SECOND EDITION

MATERIALS AND PROCESSES

FOR NDT TECHNOLOGY

THE AMERICAN SOCIETY FOR NONDESTRUCTIVE TESTING

second edition
  first printing 1/16
  second printing with corrections 9/20
  third printing 10/21
  ebook 10/18

Errata, if available for this printing, may be obtained from ASNT's website, asnt.org. Ebooks contain all corrections and updates, including the latest errata.

ISBN-13: 978-1-57117-328-7 (print)
ISBN-13: 978-1-57117-329-4 (ebook)

Printed in the United States of America

Published by:
The American Society for Nondestructive Testing Inc.
1711 Arlingate Lane
Columbus, OH 43228-0518
asnt.org

Edited by: Robert B. Conklin, Ph.D., Educational Materials Editor
Assisted by: Cynthia M. Leeman, Educational Materials Supervisor
Synthia Jester, Illustrations and Layout
Joy Grimm, Production Manager

Tim Jones, Senior Manager of Publications

ASNT Mission Statement:
ASNT exists to create a safer world by advancing scientific, engineering, and technical knowledge in the field of nondestructive testing.

ASNT *Code of Ethics*:
The ASNT *Code of Ethics* was developed to provide members of the Society with broad ethical statements to guide their professional lives. In spirit and in word, each ASNT member is responsible for knowing and adhering to the values and standards set forth in the Society's Code. More information, as well as the complete version of the *Code of Ethics*, can be found on ASNT's website, asnt.org.

About the Authors

Dr. Neda Fabris received her B.S. and M.S. degrees in mechanical engineering from the University Sarajevo, Bosnia and Herzegovina, with a Number 1 standing in the Production Option out of a class of 80 students. Subsequently, she conducted graduate study and research in manufacturing engineering at the Technical University of Aachen, Germany, and graduated with M.S. and Ph.D. degrees in mechanical and aerospace engineering from the Illinois Institute of Technology, Chicago, Illinois. She was a member of the technical staff at Bell Telephone Laboratory before joining the Mechanical Engineering Department at California State University Los Angeles where she taught 34 years and served as a chair of the department for three years. She taught 24 different undergraduate and graduate classes and introduced eight new manufacturing and material classes.

Dr. Fabris has conducted research in tool wear in metal cutting, and has developed analytical stability analysis of nonlinear chatter in metal cutting using her own experimental data. She has published numerous articles on manufacturing, as well as the pedagogy of teaching. She has received several grants including a National Science Foundation (NSF) grant for an innovative project, the "Mother Daughter Workshop" with the purpose of encouraging high school girls to study engineering. Her major honors and awards include the 2001 Society of Women Engineers (SWE) Award for Distinguished Engineering Educator (awarded to one educator in the nation per year), Outstanding Mechanical Engineering Professor Award in 1999 and 2006, and 1998 Manufacturing Educator of the Year, awarded by the Society of Manufacturing Engineering (SME), Desert Pacific Region 12.

Dr. Fabris resides in Glendale, California, with her husband, a retired scientist, and enjoys traveling and spending time with their two children and two granddaughters.

Richard D. Lopez is the Enterprise NDT Competency Lead for Deere & Company, based out of Deere's Moline Technology Innovation Center. His work centers on technology development, training, and standards, but also includes working with suppliers and periodic production challenges in any of Deere's business divisions or plants. He has a master's degree in materials science and engineering from Iowa State University, a B.S. degree in metallurgical engineering, also from Iowa State University, and an A.A.S. degree in nondestructive testing from Northeast Iowa Community College.

Previous employment experience includes Iowa State University, Mercury Marine, Boeing, and work as an ASME Code welder and radiography technician for a pressure vessel manufacturer. Half of his time with Iowa State was dedicated to no-cost NDT and metallurgical engineering outreach assistance to Iowa manufacturers, and the remainder was dedicated to NDT research and development funded primarily by the Federal Aviation Administration (FAA). Two projects that he was involved in were recognized by "Better Way" awards in 2004 and 2009 by the FAA and the Air Transport Association (now Airlines for America).

Lopez currently holds ASNT Level III certification in four methods (PT, MT, UT, and VT), and actively participates in NDT standards writing and review committees, as well as ASNT technical committees. He has authored or coauthored several peer-reviewed technical papers, contributed and reviewed ASNT Handbook material, and has presented at several conferences.

Acknowledgments

The second edition of *Materials and Processes for NDT Technology* builds upon the first edition edited by Harry D. Moore. The American Society for Nondestructive Testing, Inc., is grateful for the contributions, technical expertise, knowledge, and dedication of the following individuals who have helped make this new edition possible.

Authors

Dr. Neda Fabris – Professor of Mechanical Engineering, California State University, Los Angeles (Sections One & Two)
Richard D. Lopez – Deere & Company, Moline Technology Innovation Center (Section Three)

Editorial Direction

Gerard K. Hacker – Teledyne Brown Engineering
Dr. Shant Kenderian – The Aerospace Corporation

Technical Contributors and Reviewers

Paul Bansal – Lockheed Martin
Jonathan R. Bellos – Shawndra Products, Inc.
John A. Brunk
Eugene V. Charpia – Bluegrove NDT Consulting
L. Terry Clausing – Drysdale & Associates, Inc.
Dwayne E. Cooper – Wyman Gordon Forging, Inc.
Aaron M. DePoala – K Machine Industrial Services
Dr. Peter Huffman – Deere & Company
Steven Craig Johnson, Sr. – OneSubsea
Timothy Kinsella – Dassault Falcon Jet Corp.
Donald P. LeMaire – Citgo, Lake Charles Manufacturing Complex
Thomas E. McConomy – ATI
John W. Newman – Laser Technology, Inc.
Stephen R. Parkes – UTC Aerospace Systems
Glenn Peloquin – Welding Testing, Inc.
Mark R. Pompe – West Penn Testing Group
Douglas P. Shoup – Airfasco Industries
Dharmveer V. Singh – Alstom Group
Samuel G. Tucker – United Airlines
Roland Valdes – Inspection Solutions

Publications Review Committee

Joseph L. Mackin, Chair – International Pipe Inspectors Association
Marty Anderson – Global Technical Services
Mark R. Pompe – West Penn Testing Group

Preface

Materials and Processes for NDT Technology is intended as a reference and source of information concerning manufacturing for use by personnel involved in designing, using, or evaluating nondestructive testing (NDT) of products and structures. The text material has been kept as general as possible to still retain technical value but broad enough to include most phases of manufacturing and the materials used.

New to this edition is a section on NDT technology. Section III covers many of the NDT methods and techniques commonly used to test materials and structures in a variety of industries. One of the essential needs for satisfactory use of NDT is recognition of its limitations. Knowledge of the source of discontinuities, the materials in which they are found, and the processes by which they are created is an aid of determining the validity of any test and its evaluation.

The subject of materials and manufacturing processes is truly a single subject when the orientation of discussion is toward the end product that must be manufactured to fulfill some function. Although the attempt has been made in this book to show this singleness of subject matter, it is still necessary to treat specific areas as isolated topics. The enormous quantity of knowledge available about manufacturing processes can be discussed in varying degrees of depth and coverage. The following sections of this book have been chosen with the hope that the order will seem logical and conducive to maximum learning.

Industrial Materials. The bonding, structure, and solidification of a variety of materials are presented with an emphasis on composition and crystalline structure, as well as potential imperfections and impurities that call for NDT. In addition to metals and alloys, including aluminum and titanium, other, newer material technologies are presented, such as bio-, nano-engineered, and so-called intelligent materials. The properties and uses of polymers, ceramics, and composites are also discussed.

Manufacturing Processes. The major processes of casting, deformation shaping, welding, machining, and finishing are discussed with an emphasis on their use and importance to NDT personnel. The interrelationships of manufacturing processes are such that no one area can exist alone, and the importance of any process in an individual case is entirely dependent upon its relation to the product with which it is associated.

Nondestructive Testing. The final section of this book provides an overview of 16 nondestructive testing methods plus spectroscopy used in industrial applications. Basic terms are defined and qualifying procedures for NDT personnel discussed. The role of NDT for detecting material failure as well as material characterization is also presented. Finally, the importance of engineering with regard to the reliability of NDT inspections is examined.

Since NDT is an inseparable part of the manufacturing system, it is imperative that NDT personnel in responsible positions have general knowledge of the elements of manufacturing technology. The NDT specialist will devote many hours in analysis and interpretation of the discontinuities resulting from manufacturing operations. In order to provide input to corrective action, he or she will be called upon many times to furnish technical guidance to the design, materials, manufacturing, and quality assurance functions. With knowledge of the total manufacturing process, the NDT specialist will more effectively fulfill these responsibilities.

Contents

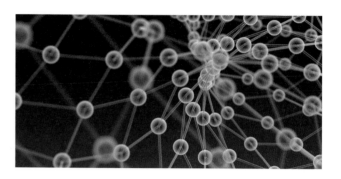

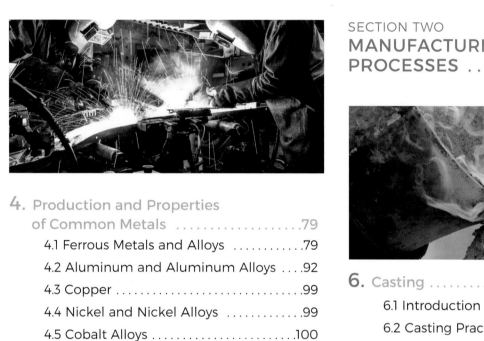

SECTION THREE
NONDESTRUCTIVE TESTING....283

INDUSTRIAL MATERIALS

CONTENTS

1 Manufacturing and Materials

1.1 INTRODUCTION TO MANUFACTURING

The term *manufacture* may be defined as the process of making raw materials into finished products especially when carried out systematically by machinery and the division of labor in large-scale industrial operations.

Such a definition is all-inclusive. It covers the making of foods, drugs, textiles, chemicals, and, in fact, everything made usable or more usable by the conversion of shape, form, or properties of natural materials.

Special interests have developed in the mechanical and industrial phases of industry concerned with the making of durable goods of metals and plastics. The majority of metals and some other materials fall in a class that is often referred to as *engineering materials.* Characteristic of this group are the properties of relatively high hardness, strength, toughness, and durability. Glass, ceramics, wood, concrete, and textiles, although they may compete with metals in many applications, have usually been excluded from these structural materials because of a difference in the combination of properties, processing requirements, and type of goods produced. The list of so-called engineering materials continues to grow with the addition of new metallic combinations, plastics, and even materials that have been previously excluded from the list, as they are developed with better properties or used in new applications.

"Characteristic of this group are the properties of relatively high hardness, strength, toughness, and durability."

Interpretation of the term *engineering materials* includes most metals and those plastics that are solids and have reasonable strength at room temperature. This book will be concerned with these materials and the processes that are used to shape them or change their properties to a more usable form.

1.2 HISTORY OF MANUFACTURING

The growth of industry in the United States is typical of industrial development throughout the world. Early settlers were concerned primarily with food and shelter. Most manufactured goods were imported, but some manufacturing was done in family units. Eventually, as conditions were stabilized, efficiency improved and excess goods were available for sale and trade. The factory form of industry finally resulted, under control of single families. Some of these still exist, but most have changed to corporate enterprises under ownership of many individuals.

Early Manufacturing. The first manufacturing was devoted mainly to agricultural and military needs. One of the earliest industrial operations to grow to large size was the reduction of ore to metal. By its very nature, particularly for ferrous metals, this process is not adaptable to very small operations. The trend in this industry toward increasing size has continued to the point where a few very large corporations produce nearly all of the basic metals, even though there are many small fabricators.

Interchangeability. The Civil War and the expanding frontier created much incentive for the manufacture of firearms. The first example of true interchangeability and the development of better transportation following the Civil War resulted in rapid growth of production goods. Many of the products were considered luxuries at the time but since have become necessities to the modern lifestyle.

Importance of Manufacturing. Manufactured products are an integral part of everyone's life, but most persons do not realize the great amount of investment and labor that makes those products possible. Almost every activity, regardless of field, is in some way dependent on hardware produced by the manufacturing industry. According to data cited by National Association of Manufacturers, the manufacturing sector accounted for 12.0 percent of the gross domestic product (GDP) in the U.S. in 2014. Further data taken from the Bureau of Labor Statistics indicates that manufacturing accounts for about one in six private sector jobs in the U.S.

1.3 INDUSTRIAL RELATIONSHIPS

1.3.1 COMPETITION IN INDUSTRY

In capitalistic economies, such as in the U.S., the profit motive is the root of most business, including manufacturing. The system presumes direct competition, so that if a number of companies are engaged in the manufacture of similar products, the sales volume will be in proportion to the product quality, promotional activities, service policies, and price. The cost of manufacturing, therefore, becomes of prime importance, for the company that can produce at the lowest cost and maintain quality can spend more for sales activities, can sell at a lower cost, or can make a larger profit per sale than less fortunate competitors. For this reason, industry is continually engaged in a battle to lower production costs.

1.3.2 PERSONNEL

Several kinds of workers are needed in any manufacturing operation. Some work directly with the product, and some are only indirectly connected with the product but are more concerned with the organization producing the goods. Those directly connected with the product include the designer; those responsible for choosing the processes, establishing control over the operation, and supervising the manufacturing; and the machine and equipment operators who perform the actual work of converting raw material into useful objects. Each of these, to function effectively in his or her job, must have varying degrees of knowledge concerning the product requirements, the material properties, and the equipment limitations. Most jobs directly connected with the product call for specific knowledge in depth concerning certain phases of the work and more general knowledge of related areas.

Products, from the simplest single part items to the most complex assemblies costing millions of dollars, go through a series of manufacturing steps as they proceed from raw materials to completed useful products. In order to conserve energy, material, time, and effort, as well as to reduce cost, it is necessary at each stage of product development that qualified personnel examine the processed material to ensure that the final product has the quality and reliability expected from the design. A large part of the manufacturing effort, therefore, is in addition to modifying material and adding to the product development. Essentially, all products require a degree of inspection of the material to see that it conforms to the requirements that provide a high-quality product.

Although not normally classed as direct labor, sales personnel usually must have complete familiarity with the product and its manufacture. They are called upon to recommend, compare, troubleshoot, and even install a product.

Indirect. Other personnel are only indirectly connected with the product or the manufacturing operation. These include most workers in administration, accounting, finance, purchasing, custodial service, and other support areas. The personnel who work in these areas may be highly skilled or trained in their own field. They do not need extensive technical knowledge of the product or its manufacture. However, they may still make decisions that are far-reaching in effect on the products. Therefore, they do need broad understanding of the product and the manufacturing facility.

1.3.3 NOMENCLATURE

The ability of personnel from one area of manufacturing to discuss and understand problems with people from another area depends directly on their knowledge of the nomenclature used in the area of concern. A designer, to discuss intelligently with a production person the effects of various design changes on the method and cost of production, must be able to understand and use the language of the production person. In most cases, he or she needs to know at least the names of the various machines and tools that might be used and have some understanding of their capabilities. In the final analysis, the problems of the production of a product become the problems of the machine and equipment operators. The loyalty, cooperation, and respect for supervision of these operators, necessary for the proper solution of production problems, can be gained only when a full understanding exists between the two groups. Of necessity, this understanding must be based on suitable language, including proper terminology, even to the point of using local terms and nicknames when appropriate. Similarly, NDT personnel must communicate with production and other personnel.

1.4 DIFFERENT CATEGORIES OF MANUFACTURING PROCESSES

Manufacturing consists of converting some raw material, which may be in rough, unrefined shape, into a usable product. The selection of the material and the processes to be used seldom can be separated. Although in a few cases some unusual property requirements dictate a specific material, generally a wide choice exists in the combination of material and processing that will satisfy the product requirements. The choice usually becomes one of economic comparison. In any case, a material is usually selected first, sometimes rather arbitrarily, and a process must then be chosen. Processing consists of one or many separate steps producing changes in shape or properties, or both.

Shape Changes. Shape changing of most materials can be accomplished with the material in one of several different forms or states: liquid, solid, or plastic. Melting of a material and control of its shape while it solidifies is referred to as *casting*. Reshaping of the material in the plastic or semisolid form is called *molding, forging, pressworking, rolling,* or *extrusion*. Shaping by metal removal or separation in the solid state is commonly performed to produce product shapes. If the removed material is in chip form, the process is *machining*. The joining of solid parts by *welding* usually involves small, localized areas that are allowed to solidify to produce a complete union between solid parts.

Energy Form. The material condition and the energy form used to effect these shape changes may vary. As noted, the material may be in a liquid, solid, or plastic form. The energy may be supplied in the form of heat, mechanical power, chemical reaction, electrical energy, or even light sources. In nearly every instance, one principal objective is changing of shape, but usually part of the energy is consumed in property changes, particularly in those processes involving state changes or solid deformation. Different materials react differently to the same energy system, and the same materials react differently to different energy systems.

Process Effect on Properties. Many concepts and fundamentals in reference to materials are common to different kinds of processes. When studied in connection with the material, these concepts, then, can be applied regardless of the kind of process by which the material is treated. The metallurgical changes that take place during solidification during casting are of the same nature as those that take place in fusion welding.

Auxiliary Steps. The completion of a product for final use generally includes the various finishing procedures apart from basic shape-changing processes. The dimensions and properties that are produced by any process are subject to variation, and, in practically all cases, some form of nondestructive testing (NDT) is necessary for controlling the process and for ensuring that the final product meets certain specifications as to size and other properties. As one of the final steps, or sometimes as an intermediate step, control of properties by *heat-treatment* or other means may be necessary. The final steps may also require surface changes for appearance, wear properties, corrosion protection, or other uses. These steps may involve only the base material or may require the addition of paints, platings, or other coatings.

Few finished products are constructed of single pieces of material because of the impracticality of producing them at a reasonable cost. Also, it is frequently necessary that properties that can be obtained only from different materials be combined into a single unit. The result is that most manufactured articles consist of *assemblies* of a number of separate parts. The joining of these parts can be accomplished in many ways, with the best method being dependent on all the factors of shape, size, and material properties involved in the particular design.

1.5 PROCESSING STEPS

Manufacturing Usually a Complex System. While the problems of design and processing are interrelated, once the design decisions have been made, the problems of processing are more clearly defined. A design may indicate certain processing steps, but basically the problem in processing is to make a product whose material, properties, shapes, tolerances, size, and finish meet specifications laid down by the designer.

Manufacturing is a term usually used to describe that section of processing starting with the raw material in a refined bulk form, and is concerned mainly with *shape changing*. While the single operation of sawing to length might produce a product useful as fireplace wood, for most manufactured products of metals, plastics, and other materials, a complex series of shape- or property-changing steps is required.

The Usual Processing Steps for Metals. Figure 1.1 shows the basic processes that are used in shaping metals. The reduction of ores is essential to any further processing, and the choices in processing come later. All but a very small percentage of the metal that is refined is first cast as a *pig* or *ingot*, which is itself always the raw material for further processing. Ingots are shown in Figures 1.2 and 1.3.

From this point on, any process may either produce a finished product or furnish the raw material for further processing. The reverse flow shown in the lower part of the diagram in Figure 1.1 refers particularly to parts that have been heat-treated or welded and must then be machined. This step generally would occur only once for any product.

That many reversals may occur within some of the blocks in the diagram is the rule rather than the exception. Steel is commonly subjected to several different rolling operations in a steel mill. Pressworking operations most often involve several separate steps to produce a product. The greatest amount of repetition occurs in machining. It is not unusual for a complex part, such as an automobile engine block, to be subjected to as many as 80 separate machining operations.

The majority of manufacturing organizations specialize in one type of manufacturing operation, and even the extremely large companies that may operate in several fields of manufacturing generally have specialized plants for the separate manufacturing areas.

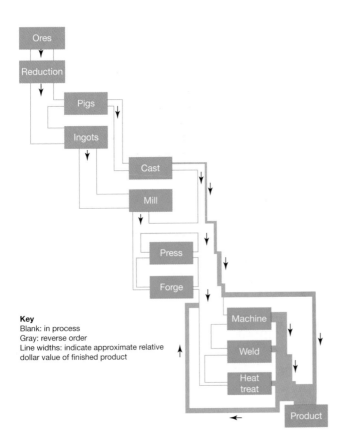

Figure 1.2: Ingot.

Figure 1.1: Metal process flow.

Figure 1.3: Forged ingots and rough forged ingots.

1.6 MATERIAL CONSIDERATION IN SELECTION OF PROCESSES

1.6.1 MATERIALS

An understanding of materials is important to any manufacturing procedure. One or more materials are required for any product, and most can be processed in a number of different ways. However, for many materials, the processing possibilities are very limited, and the process may be dictated by the particular material chosen.

Properties. The practical difference between various materials is in their properties or combinations of properties. Compared to many other materials, steel is hard and strong and may be chosen as a manufacturing material for these reasons. To some extent, steel is also elastic. If elasticity is the important property of interest, it may be necessary to choose a material like rubber for the application. An intelligent comparison of materials depends on precise meanings of the terms used and an understanding of how properties are defined and measured.

Some properties are defined by tests, such that the results may be used directly as design data. For example, from a standard tensile test, the modulus of elasticity of a material may be determined, and a designer can use this value to predict accurately the deflection of a certain-size beam under known loads. On the other hand, many properties are defined no less specifically but in a more arbitrary manner, which makes the use of the test results for calculation difficult or impossible. However, the tests still provide the opportunity for accurate comparisons with data obtained from similar tests from other materials. For example, hardness measurements may give an indication of relative wear resistance for different materials, or hardness numbers may correlate with tensile strength for a given material, but the number values can seldom he used directly in computation for design loads.

Property Variations. Each elemental material has at least some properties different from those of all other elemental materials. Some or all of the properties of an element may be changed by the addition of even small parts of another element. In many cases, the properties obtained from the combination will be better than those of either element alone. In a similar manner, the properties of elements or combinations of elements (compounds) can be varied by the type of treatment given the material. The treatments that affect properties are often intentionally selected for this purpose. However, the properties are no less affected, often in an undesirable way, by the processes being used with the objective of shaping the material. Sufficient knowledge of the relationship between the properties and the processing of materials may permit the improvement of the properties as a natural result of the processing for a different main objective. Reducing the cross-sectional size during the shaping of most metals results in an increase in hardness and strength that may be undesirable if the metal must undergo further deformation processing. In many cases, this increase in hardness and strength that occurs as a result of the processing can be beneficial and part of the product design.

1.6.2 ECONOMICS

The private ownership systems of business and industry in the U.S. and similar countries are profit motivated. In a competitive market, the manufacturer who makes the most profit will be the one who has the best combination of design, materials choice, and manufacturing processes. Ultimately, most decisions become a compromise between the most desirable from design, life, and function standpoints and the most practical from a production and cost perspective.

Design. Designers must not only know the functional requirements of the product but also have some knowledge of the probable market demands for various levels of quality and appearance. They certainly must be familiar with the mechanical properties of the various materials they might choose.

Less obvious at times is the importance of the part the designer plays in the selection of manufacturing processes. If the designer designates a sheet metal housing for a radio, obviously, the housing cannot be a plastic molded part or a die casting. If he or she specifies certain tolerances, these not only may dictate that a certain dimension be achieved by machining but also may even dictate the specific type of machine to be used. Clearly then, in every case, the designer's choices of materials, shapes, finishes, tolerances, and other factors restrict the possible choices to be made in the manufacturing process. The designer may also specify the NDT criteria, thus influencing the choice of NDT method.

Choice of Materials. Engineering materials, metals and others, have properties that vary over wide ranges with many overlaps. Costs also vary widely, but the cheapest material suitable for the product does not necessarily ensure the product will have the lowest cost. For example, a lower-cost steel substituted for another may satisfy the functional requirements of the product but may lead to increased inspection costs, thus decreasing or eliminating the margin of necessary profit.

Quantity. The number of a product that is made can have more influence on the cost than the design or the type of material used. Most manufacturing processes involve both a get-ready, or setup, cost and a production cost. The setup cost can range from nothing to many thousands of dollars, depending on the type of process and the amount of special tooling needed. The actual production time for each product is usually inversely related to the setup cost.

Quality. Quality costs money. Higher quality implies longer life, better finishes, better materials, quieter operation, and more precision. These factors all involve greater costs that may be justified by market demand. If not justified, competition will satisfy the demand with lower quality at lower cost.

Inspection. Inspection also costs money to perform, but, in another sense, like advertising, it pays; in fact, it is essential to ensure better quality product output and to improve customer relations.

Modern technology has produced a variety of inspection equipment needed for nondestructive testing. However, proper application of inspection methods and interpretation of their test indications is not possible without relying upon qualified nondestructive testing personnel. Capable individuals are needed to provide input to the decision-making processes regarding the integrity and serviceability of the test objects, stemming from the indirect indications provided by nondestructive tests. NDT technicians must have an adequate background of knowledge concerning the materials and manufacturing technologies involved in their specific industries, as well as the service conditions to which their products will be subjected, in order to make valid decisions.

1.6.3 DESIGN

Appearance in Addition to Function Usually Important. In the case of every product, the manufacturing process must be preceded by the design. The relationships that exist between design and processing are of extreme importance. The designer normally starts with some definite functional requirement that must be satisfied. The environmental conditions of use, expected life, and loading conditions dictate certain minimum shapes and sizes and limit the possible choice of materials. The designer's problems arise mainly from the fact that a single solution is seldom indicated. Of the many possible materials and shapes that may satisfy the functional requirements, some may have better appearance than others. For many consumer goods, the appearance may actually govern the final choice. Even in the designing of parts that may be completely hidden in a final assembly, the designer seldom disregards appearance completely.

Quality and Costs Must Balance. Even the original design will be influenced by the method of processing that is anticipated and, to give proper consideration to all the alternatives, it is essential that the designer have knowledge about the costs and capabilities of various production methods. It is generally true that costs will be different for different material and processing choices, and considerable screening of the alternatives can be done purely on a cost basis. However, the quality obtained with more expensive materials or methods may be superior to that of the cheaper choices, and decisions must often be made regarding some combination of quality and cost. A rational decision as to the quality to be produced can only be made with adequate information as to how the market will be affected by the quality.

Availability of Facilities Affects Choices. Obviously, the decisions made by the designer are far-reaching and of extreme importance. The materials and shapes that are specified usually determine the basic processes that must be used. Specified tolerances may even dictate specific types of machines and have a large influence on costs. In many cases, choices are limited by the equipment and the trained personnel that are available. Economical manufacture of small quantities can frequently be best accomplished by use of equipment and processes that under other circumstances would be inefficient. Certainly a designer for a plant producing castings would not design a part as a weldment if the continued operation of the plant depends on the production of castings.

In many cases, the decisions that govern the choice of materials and processes must be made in an arbitrary manner. The gathering of enough information may not be economically feasible, or time may not be available. Particularly when only small quantities are being produced, the cost of finding the most economical method of production may be more than any possible gain over some arbitrary method that is reasonably certain of producing an acceptable product. In some cases, custom governs the choice simply because some set of choices was known to give acceptable results for similar production in the past.

Designers cannot be expected to be experts in all the phases of production that influence the final quality and cost of a product. Production personnel must be relied on to furnish details of process capabilities and requirements.

NDT in Design. Similarly, the design engineering function must receive technical guidance from key NDT personnel in order to ensure that the design requirements can be met. It is essential that the design requirements contain the proper balance between the contribution from NDT to safety and reliability of the product and the economic realities. Both the capabilities and limitations of the various methods of NDT must be considered in the design phases of the product life cycle in order to achieve optimum product effectiveness.

1.7 EFFECT OF MANUFACTURING PROCESS ON THE PROPERTIES OF THE PRODUCT

1.7.1 STATES OF MATTER

Material may exist in one of three states of matter, gas, liquid, or solid, but except for some special processes with relatively small use, such as vapor deposition, or for zinc refining, the gaseous state is of small importance in manufacturing.

Most Manufacturing Processes Are to Change Material Shapes. For manufacturing purposes in which shape changing is the objective, the solid state may be thought of as existing in two forms. Below the *elastic limit*, materials are dealt with as rigid materials. Processing involving this form causes no significant relative movement of atoms or molecules of the material with respect to each other. Above the elastic limit, solid materials may flow plastically, and shape changing may be accomplished by application of external loads to cause permanent relocations within the structure of the material. The end results of dealing with materials in the liquid form are similar to those with materials above the elastic limit. No appreciable density or volume change occurs, and the shape may be changed without loss of material.

1.7.2 SHAPE-CHANGING PROCESSES

Shapes Changed with No Volume Change, by Additions, and by Subtractions. Shape changing is possible in any of these states, but most manufacturing processes by definition or nature deal with materials in only one of these possible forms. Figure 1.4 shows the processes for shape changing without material loss and those in which material is added or taken away.

No Volume Change. In those processes in which no volume change occurs, property changes are usually large and distributed throughout the material. In casting, the shape change occurs by melting and subsequent solidification to a prescribed shape. This process can be used with practically all metals and most plastics. The material properties depend on composition and the conditions of the particular casting process but not on the condition of the material prior to melting. Casting is often the most economical method for producing complex shapes, particularly where reentrant angles exist.

Wrought materials are produced by plastic deformation that can be accomplished by *hot-working* (above the recrystallization temperature) or *cold-working.* Property changes also occur throughout the material with these processes; the greatest changes are usually caused by cold-working.

Additions or Combinations. New shapes can be produced either by joining preformed shapes mechanically or by any of various bonding means. In welding, soldering, and brazing, metallurgical bonds are established by heat, pressure, or sometimes by chemical action with plastics. Mechanical fastening by use of bolts, rivets, or pins is primarily an assembly procedure and is often an alternative and competitive joining procedure to welding or adhesive fastening.

Shaping from powders by pressing and heating involves the flow of granular materials, which differs considerably from deformation processing, although some

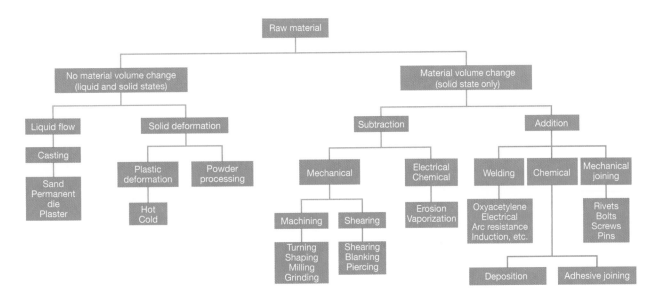

Figure 1.4: Shape-changing processes.

plastic flow undoubtedly occurs in individual particles. Powder processing is a somewhat specialized process, but, as in casting or the deformation processes, the material is shaped by confinement to some geometric pattern in two or three dimensions. Because the total volume of work material is affected by these processes, large sources of energy, pressure, or heat are required.

Subtraction or Removal. Shape changing may also be accomplished by taking material away in chip or bulk form or by material destruction. The property changes in these processes are more localized, and energy requirements are generally smaller.

Mechanical separation can be performed by removal of chips or by controlled separation along predetermined surfaces. Chip removal by machining can be used with some success for all materials, shapes, and accuracies and is probably the most versatile of all manufacturing processes. Separation by shearing, with localized failure caused by externally applied loads, is limited primarily to sheet materials but frequently turns out to be the cheapest method for producing many shapes in large quantities.

Special Shape-Changing Methods. With the advent of new materials difficult to fabricate by conventional means and of many designs requiring shapes and tolerances and material combinations difficult to achieve with conventional processes, a number of electrical and chemical processes have been developed for removing or adding material. Many of these are restricted in use to a few materials, and most are specialized to the point that they have only a few applications. Included is *metal plating* by electrical or chemical means, used primarily as a finishing process. Other developments are *electrical discharge machining* (EDM), *chemical milling, ultrasonic grinding,* and *electron beam machining,* which are specialized metal removal processes that compete with conventional machining or press-working operations and involve hard materials, special shapes, or low quantities.

1.8 SUMMARY

Manufacturing is a complex system. A product always originates as a design concept required to serve some purpose. A multiplicity of choices and decisions nearly always comes between the establishment of the need and the manufacturing of the product. The designer, because no logical means are available, frequently arbitrarily makes decisions that usually, at least broadly, determine the processes that must be used to produce the product. Within this broad framework, however, exist many other choices of specific materials, processes, and machines. Material properties, qualities, quantities, and processes are strongly interrelated. The prime effort, from original concept to the completion of manufacture, is aimed at finding the optimum combination of these variables to provide the best economic situation.

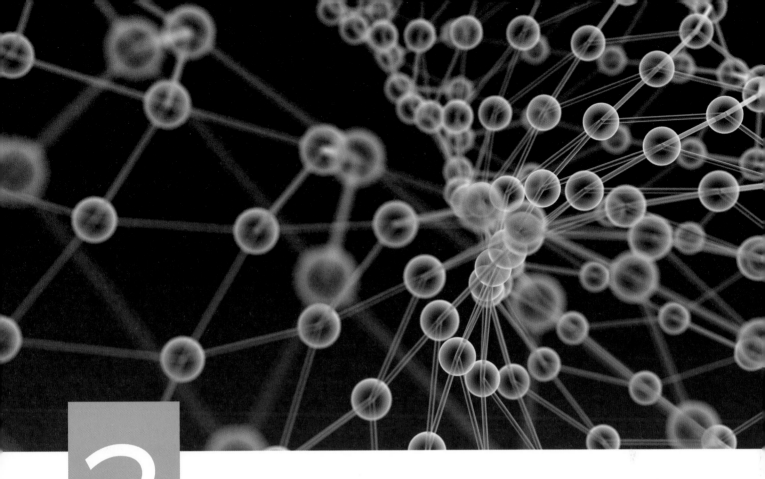

2 Classification, Structure, and Solidification of Materials

2.1 CLASSIFICATION OF MATERIALS

Human progress is closely related to the ability to utilize existing and develop new materials for use in different products. Early civilizations have been named by the predominant material adapted for tools and weapons in that period, such as Stone Age, Bronze Age, and Iron Age. Today we are utilizing a wide variety of materials and combinations of them. We are producing sophisticated objects, from miniature elements of electronic circuits to huge complicated systems, such as airplanes and satellites, consisting of millions of different components. Regardless of how complicated products may appear, everything around us (including ourselves) is made from combinations of a hundred or so stable elements. In this chapter, we will briefly review these elements, the way they are bonded, and their influence on properties of the final product. We are going to limit ourselves to engineering materials—that is, materials used to produce devices, structures, and machines in contrast to materials in biology, food, agriculture, and so on.

Four Main Categories. Although there are a number of ways to classify materials, engineering materials are often divided into four groups: *metals, ceramics, semiconductors,* and *polymers.* There are also several categories of materials that represent combinations of the above-mentioned groups, either in a special form or for use in specific applications. For example, *composites* are made of two or more materials

"... everything around us (including ourselves) is made from combinations of a hundred or so stable elements."

of the above-mentioned groups (carbon fiber is produced by carbonizing a polymer; concrete is a composite of multiple different ceramics), *foams* are special forms of basic materials, and *intelligent materials* are alloys of different metals that have special properties. In this chapter, we will briefly describe the general properties of each group and subgroup of materials.

Properties and performance of engineering materials depend mainly on four factors:
1. Types of atoms as well as atomic and crystalline structure.
2. Fabrication, processing, and thermal treatment of the product.
3. Surface treatment.
4. Environment where the product is used.

We will discuss each of these factors in more detail in subsequent chapters, as well. In order to ensure the quality of the product, we have to perform inspections. The type and accuracy of the inspection will greatly depend upon knowledge of the structure and behavior of the material being inspected. A comprehensive understanding of materials and processes requires several large volumes of specialized books. This book presents the prevailing concepts and an overall introduction to materials and processes in ways that would benefit the NDT practitioner.

2.2 GENERAL PROPERTIES OF ENGINEERING MATERIALS

2.2.1 METALS

Metals and metal alloys consist of one or more metallic elements often with nonmetallic elements in small amounts. Metallic elements are located in columns IA, IIA, IIB, IVB, VB, VIB, VIIB, VIII, IB, and IIB and IIIA of the periodic table of elements (numbering used by Chemical Abstracts Service) with the exception of boron (B), which is considered to be a semiconductor. (See Figure 2.14.) Also, the rare earth series and active series (the lanthanides and actinides) belong to the metallic group.

The most abundant metals used in engineering applications are: iron (Fe), nickel (Ni), copper (Cu), zinc (Zn), aluminum (Al), magnesium (Mg), tungsten (W), titanium (Ti), and tin (Sn) as well as gold (Au) (in electronic applications). Many other metals are used in smaller amounts, as alloying agents. For example, a steel alloy

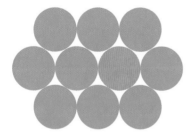

Figure 2.1: An example of a substitutional alloy. In the example of brass, the reddish atoms are copper and the gray atom represents zinc.

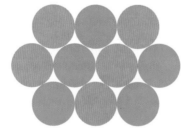

Figure 2.2: An intermetallic compound is composed of sets of atoms bonded to each other. In this example, each gray atom is bonded to two other gray atoms and four orange atoms in the same plane. The direction of the bonding will be the same for each set of atoms. For the sake of simplicity, out-of-plane bonding is not presented.

Figure 2.3: Interstitial metal alloys have alloying elements that sit between the regularly arranged atoms. They tend to be slightly too large to properly fit and will cause distortion of the nearby atoms.

might contain one or more of the elements chromium (Cr), vanadium (V), manganese (Mn), tungsten (W), molybdenum (Mo), and others, in addition to nonmetals such as carbon (C), silicon (Si), and boron (B).

Metals can be used in their pure form, for example, aluminum and copper, but they are more likely to be alloyed with other metals or nonmetals. The metal atoms in alloys can be arranged in three ways:

1. A specific atom in a metal is replaced by another from a different element; for example, in *brass*, copper atoms are partially replaced with zinc atoms. (See Figure 2.1.)
2. Different atoms make a compound inside a metallic structure; for example, a number of such compounds can form if gold and aluminum come in contact with each other. These are known as intermetallic compounds. (See Figure 2.2.)
3. Some smaller atoms "squeeze" themselves between metallic atoms, such as carbon in iron. These are known as *interstitial alloys.* (See Figure 2.3.)

Basic Properties. The nature of these alloys, in terms of the atomic bonds that form, can strongly influence the speed of sound and the electrical conductivity of the material. In addition, the Z-number of elements used strongly affects the penetrating ability of ionizing radiation. (Z is the number of protons in the nucleus of an atom, referred to as the *atomic number* of an element.) For that reason, it may be useful to understand the different classifications in which atoms might be arranged in an alloy. How bonding affects these measureable properties will be discussed in more detail later.

Basic properties of metals are:
- Metals tend to be good conductors of electricity and heat.
- They are often malleable—that is, they can be extensively deformed without fracturing at room temperature, and at relatively high strain rates.
- They are relatively hard and strong at room temperature.
- Metals cannot be made transparent, unless the metal is thinner than the wavelengths of visible light. For example, with physical vapor deposition (PVD), aluminum can be formed in thin enough layers to see through. Also, anything thinner than visible light is transparent.
- They can be made stronger or tougher by thermal and chemical treatments as well as mechanical strengthening methods.
- Some metals, such as Fe, Co, and Ni, have desirable magnetic properties.
- Metals can be remelted and recycled.

Malleability. Atoms in metals are arranged in a very orderly manner (as we will see later), but some of the electrons are not strongly bonded to any particular atom. Hence, when metals are connected to an electrical potential, such as the positive and negative terminals on a battery, they conduct current. Metals can be polished to high luster. Atoms in most metals can move away from their nearest neighbors by sliding and make bonds with other atoms. This is known as *dislocation motion*, and it is related to how metals can be extensively deformed without producing cracks and voids in the structure. For this reason, we can make different shapes out of metals without fracturing them. That property, known as *malleability,* is the reason that we can make large numbers of engineering products by forging, rolling, deep drawing, extruding, and other processes.

Conductivity and Other Factors. Other reasons for using large quantities of metals in engineering include their electrical and thermal conductivities, wide variety of mechanical properties, and their abundance and the ease and cost of extracting them from ore, which can make them relatively low cost. Some metals, because they are rarer or more difficult to extract from ore, such as titanium, silver, and gold, are expensive. (So-called *rare earth elements* are not necessarily rare in quantity, just difficult to extract.) Also, the emphasis on keeping waste and pollution down and preserving limited resources often favors the use of metals due to ease and low cost with which they can be recycled. In general, however, materials are selected based on desired properties, such as strength, fatigue resistance, high-temperature characteristics, wear properties, electromagnetic properties, and corrosion resistance.

Abundance of Metals. Metallic products are all around us: from parts of a paper stapler made from steel and electrical wire made from copper to airplane fuselages made from aluminum, engine components made from cast iron, doorknobs made from brass, electrical integrated circuits plated with gold, and U.S. pennies (from 1982) made from zinc plated with copper. Some products made from metals in their early processing stages are shown in Figures 2.4 and 2.5. In industries where NDT is commonly performed, for example, nuclear, military, petro-chemical, and aerospace, metallic products include steel drill pipes, aluminum aircraft fuselages, and iron or aluminum engine components. Metal inspected with nondestructive testing methods is shown in Figure 2.6.

Figure 2.4: Billets.

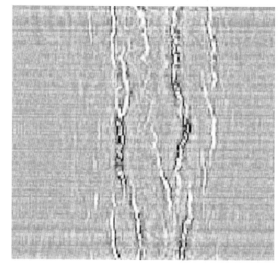

(a)

Figure 2.5: Slabs.

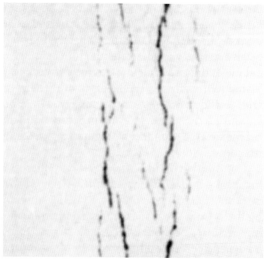

(b)

Figure 2.6: Stress-corrosion cracks on stainless steel sample: (a) laser ultrasonic image; (b) liquid penetrant test.

2.2.2 CERAMICS

Ceramics are most frequently composed of oxides (compounds of metal and oxygen [O]), nitrides (compounds of metal and nitrogen [N]), or carbides (compounds of metals and carbon [C]). However, some nonmetals can form ceramics free from metals, such as pure carbon, forming diamonds. In the periodic table of elements, nonmetals are located in the VA, VIA, and VIIA columns (Figure 2.14); however, several elements among them are considered *semiconductors*, or *metalloids*, because they behave like metals at certain times and nonmetals at other times. In ceramics, the electrons are more tightly bonded to specific atoms, as opposed to the free electron behavior of metals. Because the electrons tend to be relatively immobile, ceramics are often poor conductors of heat and electricity. Also, most ceramics cannot be easily deformed without forming cracks; hence, ceramics are *brittle* (not malleable). Atoms in ceramics tend to be strongly bonded to each other. This makes ceramics *hard* (resistant to penetration of surfaces) and *strong* (capable of carrying a significant load without permanent deformation). In spite of their high strength, most ceramics fracture easily (low toughness) because of their brittle nature.

Properties of Ceramics. Ceramics keep their strength at high temperature (higher than most metals and polymers), and they are resistant to most chemicals because of the strength and stability of their bonds.

The properties of most ceramics can be summarized as:
- Ceramics are electrical and thermal isolators.
- Ceramics are strong.
- Ceramics are very sensitive to notches. Small cracks can initiate fracture and result in catastrophic failure of the whole structure due to low toughness.
- Ceramics are chemically stable.
- Some ceramics are used as soft or hard magnetic materials.

There are exceptions to almost every one of these rules: some complicated ceramics are not only electrical conductors but superconductors; some ceramics are superplastic, that is, they can be deformed to a large extent at high temperatures. Pure carbon in the form of diamonds is an interesting example of a ceramic that is a poor electrical conductor but an excellent thermal conductor.

Uses of Ceramics. Large quantities of ceramics are used as building materials, including concrete blocks, bricks, cements, plasters, ceramic tiles, and refractory tiles (resistant to high temperatures) used as the lining of melting furnaces and thermal shields on space rockets. Advanced, high-performance ceramics are used as substrates (that is, in support of computer chips and integrated circuits), as well as electronic structural parts, including gears, sparkplugs, and prosthetic devices. Hot-pressed ceramics containing two or more ceramics, called *cermets* (from ceramic and metals) and *carbides* are often used in coatings for cutting tools, greatly increasing tool life and decreasing wear. Most grinding and polishing abrasives are ceramics. We are all familiar with ceramic and porcelain dishes as well as products made of glass, including glass windows and structural glass panels. In this category are included carbon products ranging from graphite (mostly used as a solid lubricant) to industrial diamond (used as an abrasive). Nondestructive testing of a ceramic cup is shown in Figure 2.7.

2.2.3 SEMICONDUCTORS

Semiconductors conduct electricity better than insulators, such as most ceramics and polymers, but not as well as most metals. Most semiconductors could be classified as ceramics, but some are polymers. Ceramic semiconductors can be modified with chemical impurities, which drastically change their electronic properties. Adding

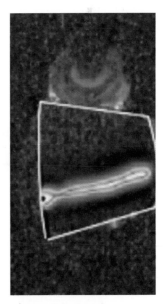

Figure 2.7: Crack detection with lock-in thermography with ultrasonically generated thermal waves in ceramic cup.

these impurities is called *doping*, which is similar to alloying, except that alloys are *usually* included in amounts on the order of 0.01 to 10 percent (by weight or atomic fraction), and doping is usually on the order of parts per billion to parts per thousand. An example of doping is adding phosphorus to silicon. In simple terms, phosphorus has one more valence electron than silicon, which doesn't get included in the phosphorus-silicon bonds. That electron is then free to move about, conducting electricity. This is an extreme simplification of the situation. In reality, it's related to the availability of quantum states in which electrons can exist, which changes when atoms move close to each other and bond.

Energy States. When enough atoms come together, the number of states with similar energy becomes very large and is treated as a nearly continuum "band" of states. The universe tends toward low energy, so the low-energy band, or "valence band," will fill up first. The next band, the conduction band, will be empty (at zero degrees kelvin [0 K]). Much like cars in a traffic jam, electrons can't move in the valence band because all of the places to go are full. The only way they can be mobile is if they have enough energy to move to the conduction band. They can get that energy from heat (thermal excitation) or from light (photon excitation). In metals, the bands overlap, and electrons can move freely from one to the other. In insulators, the bands are far apart, and a lot of energy is needed for an electron to move up to the conduction band. In a semiconductor, the bands are close but not overlapping, and visible light has enough energy to promote electrons to the conduction band. An example is pure silicon, which looks metallic, but doesn't behave like a metal.

2.2.3.1 INTRINSIC SEMICONDUCTORS

Materials that have two energy states close enough for electrons to jump over from the full state to the empty conduction band are called *intrinsic semiconductors.* Only two pure elements, silicon (Si) and germanium (Ge), have that property, and they are in group VI in the periodic table of elements. Several compounds formed from elements in groups IIIA and VA—for example, gallium arsenide (GaAs) and indium antimonite (InSb), as well as those formed from the IIB and VIA groups, such as cadmium sulfide (CdS) and zinc telluride (ZnTe)—have the same properties. Some applications of these semiconductors are listed here:

1. Precise measurements of elevated temperatures are made using *thermistors,* which are made from intrinsic semiconductors. Excitation energy is heat, and the conductivity of the semiconductor is an exponential function of the temperature. By using a calibrated instrument to measure electrical conductivity, the temperature of the medium can be accurately measured. Thermistors are used to precisely measure high temperature, much higher than temperatures that can be measured with regular mercury thermometers.
2. Road signs and safety strips on runners' shoes rely on a phenomenon called *fluorescence,* whereby electrons that are excited into the conduction band with the vehicle's light "fall down" almost immediately to the valence band, releasing light.
3. Some types of solar cells, whereby light energy excites electrons and produces electricity are made with intrinsic semiconductors.

Even nature has provided us with the light produced by semiconductors in the form of the *chemical luminescence* of fireflies. A chemical reaction in the insect provides enough energy for strategically located electrons of semiconductors to "jump" into conduction bands and then, after the energy is exhausted, "fall down" into a lower state, emitting light.

2.2.3.2 EXTRINSIC SEMICONDUCTORS

Another category of semiconductors is called *extrinsic semiconductors*. In this case, impurities are added in small, carefully controlled amounts (number of atoms) to provide either electrons near the conduction band (*n-type semiconductors)* or energy levels near the valence band (*p-type semiconductors*). For consumer electronics, such as computer processors, the base material is pure, single-crystal silicon. Consider a piece of silicon containing one atom of phosphorus. Phosphorus has one electron more than silicon in the valence shell. This electron is easily excited into a new state in the conduction band, where it is highly mobile and can be conducted.

If an element with three electrons in the conduction bands is added to silicon—for example, aluminum (Al), boron (B), gallium (Ga), or indium (In)—a p-type semiconductor is formed. Although pure silicon is also a semiconductor (intrinsic), its conductivity is usually much smaller at working temperatures than extrinsic conductivity of doped silicon, so much so that it can be neglected for most practical purposes.

Here, we will mention only three applications of extrinsic semiconductors in integrated circuits, but they are extremely important:

1. Clever combinations of n- and p-type extrinsic semiconductors are used for junction devices (*diodes*). Diodes allow high current flow only in one direction. Rectifiers are arrays of these diodes that change alternating current into direct current.
2. Another type is the *light-emitting diode* (LED) used in digital displays, where electrons in the conduction band move to the valence band, and in that process light is emitted.
3. Another critical semiconductor device is a *transistor* consisting of three semiconductors arranged in a p-n-p or n-p-n combination. Transistors serve either as a *gate* or as an *amplifier*. Millions or even billions of transistors are incorporated in "chips," or integrated circuits, providing the basis for calculators, computers, cellphones, and other devices and gadgets without which we cannot imagine our life today. A radiograph of a semiconductor is shown in Figure 2.8.

2.2.4 POLYMERS

Polymers (often called plastics) are substances composed of long-chain repeating molecules. The name comes from the Greek words *poly*, which means "many," and *mers*, which means "parts." In most cases, the carbon element forms the backbone of the chain, and therefore these materials are categorized as organic. Bonds between atoms in the chain are very strong. The bond between chains can be much weaker, forming *thermoplastic* polymers, or equally strong, forming *thermosetting* polymers. Individual products made from polymers are often called *plastics*, whereas non-finished products, such as *elastomers* (rubbers), *adhesives*, coatings, and fibers for composites, are called only *polymers* (not plastics). In this text, we will use the terms *plastics* and *polymers* interchangeably for discrete products, while others will be referred to as *polymers* only.

Origins. The word *polymer* was first used in 1866 to identify materials made from vegetable and animal products. The most common example of raw material was *cellulose*, which was modified chemically into *cellulose nitrite* and used in photographic films (thermoplastic polymers).

The first thermosetting polymer, *phenol formaldehyde*, known as *bakelite*, was developed in 1906. From that time until now, in a relatively short period of time (compared with metals and ceramics that have been known for thousands of years), more than 15 000 types of polymers have been made commercially available. There

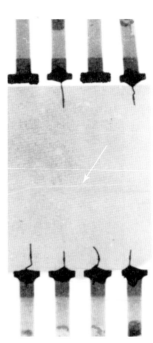

Figure 2.8: Radiograph of fine crack in plastic casing material of semiconductor.

are variations of about 20 basic polymer families. Thermoplastics are used at least five times more than thermosetting polymers.

Uses of Plastics. Examples of parts made from plastics are all around us: milk and soft drink bottles, plastic cutlery, clothing, car tires, car bumpers (often plated to look like metals), toys, gears, parachutes, packaging foam, furniture, epoxies, latex paints, rubber balls, fluorocarbon resin coating on dishes, aramid for bulletproof vests—the list goes on and on. Although concrete (composite) is produced most often, the production of plastics is increasing continuously. Nondestructive testing of a plastic test object is shown in Figure 2.9.

Widely used plastics for everyday products are called *commodity plastics*; those used for engineering products are called *engineering plastics*. Many plastics can be used for commodity as well as engineering products. For instance, *polyethylene,* which is produced in larger quantities than any other polymer, is used for plastic shopping bags and blow-molded bottles (commodity plastics) as well as in under-ground piping and wear-resistant machine parts (engineering plastics). Both groups of polymers, thermosetting and thermoplastics, can be used as commodity and engi-neering plastics.

Properties of Plastics. Compared with metals and ceramics, polymers (plastics) have the following characteristics:

- Much less stiff; that is, for the same load, they deflect and deform much more than metals or ceramics (for example about 30 times more than steel).
- At room temperature, many plastics "creep" or slowly deform with time, which can cause undesirable deformation and lead to breaking.
- Thermosets are less strong than metals. However, they often have low density so that their strength divided by density (specific strength) might be close to that of metals.
- Expandable when heated, at a rate often 10 times higher than for metals. They also soften and melt at much lower temperatures than most other engineering materials.
- Flammable to different degrees.
- Chemically inert and do not corrode, but most of them disintegrate when repeat-edly exposed to ultraviolet radiation.
- Some polymers (for example nylon) absorb water and swell.
- Most plastics are more affordable than other engineering materials.

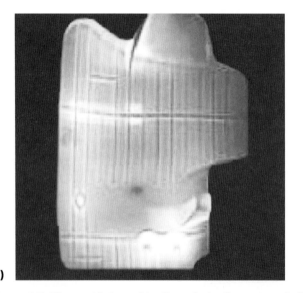 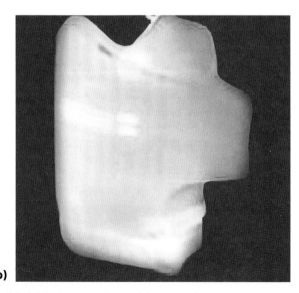

(a)   (b)

Figure 2.9: Thermal/infrared testing of plastic part made in mold: (a) bottom surface; (b) top surface.

- Most thermoplastic polymers are extremely ductile and malleable and can be easily formed into complex shapes. The same is true for thermosetting polymers before they are cured. That is probably the main reason that they are so often used in everyday life and are gaining a competitive edge in engineering applications.
- Bioplastics are biodegradable and other thermoplastics, such as fluorocarbon resins, have advantageous wear properties.

Polymers exhibit a wide range of properties due to variations in bonding, chemical elements, added fillers, and modification techniques. We will briefly discuss different types of polymers and modification techniques in a later chapter. Here we will only describe the most common properties of thermosetting and thermoplastic polymers and compare them with properties of metals and ceramics.

2.2.4.1 THERMOPLASTIC POLYMERS

The majority of produced polymers (approximately 85%) are thermoplastic. The main reason for this is that common thermoplastic polymers (such as polyethylene, which is the most common of all) are produced from relatively inexpensive base materials (petroleum and natural gas). In addition, the final product can be produced at low cost in large quantities using injection molding, blow molding, and thermoforming processes. As mentioned, the bonds between adjacent long-chained molecules in thermoplastics are about ten times weaker than bonds between atoms within the long chains. These weak bonds (called secondary bonds) determine the overall strength of the polymers. It is hard to break covalent bonds within long molecules, but it is relatively easy to break the secondary bonds, separating molecules from each other either by applying a mechanical force (pulling apart) or thermal energy (melting). The material will disintegrate, although the long molecules might still be intact. Therefore, thermoplastic polymers are in general less strong and melt at lower temperatures than thermosetting polymers (where bonds in all three directions are relatively equally strong). Thermoplastic polymers are more ductile and tough compared with thermosetting polymers. One big advantage of thermoplastic polymers is that they can be remelted and recycled, while thermosetting polymers cannot. There are two types of thermoplastics: *semi-crystalline* and *amorphous*. Crystallinity can strongly affect the properties of a polymer.

2.2.4.2 THERMOSETTING POLYMERS

In thermosetting polymers, long-chained molecules are cross-linked in a three-dimensional (spatial) arrangement so that often the whole product becomes one huge molecule. Cross-linking, also called *curing*, can be done at high as well as room temperatures with the help of chemicals. The polymerization (linking into long chains) of the product generally takes place in two stages: the first in a chemical plant where the particles are partially polymerized but still deformable, and the second at the part-producing facility where cross-linking is completed under heat and pressure during the shaping of the part. Once the part becomes "thermoset," it cannot be remelted or recycled. The difference between the recyclability of thermoplastics and thermosets is often compared to freezing water versus making a cake. Thermoplastics can be recycled like the freezing of water and melting of ice, although less often or readily, as the polymer will eventually degrade or thermally age. Thermosetting polymers, however, behave like a cake, where ingredients (flour, eggs, and butter) cannot be "recovered" from the baked cake. Thermosetting polymers (also called *thermosets*) exposed to additional heat will burn and char just like a cake left too long in the oven.

2.2.5 COMPOSITES

Composites are a combination of two or more materials where each material can be visually distinguished from the other. As mentioned, alloys also contain more than one element, but the atoms or group of atoms cannot be distinguished from each other with the naked eye. Composites have improved properties than the materials that constitute them. They can have greater strength, greater toughness, and lighter weight for the same strength.

Wood, marble, and granite are natural composites. Engineering composites are formed by coating internal additives and by laminating. Fiberglass is an example of a coated composite; glass fibers are coated by a polymer to produce a strong and light structure. Sporting equipment, such as tennis racquets, may be made of thermosetting polymers reinforced with carbon fibers.

The U.S. penny is another example of a coated composite, where copper is pressed on zinc. The material cost for producing a copper-clad zinc penny is much lower than using pure copper. Honeycomb structures, where an aluminum core or sheet, for example, is sandwiched between layers of graphite and polymer composites, are lighter than solid aluminum and provide the same strength. Another honeycomb structure is flame-resistant meta-aramid paper and pressboard. Particleboard is a composite of wood chips with epoxy (polymer). Plywood is a composite of wooden panels layered in different directions to overcome directional differences in the strength of the wood.

The most common composites used today in engineering consist of high-strength, crack-sensitive materials (glass, carbon, boron, and others) dispersed as particles, continuous fibers, or woven mats immersed in the matrix of thermosetting or thermoplastic polymers. Composites with the matrix consisting of thermosetting polymers are easier to manufacture. Thermoplastics do not easily wet the fibers to make continuous structures, and they are mostly used in composites with chopped glass fibers. In 2003, only 10% of manufactured composites had a thermoplastics matrix. However, attempts have been made to increase this percentage due to the advantages thermoplastics offer in recyclability and less time needed for manufacturing.

Properties of Composites. Properties of composites are greatly influenced by the type of matrix and the type, shape, and size of reinforcement materials used. Here we are going to give a very brief and general comparison between composites and other materials used in engineering applications. A more detailed discussion will be left for later.

Figure 2.10: Ultrasonic testing of aircraft composite assembly using squirter technique.

Compared with other engineering materials, engineering composites, in general, have the following characteristics:

- Composites are stronger than unreinforced matrices.
- High-performance polymers with a thermosetting matrix can have a specific strength (that is, strength per unit weight) higher than metals. Composites with a thermoplastic matrix are not so strong, but they are stronger than unreinforced plastics.
- Composites are corrosion resistant.
- Composites used in everyday applications are often less expensive than the materials they replace. For example, concrete is more often used, cheaper, and tougher than tiles or stone for paving roads.

New manufacturing methods had to be developed to manufacture composites, and special care has to be exercised to keep tolerances.

Applications of Composites. Composites find applications in fiberglass boats, airplanes, and satellites. For example, stealth planes are made from composites with special coatings or skins made with radar-absorbent materials (RAMs). Tennis rackets, golf clubs, and bicycles as well as bicycle helmets and hardhats are made mainly of composites. Melamine cafeteria trays as well as Formica® countertops are made from composites. However, the largest quantity of composites is still used in construction as concrete. Nondestructive testing of a composite is shown in Figure 2.10.

2.2.6 BIOMATERIALS

Biomaterials can be implanted in the human body without causing adverse biological reaction or rejection. They are used to replace damaged or diseased body parts. Several materials from each group mentioned above can be used for biomaterials, and every day, new materials are developed and adapted for use in the human body. Among metals, titanium is used most often for hip and other bone replacement, whereas ceramics are very suitable for bone replacement due to their strength, hardness, and inertness.

Ceramics used in the human body are called *bio-ceramics*. They are classified into the following groups:

1. **Nearly inert:** the ceramic device or replacement is cemented or press-fitted into the bone.
2. **Porous ingrowth:** without using cement or press fittings due to the porous nature of the ceramic, bone ingrowth occurs, attaching the ceramic implant to the bone.
3. **Surface reactive:** ceramics attach themselves directly by chemical reaction to the bone.
4. **Absorbable:** ceramics are absorbed into and slowly replaced by the bone.

Ceramics are used in hip and knee replacements as well as dental bone growth and implants. One widely used application involves ceramic tooth caps and artificial teeth made from porcelain.

Polymers are also often used for hip replacement. In the U.S., most often aluminum oxide (Al_2O_3) (ceramic) is used for the ball of the hip joint, while the ultra-high-molecular weight polyethylene (polymer) is used for the socket components. Polymers have found use in cosmetic implements, artificial eyes, and contact lenses.

Many devices implanted into the human body—heart pacemakers, for one—contain chips made of semiconductors. Also gels, intelligent, and nano-engineered materials are often used as biomaterials. Although biomaterials do not represent a new type of material, they have common characteristics that distinguish them from other materials.

2.2.7 NANO-ENGINEERED MATERIALS

Until recently, scientists could not manipulate the properties of materials on the atomic level; for example, they could add some alloying elements to the molten metal but could not move the atoms of that addition and place them precisely in a desired position. The development of scanning probe microscopes (in the 1980s) enabled the observation and manipulation of individual atoms to form new structures. This ability to arrange the atoms provides opportunities to develop mechanical, electrical, and magnetic properties that are not otherwise possible. Also, very small devices and mechanical components can be manufactured with this "bottom up" approach. Study of the properties and manufacturing of these materials is called *nanotechnology*. The prefix "nano" refers to the size of these particles, which are on the order of nanometers (10^{-9} m or 1 billionth of a meter), although this is often true in only one direction. For instance, in thin films, the thickness is in the nanometer range (1 to 100 nm), while the other two dimensions are not. One nanometer is approximately equal to five atom diameters; one red blood cell has dimensions of 2000×7000 nm.

Nanotubes and Fullerene Structures. One of the recent and most interesting findings in materials science is the discovery of a new molecular form of carbon called *graphene*. One of the allotropes of graphene is in the form of *carbon nanotubes* (in addition to widely known graphite and charcoal). Each nanotube represents one molecule. The diameter of the tube is on the order of 100 nm, while its length is much greater. Each nanotube consists of millions of carbon atoms, and both ends are capped with a hemisphere resembling one half of a soccer ball, or so-called *fullerene structure*. These tubes are extremely strong and stiff and relatively ductile. They have comparatively low density and are electrical conductors. On the basis of these properties, carbon nanotubes are called an *ultimate fiber* because the carbon-carbon bond is so strong. They are extremely promising as reinforcement in composite materials, where often, in addition to being strong and lightweight, electrical conductivity is highly desirable in order to conduct the static electricity that develops in the polymer matrix.

Nano-materials are available in granular form, fibers, films, and composites. The composition of nano-materials may consist of any combination of chemical elements. The most important nano-engineered materials are carbides, oxides, nitrides, metals and alloys, polymers, and various composites. Applications of nano-materials include cutting tools, metals, powders, computer chips, flat-panel displays for laptops, sensors, and various electrical and magnetic components.

Significant effort is being focused on developing very tiny motors, pumps, gyroscopes and accelerometers, implantable drug delivery systems, artificial body parts, and tiny bio- and chemical sensors. Whole miniature systems, for example, fly–size helicopters used in surveillance behind enemy lines, although more micro than nano in size, incorporate many nano-mechanical elements.

Nano-manufacturing. In order to perform nano-manufacturing, nano-robots and automated manufacturing are being developed so that novel systems can be manufactured as well as current precision manufacturing operations accomplished at a significantly lower cost. Small machines and robots are considered to be faster, lighter, cheaper, and more energy efficient. In addition, they can access small openings and perform well in small places. A magnified nano-device is shown in Figure 2.11.

Figure 2.11: Magnified nano-device.

2.2.8 SMART (INTELLIGENT) MATERIALS

Smart or intelligent materials are nonorganic materials that are able to sense and respond to changes in their environment in predetermined manners. Until recently, this behavior was reserved only for living organisms. Smart materials can be sophisticated systems that include smart and traditional materials. Although they are a relatively new invention, many of us are benefiting from them daily without being aware of it or considering them to be "smart." One example is eyeglasses that darken when exposed to sunlight, or ultraviolet or *photochromic radiation*, blocking the ultraviolet light to protect the eyes from sun damage.

Currently, the most important engineering materials that belonging to the "smart" category are shape-memory alloys, piezoelectric ceramics, and magnetostrictive materials:

1. **Shape-memory alloys:** nickel-titanium and copper-based alloys (CuZnAl and CuAlNi) as well as some iron alloys are materials that change their crystallographic structure with temperature and, once the temperature is restored, revert to their previous crystallographic structure and shape they had at that temperature. Simply stated, they can be deformed at room temperature but change back to their original shape when heated. The behavior of shape-memory alloys can be reversible, that is, their shape can switch back and forth repeatedly upon periodic application and removal of heat.

    One of the benefits of smart materials is the use of shape-memory alloys for dental braces. Braces are made to fit tightly over the biting edges of the teeth. Dentists experience difficulty when trying to pull them over the relatively larger arc along the gum portion of the teeth. This can be a hard and painful process. In contrast, braces made of smart materials undergo a crystallographic change at the mouth temperature. They are made smaller (tighter) at that temperature, then stretched to a larger size at room temperature. The larger braces can be easily inserted in the patient's mouth. At body temperature in the mouth, which is higher than room temperature, the smart material will "remember" its previous shape and squeeze the teeth upon shrinking to the right size.

    Shape-memory alloys are also used for eyeglass frames, collapsible antennas, greenhouse window openers, temperature regulators, and fire sprinklers. They can be used for clamps, connectors, and easy-to-install fasteners and seals. In biomedical applications, they are used as blood-clot filters, self-extending coronary stents, and bone anchors. The main advantage of these materials is that they function without any input of external energy (except changes in temperature).

2. **Piezoelectric ceramics:** often called *piezoelectric crystals*, materials that produce a voltage when they experience a change in dimension (strain) under an applied load (stresses). This effect is reversible. When a voltage is applied across the piezoelectric ceramic, it will undergo a dimensional change, that is, portions of the ceramic will extend or contract. Piezoelectric ceramics are sensitive to displacements on the order of a few nanometers when used as transducers to generate and detect ultrasonic waves in other materials. They can also be calibrated to measure applied loads, strains, accelerations, or force by measuring the voltage or current output that is produced. They have a very fast response and are more sensitive to changes in load than commonly used strain gages. One example of use is in dynamometers that measure fluctuating forces in metal cutting under chatter (vibrating) conditions.

On the other hand, very high voltages correspond to only tiny changes in the width of the piezoelectric crystals; this width can be changed with better-than-micrometer precision, making piezoelectric ceramics very suitable for actuators that are used for positioning objects with extreme accuracy. High-precision motors can be designed by positioning piezoelectric elements on the axis so that they apply a directional force causing it to rotate. Suitable design structures made from these materials can therefore be made that bend, expand, or contract when a voltage is applied.

3. **Magnetostrictive materials:** the behavior of which is analogous to that of piezoelectric ceramics except they respond to a magnetic field; that is, they produce a magnetic field when strain is applied or produce changes in dimension (strain) when a magnetic field is applied. Like piezoelectric ceramics, magnetostrictive materials are also used as ultrasonic transducers.

Materials scientists, chemists, and engineers are working on the development of smart materials that can be used in micromechanical and nano-devices as well as in everyday life applications. One of many interesting applications is pH sensitive material, that is, material that changes its color as a result of changing acidity. (It is interesting to note that the flowering plant hydrangea does the same thing in nature.) One suggested application is for paints that can change color to indicate corrosion in the metal underneath them. Other research is focused on development of roof tiles that are light color in the summer to reflect sunrays and heat and are black in the winter to absorb radiation. What will be developed next, only the future can tell. Certainly, engineering will continue to make great progress in the development and use of intelligent materials.

2.2.9 FOAMS, GELS, AND METALLIC GLASSES

Foams, gels, and metallic glasses are not new materials but new forms of known materials having different structures.

2.2.9.1 FOAMS

Foams are made from metals and graphite. Metal foams are usually made from aluminum and, less frequently, titanium or tantalum. In the foam, the solid metal represents only 5% to 20% of the volume; therefore, the weight of the foam is only 5% to 20% compared to the solid metallic piece. However, the specific strength (how much load the material can carry per unit weight) and the specific stiffness (deformation under load divided by unit weight) of the foam are larger than for solid metal, giving it an advantage in the aerospace industry. Foams often compete with honeycomb composites used for the same reason. Other applications include filters, lightweight beams, and orthopedic implants.

Current methods of metallic foam productions are:

- Blowing air into molten metal and tapping the froth that forms on the surface. When the froth solidifies, it becomes foam.
- Chemical vapor deposition on a polymer or carbon lattice that is later burned away.
- Slip casting powders onto polymer foam.
- Doping molten or powder metals with titanium hydride, which, at the casting or sintering temperature of the product, releases hydrogen, leaving a large number of cavities in the structure.

Carbon foams with very finely dispersed porosity, called *microcellular foams*, have isotropic properties (that is, equal in all three directions) and can be shaped directly into complicated aerospace structures. Figure 2.12 shows an example of a metallic foam.

Figure 2.12: Foamed aluminum.

2.2.9.2 GELS

By definition, gels are a "colloidal state comprised of inter-dispersed solid and liquid, in which the solid particles are themselves interconnected or interlaced in three dimensions" (*ASM Materials Engineering Dictionary*). Gels have a jellylike consistency and often are just a phase in the production of polymers. For instance, very strong polymer fibers are produced with a gel-spinning process. Polymer is not completely melted or dissolved in liquid, but molecules are bonded together in liquid crystal form. This operation produces strong forces between chains in the resulting filament. In this case, the gel is just the starting consistency of polymers in the production of polymer fibers.

One interesting development is so-called "aerogel" discovered in 1930 but getting more attention recently. It is not gel at all but foam, consisting of gas (air) and solid (silicon), not liquid and solid, as a strict definition of gel requires. The aerogel is silica-based substance that is 97% air. It is the lightest of all solid materials known. You cannot feel its weight when held in your hand; however, when dropped on a hard surface, it bounces and rings like a piece of light metal. Aerogel is produced from an alcohol-based gel with silica particles that resemble a wet cube of gelatin. It is then soaked in liquid carbon dioxide, which evaporates at high pressure. This process allows the gel to dry without collapsing. The resulting aerogel is a weave of air pockets and tiny silica beads, each one millionth the thickness of a human hair. Scientists think that Earth's gravity causes air pockets to form in different sizes, giving aerogel a hazy blue appearance that has inspired the names "frozen smoke" or "pet cloud."

Although it's nearly as light as a spider web, aerogel is surprisingly strong. A block the size of a human body weighs less than a pound and can support the weight of a subcompact car, about 450 kg (0.5 ton). However, the largest potential application of aerogel is as an extraordinary heat, sound, and electrical energy isolator. Its vast internal surface area completely absorbs heat, sound, and electrical energy. It is estimated that a 25.4 mm (1 in.) thick sheet of the substance provides the same thermal isolation as 10 double-pane windows, making it attractive for use in houses, cars, and appliances. The problem with aerogel is that it is very brittle and fragile. In 1998, an experiment was conducted by astronaut John Glenn on the Space Shuttle *Discovery* to produce aerogel in space with air pockets of uniform size to make it completely transparent.

The National Aeronautics and Space Administration (NASA) has used aerogel on the Mars Pathfinder mission to keep the rover *Sojourner* warm in freezing temperatures. It was also used on the Stardust mission to capture cometary samples and interstellar dust. More development is needed before aerogel reaches the commercial market, but the results could bring great benefits.

2.2.9.3 METALLIC GLASSES

As we will see later, when cooled from a melted state, metals ordinarily form long-range very uniform crystalline structures. However, since the late 1960s, it was found that some metallic alloys, when cooled very rapidly (from one million to 100 million degrees celsius per second), do not have enough time to crystallize. Instead, they form *amorphous* (without order) structures. Because their structure resembles that of glasses, which are also amorphous, they are called *metallic glasses.*

Metallic glasses are composed predominantly of iron, nickel, and chromium alloyed with carbon, phosphorus, boron, aluminum, zirconium, and silicon. They are formed with special techniques, such as *splat cooling* or *melt spinning*, in which molten alloys are propelled under high gas pressures at a very high speed against a rotating copper disk (chill surface). They can be also produced by vapor deposition and electrochemical deposition. Metallic glasses are now available in bulk quantities, as well as wire, ribbon, strip, and powder form.

Figure 2.13: Removal of disc of metallic glass from spacecraft capsule.

Atoms in metallic glasses are randomly and tightly packed. Because they do not form crystals, neither do they have grain boundaries. Grain boundaries represent the borders between grains or crystals. Within each crystal, atoms are uniformly aligned along a specific orientation. The atomic orientation, grain size, and boundaries play a great role in facilitating deformation of crystallographic structures (as we will see later). Lack of grain boundaries and crystallographic structure renders metallic glasses extremely strong (up to 10 times stronger than crystalline metals and alloys). Due to their strength and toughness, they are candidates for armored vehicles.

Metallic glasses have metallic luster and electrical conductivity similar to those of the metals from which they are formed. They have excellent corrosion resistance and high moduli of elasticity. Balls made from metallic glasses bounce off of a surface similar to rubber balls but emit a typical metallic sound or clang. This lack of energy loss during impact makes metallic glasses candidates for sporting equipment, such as golf clubs. Similarly metallic glasses lose very little energy from magnetic hysteresis, making them suitable for magnetic steel cores for transformers, generators, motors, magnetic amplifiers, and linear accelerators.

Production and application of metallic glasses is currently being researched extensively as an important and emerging form of materials. In 2004, a disc of bulk metallic glass was placed in a canister aboard the *Genesis* spacecraft launched by NASA to collect data about particulate exposure and molecular contamination in space. (See Figure 2.13.)

2.3 COMPOSITION OF MATERIALS

2.3.1 ATOMIC STRUCTURE

As it was described in previous section, different materials can exhibit a wide range of properties and many of them can be related to the type of atoms and arrangement of atoms in the structure.

By definition, an *atom* is the smallest part of an element that retains the properties of that element. A *molecule* is the smallest part of the compound (a substance consisting of more than one kind of atom) that retains properties of that compound.

The science that governs the system of atomic and subatomic particles and their behavior in atoms and solids is called *quantum mechanics*. A detailed explanation of quantum mechanics is beyond the scope of this book, and we will give only a simplified explanation of principles involved.

Each atom consists of a nucleus composed of protons, positively charged particles (arbitrary convention), and neutrons, which are not electrically charged. The nucleus is relatively stationary and very small, about 10^{-14} m. It is encircled by a thinly dispersed moving electron cloud of varying density so that the diameter of the atom is on the order of 10^{-10} m (about 10 000 larger than the nucleus). Both protons and electrons have an equal magnitude of electrical charge of 1.60×10^{-19} C (coulombs), but the charge of electrons is considered negative (-1.60×10^{-19} C) while that of protons is positive ($+1.60 \times 10^{-19}$ C).

Due to the very small size of atoms, only since the mid 1990s has it been possible to "see" atoms with available microscopes. With optical microscopes (also called inverted microscopes), scientists are able to distinguish different microstructures, grains, and grain boundaries. The human eye can distinguish down to 10^{-4} of a meter (or 1/10 of a millimeter). Optical microscopes can resolve features of 10^{-7} m, or 1000× smaller than the human eye can see.

Recently developed microscopes can distinguish features on the order of nanometers (nm), where one nanometer, as mentioned, equals 10^{-9} of a meter. Currently available microscopes with very high resolutions include:
- Scanning electron microscope (SEM) – with 1 nm resolution.
- Transmission electron microscope (TEM) – with 0.1 nm resolution.

- Atomic force microscope (AFM) – with 0.1 nm resolution.
- Scanning tunneling microscope (STM) – with 0.01 nm depth and 0.1 nm lateral resolution.

These sophisticated microscopes are bringing humans into the range of "seeing" individual atoms, although the processes that they use do not create images using light, as with optical microscopes.

Although specific scanning probe microscopes differ from one another with regard to the type of interaction that is monitored, these instruments have provided a wealth of information about a variety of materials, from integrated circuit chips to biological molecules, and have helped us move into the era of nanomaterials and engineered atomic and molecular structures.

2.3.2 ATOMIC NUMBER, ATOMIC MASS, MOLECULAR MASS

Atomic Number. The *atomic number*, referred to as the *Z-number*, is the number of protons in the nucleus. For a neutral atom—that is, completely without missing electrons—the number of protons is equal to the number of electrons. This atomic number ranges in integers from 1 for hydrogen to 92 for uranium, the highest of naturally occurring elements. It is given in the top of each square in the periodic table of elements, as shown in Figure 2.14.

IUPAC	1	2	3	4	5	6	7	8	9	10	11	12	13	14	15	16	17	18
Old	IA	IIA	IIIA	IVA	VA	VIA	VIIA	VIIIA	VIIIA	VIIIA	IB	IIB	IIIB	IVB	VB	VIB	VIIB	VIIIB
Group CAS	IA	IIA	IIIB	IVB	VB	VIB	VIIB	VIII	VIII	VIII	IB	IIB	IIIA	IVA	VA	VIA	VIIA	VIIIA
1 AN	1																	2
ES	H																	He
AW	1.01																	4.00
2 AN	3	4											5	6	7	8	9	10
ES	Li	Be											B	C	N	O	F	Ne
AW	6.94	9.01											10.81	12.01	14.01	16.00	19.00	20.18
3 AN	11	12											13	14	15	16	17	18
ES	Na	Mg											Al	Si	P	S	Cl	Ar
AW	22.99	24.31											26.98	28.09	30.97	32.07	35.45	39.95
4 AN	19	20	21	22	23	24	25	26	27	28	29	30	31	32	33	34	35	36
ES	K	Ca	Sc	Ti	V	Cr	Mn	Fe	Co	Ni	Cu	Zn	Ga	Ge	As	Se	Br	Kr
AW	39.10	40.08	44.96	47.87	50.94	52.00	54.94	55.85	58.93	58.69	63.55	65.39	69.72	72.61	74.92	78.96	79.90	83.80
5 AN	37	38	39	40	41	42	43	44	45	46	47	48	49	50	51	52	53	54
ES	Rb	Sr	Y	Zr	Nb	Mo	Tc	Ru	Rh	Pd	Ag	Cd	In	Sn	Sb	Te	I	Xe
AW	85.47	87.62	88.91	91.22	92.91	95.94	(98)	101.07	102.91	106.42	107.87	112.41	114.82	118.71	121.76	127.60	126.90	131.29
6 AN	55	56	57	72	73	74	75	76	77	78	79	80	81	82	83	84	85	86
ES	Cs	Ba	La	Hf	Ta	W	Re	Os	Ir	Pt	Au	Hg	Tl	Pb	Bi	Po	At	Rn
AW	132.91	137.33	138.91	178.49	180.95	183.84	186.21	190.23	192.22	195.08	196.97	200.59	204.38	207.20	208.98	(209)	(210)	(222)
7 AN	87	88	89	104	105	106	107	108	109	110	111	112	(113)	114	(115)	116	(117)	118
ES	Fr	Ra	Ac	Rf	Db	Sg	Bh	Hs	Mt	Uun	Uuu	Uub	Uut	Uuq	Uup	Uuh	Uus	Uuo
AW	(223)	(226)	(227)	(261)	(262)	(266)	(264)	(269)	(268)	(271)	(272)	( )	—	( )	—	( )	—	( )

Lanthanide series	AN	58	59	60	61	62	63	64	65	66	67	68	69	70	71
	ES	Ce	Pr	Nd	Pm	Sm	Eu	Gd	Tb	Dy	Ho	Er	Tm	Yb	Lu
	AW	140.12	140.91	144.24	(145)	150.36	151.96	157.25	158.93	162.50	164.93	167.26	168.93	173.04	174.97
Actinide series	AN	90	91	92	93	94	95	96	97	98	99	100	101	102	103
	ES	Th	Pa	U	Np	Pu	Am	Cm	Bk	Cf	Es	Fm	Md	No	Lr
	AW	232.04	231.04	238.03	(237)	(244)	(243)	(247)	(247)	(251)	(252)	(257)	(258)	(259)	(262)

Legend

IUPAC = period numbering system (1 to 18) used by International Union of Pure and Applied Chemistry
Old = period system (with roman numerals) formerly used by International Union of Pure and Applied Chemistry
CAS = period numbering system (with roman numerals) used by Chemical Abstracts Service
AN = atomic number
ES = element symbol
AW = atomic weight
•••••• = lanthanide series occurs here
▬ ▬ ▬ = actinide series occurs here

Figure 2.14: Periodic table of elements.

Atomic Mass. Masses of atomic particles are very small; protons and neutrons have approximately the same mass, of 1.67×10^{-27} kg, while the mass of an electron is equal to 9.11×10^{-31} kg, or approximately 1/1836 the mass of a proton. The total mass of the atom is found when the masses of protons and neutrons are added together, while the masses of electrons are mostly neglected. While neutral atoms have an equal number of protons and electrons (that is the reason they are neutral, since the positive and negative charges cancel each other), the number of neutrons can vary, causing the atomic mass to vary. The atoms of the same element that have a different number of neutrons in their nucleus and therefore a different atomic mass are called *isotopes*.

For simplicity, a new unit of mass was introduced, the *atomic mass unit* (amu). The amu is equal to 1/12 of the atomic mass of carbon-12, the most common isotope of carbon. It contains 6 protons, 6 neutrons, and 6 electrons. Therefore, the amu is approximately 1.67×10^{-24} g (1.67×10^{-27} kg). Conversely, one gram is equal to 6.023×10^{23} amu. The mass of every atom in the periodic table of elements, expressed in amu units, is given at the bottom of each square below the chemical symbol for that element. For example, iron has an atomic mass of 55.845 amu; that is, one atom of iron has a mass of approximately $55.845 \times 1.67 \times 10^{-24}$ g $= 93.264 \times 10^{-24}$ g.

Another way of specifying the mass of an element is specifying the mass per one *mole of atoms*, where a mole represents 6.023×10^{23} (so-called Avogadro's number) of atoms or molecules. For instance, one mole of iron atoms, or Avogadro's number of atoms, has a mass of 55.845 g. This can be obtained by multiplying the mass of one iron atom (93.264×10^{-24} g) with Avogadro's number. This gives the approximate mass of 56.1 g, which is slightly different from 55.854 because of the approximations involved. While one atom of iron has a mass of 55.845 amu, one mole of iron has a mass of 55.854 g.

Atomic Weight. Instead of mass, material scientists often use the term *atomic weight*, where weight is mass multiplied by gravitation (it is what you read when you put something on the scale), and it can be represented in grams or kilograms. For example, often-used terms in materials science for iron are as follows: atomic weight of iron is 55.845 amu and molecular weight (or weight of one mole) of iron is 55.845 g. *Note:* In engineering, the unit for weight (or force) is one newton (N), which is approximately 1/10 of 1 kg.

2.3.3 ATOMIC BONDING

Atoms are assumed to be spherical, although this assumption is not always justified. Electrons exist around the nucleus in orbits with different radii, each representing a different energy level. Only two electrons, which must have different "spins," can have the same energy level (the so-called *pauli exclusion principle*). Some different energy levels are combined into shells.

The electrons that occupy the outermost shell are called *valence electrons*, and these electrons are extremely important, as they participate in the bonding between atoms to form atomic and molecular groups. Furthermore, many of the physical and chemical properties of solids are based on these valence electrons.

Some atoms have stable electron configurations; that is, their valence electron shells are completely filled. These elements (He, Ne, Ar, Kr, and Xe) are the inert, or noble, gases, which virtually do not react chemically with other elements. Some atoms of the elements that have unfilled valence shells assume stable electron configurations by gaining or losing electrons or by sharing electrons with other atoms.

Atoms that have an electrical charge are called *ions*; those positively charged are called *cations*, and negatively charged atoms are called *anions*. Cations have smaller atomic radii than neutral atoms, while anions have larger radii.

Metals are also called *electropositive elements* because they easily "give up" their valence electrons and became positively charged. Most elements in the periodic table are metals. Elements located on the right side of the periodic table are *electronegative*, meaning they readily accept electrons to form anions.

Chemical Bonding between Atoms. A scientific principle is that every object seeks to decrease its potential energy. Chemical bonding between atoms is accompanied by a net decrease in the potential energy of atoms in the bonded state. For our purpose, it is important to discuss different types of bonding between atoms and their influence on properties of materials.

In general, chemical bonding between atoms can be divided into two groups:
- Primary or strong bonds.
- Secondary or weak bonds.

Three different types of primary bonds are found in solids: ionic, covalent, and metallic. Strong bonds mean that large amounts of energy have to be spent to separate atoms. This energy can be *mechanical* (work done to break the part) or *thermal* (energy necessary to melt the part). Therefore, stiffness of the part and melting temperature (T_m) are indications of the strength of the bonds. Ionic materials have high melting and boiling points due to a strong ionic bond force. However, if the strong bonds are present only between certain sets of atoms—as with covalent bonds— material can be easily broken or melted into molecules at low temperature without separating strong primary bonds in each molecule.

It is important to understand these key aspects of atomic bonds, in order to predict how measureable properties might change due to differences in chemistry or temperature. Figure 2.15 shows how the energy of two atoms, interacting with each other, changes depending on how close they are to each other. The steep "wall" near the Y-axis indicates that two atoms cannot easily be pushed into each other so that they occupy the same space. This *can* be done, of course, and it is known as *nuclear fusion*. As the two atoms get farther apart, they interact less. There is a trough in the curve, which is the equilibrium bonding distance at 0 K.

Atomic Responses to Increases in Temperature. When atoms increase in temperature, they gain kinetic energy and vibrate. Temperature is essentially a measurement of the kinetic energy of atoms. Because the bonding curve is not symmetrical, an atom that vibrates more and more will be, on average, slightly further away from the minimum of the bonding curve. (See Figure 2.16.)

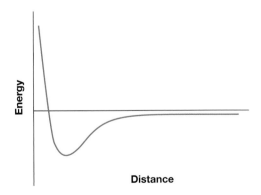

Figure 2.15: The energy versus distance diagram for atomic bonding. The low point on the graph shows the equilibrium atomic separation at 0 K.

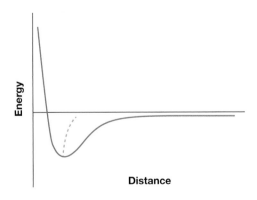

Figure 2.16: The average position of an atom is indicated by the gray dotted line. As temperature increases, the position gets farther away from the origin.

This is the cause of *thermal expansion*, which is why most materials, with the exception of polymers, expand when heated. Some exceptions exist during phase transformations, such as ice melting, as well. This causes a change in material stiffness. The stiffness of a material is directly related to the shape of the bonding curve. As a material heats up, and the atoms move farther apart, they will also be at a position on the curve with less sharp curvature. That means that the elastic modulus will *decrease* as temperature *increases*. If the stiffness of a material decreases, the speed of sound, or *shear modulus*, in that material also decreases. Acoustic velocity, as measured with ultrasonic testing (UT), for instance, is governed by material density. Thus, the stiffness of a material and, correspondingly, the speed of sound in that material are related to the strength of the atomic bonds.

The strength of those bonds is dependent on which atoms are present and how they are arranged relative to each other. For this reason, most steels will have very similar stiffness. In other words, steels almost all have an elastic modulus between 195 GPa and 210 GPa. Aluminum alloys will have elastic moduli around 70 GPa. This is very useful information in practice because you can make a very accurate guess about the stiffness of a material and therefore the speed of sound, if you know the stiffness of a similar chemistry. Knowing that the stiffness changes with chemistry and temperature can be very useful when analyzing the results of ultrasonic testing.

2.3.3.1 IONIC BONDING

Ionic bonding is perhaps the easiest to describe and visualize. It is always found in compounds that are composed of both metallic and nonmetallic elements. Atoms of a metallic element easily give up their valence electrons to the nonmetallic atoms. In the process, all atoms acquire a stable configuration with two electrons in the valence band. In addition, they acquire an electrical charge, therefore becoming ions. Metals have more protons than electrons in each atom; therefore, they are positively charged (cations). Nonmetallic materials accept one or more extra electrons and are negatively charged (anions). A classic example of ionic material is sodium chloride ($NaCl_2$), or table salt. In this case, the sodium atom loses one electron while the chlorine atom gains one. Both atoms are now electrically charged, and they attract each other with *coulombic* forces and form an ionic bond. Ionic bonding is termed nondirectional— that is, the magnitude of the bonding force is equal in all directions around an ion. It follows that in materials bonded by ionic bonds, each cation has to have as its closest neighbor an anion. Figure 2.17 illustrates schematically ionic bonding.

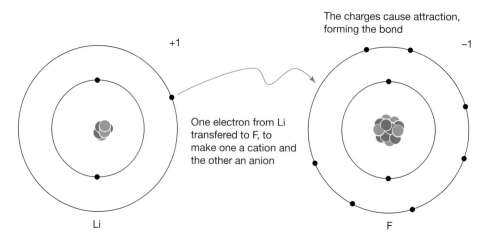

The charges cause attraction, forming the bond

+1

−1

One electron from Li transfered to F, to make one a cation and the other an anion

Li

F

Figure 2.17: Ionic bonding between lithium and fluorine to form lithium fluoride.

Ionic materials are characteristically hard and brittle and melt at high temperatures. For example, NaCl melts at 800 °C (1472 °F), while M$_g$O melts at 2800 °C (5072 °F). Materials with ionic bonds are electrical and thermal isolators. For example, ceramics are predominantly bonded ionically.

2.3.3.2 COVALENT BONDING

In covalent bonding, a stable electrical configuration is achieved by the sharing of electrons between adjacent atoms. Two atoms that are covalently bonded will each contribute at least one electron to the bond. The shared electrons belong to both atoms.

The covalent bond is directional; it exists only in the direction between one atom and another that participates in electron sharing. Many nonmetallic elements form molecules where two identical atoms share electrons (for example, H$_2$ Cl$_2$ and F$_2$), as well as molecules containing dissimilar atoms, such as CH$_4$, H$_2$O, HNO$_3$, and others. In figure 2.18, a covalent bond between two hydrogen atoms is shown.

Some elemental solids, such as carbon in diamond form, silicon, and germanium, bond with covalent bonds. Other such solids include compounds made from elements located on the right-hand side of the periodic table (beginning with IIIA [CAS numbering]: gallium arsenide (GaAs), indium antimonide (InSb), and silicon carbide (SiC). Most are semiconductors. Diamond is simply a three-dimensional interconnected structure wherein each carbon atom covalently bonds with four other carbon atoms.

Polymeric materials are also bonded covalently. Each carbon atom has four electrons in the valence band, and two of them are used to bond with two neighboring carbon atoms (shared), while the remaining two are shared with different atoms making different types of polymers.

Most covalent bonds are very strong as indicated by their melting temperature (T_m). For example, Si melts at 1410 °C (2570 °F) and diamond at a temperature higher than 3550 °C (6422 °F). On the other hand, due to the directional bonding and lack of shared electrons in three dimensions, many covalently bonded elemental molecules, for example, H$_2$, Cl$_2$, and F$_2$, as well molecules containing dissimilar

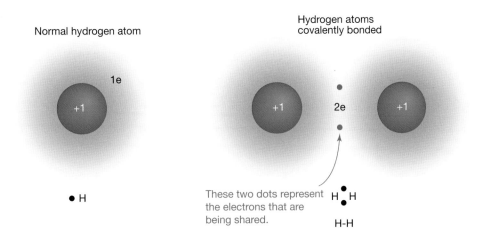

Figure 2.18: Covalent bond forming H$_2$ (right) with two hydrogen atoms sharing two electrons.

atoms, such as CH_4 or HNO_3, are gases or liquids (H_2O) at room temperature. Also, as mentioned, thermoplastic polymers are not strong due to the lack of primary bonding in three directions.

2.3.3.3 METALLIC BONDING

Metallic bonding, as the name implies, is found in metals and their alloys. Metallic materials have one, two, or mostly three valence electrons, which are not bound to any particular atom in the solid, which means that there is room in each atom for electrons to travel in the valence band. They are free to drift throughout the entire material and are considered to belong to the metal as a whole, forming a "sea of electrons" or an electron cloud. The remaining nonvalence electrons and atomic nuclei form so-called *ion cores*, which possess a net positive charge equal in magnitude to the total valence electron charge per atom (number of valence electrons × the charge of each electron of 1.6×10^{-19} C).

The free electrons shield the positively charged ion cores from the other core. Both cores are positively charged, and if electrons are not present, the cores repel each other. In addition, these free electrons act as a glue to hold the ion cores together. The metallic bond is nondirectional in character. Bonding energy and melting temperature (T_m) are proportional.

For example, bonding energy for mercury (Hg) is 68 kJ/mol, aluminum (Al) 324 kJ/mol, iron (Fe) 406 kJ/mol, and tungsten (W) 849 kJ/mol. The corresponding T_m is –39 °C (–38.2 °F) for Hg (mercury is liquid at room temperature), 660 °C (1220 °F) for Al, 1538 °C (2800 °F) for Fe, and 3410 °C (6170 °F) for W.

If the metal is not connected to a source of electricity, the movement of electrons is random. If the material is connected to a source of electricity, electrons are attracted to the positive electrode, and holes (positive charge or missing electron) to the negative electrode.

Most metals and their alloys are ductile at room temperature, meaning they can be plastically deformed without fracture. In other words, their atoms can change position without the metallic bond being broken. In contrast, in covalent- and ionic-bonded solids, the bond between atoms has to be broken before atoms can move, rendering these materials brittle. Figure 2.19 schematically illustrates metallic bonding.

Actually, very few compounds exhibit only one type of bonding. It is possible that interatomic bonds (named after the dominant effect) are partially ionic and

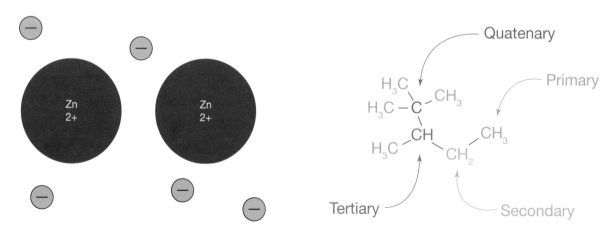

Figure 2.19: Metallic bonding of zinc.

Figure 2.20: Schematic of secondary bonds.

partially covalent, or partially covalent and partially metallic. The farther apart elements are on the periodic table, the greater their difference in electronegativity and their affinity to form ionic bonds. Electronegativity is a measure of the tendency of an atom to attract a bonding pair of electrons and is a root cause of corrosion and hydrogen embrittlement. Elements close to each other tend to form covalent or metallic bonds. The properties of materials are dependent on the percentage of each bond type.

2.3.3.4 SECONDARY BONDING

Secondary or so-called *van der waals bonds* are much weaker than primary bonds. They are on the order of only 0.4 to 4 kJ/mol (compared to the primary bond for iron of 406 kJ/mol and others given above) and are always present, although they can be obscured by primary bonds, if also present. They are evident in inert gases, which have stable electron structures and do not bond with primary bonds but still become liquid (bonding) at low temperatures. Also, these secondary bonding forces are important in covalent bonding; they act between large molecules of polymers making three-dimensional solids. (See Figure 2.20 for an illustration of secondary bonds.)

2.4 CRYSTALLINE STRUCTURE

At a given high temperature, any material will transform into a gaseous state. How high that temperature is depends upon the strength of the bonds between molecules and atoms. With dipole interactions, differences in electronegativity are also involved. In a gaseous state, atoms have high kinetic energy, causing them to vibrate rapidly and to break intermolecular attractive forces. So "free" molecules or atoms can expand and fill the available volume.

If the energy of the material is lowered (through condensation), atoms or molecules move less rapidly (that is, condense) and attractive forces play a more significant role. In this state, the molecules or atoms take random positions and structures that vary in time but maintain a constant average spacing. This state is a *liquid*, and the materials have fixed volume but assume the shape of the container in which they are placed.

As the energy level is further decreased, the mobility of the atoms decreases, atomic bonding occurs, and a solid is formed. If the atoms or ions in a solid are arranged in a pattern that repeats itself in three dimensions, they form a solid with a *crystalline structure*. The reader is certainly familiar with the term "crystal," used for special glass or precious material. The same term applies to many other materials that are neither transparent nor termed precious but could be very useful nonetheless.

Crystallization. Essentially, all metals (except when cooled at an extremely rapid rate, forming metallic glasses, as explained earlier), a major fraction of ceramic materials, and certain polymers *crystallize* when they solidify. Those materials that do not crystallize are called *amorphous* (literally without form) as in many polymers and ceramics (including optical glasses). Some materials partially crystallize, leaving parts of the structure amorphous, for example, some solid state polymers. Often, these amorphous regions crystallize with time, resulting in a volume decrease of the polymer.

Crystals possess a *periodicity* that produces *long-range order*. That really means that equal atomic arrangements repeat at regular intervals millions of times in a three-dimensional lattice. Some of the properties of crystalline solids depend on the *crystalline structure* of the material, that is, the manner in which atoms, ions, or molecules are spatially arranged. There is an extremely large number of different crystalline structures all having long-range atomic order. They vary from relatively simple structures for pure metals to exceedingly complex ones, as in some metallic compounds, minerals, ceramics, and polymers. Here we will discuss the most common metallic crystalline structures.

The atomic order in crystalline solids means that a group of atoms forms a repetitive three-dimensional pattern, called a *unit cell,* which is the basic building block of the material. The periodicity of the unit cell creates a lattice structure. The different lengths of the axial distances of the unit cell—a, b, c—and the angles between them define the type of lattice. The axial distances are called *lattice vectors* or *lattice constants*, and the angles between them are not necessarily perpendicular to one another. If the lengths of the three lattice constants are equal, the angles between them are all 90° and the unit cell is cubic. If the angles are 90° but the length of one side is different, then the unit cell is tetragonal. If all three lengths are different and the angles are 90°, then the unit cell is orthorhombic. If the length and angles are all different and none of the angles is 90°, then the unit cells is triclinic. In the hexagonal unit cell —a equals b but not c— the angle between a and b is 120°, and the remaining two angles are 90°. For further information, the reader is encouraged to look up information on the *bravais lattice*. There are only 14 possible lattice structures.

Common Unit Cell Structures. The type of unit cell and atomic arrangement within it has a strong influence on the physical and mechanical properties of that material. The most common unit cells in metals are the body-centered cubic (BCC), face-centered cubic (FCC), and hexagonal close-packed (HCP) structures or lattices, as shown in Figure 2.21. Unit cells are often sketched as shown in the figure with circles in the cubic structure representing the centers of atoms. This is known as the *ball and stick model* or the *simple model*. In fact, nearly all metals fall under one of these three unit cell types.

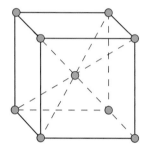

Body-centered cubic lattice

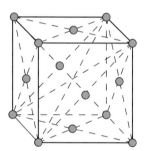

Face-centered cubic lattice

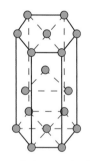

Hexagonal close-packed lattice

Figure 2.21: Common metallic lattices.

2.4.1 BODY-CENTERED CUBIC STRUCTURE

Iron has a cubic structure but two different types of unit cells at different temperatures. At room temperature, the unit cell has one atom at each corner of the cubic structure and one atom in the middle of the cubic structure. It is known as the *body-centered cubic* (BCC) structure. The atoms are touching along the diagonal of the cubic structure. Because of that arrangement, the body diagonal of a BCC unit cell can be written as:

(Eq. 2.1)
$$4R = a_{BCC} \text{ unit cell } \sqrt{3}$$

Where R is the radius of the atom and a_{BCC} is the lattice constant, which is equal on all sides of the BCC. This is illustrated in Figure 2.22.

Every atom has the same surroundings. If the unit cell is selected so that a corner atom is now in the middle, we would get the same arrangement of atoms in the new unit cell.

It is important to notice that although eight atoms are placed in the corners of the simple model of the BCC structure, only 1/8 of each belongs to the unit cell being represented. The remaining 7/8 belong to the neighboring unit cells. With eight corners of 1/8 atoms each and one atom in the center, two whole atoms make up the BCC unit cell.

If we assume that atoms are spherical (hard-ball model) we can calculate the *packing factor* of the unit cell as a volume of the spherical atoms with radius R and divide that with the volume of the unit cell.

For a BCC unit cell, the total volume of atoms in a unit cell is:

(Eq. 2.2)
$$2 \times \left(\frac{4}{3} \pi R^3 \right) = \frac{8}{3} \pi R^3$$

The total volume of the unit cell is:

(Eq. 2.3)
$$a^3 = \left(\frac{4}{\sqrt{3}} R \right)^3$$

The packing factor (PF_{BCC}) equals:

(Eq. 2.4)
$$\frac{\text{volume of atoms}}{\text{volume of unit cell}}$$

This can be expressed as:

(Eq. 2.5)
$$\frac{\left(\frac{8}{3} \pi R^3 \right)}{\left(\frac{4}{\sqrt{3}} R \right)^3} = 0.68$$

This really means that 68% of the space in a BCC unit cell is occupied with atoms, while 32% is empty interstitial space. Note that the packing factor is independent of the size of the radius of the atom. Foreign atoms can occupy this interstitial space and create new alloys, such as when carbon and other elements are introduced to iron in making steel.

Iron is the most common metal with a body-centered cubic (BCC) structure. Chromium, tungsten, titanium, lithium, sodium, and potassium also have the BCC structure.

Figure 2.22: Schematics of body-centered cubic (BCC) structure.

2.4.2 FACE-CENTERED CUBIC STRUCTURE

As one can gather from the previous section, some metals have the BCC structure, but the majority of metals have a *face-centered cubic* (FCC) structure. The FCC unit cell has one atom at each corner and another in the center of each face of the cubic structure. The atoms are touching along the diagonal of each side, or face, of the cubic structure.

The face diagonal of an FCC unit cell is:

(Eq. 2.6)
$$4R = a_{\text{FCC}} \text{ unit cell } \sqrt{2}$$

The side of a unit cell is equal to:

(Eq. 2.7)
$$4 \times \left(\frac{4}{3} \pi R^3 \right) = \frac{16}{3} \pi R^3$$

The FCC unit cell is shown in Figure 2.23.

There is a total of four whole atoms in the FCC structure unit cell: six 1/2 atoms in the center of each side and eight 1/8 atoms at each corner. The lattice constant of the FCC is larger than that for the BCC unit cell, but it contains four atoms, resulting in a higher packing factor.

For the FCC unit cell, the total volume of atoms in unit cell is:

(Eq. 2.8)
$$4 \times \left(\frac{4}{3} \pi R^3 \right) = \frac{16}{3} \pi R^3$$

The total volume of a unit cell is:

(Eq. 2.9)
$$a^3 = \left(\frac{4}{\sqrt{2}} R \right)^3$$

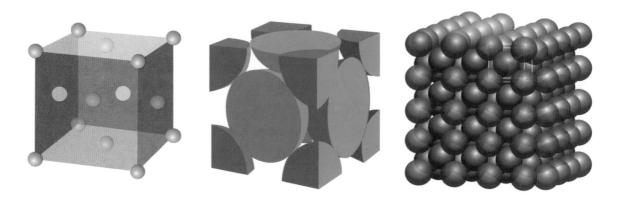

Figure 2.23: Schematics of face-centered cubic (FCC) structure.

The packing factor (PF_{FCC}) is:

(Eq. 2.10)
$$\frac{\text{volume of atoms}}{\text{volume of unit cell}}$$

This can be expressed as:

(Eq. 2.11)
$$\frac{\left(\dfrac{16}{3}\pi R^3\right)}{\left(\dfrac{4}{\sqrt{2}}R\right)^3} = 0.74$$

Larger packing factors mean that the FCC metals are more densely packed. Iron has an FCC structure at higher temperatures, and it weighs more per unit volume than at room temperature where it is more "loosely" packed in a BCC structure. Aluminum, copper, nickel, silver, lead, gold, and some other materials form FCC crystallographic structures. Some compounds, such as NaCl (table salt) also have the FCC structure. The unit cell may be viewed as an FCC structure of one type of atom, for example, Na, with the other, Cl, occupying the interstitial vacancies. Both elements for an FCC structure are intertwined.

2.4.3 HEXAGONAL CLOSE-PACKED STRUCTURE

A hexagonal close-packed (HCP) structure with the center of atoms represented as hard balls is shown in Figure 2.24a. The hard-ball representation of whole atoms is shown in Figure 2.24b. This structure represents three HCP unit cells, which are skewed prisms. As can be seen, each atom in one layer is located directly above or below the interstices created by the space between three adjacent atoms in neighboring layers. Atoms are touching along the side of the base. In an ideal HCP structure, c/a = 1.633, but for most HCP metals c/a ratios differ slightly due to the presence of mixed bonding conditions—metallic and some covalent.

The FCC and HCP are close-packed structures; that is, they are packed very efficiently with the highest possible packing factor of 0.74. Several metals have the HCP structure including zinc, magnesium, titanium, and cobalt.

2.4.4 AMORPHOUS STRUCTURES

As mentioned earlier, solids can be generally classified into two types: (1) crystalline, which can form a regular repeating three-dimensional structure called a crystal lattice, and (2) amorphous, which can aggregate with no particular order. The word *amorphous* is derived from Greek word "amorphos" meaning "without order."

In an amorphous solid, the local environment, including both the distances to neighboring units and the numbers of neighbors, varies throughout the material. Different amounts of thermal energy are needed to overcome these different interactions. Consequently, amorphous solids tend to soften slowly over a wide temperature range rather than having a well-defined melting point like a crystalline solid. If an amorphous solid is maintained at a temperature just below its melting point for long periods of time, the component molecules, atoms, or ions can gradually rearrange into a more highly ordered crystalline form.

Amorphous solids include both natural and manufactured materials. The most frequently cited example of an amorphous solid is glass. However, amorphous solids are common to all subsets of solids. Additional examples include thin film lubricants, metallic glasses, polymers, and gels.

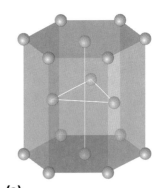
(a)

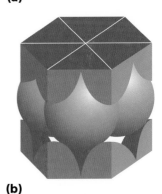
(b)

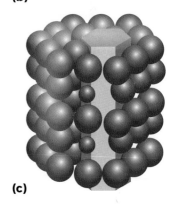
(c)

Figure 2.24: Schematics of hexagonal close-packed structure.

2.4.5 POLYMORPHISM

Materials that can have more than one structure are called *polymorphic* (or *allotropic*). As you might notice, Fe and Ti are listed as having two different structures: iron as BCC and FCC, and titanium as BCC and HCP. At temperatures higher than 912 °C (1674 °F) but lower than 1394 °C (2541 °F), pure iron has the FCC structure. Below 912 °C (1674 °F) or above 1394 °C (2541 °F), Fe has the BCC structure until melting at 1538 °C (2800 °F). This temperature is different for steels depending on their carbon content. (*Note:* The reader may wish to explore "phase diagrams" for further information on this topic.) Titanium has the HCP structure at low temperatures and BCC above 882 °C (1620 °F). These transformations provide the basis for the heat treatment of steel and titanium, as will be explained later. Many ceramic materials such as silica (SiO_2) are also polymorphic, as is carbon, which can have a graphite, diamond, or fullerine structure.

Volume Change. A volume change often accompanies these crystallographic transformations. For instance, when iron is cooled from a high temperature to below 912 °C (1674 °F), its packing factor changes from 0.74 to 0.66, as it changes from FCC to BCC and expands in volume. If we consider an iron atom with a given diameter, then we can compute the change in volume of the iron unit cell as it cools from 913 °C (1675 °F) to 912 °C (1674 °F).

The volume of the FCC cell (V_{FCC}) equals:

(Eq. 2.12)
$$\left(a_{FCC}\right)^3 = \left(4R\sqrt{2}\right)^3 = \left(0.3591 \text{ nm}\right)^3 = 0.046307 \text{ nm}^3$$

The volume of the BCC cell (V_{BCC}) equals:

(Eq. 2.13)
$$\left(a_{BCC}\right)^3 = \left(4R\sqrt{3}\right)^3 = \left(0.2683 \text{ nm}\right)^3 = 0.023467 \text{ nm}^3$$

The volume in the FCC unit cell is occupied by four atoms and in the BCC unit cell by two. So we have to compare two BCC unit cells with one FCC cell. Two BCC unit cells have a total volume of $2 \times 0.023467 = 0.046934$. The volume change per atom during the crystallographic transformation can be calculated as:

(Eq. 2.14)
$$\frac{\left(0.046307 - 0.046934\right)}{0.046934} = -0.0134$$

This represents a percentage change of –1.34%.

Upon further cooling, from 912 °C (1674 °F) to room temperature, the volume will decrease slightly because the diameter of the atom decreases, but this change is much less than the volume increase due to the change in crystallographic structure.

Residual Stress. This substantial change in volume can cause *residual stresses*, which result in warping and fracture. When FCC iron is cooled to room temperature, the surface of the part is cooled first and transforms to a BCC structure. The surface expands, while the interior is still hot and has the FCC structure. When the interior cools down and transforms to the BCC structure, it will start to expand, but the exterior, already cold and strong, tends to prevent this expansion. As a consequence of this "tug of war" situation, the surface is stretched and the core is compressed so that the forces in the part are in equilibrium. During this process, the surface may crack and warp. If a section of this part is cut off, the equilibrium of internal and external forces will be disrupted, which results in further warping until a new equilibrium is attained.

Residual stress can be caused by thermal gradients, crystallographic transformations, and plastic deformation. Plastic deformation can occur across the cross section of the part (for example, rolling or forging), or be localized to the surface (for example, peening). Residual stress can be problematic because very little external load could be required before the total stress exceeds the material's capacity. Residual stress can also be beneficial because localized compressive stress at the surface from peening must first be overcome by applied stresses, thus extending the fatigue life of the part. (Residual stresses and how they can be relieved are discussed in other sections of this book.)

2.4.6 SLIP LINES, PLANES, AND SYSTEMS

Different crystallographic structures deform differently under applied loads. Most materials experience some elastic deformation before they permanently (plastically) deform. During elastic deformation, the bonds between atoms are "stretched" or "compressed" but not broken. The volume of the material increases or decreases slightly depending on the type of the applied force: tension or compression. When the force is removed, the material "springs back" to the original shape and volume. (For more information on this type of action, the reader may wish to research *Hooke's law*. Hooke's law is a principle of physics that states that the force needed to extend or compress a spring by some distance is proportional to that distance. Essentially, Hooke's law shows the relationship between the forces applied to a spring and its elasticity. Derived from Hooke's law, the *modulus of elasticity* is the ratio of the stress to the strain.) A perfect example of an elastic material is rubber. Metals and many polymers exhibit an elastic behavior but to a much lesser degree than rubber. Ceramics and other brittle materials, as well as so-called *perfectly plastic* materials (materials that deform only permanently like clay), are not elastic.

Stress-Strain Ratio. The amount of force needed to deform a single crystal elastically depends on the crystallographic direction in which a load is applied. If the load is applied in the direction where the atoms are touching, more force is needed to separate the atoms than if the load is applied in a less dense direction. The ratio between *stress* (amount of force per unit area) and *strain* (change in length per unit length) is known as the *modulus of elasticity*. We will talk more about these quantities in the next chapter. The densest direction in a BCC unit cell is along the body diagonal. The modulus of elasticity has the highest value in that direction and lowest in the direction of the side diagonal of the unit cell. For an FCC unit cell, the densest direction is the side diagonal of the unit cell. For example, the modulus of elasticity for polycrystalline aluminum (FCC) is 63.4 GPa (9.2×10^6 psi). However, along the side diagonal of a single crystal of aluminum, the modulus of elasticity is 75.9 GPa (11×10^6 psi). In the same manner, the measurement of sound velocity with ultrasonic testing (UT) varies with respect to the crystallographic direction of a material. To date, both steel and aluminum have been experimentally explored.

Anisotropic Behavior. If the whole piece of the material is only one crystal or all the crystals are oriented in the same direction, the material would exhibit *anisotropic* behavior, meaning its properties vary with direction. On the other hand, if the crystals are small (as they usually are) and randomly oriented, then the material is *isotropic*, meaning it has identical properties in all directions. If the metal is cooled under normal circumstances (in air, quenched, or slow-cooled in an oven), it becomes less isotropic. However, to take advantage of different properties in different directions, some special cooling methods can be applied to employ anisotropy for specific applications. We will discuss these methods in the chapter on casting.

Plastic Deformation. Permanent or *plastic deformation* implies moving layers of atoms with respect to each other and changing the shape of the part without changing the volume or causing fractures or cracks. Contrary to elastic deformation, plastic deformation is easier along directions where the atoms are closely spaced and the distance between planes is relatively large. For an analogy, we can use domino lines: it is easier to push dominoes if they are close to each other and one line does not interfere with another than if they are far away from each other. These planes are called *slip planes*, and the most dense directions where the spilt occurs are called *slip directions*. Slip planes and slip directions make *slip systems*. Each structure—FCC, BCC, and HCP—has a different number of slip systems. FCC crystallographic structures have more slip systems and are more malleable, that is, easier to deform plastically.

2.5 SOLIDIFICATION, PHASES, AND MICROSTRUCTURES

2.5.1 SOLID SOLUTIONS

We tend to think of pure substances as ideal, but in many instances, because of cost, availability, and properties, it is desirable to have impurities present. An example is *sterling silver,* which contains 7.5% copper and 92.4% silver. We rate silver highly and we can refine it to over 99% purity. It would cost more, however, and it would have inferior qualities. Without altering its appearance, 7.5% Cu makes the silver stronger and harder, therefore more durable at a lower cost.

Another common example is *brass*, which is formed when zinc is added to copper. Brass is harder and stronger than copper, but pure copper has better electrical conductivity. Adding copper to silver or zinc to copper is called *alloying*. One very common alloy is steel, where iron contains small amounts of carbon.

Common Metallurgical Terms. To understand the formation and properties of alloys we first have to introduce several common terms used by materials scientists and metallurgists. They do not necessary correspond to terms used in other branches of science and engineering or in everyday life. These are:

- *Equilibrium condition*: The condition of the material when all reactions are completed and the structure would not change regardless of how long the material is kept at that temperature. In contrast, *nonequilibrium conditions* represent the structure before the material transformation is finished. By keeping material at that temperature, phase changes can be completed and equilibrium conditions can be achieved.
- *Phase*: A material having the same composition, structure, and properties everywhere. There is a definite interface between the phase and any surrounding or adjoining phases.
- *Solid solution*: Solid single phase that contains more than one element.
- *Solid mixture*: Solid material where more than one phase is present.
  Examples of Alloys. Alloys can be obtained by:
- substituting one type of atom with another in a structure, referred to as a *substitutional solid solution.*
- squeezing one foreign atom between atoms of the host material, referred to as an *interstitial solid solution.*
- producing a mixture of two or more different phases.

Brass is an example of a substitutional solid solution. Zinc atoms replace some copper atoms. Brass takes in the FCC (face-centered cubic) structure of copper rather than the HCP (hexagonal closed-packed) structure of zinc. This is possible because the zinc atoms and copper atoms have similar sizes and comparable electron structures. However, only a limited number of copper atoms (39%) can be replaced by zinc atoms. If more Zn atoms are added, a mixture is formed which does not have the property of brass and is not used in engineering. So we say that zinc has limited solubility in copper.

Solubility. On the other hand, copper atoms and nickel atoms can substitute each other in any quantity; that is, they have unlimited *solubility*. We can have a single-phase alloy at room temperature of almost 100% copper with nearly 0% nickel, almost 100% nickel with almost 0% copper, and anything in between. This is because copper and nickel atoms are even closer to each other in size and electron structure than zinc and copper, and both of them have the FCC crystallographic structure.

We can compare *solid solubility* with more familiar *liquid solubility*. Milk in coffee, for example, has unlimited solubility, while sugar in coffee has only limited solubility, and if we exceed the limit (add more sugar), we form a mixture with two phases: liquid (sweet coffee) and solid (sugar on the bottom of the cup). While in this case we have solid and liquid phases, we can also have a mixture of two liquids, such as oil and water, where oil represents one phase floating on the top, while the heavier water is on the bottom. We can see readily the interference between these two phases.

Steel at higher temperatures (above 912 °C [1674 °F]) is an interstitial solid solution of carbon and iron. Above that temperature, iron takes on the FCC structure, which includes an interstitial cavity at the center of the unit cell where the small carbon atoms can squeeze themselves into that cavity.

Although in our examples only metals are mentioned, other materials like ceramics and polymers can form a single phase with more than one component; therefore, by definition, they are solid solutions. We will discuss these solutions in the sections on plastics and ceramics.

2.5.2 SOLID SOLUTIONS AND MIXTURE STRENGTHENING

As mentioned, the addition of alloying elements changes the properties of the host material. How much the properties change depends on the amount of alloying elements and differences in atomic size between the alloying elements and the host or base material.

In general, we can say that the effect of solid solution strengthening on the properties of material includes following:

- The strength and hardness of alloys are greater than those of pure metals.
- Almost always, the ductility of the alloy is much lower than that of pure metal. Only rarely, as in copper-zinc alloys, does the solid solution increase both strength and ductility.
- Electrical conductivity of the alloy is much lower than that of pure metal. The conductivity of a metal changes as increasing amounts of alloying elements are added. Even small amounts of foreign atoms can reduce conductivity, as shown in Figure 2.25.
- The loss of strength in use at high temperature due to "creep" is improved by solid solution strengthening. Many high-temperature alloys, such as those used for jet engines, rely partly on extensive solid solutions strengthening.

Mixtures. When the solubility limit of a material is exceeded by adding too much of another material, a second phase forms, as we have seen when we add too much zinc to copper or too much sugar to coffee. The boundary between the two phases is a surface at which the atomic arrangement is not perfect. This type of material is called a *mixture*. Many common engineering materials are mixtures of two or more phases: solder, steel, concrete, copolymers, and composites are just five examples. The addition of a second (or third) phase improves the properties of the material.

The base material is called the *matrix* (the one that represents the larger component in the structure), and the added material is called the *solute*. The general rule to obtaining good properties of a mixture is that the matrix should be relatively soft and tough and the solute should be hard, finely dispersed, and round. We can relate this rule to concrete: cement in concrete is the matrix and sand is the solute. Better concrete can be obtained if the sand is fine and round than if the same amount of sand is added in the form of huge rocks. The same situation is seen in the case of composites. For example, polymer is the matrix (soft and tough), while strong, hard glass or graphite fibers are added for reinforcement. Other common mixtures include the different carbides: tungsten (WC), titanium (TiC), and other carbides in a matrix of cobalt as a binder, all used for cutting edges in cutting tools.

How much the properties of a single phase are improved by adding a second phase depends upon the amount of the solute phase and its size, shape, and distribution. It should be noted that each phase in the mixture could be a solid solution consisting of more than one material. For example, in carbide cutting tools, WC carbides (one phase) consist of tungsten (W) and carbon (C).

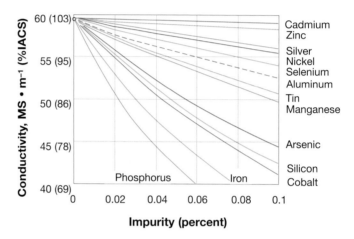

Figure 2.25: Decrease in conductivity of copper caused by various impurities (%IACS = percentage of International Annealed Copper Standard).

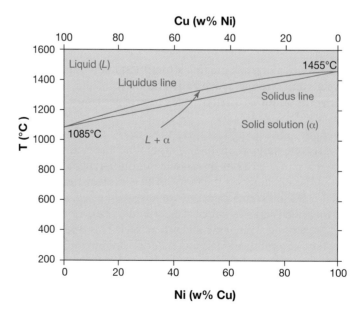

Figure 2.26: Cu-Ni phase diagram.

2.5.3 EQUILIBRIUM PHASE DIAGRAM

An *equilibrium phase diagram* graphically illustrates the relationship between temperature, composition, and the phases present in the particular alloy system. It is a collection of curves showing *solubility limits* for different compositions at different temperatures. The diagrams are constructed using experimental data. Alloys with different composition are heated to different temperatures and held as long as necessary for any reaction to stop when equilibrium is reached. At that temperature, the chemical composition of each phase is determined. When these values are plotted for different temperatures, the phase diagram is formed. In Figure 2.26, the Cu-Ni phase diagram is shown. The upper line is called *liquidus*, and it represents the temperatures above which each alloy is 100% liquid. The lower line is called *solidus* and shows at what temperature each alloy is completely solid. For example, for an alloy that contains 40 w% Ni (w% stands for weight percentage) and 60 w% Cu, the liquidus temperature is 1280 °C (2336 °F), whereas 1240 °C (2264 °F) is its solidus temperature. Above the liquidus temperature, the material is only one phase liquid (L), and below the solidus temperature, it takes on only the solid phase (α). Between these two temperatures, the material is a mixture of solid and liquid phases. The right side of the figure represents the change in temperature per time. It can be seen that material cools faster in liquid than in the solid region.

Single- and Multiple-Phase Regions. In the *single-phase region*, a particular phase has a known chemical composition of the given alloy. Similarly, in a *multiple-phase region*, the chemical composition and amount of each phase in the mixture can be deduced from the phase diagram, as well. As can be seen from the figure, Cu has a lower melting temperature than Ni. When we cool an alloy of 40 w% Ni 60 w% Cu below 1280 °C (2336 °F), most of the solids that are formed in the beginning mainly contain Ni, while later they mostly contain Cu. Uniform one-phase solid (α) is formed when equilibrium is reached.

More complicated diagrams are obtained when the alloy has limited solubility into the host material and when more than one solid phase is present at room temperature.

2.5.4 IRON-CARBON DIAGRAM

Pure iron melts at a temperature of 1538 °C (2800 °F) as shown at the left side of the diagram in Figure 2.27. As it cools, it takes on a BCC crystallographic structure forming the δ-iron phase. At 1394 °C (2541 °F), the structure changes to an FCC structure, forming the γ-iron phase. Then, upon further cooling, it changes to a BCC structure again, where it is known to have the α-iron phase. The ability of a solid material to exist in multiple forms of a crystallographic structure is known as *polymorphism*. It exists in other metals and ceramics, such as Ti and ZrO_2.

Changes in Crystallographic Structure. Change in the crystallographic structure causes change in the volume of the piece of iron. Remember that the BCC structure has a lower packing number than the FCC structure. Therefore, the same number of iron atoms in γ- iron will occupy less space than in α-iron. Although atoms at lower temperature vibrate less (so they are considered smaller in size) than at high temperature, the volume of an equal number of atoms or iron cooling from the δ-phase into the γ-phase will contract and then, from γ- to α-iron at room temperature, will expand approximately 1.4% in volume—a 0.047% linear expansion. This change in volume is opposite to the change commonly undergone for most other materials. While other materials shrink when they are cooled to room temperature, iron expands!

Pure iron is rarely used; for engineering applications, steel or cast iron is mostly used. Both are alloys of iron and carbon. Many steels and cast irons also contain other alloying elements. Even commercially available "pure" iron contains up to 0.008% C, steels contain up to 2.11% C, and cast iron up to 6.67% C. As can be seen from Figure 2.27, the iron-carbon diagram or Fe-Fe$_3$C diagram, as it is often called, is more complicated than previous phase diagrams. The main reason is that in the solid region, the change of crystallographic structure is also indicated, meaning that regions of γ- and α- steels are separated. Besides Greek letter notations (α, γ, δ), many phases in the diagram also have specific names that are used in metallurgy and material science. For instance, the α phase is called *ferrite,* γ phase *austenite,* and Fe$_3$C phase *cementite* or *carbide.* These phases and their properties will be briefly described in next section.

2.5.5 EQUILIBRIUM PHASES AND MICROSTRUCTURES IN STEEL AND CAST IRON

The iron-carbon diagram in Figure 2.27 is obtained under equilibrium conditions, which really means that the material is heated to different temperatures and kept at these temperatures as long as necessary to obtain any change in phases or microstructures present. As explained earlier, phase can be defined as a homogeneous part of the material structure with identical physical or chemical characteristics. The boundary between phases represents an abrupt change of these properties. A system composed of two or more phases is called a mixture. The properties of a material will depend not only on the phases present but also on their distribution. The best mixtures of materials are those where the matrix (predominant phase) is relatively soft and the precipitant (second phase) is hard and distributed in the matrix as relatively fine particles. Differences in the shape, size, and distribution of phases and grains result in different *microstructures.*

To make these concepts a little easier to remember, we will use analogy with cloth materials and colors as follows:

- Red cloth (pure primary color) = only one phase, equivalent to single-phase metal, such as copper or pure iron.
- Purple cloth (an indistinguishable mix of blue and red) = substitutional alloy, such as brass, or interstitial alloy, such as austenite in steel. With purple, we cannot distinguish between red and blue colors.

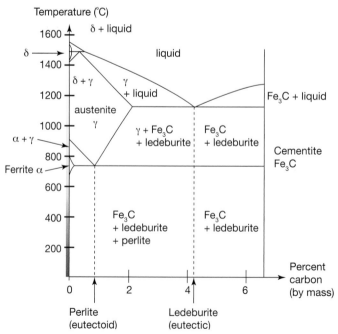

Figure 2.27: Iron-carbon phase diagram.

- Red or purple cloth with blue dots = a mixture such as spheroidate.
- Red cloth with blue stripes = different microstructures, such as pearlite, a common microstructure of steel.

This example illustrates different concepts used in materials science, including single-phase alloys, mixtures, and microstructures. Just as we get different effects in cloth if we have a red base (matrix) with blue dots or red base with blue lines, we get different properties if we have a relatively soft iron matrix with hard carbon particles in round form or in the form of strips.

Regions Based on Temperature Differences. At temperatures below 1394 °C (2541 °F), as mentioned, pure iron is called δ-iron and has the BCC crystallographic structure. It does not have any special name. Because of its high temperature, neither does it have any technological importance. It contains only small amounts of carbon.

Below the δ-iron region, iron and steel have the FCC structures and are called γ-iron or *austenite*. Depending on the temperature, small amounts of carbon can dissolve in *austenite* by filling interstitial vacancies, forming only the γ-iron phase. As can be seen from Figure 2.27, the maximum amount of carbon in austenite, also referred to as *gamma iron* or *gamma-phase iron*, is 2.14 w% at 1147 °C (2097 °F). On the left side of this point, iron alloys are called steels (although most steels used in engineering have 1% or less carbon). The lowest temperature at which austenite can exist is 727 °C (1341 °F), at which temperature steel has 0.76 w% carbon. Austenite is important in the heat-treatment process of steel. It is single phase, nonmagnetic, and ductile at higher temperatures, where hot working (forging, extrusion, and other processes) is usually done. Austenite in plain carbon steel cannot exist at room temperature. With the addition of manganese, the diffusion process is obstructed, reducing the mobility of iron atoms, resulting in a stable form of austenite at room temperature.

Below 912 °C (1674 °F), the BCC structure of pure iron has a BCC and it is called α-iron or *ferrite*. Ferrite can contain a maximum of 0.022% carbon (at 727 °C [1341 °F]), but at room temperature, it is almost pure iron. Ferrite is relatively soft and it is magnetic.

On the right boundary side of the equilibrium steel phase diagram, we find *cementite* or iron carbide (Fe_3C) . It contains 6.67% of carbon. Cementite is very hard and brittle. In the region between the left and right boundaries in the $Fe-Fe_3C$ diagram, the material is a mixture of ferrite and cementite. If it consists mostly of iron and carbon and has less than 2.1% C, it is called *plain carbon steel*. When other elements are added, it is called *alloyed steel* (if it consists mostly of iron and carbon). There is a wide variety of steel alloys, some of which will be mentioned in Chapter 4.

An iron-cementite mixture with more than 2.11% iron is called *cast iron*. Most common cast iron has 4.30% carbon. This material can be heated at the lowest temperature of any material in the $Fe-Fe_3C$ diagram to become liquid (1148 °C [2098 °F]). That is the main reason that it is used in casting practices to produce different objects.

Pearlite. It is important to mention a special microstructure called *pearlite*, which is present in most steels and cast irons at room temperature, if cooled slowly under equilibrium conditions. This microstructure has alternating lamellas of cementite and ferrite. Upon polishing, the soft ferrite erodes quicker than the hard cementite under the abrasive surface of a polishing wheel and subsequent etching action. The erosion patterns leave high and low ridges that define the inter-laminar boundaries of this microstructure. Light reflecting from this surface produces interference patterns that result in a shimmering effect similar to that observed on soap bubbles or a thin oil film floating on water. This shimmer gives pearlite its pearly appearance, hence its name. Incidentally, pearls also obtain their shimmer from a layered calcite deposit. All soap bubbles, pearlite lamellas, and pearl deposit layers are comparable in size, which is the favorable condition for interference patterns of the visible light.

Steel with approximately 0.77% C consists entirely of a pearlitic microstructure. If steel has less than 0.77% C, it becomes a mixture of pearlite and ferrite, where pearlite will require 0.77% C and the leftover iron precipitates as pure α-iron (ferrite). Alternatively, if steel has more 0.77% C at room temperature, it becomes a mixture of pearlite and cementite. The amount of pearlite at room temperature is proportional to the carbon concentration difference of a particular steel from the optimum 0.77%. Pure pearlite is generated at 0.77% C, pure ferrite at 0% C. All steels in between have a linear proportion of pearlitic grains spread within an α-matrix (ferrite). For example, steel with 0.38% carbon contains approximately 50% pearlite and 50% ferrite at room temperature, whereas 0.25% C steel has approximately 33% pearlite and 67% ferrite. On the other side of pure pearlite (steel with more that 0.77% C), cementite begins to precipitate. The amount of pearlite is linearly proportional from 0.77% C to 6.77% C. For instance, cast iron with 3.72% C (in the middle between 0.77 and 6.67% C) has 50% pearlite and 50% cementite.

As will be seen, thermal treatment of steel and mechanical properties of the final product are very much dependent upon the amount, shape, and form of phases and microstructures present at room temperature.

2.6 HEAT TREATMENT OF METALS

2.6.1 TYPES, PURPOSE, AND APPLICATIONS

In the preceding sections, we have discussed phases and microstructures of steels and cast iron, given that the alloy is allowed to cool slowly and under equilibrium conditions (that is, waiting at each temperature until each transformation is completed). Any increase in cooling speed will influence the properties of the final product. Phases present, as well as the shape, size, and distribution of particles, will largely differ from those obtained with slow cooling.

Heating the material to various temperatures and controlled cooling at the desired speeds is called *thermal treatment*. Most materials can be thermally treated to some degree. Thermal treatment of metals, in particular steel, is widely used to obtain alloys with a broad range of desired mechanical and physical properties. This is one of the reasons that make steel an important engineering material.

Thermal Treatment in General. Thermal treatment of metals is a vast subject by itself. Only a brief description of the most common thermal processes and treatments will be given here. It is important to emphasize that improper execution of heat treatment can cause distortions and imperfections in the product that the material testing specialist needs to be aware of.

There are a wide variety of thermal treatments used for metals. However, they may be divided into two basic groups: (1) those that increase the strength of materials and (2) those that increase their ductility and toughness. As will be seen, it is rarely possible to obtain an increase in both properties simultaneously. Most of the time, an increase in strength and hardness is accompanied with a decrease in toughness and ductility. It was explained earlier that an increase in hardness and strength is often caused by an increase in the number and length of dislocations, which causes the material to be more brittle, that is, less tough.

2.6.2 QUENCHING AND MARTENSITE FORMATION IN STEELS

When steel is quenched (cooled rapidly) from the austenitizing temperature, an entirely different type of transformation occurs, the austenite transforms to *martensite*. Martensite is metastable and has the same composition as the austenite from which it forms, but instead of a face-centered cubic (FCC) structure it has a structure known as body-centered tetragonal (BCT). Depending on the chemical composition of the steel, martensite starts forming at a temperature of 230 °C (446 °F) or lower. The extent of martensite formation is dependent on the chemical composition of the steel and the cooling rate. Because the formation of martensite requires no change in composition, no diffusion is required for the transformation. That is why the martensite can form at such low temperature. A very significant characteristic of martensite is that it has a potential for very high hardness. Depending on the chemical composition of the steel, the hardness can be as high as 65 HRC (Rockwell C). There is also a volumetric increase as austenite transforms to martensite. This volumetric increase is the source of distortion and other defects in the parts.

2.6.3 NORMALIZAING AND ANNEALING PROCESSES

The term *annealing* originally was used by craftspeople who discovered the benefits of heating some materials to elevated temperatures, then cooling them slowly. The structural changes that occur during annealing are not the same for all materials. Annealing typically involves the following sequence: (1) heating the piece to a specific temperature range, (2) holding at that temperature for a period of time (soaking), and (3) cooling it slowly at a specific cooling rate. Annealing processes are categorized into the following groups:

- **Process Anneal:** (also called intermediate annealing) is used to remove strain hardening due to previous cold working and to restore ductility so that additional cold working can be performed on the product. For instance, after each pass of cold-rolled brass (or steel) between rollers, the sheets are reheated before their thickness is further reduced in the following step. This process is often done in an inert atmosphere to prevent oxidation. During reheating, the material is recrystallized, that is, new grains free of dislocations are formed. The temperature of recrystallization is approximately 0.3 to 0.6 T_m. For example, the recrystallization temperature for copper is in the range between 200 °C and 300 °C (392 °F and 572 °F). Annealing temperatures are slightly higher, between 260 °C and 650 °C (500 °F and 1202 °F), for copper. Selecting the temperature and the annealing time is an art in itself. Too high a temperature and too long a duration of the process cause excessive grain growth, which makes the material brittle. In hot-working processes, deformation and recrystallization occur almost simultaneously so that the annealing between processing steps is not necessary.
- **Full Anneal:** is normally used for steels with medium carbon content (0.35 to 0.65% carbon) to improve machinability and formability. Steel is first fully austenized, where it is heated 25 °C to 30 °C (77 °F to 86 °F) above the so-called A_{c3} line, which separates the γ-region from mixed γ- and α-regions in the phase diagram, then cooled slowly in the furnace. Furnace cooling produces very coarse pearlite that has the softest microstructure possible for that steel. Typically, the product receives additional heat treatments after machining or forming to improve strength.
- **Normalizing:** is a process used to homogenize alloy steels. Austenization is performed at approximately 50 °C to 60 °C (122 °F to 140 °F) above the A_{c3} temperature for that steel for a short time. The temperature is higher than that in the full annealing process to accelerate the diffusion required for dissolution of the alloying elements (Ni, Cr, Mo, V, and others), while avoiding the excessive grain growth that would occur at longer exposure to still higher temperatures. Steels are held at the normalizing temperatures for a sufficient period of time to effectively dissolve most of the alloying elements. Excessively long soaking times are avoided as they may cause grain growth, which will adversely affect the mechanical properties. Heating is followed by circulated air cooling, which is faster than furnace cooling used in full annealing.

- **Stress Relief:** is a process designed to eliminate internal stresses in the part, referred to as *residual stresses*, which occur due to welding, forming, or machining, or may be due to volumetric change, such as when quenching steel during hardening. These stresses are particularly present in steels due to the expansion of iron as it transforms from an FCC to a BCC structure upon cooling. The surface of the part cools first and transitions to the BCC crystallographic structure, which is larger in volume than the FCC structure of the hot interior. Later, the interior cools and expands as it transitions to the BCC structure, while the rigid exterior tends to restrain the interior. Eventually, the process ends with the outer region under tension and the interior under compression, at equilibrium. Therefore, the material is under stress even when no external loads are applied, hence the term "residual," meaning "left over," stress. When the part is subsequently machined, the equilibrium will be disturbed and the part may distort and sometimes crack.

Residual stress. Residual stresses are hidden hazards in design and manufacturing, and should be minimized. The most common method of residual stress mitigation is by heating to temperatures substantially below the austenite-to-ferrite transformation to allow some diffusion of atoms at short distances. This heating is then followed by slow cooling. Other methods include mechanical working of the part.

It is important to mention that residual stresses can also be introduced by mechanical deformation in the plastic region, especially under nonuniform loading, such as in bending. In some cases, these stresses can be eliminated. Product designers should be aware that the elimination of residual stresses in a part is one of the most formidable problems in design. Nondestructive test specialists must recognize the significance of residual stresses on component integrity, as well.

2.6.4 AGE HARDENING

Several alloys (for example, 2024, 6061, or 7075 aluminum) when quenched from an elevated temperature (from a single phase solid solution) are supersaturated with solute atoms at room temperature. These alloys, when aged at room or slightly elevated temperature, will strengthen by a process known as *age hardening* or *precipitation hardening*. The increase in mechanical properties is due to the precipitation of alloying elements. Several alloy systems, including Cu-Be, follow this mechanism where tensile, yield, and hardness increase as the alloy is aged at room temperature or at an elevated temperature and ductility is reduced. The exact treatment (time and temperature) varies from alloy to alloy.

2.6.5 STRAIN RATE INFLUENCE ON PROPERTIES OF MATERIALS

Strain rate is defined as the rate of change in strain with respect to time. The strain measured on the specimen gage length is used to calculate the strain rate. The unit of strain rate is reciprocal of time. The rate at which strain is applied to a specimen has an important influence on the stress-strain curve. Increasing strain rate increases flow stress. Strain-rate dependence of strength increases with increasing temperature.

Strain Rate as Variable. The strain rate is a variable that can range from the very low rates observed as in creep to the extremely high strain rates during impact or shock loading. Very low strain rates ($\sim 10^{-9}$ to 10^{-7} s^{-1}) can result in creep rupture, with the accompanying changes in fracture mode. A moderately high strain rate ($\sim 10^2$ s^{-1}), such as experienced during charpy impact testing, changes the mode of fracture (size and depth of the dimples or changes the mode from dimple rupture to quasi-cleavage or intergranular separation). At extremely high strain rates, materials exhibit a highly localized deformation known as *adiabatic-shear*. In adiabatic shear, the bulk of the plastic deformation of the material is concentrated in narrow bands within a relatively undeformed matrix. Materials where adiabatic shear has been observed include steels, aluminum and titanium alloys, and brass. At low values of plastic strain, the yield and flow stress are affected more by strain rate than tensile strength.

The concept of strain rate is best understood by the following. Many materials (like plastics and nylons), if a gradual tensile force (low strain rate) is applied, will elongate a large amount before they break. This is because the molecules have enough time to reorient themselves and move past each other, causing the stretching to occur and redistribute the stress. If an impact load or sudden force is applied (as in high strain rate loading), the material will break without stretching, and break in a brittle manner.

2.7 INFLUENCE OF ENVIRONMENT ON PROPERTIES

Each material has its own unique chemical, mechanical, and physical properties. These properties may be subjected to change or tend to change once the material is influenced by the environment.

2.7.1 INFLUENCE OF TEMPERATURE AND HUMIDITY

The mechanical properties of the material are affected by a number of factors such as applied load, time, temperature, humidity, and other conditions. It has been observed that with increasing temperature, the modulus of elasticity diminishes.

Thermal effects include:
- Phase change: basically melting and boiling (phase transition temperatures).
- Dimensional change: basically thermal expansion (contraction if negative).
- Elastoplastic changes, due to thermal stresses.
- Brittle/ductile transition temperature.
- Chemical change, decomposition, oxidation, and ignition.
- Other physical changes such as drying, segregation, outgassing, and color change.
- Thermal effects due to nonthermal causes, for example, frictional heating, electrical heating, chemical heating, and nuclear heating.

Excessive humidity may also be costly or inconvenient. The main effects of humidity or moisture include:
- Corrosion.
- Condensation.
- Storage issues.
- Problems associated with environmental control.

2.7.2 CORROSION AND ELECTROLYTIC REACTION

Corrosion. Corrosion is an undesirable process. Corrosion can be defined as the degradation of a material due to a reaction with its environment. Degradation implies deterioration of physical properties of the material. Generally, this means electrochemical oxidation of the metals in the reaction with an oxidant such as oxygen. The term *corrosion* is sometimes also applied to degradation of plastics, concrete, and wood, but generally it refers to metals. Metals corrode because they are used in environments where they are chemically unstable. Only copper and the precious metals (gold, silver, platinum) are found in nature in their metallic state. All other metals, including iron, are processed from minerals or ores and become inherently unstable in their environments.

Electrolytic Reaction (Electrochemical Reaction). Most metals are electrochemical in nature where oxidation and reduction take place. A common oxidation reaction in corrosion is the oxidation of neutral metal atoms to positively charged metal ions as follows:

(Eq. 2.15)
$$Fe \rightarrow Fe^{+2} + 2e^{-}$$

Usually, these electrons move up in a nonmetallic atom forming a negatively charged ion. Since the charge of these ions is reduced, this is why these types of reactions are called *reductions*. For example:

(Eq. 2.16)
$$2H^{+} + 2e^{-} \rightarrow H_{2}$$

2.7.3 TYPES OF CORROSION

Corrosion can be classified into various categories based on the material, environment, or morphology of corrosion damage. Several of the most important types of corrosion are described below.

- **General corrosion**, also referred to as *general attack* or *uniform corrosion*, is the most common type of corrosion and is caused by a chemical or electrochemical reaction, which deteriorates the entire exposed surface of the material. It is the easiest to recognize as the entire surface of the metal shows a uniform spongelike appearance.
- **Localized corrosion** attacks or targets one area of the material. Pitting, crevice, and feliform are localized types of corrosion.
- **Pitting** results when a small hole, or cavity, forms in the metal, usually as a result of depassivation of a small area. This type of corrosion is very difficult to detect because it is present only in a limited area, which can lead to failure of the material.
- **Crevice corrosion** is another type of localized corrosion that occurs in confined spaces where the access of working fluid from the environment is limited. Crevice corrosion occurs under gaskets or seals, inside cracks and seams, or in spaces filled with deposits and under sludge piles.
- **Filiform corrosion** occurs under painted or plated surfaces when water breaches the coating. Filiform corrosion begins at small discontinuities in the coating and spreads to cause structural weakness.
- **Galvanic corrosion** occurs only when two electrochemically dissimilar metals are in contact in an electrolyte solution and one metal becomes the anode while the other becomes the cathode. The cathode corrodes slowly while the anode or sacrificing material corrodes faster.
- **Environmentally induced corrosion** in a material is the result of the presence of a corrosive or chemically reactive environment. When materials are present in this type of environment, a small mechanical stress can form and propagate a crack. Exposure to aqueous solution, organic solvents, liquid metals, solid metals, and gases has been found to cause failure in this manner. Stress-corrosion cracking (SCC), hydrogen embrittlement, liquid metal embrittlement, and corrosion fatigue are alternative names of environmentally induced corrosion depending on the environment and type of loading.
- **Flow-assisted corrosion**, or flow-accelerated corrosion, results when a protective layer of oxide on a metal surface is dissolved or removed by wind or water, exposing the underlying metal to further corrosion and deterioration.
- **Erosion-assisted corrosion.** Impingement, and cavitation are examples of this type of corrosion.

- **Erosion corrosion** is an accelerated or increased rate of deterioration or attack on a metal because of relative movement between a corrosive fluid and the metal surface, resulting from the combination of mechanical and chemical wear. Usually, this type of corrosion appears near the eye of a pump impeller. Erosion corrosion is characterized in appearance by grooves, waves, round holes, and valleys, which usually exhibit a directional pattern.
- **Intergranular corrosion** occurs as a result of a localized attack at or nearer to the grain boundaries in a metal or alloy. Impurities and precipitation at grain boundaries, along with depletion of an alloying element in the grain boundary area, are the main factors contributing to intergranular corrosion.
- **Dealloying or selective leaching** refers to selective dissolution of the active metal phase from an alloy in a corrosive environment. Brass containing copper and zinc is one such example of a material being anodic to copper dezincification in a corrosive medium.
- **Fretting corrosion** occurs as a result of repeated wearing, weight, and/or vibration on an uneven, rough surface. Corrosion, resulting in pits and grooves, occurs on the surface. Fretting corrosion is often found in rotation and impact machinery, bolted assemblies and bearings, as well as on surfaces exposed to vibration during transportation.

2.7.4 CORROSION PROTECTION

The rate of corrosion can be reduced by retarding either anodic or cathodic reactions. This can be achieved by several means.

2.7.4.1 CONDITIONING THE METAL

This can be broadly categorized in to two groups:
- **Coating the Metal:** Corrosion-resistant coating is coated at the metal to avoid the contact between the metal and a corrosive environment corroded any one or both. This coating can be (1) from another metal like zinc or tin coatings on steel; (2) a protective coating derived from metal itself, for example, aluminum oxide on anodized aluminum; or (3) an organic coating, such as resins, plastics, paints, enamel, oil, and grease.
- **Alloying the Metal:** A corrosion-resistant alloy is added to a metal to provide more resistance to corrosion. For example, ordinary steel is alloyed with Ni and Cr to make stainless steel more corrosion resistant, as an invisible layer of Cr_2O_3 protects the stainless steel.

2.7.4.2 CONDITIONING THE CORROSIVE ENVIRONMENT

Conditioning can be done by one of two methods.:
- **Removal of Oxygen:** Oxygen is one of the main agents in corrosion. Sulphite or any other such solution can work as a strong reducing agent to remove oxygen from water in the 6.5–8.5 pH range. However, this approach is not suitable for an open evaporative cooling system.
- **Corrosion Inhibitors:** A corrosion inhibitor is a chemical additive, which, when added to a corrosive aqueous environment, reduces the rate of metal wastage. It can work in four ways: (1) anodic inhibitors, (2) cathodic inhibitors, (3) absorption-type corrosion inhibitors, and (4) mixed inhibitors.

The rate of corrosion reaction can be controlled by passing anodic or cathodic currents into the metal; for example, if electrons are passed into the metal and reach the metal/electrolyte interface (a cathodic current), the anodic reaction will be stifled while the cathodic reaction rate increases. This process is called *cathodic protection* and can only be applied if there is a suitable conducting medium such as earth or water through which a current can flow to the metal to be protected. In most soils or natural waters, corrosion of steel is prevented if the potential of the metal surface is lowered by 300 or 400 mV.

In certain chemical environments it is sometimes possible to achieve anodic protection, passing a current that takes electrons out of the metal and raises its potential. Initially this stimulates anodic corrosion, but in favorable circumstances this will be followed by the formation of a protective oxidized passive surface film.

2.8 IMPERFECTION IN MATERIALS

2.8.1 IMPURITIES IN SOLIDS

Up to now, we have discussed only perfect crystals, where all positions in the unit cell are occupied with the same type of atoms. However, the arrangement of atoms in all materials contains imperfections, which have a profound effect on the behavior of the material. By introducing and controlling lattice imperfections, we create stronger metals and alloys, more powerful magnets, improved transistors and solar cells, glassware of striking colors, and many other materials of practical importance.

We will discuss in this section point imperfections, line imperfections (dislocations), and surface imperfections. In materials science, imperfections are often called *defects*. We must emphasize here that defects represent imperfections in the perfect atomic structure and not defects in the part, as the term is often used in nondestructive testing. As mentioned earlier, many of these imperfections are intentionally introduced. For instance, pure copper can have a perfect crystallographic structure. However, by adding zinc to copper, we obtain brass. Despite its "imperfect" crystallographic structure, brass has some superior properties over pure copper: it is harder, stronger, and less expensive to produce. Actually, the goal of alloying metals is to produce imperfect structures but with improved properties.

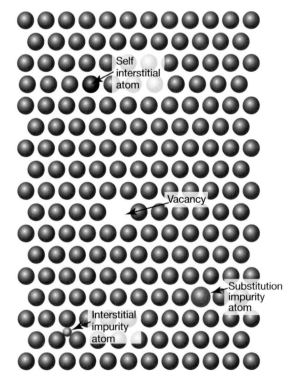

Figure 2.28: Point defect.

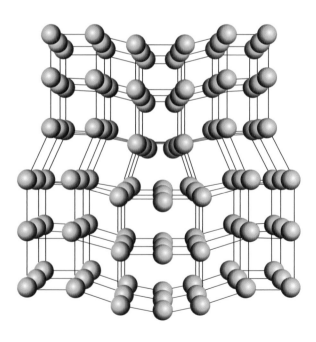

Figure 2.29: Edge dislocation.

2.8.2 POINT DEFECTS (VACANCIES)

If crystals have missing or have few extra atoms, the imperfection is called a *point defect*. In particular, if one or a few atoms are missing, it is termed a *vacancy*. Vacancies can result from imperfect atomic packing within the lattice during the crystallization process. They might also arise from thermal vibrations of atoms at elevated temperature. As thermal energy is increased, atoms become more agile, giving some sufficient energy to jump out of their positions, leaving an empty space behind. Vacancies might be single, as shown in Figure 2.28, or two or more of them may condense into di-vacancy or tri-vacancy.

2.8.3 LINE DEFECTS OR DISLOCATIONS

A dislocation is a line of imperfection, representing a missing row or an extra row of atoms, in an otherwise perfect crystal. If one extra line of atoms is squeezed in the part of one crystal, as shown in Figure 2.29, it is called a *line dislocation* or *edge dislocation*. As can be seen from the figure, atoms in the upper region of the crystals (above the dislocation line) are compressed, while those below are stretched. When the crystalline lattice is distorted in a spiral form, as shown in Figure 2.30, the dislocation is called a *screw dislocation*. Most dislocations are of mixed type, having edge and screw components. In Figure 2.31a, the dislocation enters the crystal from the left as a pure screw type and exits as a pure edge-type on the right. The net plastic deformation is the same as that for an edge type dislocation, shown in Figure 2.31b. Dislocations are formed: during solidification of crystalline solids, by permanent or plastic deformation, and by atomic mismatch in solid solution.

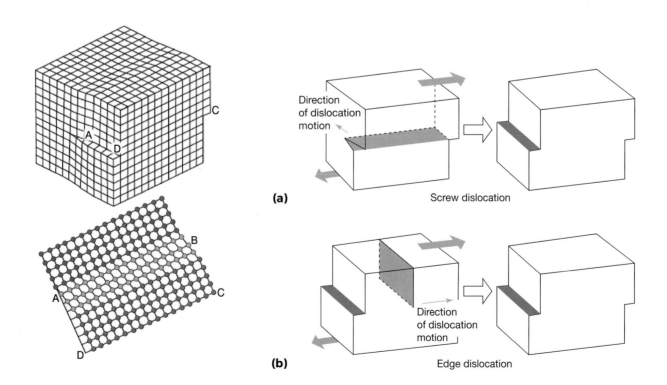

Figure 2.30: Screw dislocation.

Figure 2.31: Dislocation movement in a crystal: (a) screw dislocation; (b) edge dislocation.

Slip. The process by which a dislocation moves and causes material to deform is called *slip*. When a small amount of stress is applied on a crystallographic material containing dislocations, the atoms move a little (the material begins to change shape) but then come back to their equilibrium upon the removal of stresses. This sort of deformation falls under the elastic regime, and it resembles a spring that goes back to its original shape once the load is released. However, as in a spring, if a higher level of stress is applied, the material will experience permanent deformation, therefore transitioning into the plastic deformation regime. Once dislocations start to move, they travel relatively easily because only a few bonds between atoms are broken at one time. This process makes crystallographic structures (mostly metals and some polymers and ceramics) more plastic and much easier to deform than theoretically predicted from the strength of atomic bonds in the plane of deformation. However, this is true only to a degree.

Strain Hardening. During deformation, dislocations are also continuously formed, often running in different directions, intercepting and jamming each other. Dislocations especially pile up on the grain boundaries. Grain boundaries, inclusions, alloying additives, and other dislocations obstruct the path and restrict the mobility of dislocations. As a result, the material becomes harder to deform. An increase in deformation causes an increase in dislocations, making the material harder to deform: it becomes stronger and more brittle. This phenomenon is called *strain hardening*. Strain hardening occurs during plastic deformation at room temperature—that is, the material is "cold worked." Highly cold-worked materials can have an extremely large total dislocation length, up to 10^9 mm/mm^3, which is the length of one billion millimeters for 1 cubic millimeter of volume. Dislocations may be compared to roads and traffic: to travel more easily, you need roads; however, too many roads leading to the same intersection can cause traffic jams.

If the material is deformed at higher temperatures, atoms will have enough energy to move and relieve internal strains. As soon as dislocations are formed, they are dissolved and the material will not stain harden. It stays soft. Hot working and cold working will be discussed in more detail in a later section.

2.8.4 SURFACES, GRAINS, AND GRAIN SIZE DETERMINATION

Crystalline imperfection can extend in two dimensions as a boundary. The most obvious boundary is the external surface. Internal atoms are surrounded by other atoms on all sides. The net force on them is zero. Surface atoms have neighbors only on one side, and the net forces acting on them do not vanish to zero. They have higher energy and chemical activity. Another way to look at surface energy is that it takes work to create a new surface. If we mechanically break a piece of material, we put work into it. The resulting product has more energy because it has a larger surface. The surface is chemically more active. For example, fine particles of baking soda and charcoal have large surface areas to better absorb odors. Surface tension on water can prevent two glass surfaces from sliding against each other as well as carry a razor blade carefully placed on the surface of water in a glass. All objects tend toward a lower state of energy. To decrease their energy level, liquids under free fall or zero gravity take on a spherical shape, which has the smallest surface-to-volume ratio. This cannot happen in solids because interatomic forces are too strong for atoms to move and form spheres.

Grain Boundaries. Earlier, we mentioned dislocation pileup on grain boundaries. The individual crystals in metals (and other crystallographic ceramics and polymers) are called *grains*. Most metals, pure or alloys, and other crystallized solids, contain large number of differently oriented crystals. They are formed during solidification, which starts at a colder spot in the liquid metal: wall of a vessel, surface of a fluid, or cold inclusion (impurity or added alloying solid particle). The shape of a grain in a solid is usually controlled by the presence of surrounding grains. Within any particular grain, all of the unit cells are arranged with one orientation and one pattern. However, at the grain boundary, where two differently oriented crystals meet, there is a mismatch between the atoms as well as empty space (voids). This *grain boundary*, a two-dimensional imperfection, often runs to several layers of atoms.

We can locate grain boundaries using a metallurgical microscope. The piece of metal (in our discussion, we will use the example of metal from now on) is first smoothly polished so that a mirror-like surface is obtained and then chemically attacked for a short period of time. This process is called *etching*. The atoms on the grain boundary have more energy than atoms in the interior of the grain (the same way that atoms on the surface have), and they dissolve more readily in the acid, resulting in loose particles. When they are removed, grooves are left behind, making the grain boundary readily seen under an optical microscope.

Smaller grains have more grain boundaries per unit area. These grain boundaries stop dislocations by interrupting their slip plane. Materials with smaller grains are stronger at room temperature. Atoms can diffuse more easily in the material with smaller grains. Also, materials with small grains melt at lower temperatures because more energy is already stored in the grain boundary.

Since the grain boundary affects a material in a number of ways, it is useful to know the amount of grain-boundary surface per unit volume S_V. This area can be estimated if we place a line (straight or curved) randomly across the magnified picture of the piece of metal (or screen) with etched atoms. This line will intersect more of the grain boundary in a fine-grained material than in coarse-grained material. The relation is:

(Eq. 2.17)
$$S_V = 2P_L$$

where P_L is the number of points of intersections per unit length between the line and the boundaries.

A more common identification of the amount of grain boundary per unit area is *grain size* (*n*). A method to determine the grain size number has been standardized by ASTM International (formerly, the American Society for Testing and Materials). Although empirical, it is a quantitative and reproducible index. Grain size *G* is found from the equation:

(Eq. 2.18)
$$n = 2^{G-1}$$

Or:

(Eq. 2.19)
$$G = \frac{\ln(n)}{\ln(2)} + 1$$

where *n* is the number of grains per area of 1 in.^{2} (0.0645 mm^2) at magnification of 100×.

Grains are counted as one if they are completely inside of the area, 1/2 if they are cut by the line, and 1/4 if they are in the corners regardless of their size.

Number of Grains per Unit Area. Although there might be a little difference in *n* for different areas analyzed, the number of grains will come out the same (*n* is a rounded number). Only if you count two times more grains in one specimen than in the other (which is very unlikely) will the grain size change. To get some feel for the grain size and number of grains per unit area, we will give three examples here: ASTM grain size 3 has 64 grains per area of mm^2, grain size 7 has 1024 grains per mm^2 of area, and grain size 12 has 32 800 grains per mm^2 area.

Production of Single Crystals. Under special conditions, all atoms in a structure can be aligned, perfectly forming a single crystal. Single crystals without any imperfections (except external surfaces) are grown for use in the manufacturing of electronic chips and devices. Manufacturing of a single crystal will be discussed under the topic of casting (Chapter 6). Single crystals have different properties (for instance, elastic constant and velocity of sound) in different directions. They are stronger in the direction where there are more atoms per unit length. However, in multigrain (polycrystalline) materials, small grains are oriented in all directions. The resultant property is averaged out over the different values for each crystalline orientation. In the end, the properties of the material are independent of direction, that is, the material is *isotropic*, whereas a single crystal is usually *anisotropic*.

2.8.4.1 INFLUENCE OF GRAIN BOUNDARIES

As indicated before, grain boundaries stop dislocations. Materials with small grains (large amount of grain boundary) behave stronger at room temperature. At elevated temperatures, that effect is reversed: materials with small grains need less energy to melt (energy already exists in grain boundaries where atoms do not have close neighbors in all directions and are vibrating more than the atoms inside the grains).

Atoms at grain boundaries are more reactive; they form chemical bonds with different impurities more readily than atoms inside the grains. As a consequence, when some ductile and strong metals are brought into contact with low-melting-point metals, they can become brittle and crack under very low stresses. This phenomenon is called *grain boundary embrittlement.* Examples include aluminum wetted with a mercury-zinc amalgam and copper at elevated temperatures wetted with lead and bismuth.

Hot shortness is caused by local melting of a constituent or an impurity populating the grain boundaries of a base material below its melting temperature. When the material is subjected to hot work (plastic deformation at elevated temperature), the metal can crumble and fall apart along its grain boundaries. An example includes antimony in copper and brass.

2.8.4.2 DEFORMATION OF GRAINS

We have seen that when we plastically deform materials at room temperature, we produce dislocations, which pile up along grain boundaries. Also, grains are deformed in the direction of applied stress. If a material is compressed, as in pressing and cold forging, the grains are squeezed. Furthermore, if it is stretched, as in drawing and rolling, the grains are stretched also. Consequently, the material is no longer isotropic; it is stronger and more brittle in the direction of previously applied stress and is deformed by tension (in the direction of rolling or drawing, for example) or compression (in the opposite direction of the applied stress, in the case of forging or pressing). The texture created by a change in microstructure due to manufacturing is dependent on the process, direction of stresses, and position of grains (surface versus internal). Many other properties also lose their isotropy due to texture, most notably the speed of sound. In addition, impurities are aligned in the same way, causing so-called *mechanical fibering*.

Annealing Results in Recrystallization. If a piece of material is heated between 0.3 T_m and 0.5 T_m, where T_m is the melting temperature of that material, the atoms have enough energy to move slightly and form new grains. Their movement is due to dislocations creating local deformations in the atomic order, which results in a local unbalance of stresses. Once atoms have mobility, they find new positions and relieve stresses by creating new grains, which are free of dislocations and approximately equal in size in all three directions. This process is called *annealing*, which results in *recrystallization*. By eliminating the jamming of dislocations and allowing them to move more easily, recrystallization lowers the strength of materials but makes them more ductile. It can take place only if grains are previously deformed and dislocations are piled upon the grain boundaries. The variables that influence recrystallization are the amount of prior cold work and the purity of the material (inclusions obstruct the movement of atoms), as well as peak temperature, hold time, and cooling rate.

Materials with large grains are weaker at room temperature and often during processing cause products to have a rough granular surface, known as *orange peel*. This is often present in sheet metal forming and compression as shown in Figure 2.32.

2.8.5 ATOMIC DIFFUSION

Diffusion is just a stepwise migration of atoms from one position (lattice site) to another. It is important to notice that atoms in solid materials are in constant motion; they vibrate around their equilibrium positions. As the temperature is increased, they vibrate more energetically, and more and more atoms will have enough energy to break bonds with neighboring atoms and relocate into other positions. Surface diffusion of crystal atoms is shown in Figure 2.33.

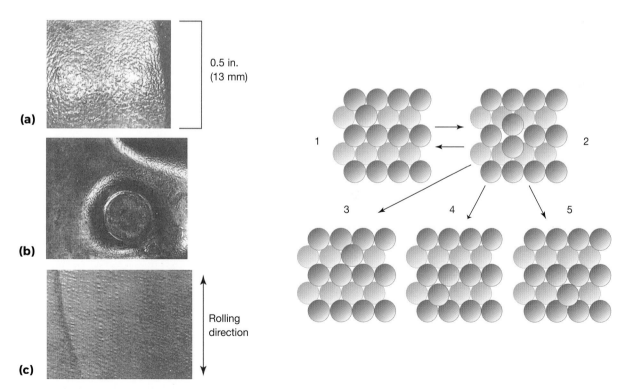

Figure 2.32: Orange peel (coarse grain) condition: (a) drawn surface; (b) formed surface; (c) orange peel strain, a pebbly surface condition that develops during drawing.

Figure 2.33: Diffusion of atoms (gray and green) on a crystal surface from (1) initial position through (2) intermediate position to one of three possible final positions (3, 4, and 5).

Activation Energy. The energy necessary to break bonds between atoms is called *activation energy.* Even at low temperatures, except at absolute zero, a small number of atoms have energy equal to or larger than the activation energy. That number increases exponentially with temperature. How many atoms will move depends not only on temperature but also on the bond strength between atoms, density of the structure, and size of the atoms. If the atoms are of approximately the same size, they can only move to vacancies or grain boundaries. Close to melting temperatures, atoms leave their lattice positions in large numbers and "jump" to the surface, leaving vacancies behind inside the structures. When the number of vacancies is large, the crystallographic order ceases to exist, causing the material to melt.

Self Diffusion. In uniform metals (for example, copper) or substitutional alloys (for example, copper-nickel alloys, where all atoms are almost the same size), no net diffusion can be observed at low temperatures because the movement of atoms is random and the atoms are identical. This type of diffusion is called *self diffusion.* However, with the use of radioactive isotopes, it is possible to determine the diffusion of atoms in their own structures. For example, radioactive nickel can be plated onto the surface of normal nickel. With time, and as a function of temperature, there is progressive self diffusion of the tracer isotopes into the adjacent nickel (movement into vacancies and grain boundaries), and there is countermovement of the untagged atoms into the surface layer.

The diffusion mechanism for atoms of different sizes and different materials is easier to trace. The flow of atoms or *atomic flux* is proportional to (1) the difference in concentrations of atoms between the start and end points along the diffusion path, (2) the length of the path, and (3) a property called *diffusivity (D).*

General rules regarding diffusivity are:

- Higher temperatures provide higher diffusivity because a larger number of atoms have the activation energy required to break atomic bonds and become "free" to move to new locations.
- It is easier for small atoms to move (diffuse) into a lattice of larges atoms. For example, carbon has a higher diffusivity than nickel in iron. Carbon atoms (radius 0.071 nm) are much smaller than nickel atoms (radius 0.125 nm).
- Diffusivity is higher in materials with weaker atomic bonds. For example, copper atoms diffuse more readily in aluminum than in copper because Al-Al bonds are weaker than Cu-Cu bonds, as evidenced by their melting temperatures, where Al melts at 660 °C (1220 °F), while Cu melts at 1084.9 °C (1984.8 °F).
- Atoms have higher diffusivity in less dense crystallographic structures, such as BCC structures of metals, than in FCC and BCT structures.
- Diffusivity is higher in materials with small grains because they have more grain boundaries with more spacing.

Diffusion can be undesirable when two parts "stick" together or plating elements dissolve into the matrix material. For example, the silver in silver-plated dishes and jewelry diffuses into the base material (such as copper) over time, resulting in a loss of aesthetic quality.

However, diffusion is the main mechanism in:

- many thermal treatment processes: annealing, tempering, and others;
- surface treatment processes, for example, carburizing and nitrating in metals and "doping" of silicon, such as in the production of semiconductor devices (diodes and transistors);
- the powder technology process where objects are formed from particles through diffusion.

We will discuss these processes in more detail further in the text.

2.8.6 COLD AND HOT WORK

The material is *hot worked* if it is plastically deformed (for example pressed, rolled, drawn, or extruded) above its recrystallization temperature. If the process is carried out below the recrystallization temperature, it is *cold worked*. The material properties resulting from hot-working conditions are different from those under cold-working conditions. As discussed earlier, the grains in cold-worked materials are deformed. A large number of dislocations are jammed along grain boundaries. Under hot-working conditions, new grains are formed, which are mostly free of dislocations.

Properties of cold-worked material compared to hot-worked material are:
- Cold-worked products are harder and stronger than hot-worked products.
- Cold-worked materials are less ductile. If further deformation is necessary, cold-worked pieces often require annealing, where they have to be heated to their recrystallization temperature so that new grains, free of dislocations, are formed. Care must be taken to avoid excessive grain growth.
- Cold-worked pieces have better surface finish. New grains formed in hot working make surfaces rougher. Also an oxide layer usually develops during hot working.
- Dimensional accuracy of cold working is better because of uneven thermal expansion during the hot-working process.

As a general rule, thinner pieces, such as sheet metal, or pieces made from softer material like solder wire are cold formed, whereas harder materials, such as steel, or parts where the reduction in area is large (as in the rolling of a thick plate into a thin sheet) are hot worked. Typical examples of cold- and hot-worked material are provided in Section II, which discusses the manufacturing of different products.

2.8.7 RECRYSTALLIZATION AND GRAIN GROWTH

Recrystallization can be defined as the nucleation and growth of stress-free grains. Recrystallization that occurs during deformation is called *dynamic recrystallization,* and *static recrystallization* when it occurs after deformation. Recrystallization may occur in a discontinuous manner when new grains form and grow, or in a continuous manner when the microstructure gradually evolves into a recrystallized microstructure.

Role of Plastic Deformation. *Recrystallization* occurs when the uppermost temperature limit of the recovery range is reached. With the onset of recrystallization, minute, new, equiaxed grains start appearing in the microstructure. These are formed by a group of atoms, known as the nucleus. Mostly nucleation starts at the sites of dislocation pile-up, slip planes, and grain boundaries. Plastic deformation is the main reason for recrystallization, and this plastic deformation leads to dislocation pile-up at the slip planes and grain boundaries, which become points of high internal energy. When recrystallization temperature is reached, these high-energy regions (highly deformed parts) give away a part of the energy as heat of recrystallization and form nuclei of small strain-free grains, which initiates the recrystallization process.

In most of modern industry, recrystallization is used to soften the material to recover lost ductility and to control the grain structure in the final product because the process of recrystallization brings reduction in strength and hardness in the material with each increment in ductility. Temperature, strain, initial grain size, and purity of metals are the main factors affecting recrystallization.

Further reduction in internal energy is possible only by reducing the total area of the grain boundary after recovery and recrystallization are completed. Reduction in grain boundary area is accomplished by increasing the size of the grains in material at high temperature. Hence, grain growth is the increase in size of grains in materials at high temperature.

Process of Grain Growth. *Grain growth* is also inherently associated with recrystallization. Part of the heat of recrystallization is absorbed by surrounding atoms so that they have sufficient energy to overcome the rigidity of the distorted lattice and become attracted to the lattice structure of strain-free grains, initiating grain growth. A larger grain will always have lower free energy than smaller grains due to the associated reduction in the grain boundary area. This is the driving force towards grain growth, since any structure will always try to attain the lowest energy state. Although the rigidity of the lattice opposes this, at higher temperatures the rigidity of the lattice is lowered and thus grain growth is accelerated.

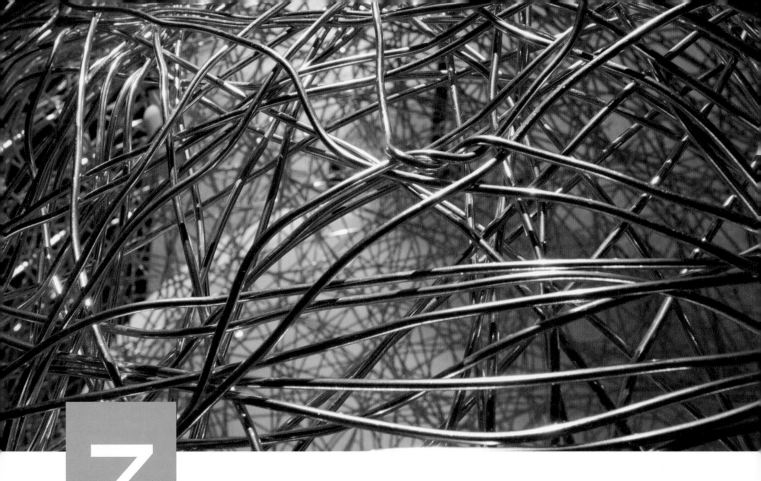

3

Properties of Materials

3.1 INTRODUCTION

The type of atoms, atomic bonding, imperfections, and processing will determine the properties of materials. Many of these properties are experimentally obtained; only a few properties can be calculated with sufficient accuracy based on atomic structures of the material. For every designer and material-testing technician, it is important to know the exact definition of the property as well as under which condition it is obtained. Changing the condition of testing will often cause a change in the value of the particular property and lead to engineering errors.

In this chapter, we will define, discuss, and relate material properties to atomic bonding and other topics discussed in Chapter 2. We will also discuss the appropriate tests used to determine these properties, and the accuracy and limitations of these tests.

Mechanical Properties. The use of the product determines the type of properties that are important in that application. Mechanical engineers are mostly interested in *mechanical properties*: strength, stiffness, hardness and toughness, fatigue, and some others. Designers, on the other hand, are also interested in availability, cost, recyclability, and often the aesthetics and "feel" of the product. You can appreciate the complexity associated with the selection of the right materials by considering the

"Changing the condition of testing will often cause a change in the value of the particular property and lead to engineering errors."

example of a car. Most customers are interested in the car that will provide the best performance at an affordable price. However, often the shape and size, as well as the quality and appearance of the interior, determine the final decision for the buyer. Many properties, such as color and texture, are indeed the *physical properties* of that material, which in this case is the car. In materials science, physical properties include magnetic permeability, specific heat, thermal conductivity, and many others.

In addition to mechanical properties, manufacturing engineers are also interested in ductility and malleability, as well as heat transfer, fluidity, solidification pattern, and melting temperature. These attributes influence the type of manufacturing process that can be used for a given material. These properties are often called *manufacturing properties.*

On the other hand, chemists would be interested in *chemical properties,* that is, from what types of elements a material is made and how it reacts with other chemicals and the environment.

The biggest difference between science and engineering is that physicists and chemists try to discover the fundamental laws of natures, mathematicians try to put them in some useable mathematical form, while engineers adapt these sciences into practical applications. They require useful data for their designs that often can be obtained only experimentally.

Moving forward, we will define in more detail the physical and mechanical properties of materials, while manufacturing properties will be discussed in connection with the described processes.

3.2 PHYSICAL PROPERTIES

An engineering materials handbook defines physical properties as "properties of a material that are relatively insensitive to structure and can be measured *without the application of force*; for example, density, electrical conductivity, coefficient of thermal expansion, magnetic permeability, and lattice parameter" (Chandler, p. 246). Other references define physical properties as the interactions of materials with various forms of energy and with the human senses. Briefly stated, physical properties can be explained by physics.

3.2.1 DENSITY AND VISCOSITY

Density of the material is defined as the mass of the material per unit volume. In the International System of Units (SI), the unit for density is kilogram per cubic meter (kg/m^3). In standard (imperial) units, lb/ft^3 or $lb/in.^3$ are used. Table 3.1 lists densities of some common engineering materials. To convert SI to standard units, multiply kg/m^3 with 3.613×10^{-5} to convert it to $lb/in.^3$ or 6.243×10^{-2} to obtain units of $lb/in.^3$.

The density of materials depends on their atomic weight, atomic radius, and their packing efficiency in their crystallographic lattice. For example, the BCC is less efficiently packed than the FCC structure. The effect of alloying elements on the total density, in general, depends on their individual densities and amounts added.

The density is very important in the selection of materials for aircraft, aerospace structures, and automobiles, where high specific strength (strength-to-weight ratio) and high specific stiffness (stiffness-to-weight ratio) are desired. Low density is also important in high-speed equipment to decrease inertia forces and vibrations and provide better accuracy. For example, low-density magnesium is used in printing and textile machinery where moving parts operate at high speed. In some applications, high-density materials are desirable, such as counterweights for various mechanisms, such as weight training equipment.

3.2.2 THERMAL PROPERTIES

While in use, many parts are exposed to various temperatures. The change in temperature might cause geometric distortions, deterioration of materials properties, changes in surface conditions, or degradation in overall performance.

The *melting temperature* or *melting point* is the temperature where materials become liquid. It depends on the energy required to separate its atoms. As discussed, pure metals have a single melting point, while most alloys have a range of temperatures where they are partially liquid and partially solid. The selection of casting operations and materials depends upon the melting point: the higher it is, the more difficult the casting process becomes.

The *recrystallization temperature* is directly related to the melting temperature (T_m). Therefore, knowledge of the melting point is very important in the selection and execution of cold- or hot-forming processes as well as thermal treatment of materials. The melting points for a range of metals and alloys are given in Table 3.2.

Specific heat is the thermal energy required to raise the temperature of a unit mass of material by one degree measured by centigrade or celsius (°C), kelvin (K), or fahrenheit (°F). At 0 °C, the temperature in kelvin is equal to 273 K. A change of 1 °C is equal to a change of 1 K. To convert celsius to kelvin, simply subtract 273. Alternatively, at 0 °C, the temperature in fahrenheit is 32 °F. A change of 1 °F is equal to 5/9 °C. At –40 °C, the fahrenheit temperature is also –40 °F. To convert celsius to fahrenheit, divide by 5, multiply by 9, then add 32. Note that celsius and fahrenheit are relative scales, where 0° does not mean the total absence of heat, whereas kelvin is an absolute scale; therefore, the term "degree" and symbol ° are not used.

The temperature rise in the workpiece during forming or machining operations is larger for materials with low specific heat, often causing (a) more distortion in the piece, (b) metallurgical change, (c) adverse effects on surface finish and dimensional accuracy, and (d) excessive tool and die wear.

Table 3.1: Densities of common engineering materials.			
Material	**Density (kg/m³)**	**Material**	**Density (kg/m³)**
Alumina (ceramic)	2700	Manganese	7440
Aluminum	2712	Mercury	13 593
Aluminum-bronze (3-10% Al)	7700-8700	Molybdenum	10 188
Bismuth	9750	Monel®	8360-8840
Brass 60/40	8520	Nickel	8908
Bronze (8-14% Sn)	7400-8900	Nickel silver	8400-8900
Calcium	1540	Nylon 6/6	1150
Carbon epoxy (61%)	1600	Palladium	12 160
Cast iron	6800-7800	Platinum	21 400
Chromium	7190	Polyethylene (HDPE)	900-1400
Copper	8940	Polypropylene	900-1240
Epoxy	1250	Silver	10 490
Glass-filled epoxy (35%)	1900	Sodium	971
Glass-filled polyester (35%)	2000	Solder 50/50 Pb-Sn	8885
Glass-filled nylon (35%)	1600	Stainless steel	7480-8000
Gold	19 320	Steel (AISI 1045)	7700-8030
Hastelloy®	9245	Tin	7280
Inconel™	8497	Titanium	4500
Iron	7850	Tungsten	19 600
Kevlar® epoxy (53%)	1350	Wrought iron	7750
Lead	11 340	Zinc	7135
Magnesium	1738	Zirconium	6570

Thermal conductivity is the quantity of the heat that will be transmitted per unit area by a material of a given thickness and temperature gradient. Thermal conductivity is important in many engineering and everyday applications: heat-sealing heads, heat exchangers, heat sinks, die casting, plastic-molding cavities, and cooking utensils. The units used are BTU/hr/ft/°F in the imperial system (BTU standing for British Thermal Unit), or W/m K (watt/meter-kelvin) in SI, where one watt is 3.4129 BTU/hr.

Thermal conductivity is especially important in insulating materials. Most insulating materials still use air as the insulating medium. At room temperature, air has a thermal conductivity of about 0.15 BTU/hr/ft/°F compared with 4 for brick, 35 for steel, and 200 for copper. When materials with low thermal conductivities are machined, the heat generated in the process is not dissipated, causing rapid softening and wear of the overheated cutting tool. This is one of the main reasons that it is difficult (and expensive) to machine titanium. In general, materials that have high electrical conductivity also have high thermal conductivity and vice versa.

Coefficient of thermal expansion (CTE) determines the change in length per unit length of the material for a one degree change in temperature, either celsius or fahrenheit. Materials that have high melting temperatures, in general, have a low CTE. This can be explained in terms of atomic bond strength as follows: the materials that have stronger bonds between atoms need more energy to separate atoms and, hence, expand less (low CTE) and need more energy to melt (high T_m). These are also stronger materials. If materials with a different thermal expansion are rigidly joined, temperature changes can cause disbond, delamination, warping, or fracture. That is often the problem in electronic devices where ceramics with a low coefficient of thermal expansion are paired with metals with high thermal expansion (such as copper or aluminum). This is the case with struts on jet engines, lightweight and complex aerospace structures, and moving parts that require certain clearances for proper functioning. Shrink-fit operations use the thermal expansion property, where a hub is usually expanded by heating, then fitted over a shaft, so that upon cooling,

Table 3.2: Melting points of metals and alloys.

Metal	Melting Point (T_m) °C	°F	Metal	Melting Point (T_m) °C	°F
Aluminum	660	1220	Molybdenum	2620	4750
Aluminum alloy	463-671		Monel®	1300-1350	2370-2460
Antimony	630	1170	Nickel	1453	2647
Beryllium	1285	2345	Phosphorous	44	111
Bismuth	271.4	520.5	Platinum	1770	3220
Brass, red	1000	1832	Plutonium	640	1180
Brass, yellow	930	1710	Potassium	63.3	146
Cadmium	321	610	Selenium	217	423
Chromium	1860	3380	Silicon	1411	2572
Cobalt	1495	2723	Silver, pure	961	1761
Copper	1084	1983	Silver, sterling	893	1640
Gold, 24K pure	1063	1945	Sodium	97.83	208
Hastelloy® C	1320-1350	2410-2260	Steel, carbon	1425-1540	2600-2800
Inconel™	1390-1425	2540-2600	Steel, stainless	1510	2750
Iridium	2450	4440	Tin	232	449
Iron, wrought	1482-1593	2700-2900	Titanium	1670	3040
Lead	327.5	621	Tungsten	3400	6150
Magnesium	650	1200	Uranium	1132	2070
Magnesium alloy	349-649	660-1200	Vanadium	1900	3450
Manganese	1244	2271	Zinc	419.5	787
Mercury	−38.86	−37.95	Zirconium	1854	3369

the hub clamps tightly against the shaft. This process, known as *autofrettage*, is applied on a number of products, especially those that experience high pressures, such as cannons and pressure vessels.

3.2.3 ELECTRICAL PROPERTIES OF MATERIALS

Electrical properties are defined as the response of materials to an applied electric field. They are important not only in designing circuitry, electrical machines, and electronic devices, but also in the selection of manufacturing processes and testing methods of products. For instance, electro-discharge machining (EDM) and electro-chemical grinding are used on hard-to-manufacture products, and electromagnetic testing (ET) is used on conductive materials.

Electrical conductivity is an expression of how well materials conduct electrical current. The opposite of electrical conductivity is *electrical resistivity*. The units that measure electrical resistivity are Ω/m (ohms per meter) or Ω/ft (ohms per foot) of the length of the specimen. Therefore, conductivity is measured in units of meter/Ω or foot/Ω. Materials with high conductivity are called *conductors*. Almost all pure metals are very good conductors. The conductivity of alloys is lower than that of pure metals. For instance, brass, which is a copper and zinc alloy, has a lower conductivity than pure copper and pure zinc. The reason for this is that the different atomic sizes of the two elements obstruct the passage of electrons within the matrix of the parent material. Metals with only metallic bonding and a uniform structure, such as copper, are better conductors than metals with mixed bonding, such as iron, which has metallic and partially covalent bonding. In covalent bonding, electrons are not free to move about to conduct electricity. Materials that are covalently bonded (for example, most ceramics) are called *resistors*. As mentioned in Chapter 2, there are materials that can conduct electricity under certain circumstances but not others. These materials are called *semiconductors*.

Under very high voltages, the resistivity of materials can be "broken." The *dielectric strength* of materials is defined as the voltage per unit length necessary for electrical "breakdown"; that is, the material becomes a conductor of direct current. *Superconductivity* is a phenomenon whereby materials below some critical temperature exhibit zero electrical resistivity. Certain metals, a large number of intermetallic compounds (combinations of two or more metals), and some ceramics exhibit superconductivity at very low temperatures. The highest temperature at which this phenomenon is observed is now approximately 88 °C (190 °F). Materials with superconductivity at appreciably higher temperatures are constantly sought, since the use of these materials greatly improves the efficiency of electrical and electronic devices.

Some ceramics and quartz crystals exhibit the *piezoelectric effect* (from Greek *piezo-* meaning to "press"). In piezoelectricity, there is a reversible interaction between an elastic strain and electrical field. When these materials are compressed, they generate an electrical current, and when they are given an electric current, they undergo a change in dimension. This property is the foundation of ultrasonic transducers, precision actuators, sonar detectors, and some microphones.

3.2.4 MAGNETIC PROPERTIES

Magnetism refers to physical phenomena arising from the force between magnets—objects that produce fields that attract or repel other objects. The origin of magnetism lies in the orbital and spin motions of electrons and how the electrons interact with one another. In most atoms, electrons occur in pairs. These electrons spin in opposite directions resulting in a cancellation of the magnetic field or no net magnetic field.

Magnetic susceptibility (χ) is one of the main properties along with magnetic field strength (H) and magnetic flux (B): $\chi \propto B/H$.

This may be surprising to some, but all matter is magnetic. It's just that some materials are much more magnetic than others. Based on their magnetic behavior, material can be classified as follows:

- Diamagnetic.
- Paramagnetic.
- Ferromagnetic.
- Ferrimagnetic.
- Antiferromagnetic.

Diamagnetism. Diamagnetism is a very weak form of magnetization that is non-permanent and persists only while an external field is being applied. In diamagnetic materials, χ is negative on the order of 10^{-6} to 10^{-5}. The negative value of susceptibility means that the magnitude of the B field within the diamagnetic solid is less than that in a vacuum, which is to say that in an applied magnetic field, diamagnetic materials acquire the magnetization in the opposite direction of the applied field. When placed between the poles of a strong electromagnet, diamagnetic material is attracted toward regions where the field is weak. Most elements in the periodic table including copper (Cu), silver (Ag), and gold (Au) are diamagnetic

Paramagnetism. In paramagnetic materials, χ is small and positive. The positive and small value of susceptibility means that the magnitude of the B field within the paramagnetic solid is slightly more than that in a vacuum; that is, in an applied magnetic field, paramagnetic materials acquire the magnetization in the direction of the applied field. In the absence of any external magnetic field, the orientation of atomic magnetic moments of these materials is random in such a way that the net magnetization remains negligible. These atomic dipoles are free to rotate, and paramagnetism results when they preferentially align, by rotation, in the direction of the applied external magnetic field. Molybdenum (Mo), lithium (Li), and tantalum (Ta) are good examples of paramagnetic materials.

Ferromagnetism. In ferromagnetic materials, χ is large (on the order of 10^6) and positive to an external magnetic field. These materials exhibit a strong attraction to magnetic fields and are able to retain their magnetic properties even after the external field has been removed. Ferromagnetic materials have some unpaired electrons so their atoms have a net magnetic moment. These materials have domains resulting in strong magnetic properties. When ferromagnetic materials are not in any magnetic field, their net magnetic field becomes zero due to random orientation of domains. When a magnetization force is applied, the domains become aligned to produce a strong magnetic field within the material. Iron (Fe), nickel (Ni), and cobalt (Co) are the best examples of ferromagnetic material.

Ferrimagnetism. Ferrimagnets possess permeability comparable to most ferromagnets, but their eddy current losses are far lower because of the material's greater electrical resistivity. Most electronic equipment contains ferrimagnetic material, for example, loudspeakers, motors, antenna rods, and transformers. The main difference between ferromagnetic and ferrimagnetic material is the change of the value of χ over the temperature range. Another difference is that in ferromagnetic material, the saturation of magnetization versus temperature behaves in a more complicated way.

Ferrimagnetic materials are usually oxides of iron combined with one or more transition metals, such as manganese, nickel, or zinc, for example, $MnFe_2O_4$. Permanent ferrimagnets often include barium (Ba). The raw material is turned into a powder, which is then fired in a kiln or *sintered* to produce a dark gray, hard, brittle ceramic material having a cubic crystalline structure. At an atomic level, the magnetic properties depend upon interaction between the electrons associated with the metal ions. Neighbouring atomic magnetic moments become locked in antiparallel alignments with their neighbours (this contrasts with the ferromagnets). However, the magnetic moments in one direction are weaker than the moments in the opposite direction, leading to an overall magnetic moment.

Antiferromagnetism. Antiferromagnetic materials have a small positive value of χ at all temperatures. This phenomenon of magnetic moment coupling between adjacent atoms or ions occurs in materials other than those that are ferromagnetic. In one such group, this coupling results in an antiparallel alignment; the alignment of the spin moments of neighboring atoms or ions in the exact opposite direction is termed *antiferromagnetism*. Manganese oxide (MnO) is one such material that shows the behavior of antiferromagnetism.

3.2.5 OPTICAL PROPERTIES

Optical properties of a material refer to the response of the material to electromagnetic radiation, particularly visible light. Electromagnetic radiation consists of a dual nature: a wave and a particle a (photon is a wave packet). Planck has quantified the energy of one photon as $E = hc / \lambda$, where λ is called *Planck's constant*.

Light interaction with a solid can be described by the following equation, which follows the law of conservation of energy:

(Eq. 3.1)
$$I_0 = I_T + I_A + I_R$$

This equation states that the intensity I_0 of a beam incident to the surface of a solid must be equal to the sum of the wave intensities I_T (transmitted), I_A (absorbed), and I_R (reflected). Based on the above properties, materials can be classified as:

- **Transparent:** a material/object that is clear so that light can pass through it.
- **Translucent:** a material/object that is cloudy and only allows part of the light to pass through.
- **Opaque:** a material/object through which light cannot pass.

A typical characteristic of metals with respect to crystal structure is that they possess a high-energy band that is only partially filled with electrons. When visible light is directed onto a metal surface, the energy excites electrons into unoccupied energy states above the fermi level, thus making metals behave as opaque materials; that is, light is absorbed. Except for thin sections, metals strongly reflect and/or absorb incident radiation for long wavelengths to the middle of the ultraviolet range. This means that metals are opaque to all electromagnetic radiation on the low end of the frequency spectrum, from radio waves, through infrared, visible, and into the middle of ultraviolet radiation. However, metals are transparent to high-end frequencies, for example, X-ray and γ–ray radiation. Most of the absorbed radiation is emitted from the metallic surface in the form of visible light of the same wavelength as reflected light. The reflectivity of metals is about 0.95, while the rest of the impinged energy is dissipated as heat.

Nonmetallic materials may be transparent to visible light because of their electron structure with characteristic energy band structures. Therefore, all four optical phenomena—absorption, reflection, transmission, and refraction—can take place in nonmetallic materials.

3.2 6 ACOUSTIC PROPERTIES

The word *acoustic* is derived from the Greek Work "akoustikos," which translates as "of or for hearing; ready to hear." Acoustic waves are mechanical waves in gases, liquids, and solids. In fluids, sound propagates primarily as a pressure wave. In solids, mechanical waves can take many forms, including longitudinal waves, transverse waves, and surface waves. These waves can be produced through vibration, sound, ultrasound, and infrasound.

Based on frequency, acoustic waves can be divided into infrasonic, sonic, and ultrasonic waves. Here is a simple concept of an acoustic wave:

- **Cause:** There must be a medium and cause to generate acoustic waves.
- **Generating mechanism:** There must be some kind of mechanism, such as a transducer, to generate acoustic waves.
- **Acoustic wave propagation:** The generated waves, for example, transverse waves, have definite patterns in propagation.
- **Reception:** The waves should be received by any means after they are propagated, generally by a type of transducer.
- **Effect:** After reception, each wave provides information that is useful for analyzing the wave pattern.

Ultrasonic testing is a nondestructive testing method that propagates ultrasound into a material in order to receive information about the soundness of the material.

3.3 MECHANICAL PROPERTIES AND DESTRUCTIVE TESTING OF MATERIALS

Mechanical properties are described as the relationship between forces (or stresses) acting on a material and the resistance of the material to deformation (that is, strains) and fracture. Depending on how much the material is strained, this deformation may or may not be present in the material after the applied load is removed. Design engineers must take into consideration the mechanical properties of the materials used in the final product. Materials chosen in engineering applications should rely on the ability of the material to meet or exceed design and service requirements. For cost, strength, and other beneficial reasons, materials should also have the ability to be fabricated within specified tolerances relatively easily. A plethora of tests and equipment, which use an applied force, measure properties such as elastic modulus, yield strength, elastic and plastic deformation, hardness, fatigue resistance, and fracture toughness.

3.3.1 STRESS AND STRAIN

Stress-Strain Curve. Engineering stress is calculated by dividing the applied load (P) by the original cross-sectional area (A_0) of the specimen. This differs from true stress, where P is divided by the actual area (A), which is constantly changing under the applied load. The engineering *stress-strain curves*, shown in Figure 3.1, are constructed from the load-elongation measurements made on a test object. The engineering stress (s) used in the stress-strain curve is the average longitudinal stress in the tensile specimen. In SI units, stress is expressed as newton (N) per square meter (m^2), otherwise known as a pascal (Pa). In standard units, stress is expressed in pounds per square inch (psi).

The shape and magnitude of a stress-strain curve of a material are greatly influenced by its composition, heat treatment, history of plastic deformation, strain rate, temperature, and state of stress imposed during testing. The parameters that are used to describe the stress-strain curve can be divided into two categories. *Tensile and yield strength* are strength parameters, while *strain* (percent elongation or reduction in area) indicates ductility.

Elastic Deformation. In the elastic region, stress is linearly proportional to strain. This relationship is known as the *modulus of elasticity* or *Young's modulus* (*E*). Simply stated, the modulus of elasticity is stress (σ) divided by strain (ε) or $E = \sigma/\varepsilon$. Materials recover their elastic deformation once the applied load is removed. When the stresses exceed the yield strength (S_y) of a material, it undergoes plastic deformation. Once the load is removed, the specimen slightly springs back, recovering the energy spent on the elastic portion of deformation, but the plastic deformation remains permanent. The stresses required to continue the plastic deformation increase progressively due to a phenomenon known as *strain hardening*. As plastic deformation increases, the dislocations in the crystallographic lattice increase. Dislocations tangle up and obstruct the movement of each other. Therefore, further deformation requires higher stresses; hence, the material's strain hardens. An unstressed copper tube, for example, can be easily bent by hand once, but after that the attempt becomes very difficult or impossible. Because the volume of the specimen remains constant during plastic deformation:

(Eq. 3.2)
$$AL = A_0 L_0$$

As the specimen elongates (*L*), its cross-sectional area (*A*) decreases uniformly along the gage length.

Instability. Reduction in area results in an increase in stress under a constant applied load. While the specimen grows weaker with the reduction of its cross section, it also becomes stronger due to strain hardening. Initially, the strain hardening more than compensates for this decrease in area, and the engineering stress continues to rise nonlinearly with increasing strain. Eventually, the effect of the decrease in

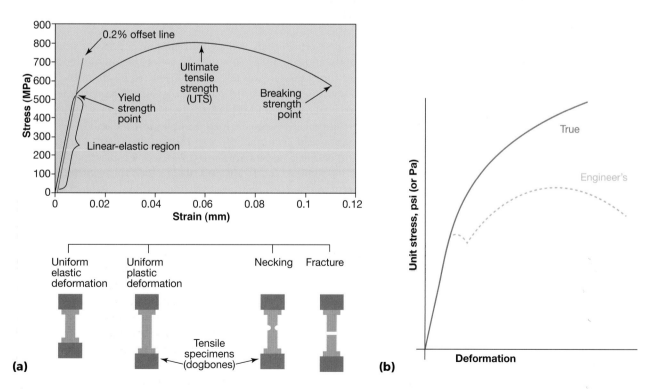

Figure 3.1: Stress-strain curves: (a) based on tensile test; (b) true versus engineering curves.

the cross-sectional area becomes greater than the compensation from strain hardening. This condition is known as *instability* and is reached at the weakest location along the gage length. All plastic deformation beyond this point is concentrated in this location. The specimen begins to neck or thin down locally. Now the cross-sectional area is decreasing more rapidly than the effects of strain hardening can overcome. Thus, the actual load required to deform the specimen drops off, and the engineering stress continues to decrease until fracture occurs.

Since engineering stress-strain is a function of the original cross-sectional area (A_O), the curve does not give a true indication of the deformation characteristics of a material as these dimensions change continuously during the test. Ductile materials that are pulled in tension become unstable and neck down during the course of the test. As stated earlier, because the cross-sectional area of the specimen is decreasing rapidly at this stage in the test, the load required to continue deformation falls off.

If the strain measurement is based on instantaneous measurement, the resulting curve is known as a *true stress-true strain curve*. In terms of engineering stress, true stress is calculated as:

(Eq. 3.3)
$$\sigma = s(e+1)$$

where *e* is the mathematical function. This mathematical expression holds true up to the point of necking. Once necking begins, true stress is then calculated using the instantaneous cross-sectional area of the specimen. The true stress-true strain curve is also known as a *flow curve* because it represents the plastic-flow characteristics of the material.

3.3.2 TENSILE AND COMPRESSION TESTS

The *tensile test* (applying tension) is one of the most common mechanical tests for evaluating materials. This is because testing under tension provides data for quantifying several mechanical properties, such as the elastic modulus, Poisson's ratio, yield and ultimate strength, and ductility properties, as well as strain hardening characteristics. In its simplest form, the tension test is accomplished by clamping or fixturing the ends of a test specimen in the grips of a test machine. The specimen is prepared following specific standards and is commonly referred to as a *dogbone* based on its shape. (See Figure 3.2.) A tensile load is applied by the machine, resulting in the gradual elongation and eventual failure of the test specimen. Throughout the test, applied force and elongation data are monitored and recorded.

The material properties deduced from tension tests are used for ensuring quality control in production, ranking performance of structural materials, evaluating newly developed alloys, and dealing with the static-strength requirements of design. However, it should be noted that as simple as the tension test is, numerous variables affect the results. To list a few, methodology (that is, applied strain-rate), human factors (for example, an improperly set test sample), equipment, and ambient conditions all affect the end results.

The *compression test* applies compressive forces and measures the deformation of a cylindrical specimen. To maintain the volume conservation principle, as the height of the cylinder decreases, the specimen cross-sectional area will increase. In real applications, the friction between the specimen and the ram causes the cylinder to deform nonuniformly. This is known as *barreling*. To understand the behavior of materials under large plastic strains during deformation, measurements must be made beyond the tensile necking limit. In this case, compression is the test method of choice. It is used for determining the stress-strain response of materials at large strains ($\varepsilon > 0.5$). Under certain circumstances, compression testing may also have

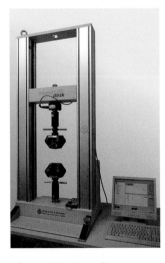

Figure 3.2: Tensile test: test objects (dogbones) made of aluminum alloy in a tensile test machine.

advantages over other testing methods. Less material is needed since the compression test does not require additional specimen length, which would be needed for fixturing. This can be very important when dealing with rare and/or exotic materials that can be very expensive or hard to find. This is also important when considering another possible mode of failure known as *buckling*. The problem of buckling is mainly a geometrical issue where the slenderness ratio is important. Thus, having a short yet wide specimen eliminates any chance for buckling.

Compression tests are also frequently used to evaluate the workability of materials. This is especially true for elevated temperature applications where deformation processes such as forging or rolling introduce large compressive stresses. Compression testing is also used with brittle materials where the machinist and technician may find it extremely difficult to machine a specimen and tensile test it in perfect alignment. Characterizing the mechanical behavior of anisotropic materials often requires compression testing. For isotropic polycrystalline materials, compressive behavior is assumed to be identical to tensile behavior in terms of elastic and plastic deformation. However, for highly textured materials that deform by twinning, as opposed to a dislocation slip, compressive and tensile deformation characteristics greatly differ from each other. The failure of unidirectionally reinforced composite materials is much different in compression than in tension, particularly along the direction of reinforcement.

3.3.3 MODULUS OF ELASTICITY AND MODULUS OF RESILIENCE

The *modulus of elasticity* (E), also known as Young's modulus, as previously described in section 3.3.1, is the quotient of the stress (σ) divided by the strain (ε) up to the yield strength or within the elastic region of the material, as illustrated in Figure 3.3a.

The *modulus of resilience*, shown in Figure 3.3b, is defined as the maximum energy that can be absorbed per unit volume without creating a permanent distortion.

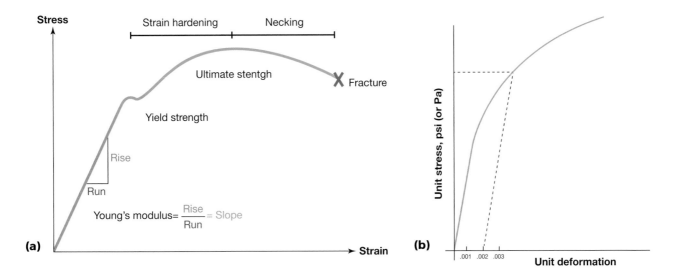

Figure 3.3: Two different moduli: (a) modulus of elasticity; (b) modulus of resilience.

Simply put, it is the area underneath the curve to the yield strength. Since strain is a dimensionless parameter, the moduli of elasticity and resilience both have the same units as stress or pressure. The modulus of elasticity is expressed as:

(Eq. 3.4)
$$E = \frac{\sigma}{\varepsilon}$$

and the modulus of resilience as:

(Eq. 3.5)
$$U_r = \frac{\sigma\varepsilon}{2} = \frac{\sigma^2}{2E}$$

Both moduli are only valid in the elastic region or below the yield strength.

3.3.4 STRAIN AND DUCTILITY

Strain is defined as the elongation change in dimension per unit length. Since strain is the quotient of a length divided by another length, the value is essentially dimensionless. Due to the inherent relationship between stress and strain, discussed in section 3.3.1, strain also can be calculated for both engineering (e) and true (ε) values. *Engineering strain* is the change in length (Δl) divided by the original length (l_o) or:

(Eq. 3.6)
$$e = \frac{\Delta l}{l_o}$$

Note: diameter can also be used in place of length.

True strain is calculated by taking the natural log of the quotient (l_o/l_f) where l_f is the final length; thus:

(Eq. 3.7)
$$\varepsilon = \ln\left(\frac{l_o}{l_f}\right)$$

Once the onset of necking occurs, true strain must be calculated by using the quotient of the original cross-sectional area (A_o) divided by the instantaneous cross-sectional area (A_i) or:

(Eq. 3.8)
$$\left(\frac{A_o}{A_i}\right)$$

Ductility is defined as the total elongation of the specimen due to plastic deformation. Upon failure, the two halves of the broken specimen recover their elastic elongation and separate. The total elongation measured by the mechanical testing instrument includes the elastic portion. (See Figure 3.4.)

3.3.5 HARDNESS

Hardness may be defined as the ability of a material to resist permanent deformation or penetration when in contact with an *indenter* under load. A typical hardness test consists of pressing an indenter of known geometry and mechanical properties into the test material. The hardness of the material is quantified using one of a variety of scales. The *brinell test* utilizes a spherical indenter, whereas the *vickers* and *knoop tests* make use of a pyramidal indenter. The most widely used *rockwell test* uses a conical indenter tool, as shown in Figure 3.5. In brinell, vickers, and knoop tests, the hardness value is the load divided by the area of the indentation, with units in kilograms per square millimeter (kg/mm²). In the rockwell test, the depth of an indentation at a prescribed load is determined and converted to a unitless hardness number, which is inversely related to depth. A wealth of information is available to converting one hardness scale to another. However, the engineer must be careful to note which case gives the correct conversion as there is more than one plot, equation, or table that covers the entire range of engineering materials.

Hardness testing is a cheap, quick, and simple method of mechanically characterizing a material since it requires neither specimen preparation nor expensive testing equipment. Hardness tests are no longer limited to metals, as current tools and procedures cover a vast range of materials, including polymers, elastomers, thin films, semiconductors, and ceramics. Experimentation and empirical studies have resulted in accurate quantitative relationships between hardness and other mechanical properties of materials, such as ultimate tensile strength, yield strength, strain hardening coefficient, fatigue strength, and creep. These relationships are accurate enough for use as quality control during the intermediate and final stages of manufacturing. Many times hardness testing is the only test alternative available to qualify finished components for end applications.

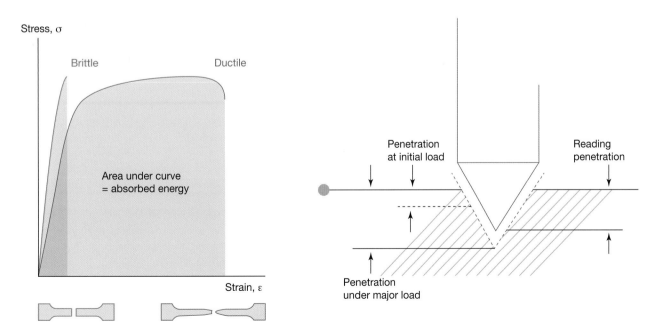

Figure 3.4: Graph comparing stress-strain for brittle versus ductile materials.

Figure 3.5: Rockwell hardness test.

3.3.6 TOUGHNESS

Toughness is defined as the total area under the stress-strain curve, which measures the energy absorbed by the specimen in the process of breaking. (Stress-strain curves from tensile tests for toughness are shown in Figure 3.6.) Unlike the modulus of resilience, toughness cannot be calculated algebraically since the plastic region is nonlinear due to strain hardening. Taking the true stress-true strain curve into account, where $\sigma = K\varepsilon^n$, toughness is calculated by integrating the true stress-true strain function from 0 to ε_f or:

(Eq. 3.9)
$$K \cdot \int_0^{\varepsilon_f} \varepsilon^n \, d\varepsilon$$

where K is the strength coefficient.

3.3.7 FATIGUE

Fatigue is the progressive, localized, and permanent structural damage that occurs when a material is subjected to cyclic or fluctuating strains at nominal stresses that have maximum values less than the static yield strength of the material. The *fatigue limit*, or *endurance limit*, is the amplitude of cyclic stress below which fatigue damage will not occur. The fatigue limit is an important parameter in the design of parts that undergo cyclic loading, such as wheel axles, airplane wings, and engine parts. Fatigue is a crucial cause of failure in many cases. It can initiate cracks at nucleation points, such as stress concentration points or inclusions, which begin to grow under the cyclic loading until they are large enough to cause fracture toughness failure. In most cases failure is catastrophic, that is, sudden and total. Fatigue can result from cyclical application of tension and compression, tension only, or compression only.

   Conditions Required for Fatigue Damage. Generally, three conditions are required for the occurrence of fatigue damage: cyclic stress, tensile stress, and plastic strain. All three conditions must be present for fatigue cracking to initiate and propagate. The plastic strain resulting from cyclic stress initiates the crack, and the tensile stresses (which may be localized tensile stresses caused by compressive loads) promote crack propagation.

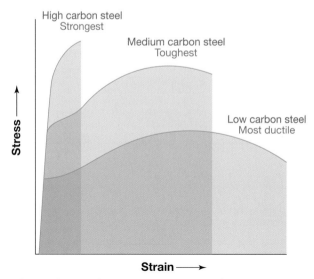

Figure 3.6: Toughness in relation to the stress-strain curve for three types of steel.

S-N Plot. A typical plot used to characterize the fatigue of a material is known as the *S-N plot* (stress versus number of cycles). Design engineers rely on these plots to determine if a part will survive its expected life cycle. Again, there exists an extensive database of these curve plots for different situations. Depending on the case, the correct S-N curve must be used to avoid catastrophic failure. Examples are shown in Figure 3.7, where the materials represented by the curves would have endurance limits, the curves have flattened out and stressing at these levels could be continued indefinitely without failure.

3.3.8 CREEP

A typical *creep test* is performed by applying a constant load and measuring the strain (elongation) as a function of time. The resulting curve has three stages, as shown in Figure 3.8. During the first stage, primary creep, dislocations climb and break free from their pinning sites and the material starts to elongate. The second stage of creep is characterized by a steady rate of strain where the rate creating new dislocations is balanced by the rate at which they annihilate each other. In the third stage, tertiary creep, necking occurs, causing the load to apply higher stresses until failure. The creep rate increases with temperature and load, so failure occurs sooner. At elevated temperatures or loads, dislocations are more mobile. Also, at higher stress, the initial strain is high, which also reduces the time for failure to occur.

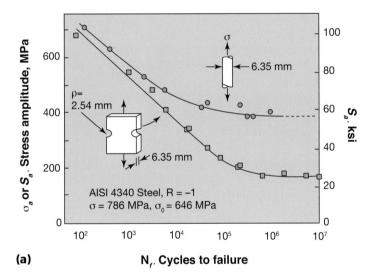

(a)

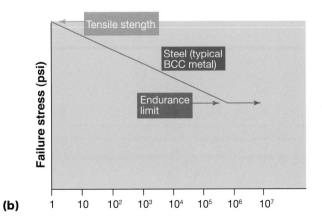

(b)

Figure 3.7: Typical S-N plots: (a) notched square sample compared to a rod; (b) endurance limit of steel

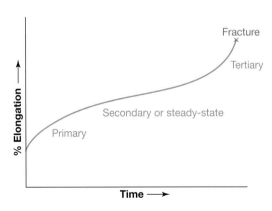

Figure 3.8: Creep test curve.

4 Production and Properties of Common Metals

4.1 FERROUS METALS AND ALLOYS

4.1.1 INTRODUCTION, PROPERTIES, AND USE

In Chapter 2, metals were discussed primarily on the basis of their atomic configurations. While it is true that this basis gives a more precise definition in the chemist's or physicist's terms, of greater practical interest in manufacturing are the metallic properties of relatively high hardness and strength, ability to undergo considerable plastic flow, high density, durability, rigidity, and luster. A distinction is sometimes made between the word *metal,* meaning a pure chemical element, and the word *alloy,* meaning a combination of materials, the predominant one of which is a metal. The term *metal* in this text will be taken to mean any metallic material, whether pure or alloyed.

   Availability of Ores. Among all the possible reasons for the choice and use of a material, one of very prime importance is availability. Table 4.1 shows the composition of the Earth's crust. Of the first 12 elements in occurrence, aluminum, iron, magnesium, and titanium are used as the base metals of alloy systems. For the other metals, although the total tonnage in the Earth's crust may be considerable, the

"The term 'metal' in this text will be taken to mean any metallic material, whether pure or alloyed."

potential use is much more restricted. Some of them, such as copper, are found in relatively pure deposits but frequently in remote locations, and the total use is dependent on relatively few of these rich deposits. Most other metals are recovered only in relatively small quantities, either as byproducts of the recovery of the more predominant metals or as products of low-yield ores after extensive mining and concentration in which many tons of material must be handled for each pound of metal recovered. The U.S. has only marginal deposits of antimony, chromium, cobalt, manganese, and nickel and imports the major quantity of these metals. It is almost totally dependent on imports for its supply of mercury, tungsten, and tin. The location and the availability of these materials have a marked influence on both the risk and cost of choosing these materials for large-use applications.

Base Metals. Approximately 70 of the elements may be classed as metals, and of these, about forty are of commercial importance. Historically, copper, lead, tin, and iron are metals of antiquity because they are either found free in nature or their ores are relatively easy to reduce. These four metals together with aluminum, magnesium, zinc, nickel, and titanium are among the most important metals for use as base metals for structural alloy systems. Most other commercially important metals either are metals used primarily as alloying metals or noble metals, such as gold, silver, or platinum, which are important only for special uses or because of their rarity.

Material Choice Affected by Process. The method of manufacture frequently affects the alloy type chosen even after the base metal has been selected. Although nearly all metals are cast at some time during their manufacture, those that are cast to approximate a finished shape without deformation are specifically referred to as *casting alloys.* When the metal is fabricated by deformation processes, an alloy designed to have good ductility is specified and referred to as a *wrought alloy.* Some alloys can be either wrought or cast. Most wrought alloys can be cast, but many casting alloys have insufficient ductility for even simple deformation processing.

Final Choice Dependent on Many Factors. The choice of a material is usually a stepwise process. Sales requirements, raw material costs, equipment availability, or specific product requirements frequently narrow the choice between the fields of metals and plastics. With the choice of either metals or plastics, some may be eliminated on the basis of properties, although a considerable number of plastics or metal alloys still satisfy the functional requirements for the great majority of products. The life to be expected from the product may also eliminate some materials from consideration. Ultimately, the choice usually becomes one based on costs. From the various materials that would produce a functionally acceptable product with sufficient life and from the various processing methods that are available to a manufacturer, the best combination must be found. Obviously, many combinations will be rather quickly eliminated, but of those remaining, the costs of some may not be entirely predictable without actual experience in producing the product. Consequently, the first choice is not always the final choice, and for this reason, as well as for reasons of sales appeal and product redesign, materials and processes frequently are changed on a trial and error basis.

Table 4.1: Elements in Earth's crust.			
Element	**Percent**	**Element**	**Percent**
Oxygen	46.71	Magnesium	2.08
Silicon	27.69	Titanium	0.62
Aluminum	8.07	Hydrogen	0.14
Iron	5.05	Phosphorus	0.13
Calcium	3.65	Carbon	0.094
Sodium	2.75	Others	0.436
Potassium	2.58		

4.1.2 PROCESSING OF IRON ORE

Ore Reduction. Both iron and steel have their start in the blast furnace. Although other methods for reduction have been proposed and will likely be developed, the tremendous investment in equipment and trained personnel that would be required for the replacement of present facilities almost ensures that the blast furnace method will remain for some time.

This device is a tall, columnar structure into which is fed, through a top opening, a mixture of iron ore (oxides of iron—Fe_3O_3, hematite, or Fe_3O_4, magnetite), coke, and limestone. A blast of hot air is supplied through the mixture from near the bottom to provide oxygen for combustion of the coke. Temperatures in the neighborhood of 1650 °C (3000 °F) are developed in the melting zone. The iron ore is reduced by chemical reactions with carbon monoxide gases and by high temperature contact directly with the carbon in the coke as well as with other impurity elements in the mixture. Near the bottom of the furnace, the iron and the slag, which is made up of other metallic oxides combined with limestone, melt and accumulate in a well; the lighter slag floats on top of the melted iron. The molten iron and slag are tapped off periodically through separate holes. The slag is disposed of, either as trash or for byproduct use, and the iron is run into open molds to solidify as *pigs,* unless it is to be further processed immediately. In large installations, the molten iron is frequently transported in large ladles to other equipment for carbon reduction in the manufacture of steel.

Pig Iron. The product of the blast furnace, whether liquid or solid, is called *pig iron.* The term *pig* refers to a crude casting, convenient for transportation, storage, and remelting of any metal, whereas the term *pig iron* refers to the composition of the metal tapped from the blast furnace, whether in liquid or solid state. Although this composition varies with ore, coke, blast furnace conditions, and other factors, the blast furnace is controllable only within broad limits. Pig iron as a natural result of the conditions within the furnace always contains 3% to 4% of carbon and smaller amounts of silicon, sulfur, phosphorus, manganese, and other elements.

Pig Iron Requires Further Processing. In the solid state, pig iron is weak, is too hard to be machined, and has practically no ductility to permit deformation work. It must therefore be treated to improve some of its properties by one of the methods shown in Figure 4.1. The simplest of these treatments are those shown on the left of the figure; the treatments involve remelting with only moderate control of composition, in particular with no attempt to remove the carbon.

4.1.3 STEELMAKING PROCESSES

Early Steel. The oldest known method of making higher carbon steel consisted of reheating wrought iron and powdered charcoal together in the *cementation* process. According to the iron-carbon equilibrium diagram, at 1148 °C (2098 °F) carbon is soluble in iron up to 2%. At this temperature, the carbon slowly diffused into the solid material; the process required a total cycle time, including heating, of about two weeks. Much of the slag in the wrought iron migrated to the surface and formed surface blisters, which resulted in the term *blister steel.* Even after this lengthy treatment, the carbon was not uniformly dispersed throughout the material, and multiple cutting and rerolling procedures were required to produce a high quality product.

Crucible Steel. Further reduction of the slag, greater uniformity of the carbon, and closer controls were later achieved by a secondary operation known as the *crucible process.* Bars made by the cementation process were remelted in a clay or graphite crucible in which the slag floated to the surface. This crucible process produced steel of very high quality; however, the process is now considered obsolete. Similar quality steel can be manufactured using an electric arc furnace.

Open-Hearth Steel. Both the modern open-hearth furnace and the bessemer converter were developed in the 1850s. These two developments greatly increased the speed with which pig iron could be refined. The modern era of industry can be tied to these developments that led to the production of large quantities of high-quality, low-cost steel.

Figure 4.2 shows the construction of an open-hearth furnace as was used for the majority of steel produced in the U.S. until superseded by the bessemer steelmaking process, which in turn has been supplanted by basic oxygen steelmaking beginning in the 1950s. By the early 1990s, most open-hearth furnaces had ceased production. Various proportions of pig iron (either solid or molten), steel scrap, limestone for flux, and iron ore are charged on the hearth of the furnace. The principal reducing action takes place between the iron ore and the carbon of the pig iron, the final carbon content of the steel being controllable by the proper proportions of the charged materials. The principal difference between this furnace and that used previously in the manufacture of wrought iron lies in the preheating of the entering combustion air. In the open-hearth furnace for steelmaking, the air enters through a brick checkerwork that has been previously heated by the exhausting flue gases. Two similar checkerworks are used, one for the exhaust side and one for the entering air side of the furnace. After a relatively short period of operation in this manner, the airflow through the checkerworks is reversed. Preheating of the air permits higher

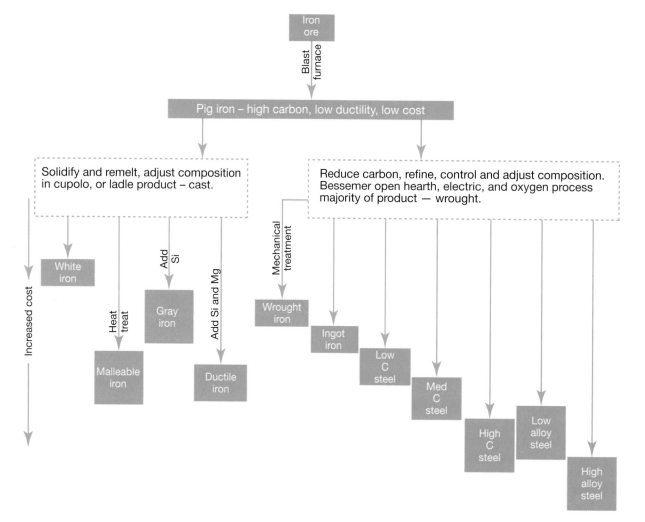

Figure 4.1: General relationship of ferrous materials.

temperatures to be developed in the furnace, and the bath of metal may be kept molten as the carbon content is reduced.

Bessemer Steel. The bessemer converter is shown in Figure 4.3. The charge consists of molten pig iron. Steel scrap may be added to help control the temperature. After charging in the horizontal position, the air blast is turned on through the tuyeres and the converter turned upright so that the air bubbles through the melt, oxidizing and burning out first silicon, then carbon. The process can be used to reduce the carbon content to about 0.05%. Although less expensive to operate than the basic-lined open-hearth furnace, the inability of the acid-lined bessemer converter to reduce the phosphorus content of the metal has restricted its use. By 1968, U.S. steel production using the bessemer process ceased and was replaced by the more efficient basic oxygen steelmaking process.

Electric Furnace Steel. Electric furnace steel is produced in a variation of the older crucible process with the furnace heated by electric arc or induction. The atmosphere can be well controlled in the electric furnace, and careful control of composition can be maintained. Steel of the highest quality is produced by this method.

Basic Oxygen Process. A steelmaking process known as the basic oxygen process was developed in Switzerland and Austria after World War II and first used in 1952. By 1957, the method was producing 1% of the world production. In 1966, the growth of use was to 25% and by 2000, 60% of the world's steel was made by the basic oxygen process.

There are a number of variations in the equipment and methods for making basic oxygen steel. Fundamentally, they all operate much as follows:

- Scrap as great as 30% of the heat is charged into the refining vessel, as shown schematically in Figure 4.4.
- Molten pig iron is charged on top of the scrap.
- The lance is positioned, and a high-velocity jet of oxygen is blown on top of the molten mixture for about 20 min. During this period, lime and various fluxes are added as aids for control of the final composition.
- The metal is then sampled and, if it meets specifications, poured through the tap hole into a ladle by tilting the vessel.
- Finally, the vessel is inverted to empty the slag and then is ready for reuse. With careful use, the vessel lining may last for as many as 400 heats.

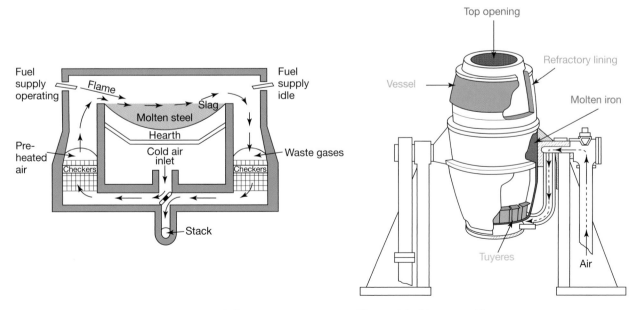

Figure 4.2: Cross section of open-hearth furnace.   **Figure 4.3: Diagram of bessemer converter.**

The total time for producing a heat by this method is 30 to 45 min. This compares very favorably with the 4 to 6 h necessary for the open-hearth methods using oxygen.

Steel made by this method can start from any grade of pig iron. The finish quality is similar to that made in open-hearth furnaces. Scrap is usable in large quantities so that the process becomes the cheapest method for remelting and reusing scrap.

A typical 227 metric ton (250 U.S. short ton) BOF vessel in the U.S. is 10.4 m (34 ft) in height with an outside diameter (OD) of 7.9 m (26 ft), a barrel lining thickness of 0.9 m (3 ft), and a capacity of 226.5 m³ (8000 ft³). (Source: Steelworks, www.steel.org.) However, sizes greater than 272 metric tons (300 U.S. short tons) are available. A 272 metric ton (300 U.S. short ton) unit can produce 3 million tons (2.7 million metric tons) of steel per year.

The growth of the basic oxygen process has been extremely fast as industrial processes go, and would probably have been even faster except for the large investments required. The immense quantities of oxygen and its use demand much in the way of special equipment.

The development of oxygen-making facilities and the reduction of cost of the gas has changed nearly all steelmaking. Even when the complete basic oxygen process is not used, oxygen is used to speed steelmaking. Both open-hearth and bessemer converters are likely to be supplied with oxygen to speed combustion and refining. An open-hearth furnace fitted with oxygen lances can approximately double production with less than one-half the fuel of earlier methods, without use of pure oxygen. The making of bessemer steel is speeded by use of oxygen combined with air, and is also improved in composition, mainly by reduction of nitrogen impurities left in the steel. Little bessemer steel is made in the U.S., however.

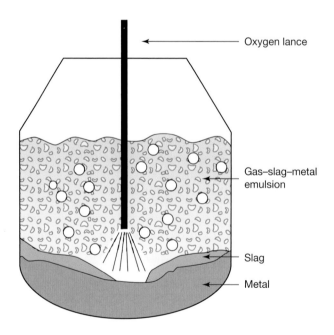

Figure 4.4: Cross section of a basic oxygen furnace vessel during oxygen blowing. (AISI)

4.1.4 STEEL REFINING

One of the largest and most influential manufacturing operations is the steel industry, which makes some finished products but is primarily concerned with the making of raw material for further processing. The annual production of more than 100 million tons (900 million metric tons) exceeds by far the total production of all other metals and plastics combined.

Comparison of Steel with Cast Iron. Assuming equal weight, castings of cast iron are cheaper than those of steel, and for those products that can be made with suitable shapes and strengths as castings, the cost of the finished product often will be lower in this form. However, all cast irons, because of their high carbon content, are subject to the definite processing limitations of casting. Thin sections, good finishes, and dimensional control are obtained at reasonable cost only by deformation processing instead of casting. Deformation can be performed only on materials having relatively high ductility. For ferrous materials, this requires reduction of carbon from the cast iron range to the extent that a material with an entirely new set of properties is produced.

All cast irons are essentially pig iron with, at most, only minor modifications of composition. The essential component of pig iron in addition to the iron is 3% to 4% carbon. When this carbon content is reduced to less than 2%, the resulting new material is called *steel.*

Wrought Iron. Prior to the introduction of currently used methods for making steel, a method of reducing the carbon content of pig iron had been used since before 1600. The product, although called *wrought iron,* was actually the first low carbon steel to be manufactured in quantity.

Early Furnace Limitations. In the early manufacture of wrought iron, molten pig iron was subjected to oxidizing agents, normally air and iron oxide, and the silicon and carbon content of the melt was reduced. The furnaces used were incapable of maintaining the iron at temperatures greater than about 1480 °C (2700 °F). Reference to the iron-carbon equilibrium diagram will show that at this temperature pig iron would be well above the liquidus line. However, as the carbon content was reduced, at constant temperature, the iron began to solidify; consequently, to keep the reaction proceeding within the melt, it was necessary to stir or *puddle* the material in the furnace.

Wrought Iron Contains Slag. Because this material included slag, which floated on top as long as the metal was liquid, the slag was mixed with the purified iron. The resulting product was withdrawn from the furnace as a pasty ball on the end of the stirring rod and, while low in carbon and silicon, contained from 3% to 4% slag, mostly SiO_2. These balls were then deformation processed by repeated rolling, cutting, stacking, and rerolling in the same direction. The resulting product consisted of relatively pure iron with many very fine slag stringers running in the direction of rolling.

Although cheaper methods have been developed for reducing the carbon from pig iron without incorporating the slag in the product, a demand for wrought iron continues, based primarily on its reputation for corrosion and fatigue resistance. It is manufactured by pouring molten refined iron into separately manufactured slag with subsequent rolling.

Properties of Wrought Iron. Wrought iron has a tensile strength of about 350 MPa (50 000 psi) and good ductility, although the material is quite *anisotropic* (properties vary with orientation or direction of testing) because of the slag stringers. Its principal use is for the manufacture of welded pipe.

While *wrought iron* originally referred to this product or to its composition, the term has frequently been extended to refer to any *worked* low carbon steel product, particularly a product shaped or worked by hand, such as ornamental iron railings and grillwork.

4.1.5 STEEL SPECIFICATION AND TERMINOLOGY

Variety of Metallic Materials Necessitates Specification Codes. During earlier industrial development, there was less need for material identification systems. A manufacturer generally had complete charge of the entire operation from raw material to finished product. In any event, there were relatively few materials from which to choose. Specialization has led to more division of the manufacturing procedure. Fabricators seldom produce their own raw materials, and the number of material choices has grown tremendously and continues to grow yearly. Reliable and universally accepted systems of material specification are essential to permit designers to specify and fabricators to purchase materials and be assured of composition and properties. The first group of materials for which standardization was needed was ferrous materials. The automotive industry set up the first recognized standards, but with broader use and more classes of steels, the most universally recognized standards are those of the American Iron and Steel Institute (AISI).

AISI Numbers for Plain and Low-Alloy Steels. The number of possible combinations of iron, carbon, and alloying elements is without limit. Some of these, for example, the low-alloy, high-strength structural steels, are not covered by any standard specification system or designation. However, the majority of commonly used steels in the plain carbon and low-alloy categories can be described by a standardized code system consisting of a letter denoting the process by which the steel was manufactured, followed by four or, in a few cases, five digits. The first two digits refer to the quantity and kind of principal alloying element or elements. The last two digits, or three in the case of some high carbon steels, refer to the carbon content in hundredths of a percent. At one time, the process used in steelmaking affected the properties of the finished product enough that it was important to know how it was made. Letter prefixes as follows were used for this purpose:

- **B:** Acid bessemer carbon steel
- **C:** Basic open-hearth steel
- **D:** Acid open-hearth steel
- **E:** Electric furnace alloy steel

With the advent of basic oxygen steel, however, the letter prefix is falling into disuse. The control exhibited in the basic oxygen process produces steel of similar quality to that from the open-hearth method.

Table 4.2 shows the average alloy content associated with some of the most frequently used classes of steels. The exact specified quantity varies with the carbon content of each steel, and even steels with exactly the same number throughout will vary slightly from heat to heat because of necessary manufacturing tolerances. Exact composition can therefore be determined only from chemical analysis of individual heats.

4.1.6 CARBON STEELS

Any steelmaking process is capable of producing a product that has 0.05% or less carbon. With this small amount of carbon, the properties approach those of pure iron with maximum ductility and minimum strength. Maximum ductility is desirable from the standpoint of ease in deformation processing and service use. Minimum strength is desirable for deformation processing. However, higher strengths than that obtainable with this low carbon are desirable from the standpoint of product design. The most practical means of increasing the strength is by the addition or retention of some carbon. However, it should be fully understood that any increase of strength over that of pure iron can be obtained only at the expense of some loss of ductility, and the final choice is always a compromise of some degree.

Figure 4.5 shows typical ferrous material applications in relation to carbon content. Because of the difficulty of composition control or the additional operation of increasing carbon content, the cost of higher-carbon, higher-strength steel is greater than that of low carbon.

Plain Carbon Steels Most Used. Because of their low cost, the majority of steels used are plain carbon steels. These consist of iron combined with carbon concentrated in three ranges classed as low carbon, medium carbon, and high carbon. With the exception of manganese used to control sulfur, other elements are present only in small enough quantities to be considered as impurities, though in some cases they may have a minor effect on properties of the material.

Low Carbon. Steels with approximately 6 to 25 points of carbon (0.06% to 0.25%) are rated as low carbon steels and are rarely hardened by heat treatment because the low carbon content permits so little formation of hard martensite that the process is relatively ineffective. Enormous tonnages of these low carbon steels are processed in such structural shapes as sheet, strip, rod, plate, pipe, and wire. A large portion of the material is cold worked in its final processing to improve its hardness, strength, and surface finish qualities. The grades containing 20 points or less of carbon are susceptible to considerable plastic flow and are frequently used as deep-drawn products or may be used as a ductile core for case-hardened material. The low plain carbon steels are readily brazed, welded, and forged.

Medium Carbon. The medium carbon steels (0.25% to 0.5%) contain sufficient carbon that they may be heat treated for desirable strength, hardness, machinability, or other properties. The hardness of plain carbon steels in this range cannot be increased sufficiently for the material to serve satisfactorily as cutting tools, but the load-carrying capacity of the steels can be raised considerably, while still retaining sufficient ductility for good toughness. The majority of the steel is furnished in the hot-rolled condition and is often machined for final finishing. It can be welded but is more difficult to join by this method than the low carbon steel because of structural changes caused by welding heat in localized areas.

High Carbon. High carbon steel contains from 50 to 160 points of carbon (0.5% to 1.6%). This group of steels is classed as tool and die steel, in which hardness is the principal property desired. Because of the fast reaction time and resulting low hardenability, plain carbon steels nearly always must be water quenched. Even with this

Table 4.2: AISI basic classification numbers.	
AISI No.	**Average Percent Alloy Content**
10xx	None
11xx	0.08-0.33 S
13xx	1.8-2.0 Mn
23xx	3.5 Ni
31xx	0.7-0.8 Cr, 1.3 Ni
41xx	0.5-1.0 Cr, 0.2-0.3 Mo
43xx	0.5-0.8 Cr, 1.8 Ni, 0.3 Mo
51xx	0.8-1.1 Cr
61xx	0.8-1.0 Cr, 0.1-0.2 V
86xx	0.6 Ni, 0.5-0.7 Cr, 1.2 Mo
87xx	0.6 Ni, 0.5 Cr, 0.3 Mo

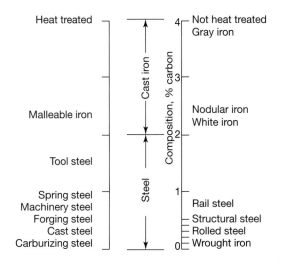

Figure 4.5: Ferrous materials.

drastic treatment and its associated danger of distortion or cracking, it is seldom possible to develop a fully hardened structure in material more than about 25.4 mm (1 in.) in thickness. In practice, the ductility of heat-treat-hardened plain carbon steel is low compared to that of alloy steels with the same strength, but, even so, carbon steel is frequently used because of its lower cost.

4.1.7 ALLOY STEELS

Although plain carbon steels work well for many uses and are the cheapest steels and therefore the most used, they cannot completely fulfill the requirements for some work. Individual or groups of properties can be improved by the addition of various elements in the form of alloys. Even plain carbon steels are alloys of at least iron, carbon, and manganese, but the term *alloy steel* refers to steels containing elements other than these in controlled quantities greater than impurity concentration or, in the case of manganese, greater than 1.5%.

Composition and Structure Affect Properties. Table 4.3 shows the general effects of the more commonly used elements on some properties of steels. Some effects noted in the chart are independent, but most are based on the influence the element has on the action of carbon. The hardness and the strength of any steel—alloy or otherwise—depend primarily on the amount and the form of the iron carbide or other metal carbides present. Even in unhardened steel, carbon produces an increase in hardness and strength with a consequent loss of ductility. The improvement in machinability and the loss in weldability are based on this loss of ductility.

Alloys Affect Hardenability. Interest in hardenability is indirect. Hardenability itself has been discussed earlier and is usually thought of most in connection with depth-hardening ability in a full hardening operation. However, with the isothermal transformation curves shifted to the right, the properties of a material can be materially changed even when not fully hardened. After hot-rolling or forging operations, the material usually air cools. Any alloy generally shifts the transformation curves to the right, which with air cooling results in finer pearlite than would be formed in a plain carbon steel. This finer pearlite has higher hardness and strength, which has an effect on machinability and may lower ductility.

Weldability. The generally bad influence of alloys on weldability is a further reflection of the influence on hardenability. With alloys present during the rapid cooling taking place in the welding area, hard, nonductile structures are formed in the steel and frequently lead to cracking and distortion.

Element	Low C 0.1-0.2%	Med. C 0.2-0.6%	Mn 2.0%	P 0.15%	S 0.3%	Si 2.0%	Cr 1.1%	Ni 5.0%	Mo 0.75%	V 0.25%	Cu 1.1%	Al 0.1%	B 0.003%
Hardenability	N	G	VG	G	B	G	VG	VG	VG	G	N	N	VG
Strength	G	VG	G	G	B	VG	G	G	G	N	N	G	G
Toughness	B	VB	G	VB	VB	B	VB	VG	G	G	N	G	?
Wear resistance	N	VG	VG	N	N	G	VG	G	VG	G	N	N	G
Machinability annealed	G	G	B	G	VG	B	B	VB	B	N	B	N	?
Weldability	B	VB	VB	VB	B	B	VB	VB	VB	G	B	N	VB
Corrosion resistance	B	VB	N	VG	VB	G	N	VG	G	N	VG	G	?

Table 4.3: Effect of some alloying elements on properties of steel.

Very good-VG   Good-G   Little or none-N   Bad-B   Very bad-VB

Grain Size and Toughness. Nickel in particular has a very beneficial effect by retarding grain growth in the austenite range. As with hardenability, it is the secondary effects of grain refinement that are noted in properties. A finer grain structure may actually have less hardenability, but it has its most pronounced effect on toughness; for two steels with equivalent hardness and strength, the one with finer grain will have better ductility, which results in improved toughness. This improved toughness, however, may be detrimental to machinability.

Corrosion Resistance. Most pure metals have relatively good corrosion resistance, which is generally lowered by impurities or small amounts of intentional alloys. In steel, carbon in particular lowers the corrosion resistance very seriously. In small percentages, copper and phosphorus are beneficial in reducing corrosion. Nickel becomes effective in percentages of about 5%, and chromium is extremely effective in percentages greater than 10%, which leads to a separate class of alloy steels called stainless steels. Many tool steels, while not designed for the purpose, are in effect stainless steels because of the high percentage of chromium present.

4.1.7.1 LOW ALLOY STRUCTURAL STEELS

Certain low alloy steels sold under various trade names have been developed to provide a low cost structural material with higher yield strength than plain carbon steel. The addition of small amounts of some alloying elements can raise the yield strength of hot-rolled sections without heat treatment to 30% to 40% greater than that of plain carbon steels. Designing to higher working stresses may reduce the required section size by 25% to 30% at an increased cost of 15% to 50%, depending upon the amount and the kind of alloy.

The low alloy structural steels are sold almost entirely in the form of hot-rolled structural shapes. These materials have good weldability, ductility, better impact strength than that of plain carbon steel, and good corrosion resistance, particularly to atmospheric exposure. Many building codes are based on the more conservative use of plain carbon steels, and the use of alloy structural steel often has no economic advantage in these cases.

4.1.7.2 LOW ALLOY AISI STEELS

Improved Properties at Higher Cost. The low alloy American Iron and Steel Institute (AISI) steels are alloyed primarily for improved hardenability. They are more costly than plain carbon steels, and their use can generally be justified only when needed in the heat-treat-hardened and tempered condition. Compared to plain carbon steels, they can have 30% to 40% higher yield strength and 10% to 20% higher tensile strength. At equivalent tensile strengths and hardnesses, they can have 30% to 40% higher reduction of area and approximately twice the impact strength.

Usually Heat Treated. The low alloy AISI steels are those containing less than approximately 8% total alloying elements, although most commercially important steels contain less than 5%. The carbon content may vary from very low to very high, but for most steels, it is in the medium range that effective heat treatment may be employed for property improvement at minimum costs. The steels are used widely in automobile, machine tool, and aircraft construction, especially for the manufacture of moving parts that are subject to high stress and wear.

4.1.8 STAINLESS STEELS

Tonnage-wise, the most important of the higher alloy steels is a group of high chromium steels with extremely high corrosion and chemical resistance. Most of these steels have much better mechanical properties at high temperatures. This group was first called *stainless steel.* With the emphasis on high temperature use, they are frequently referred to as *heat-*and *corrosion-resistant steels.*

Martensitic Stainless Steel. With lower amounts of chromium or with silicon or aluminum added to some of the higher chromium steels, the material responds to heat treatment much as any low alloy steel. The gamma-to-alpha transformation in iron occurs normally, and the steel may be hardened by heat treatment similar to that used on plain carbon or low alloy steels. Steels of this class are called *martensitic,* and the most used ones have 11% to 18% chromium.

Ferritic Stainless Steel. With larger amounts of chromium, as great as 30% or more, the austenite is suppressed, and the steel loses its ability to be hardened by normal steel heat-treating procedures. Steels of this type are called *ferritic* and are particularly useful when high corrosion resistance is necessary in cold-worked products.

Austenitic Stainless Steel. With high chromium and the addition of 8% or more of nickel or combinations of nickel and manganese, the ferrite is suppressed. These steels, the most typical of which contains 18% chromium and 8% nickel, are referred to as *austenitic stainless steels.* They are not hardenable by normal steel heat-treating procedures, but the addition of small amounts of other elements makes some of them hardenable by a solution precipitation reaction.

Composition and Structure Critical for Corrosion Resistance. In any stainless steel, serious loss of corrosion resistance can occur if large amounts of chromium carbide form. Consequently, the ferritic and austenitic grades are generally made with low amounts of carbon and even then may need special heat treatments or the addition of stabilizing elements such as molybdenum or titanium to prevent chromium carbide formation. With the martensitic grades in which the hardness and strength depend on the carbon, the steels must be fully hardened with the carbon in a martensitic structure for maximum corrosion resistance.

The austenitic steels are the most expensive but possess the best impact properties at low temperatures, the highest strength and corrosion resistance at elevated temperatures, and generally the best appearance. They are used for heat exchangers, refining and chemical processing equipment, gas turbines, and other equipment exposed to severe corrosive conditions. The austenitic steels are *paramagnetic* (practically unaffected by magnetic flux). This fact precludes the use of magnetic particle testing. In the as-cast state, and in welds, austenitic stainless steel is quite coarse-grained. In ultrasonic testing of this material, high levels of noise and attenuation serve to limit the effectiveness of the test.

Both the ferritic and martensitic stainless steels are magnetic. Most are not as corrosion resistant at high temperatures as the austenitic type but offer good resistance at normal temperatures. They are used for such products as cutlery, surgical instruments, automobile trim, ball bearings, and kitchen equipment.

Fabrication Difficult. The stainless steels are more difficult to machine and weld than most other ferrous materials. In no case can stainless steels be classed as the easiest to work, but they can be processed by all of the normal procedures, including casting, rolling, forging, and pressworking. Table 4.4 presents information on common forms of stainless steel.

4.1.9 CAST IRON

These simplest ferrous materials are produced by causing the molten metal to solidify into approximate final product form. The result is known as a casting. The processes of making castings is discussed in Chapter 6. Some of the relationships between common cast irons are shown in Table 4.5.

4.1.10 CAST STEEL

Quantity Relatively Small. Compared to the tonnage of cast iron and wrought steel produced, the quantity of cast steel is small. The high temperatures necessary make melting and handling more difficult than for cast iron and also create problems in producing sound, high-quality castings. The mechanical properties of cast steel tend to be poorer than those of the same material in wrought form, but certain shape and size relationships, together with property requirements that can be supplied only by steel, may favor the manufacture of a product as a steel casting. Steel castings may be produced with greater ductility than even malleable iron.

Cast Steel Is Isotropic. The principal advantages of steel as a structural material, mainly the ability to control properties by composition and heat treatment, apply for both the wrought and the cast material. One advantage of cast steel over its wrought counterpart is its lack of directional properties. Wrought steel and other materials tend to develop strength in the direction of working when they are deformed by

	Composition			Ten St 1000 psi (6.9 x 10⁶ Pa)	Percent Elong. (2 in.)	Characteristics and Uses
Material	**Ni**	**Cr**	**Other**			
302 Annealed	9	18		85	60	Austenitic – Work harden only. Excellent corrosion resistance to atmosphere and foods. Machinability fair. General purpose.Kitchen and chemical applications.
430 Annealed Cold worked		16	CO.12	75 90	30 15	Ferritic – Work harden only. Excellent corrosion resistance to weather and water exposure and most chemicals. Machinability fair. General purpose. Kitchen and chemical equipment. Automobile trim.
420 Annealed Hardened and tempered		13	CO.15	95 230	25 8	Martensitic – Heat treatable. Good corrosion resistance to weather and water exposure. Machinability fair. Cutlery, surgical instruments, ball bearings.
17-4PH Room temp 649 °C (1200 °F)	4	17	Cu 4	195 59	13 15	Age hardening – Good corrosion resistance. Maintains strength at elevated temperature. Machinability poor. Airframe skin and structure.

Table 4.4: Some stainless steels and properties.

Type Iron	How Produced	Characteristics	Relative Cost
White	Rapid cooling Low C+Si	Hard, brittle, unmachinable	1
Malleable	Heat treated White iron	T.S. 3.5-8 x 10⁸ Pa (50 – 120 ksi) Good malleability and ductility	4
Ductile	Ladle addition	T.S. 4-10 x 10⁸ Pa (60 – 150 ksi) similar to malleable	3
Gray	Slow cooling High C+Si	T.S. 1.4-4.1 x 10⁸ Pa (20 – 60 ksi) Good machinability, brittle	2
Chilled	Fast surface chill	Hard surface (white iron) Soft core (gray iron)	3

Table 4.5: Common cast irons.

plastic flow, that is, become anisotropic. At the same time, they become weaker and more brittle in the perpendicular directions. Steel that is cast to shape loses the opportunity for gain in properties by plastic work but, by the same token, is not adversely affected by weakness in some directions.

Wide Variety of Composition. As far as composition is concerned, no real differences exist between wrought and cast steel. It was pointed out earlier that steel is a combination of mostly iron with carbon in amounts from just above that soluble at room temperature (0.008%) to as high as 2%, the maximum soluble in austenite. This is referred to as the *eutectic temperature*—denoting the single temperature at which a mixture of substances in fixed proportions melts and solidifies that is lower than the melting points of the separate constituents or of any other mixture of them. Other elements may also be part of the composition in quantities small enough to be negligible or sufficiently large to influence the heat treating of the alloy or even exert effects of their own, as in wrought alloy steels. The carbon content can be in any of the three ranges—low, medium, or high—but the majority of steel castings are produced in the medium carbon range because nearly all are heat treated to develop good mechanical properties.

4.2 ALUMINUM AND ALUMINUM ALLOYS

4.2.1 INTRODUCTION

Major nonferrous alloys include aluminum, magnesium, copper, nickel, and titanium. Aluminum alloys have been widely used in structural applications because of their lower density and lower cost.

Aluminum is produced by electrolytic reduction of alumina (Al_2O_3) based on the hall-heroult process developed in the 19th century. In earlier days, aluminum played an important role in the automotive and electrical industries. In the 20th century, when the aerospace industry was born, aluminum grew in acceptance as a structural material because of low density, good strength, good fracture resistance, and corrosion resistance. In aerospace, aluminum use was accepted for airframes, engines, missile components, and satellite components. In the 21st century, aluminum use includes automotive, electrical, marine, household appliance, and aerospace industries. Current annual world production of aluminum is approximately 47 million tons.

ANSI System for Alloys. The system for designating aluminum alloys is covered by the American National Standards Institute (ANSI) standard ANSI H35.1. The Aluminum Association, Washington, D.C., is the registrar under ANSI H35.1 for the designation and composition of aluminum alloys and tempers registered in the U.S.

4.2.2 ALUMINUM ALLOYS

Aluminum alloys can be divided into two major categories: casting alloys and wrought alloys. Some wrought aluminum alloys can be strengthened by thermal treatment while others can only be strengthened by work hardening through mechanical means (cold work). Casting alloys, depending on the chemical composition, can be strengthened by heat treatment while others are not heat treatable and are used in the "as cast" condition.

A four-digit system is used for identification of wrought aluminum and wrought aluminum alloys, as shown in table 4.6. The first digit indicates the alloy group.

Table 4.6: Identification of wrought aluminum and aluminum alloys.	
Aluminum (alloy)	**Series No.**
Aluminum, 99% minimum	1xxx
Aluminum alloys grouped by major alloying element	
Copper	2xxx
Manganese	3xxx
Silicon	4xxx
Magnesium	5xxx
Magnesium and silicon	6xxx
Zinc	7xxx
Tin and lithium (miscellaneous compositions)	8xxx
Unused series	9xxx

Casting alloys also have a system of four-digit designations as listed in Table 4.7:

Table 4.7: Identification of casting alloys.	
Cast metal	**Series No.**
Aluminum, 99% minimum or greater	1xx.x
Casting alloys grouped by major alloying element	
Copper	2xx.x
Silicon with added copper or manganese	3xx.x
Silicon	4xx.x
Magnesium	5xx.x
Zinc	7xx.x
Tin	8xx.x
Other element	9xx.x
Unused series	6xx.x

4.2.3 TEMPER DESIGNATION SYSTEM

A temper designation system has been developed by the Aluminum Association and is published in the ANSI H35.1 standard. Basic temper designations for wrought aluminum alloys are:

4.2.3.1 BASIC TEMPER DESIGNATIONS

- **F – as fabricated:** Applies to the products of shaping processes in which no special control over thermal conditions or strain hardening is employed. For wrought products, there are no mechanical property limits.
- **O – annealed:** Applies to wrought products that are annealed to obtain the lowest strength temper, and to cast products that are annealed to improve ductility and dimensional stability. The O may be followed by a digit other than zero.
- **H – strain hardened (wrought products only):** Applies to products that are strengthened by strain-hardening, with or without supplementary thermal treatments to produce some reduction in strength. The H is always followed by two or more digits.
- **W – solution heat treated:** An unstable temper applicable only to alloys that spontaneously age at room temperature after solution heat treatment. This designation is specific only when the period of natural aging is indicated; for example: W 1/2 hr.
- **T – thermally treated to produce stable tempers other than F, O, or H:** Applies to products that are thermally treated, with or without supplementary strainhardening to produce stable tempers. The T is always followed by one or more digits.

Subdivision of H Tempers: Strain Hardened. The first digit following the H indicates the specific combination of basic operations as follows:

- **H1 – strain hardened only:** Applies to products that are strain hardened to obtain the desired strength without supplementary thermal treatment. The number following this designation indicates the degree of strain hardening.
- **H2 – strain hardened and partially annealed:** Applies to products that are strain hardened more than the desired final amount and then reduced in strength to the desired level by partial annealing. For alloys that age soften at room temperature, the H2 tempers have the same minimum ultimate tensile strength as the corresponding H3 tempers. For other alloys, the H2 tempers have the same minimum ultimate tensile strength as the corresponding H1 tempers and slightly higher elongation. The number following this designation indicates the degree of strain hardening remaining after the product has been partially annealed.
- **H3 – strain hardened and stabilized:** Applies to products that are strain hardened and whose mechanical properties are stabilized either by a low-temperature thermal treatment or as a result of heat introduced during fabrication. Stabilization usually improves ductility. This designation is applicable only to those alloys that, unless stabilized, gradually ages often at room temperature. The number following this designation indicates the degree of strain hardening remaining after the stabilization treatment.
- **H4 – strain hardened and lacquered or painted:** Applies to products which are strain hardened and which are subjected to some thermal operation during the subsequent painting or lacquering operation. The number following this designation indicates the degree of strain hardening remaining after the product has been thermally treated, as part of the painting/lacquering cure operation. The corresponding H2X or H3X mechanical property limits apply.

The digit following the designation H1, H2, H3, and H4 indicates the degree of strain hardening as identified by the minimum value of the ultimate tensile strength. Numeral 8 has been assigned to the hardest tempers normally produced.

The third digit, when used, indicates a variation of the two-digit temper. It is used when the degree of control of temper or the mechanical properties or both differ from, but are close to, the two-digit H temper designation to which it is added, or when some other characteristic is significantly affected.

Subdivision of T Tempers. Numerals 1 through 10 following the T indicate specific sequences of basic treatments as follows:

- **T1 – cooled from an elevated temperature-shaping process and naturally aged to a substantially stable condition:** Applies to products that are not cold worked after cooling from an elevated temperature-shaping process or in which the effect of cold work in flattening or straightening may not be recognized in mechanical property limits.
- **T2 – cooled from an elevated temperature-shaping process, cold worked, and naturally aged to a substantially stable condition:** Applies to products that are cold worked to improve strength after cooling from an elevated temperature-shaping process or in which the effect of cold work in flattening or straightening is recognized in mechanical property limits.
- **T3 – solution heat treated, cold worked, and naturally aged to a substantially stable condition:** Applies to products that are cold worked to improve strength after solution heat treatment or in which the effect of cold work in flattening or straightening is recognized in mechanical property limits.

- **T4 – solution heat treated and naturally aged to a substantially stable condition:** Applies to products that are not cold worked after solution heat treatment or in which the effect of cold work in flattening or straightening may not be recognized in mechanical property limits.
- **T5 – cooled from an elevated temperature-shaping process and then artificially aged:** Applies to products that are not cold worked after cooling from an elevated temperature-shaping process or in which the effect of cold work in flattening or straightening may not be recognized in mechanical property limits.
- **T6 – solution heat treated and then artificially aged:** Applies to products that are not cold worked after solution heat treatment, or in which the effect of cold work in flattening or straightening may not be recognized in mechanical property limits.
- **T7 – solution heat treated and overaged/stabilized:** Applies to wrought products that are artificially aged after solution heat treatment to carry them beyond a point of maximum strength to provide control of some significant characteristic. Applies to cast products that are artificially aged after solution heat treatment to improve strength and dimensional stability.
- **T8 – solution heat treated, cold worked, and then artificially aged:** Applies to products that are cold worked to improve strength or in which the effect of cold work in flattening or straightening is recognized in mechanical property limits.
- **T9 – solution heat treated, artificially aged, and then cold worked:** Applies to products that are cold worked to improve strength.
- **T10 – cooled from an elevated temperature-shaping process, cold worked, and then artificially aged:** Applies to products that are cold worked to improve strength or in which the effect of cold work in flattening or straightening is recognized in mechanical property limits.

Additional digits, the first of which shall not be zero, may be added to designations T1 through T10 to indicate a variation in treatment that significantly alters the product characteristics that would be obtained using the basic treatment. Additional information regarding the temper designation system can be obtained from ANSI H35.1.

4.2.4 WROUGHT ALUMINUM ALLOYS

Table 4.8 shows typical applications of aluminum alloys by series. Table 4.9 shows typical mechanical properties and chemical composition of commonly used aluminum alloys. The newer aluminum lithium alloys, for example, 2090 (Al-Cu-Li), and 2091 and 8090 (Al-Cu-Mg-Li), are not shown in the table. The density of these alloys is 7% to 10% less than the other commonly used aluminum alloys in aerospace applications. These alloys are primarily used in aerospace applications where a high strength-to-weight ratio is desired.

Strengthening of Alloys with Heat Treatment. Alloys in the 2xxx, 6xxx, and 7xxx series can be strengthened by heat treatment. Typical heat treatment consists of solution heat treatment at high temperature 467 to 538 °C (approximately 870 °F to 1000 °F, depending on the alloy) and rapid cooling (quenching) in water or polymer solution. The condition after quenching is relatively soft. Subsequently, the alloy is aged at room temperature or artificially aged at a temperature 121 to 177 °C (250 to 350 °F), that depends on the alloy to achieve optimum mechanical properties.

Aluminum alloys have good ductility and can be easily formed with normal forming operations. Machinability of most aluminum alloys is also good. Most of the aluminum alloys have good weldability. Examples of alloys that have poor weldability include 2024, 7050, and 7075. Because of deterioration of properties at elevated temperatures, their use is limited to temperatures around 93 °C (200 °F).

Table 4.8: Wrought aluminum alloys and typical applications.

Alloy Series	Properties	Typical Applications
1xxx	Lowest strength, excellent thermal and electrical conductivity, good corrosion resistance.	Electrical conductors, radiator tubing, fuel filters, railroad tank cars, chemical equipment, and decorative components.
2xxx	High mechanical properties, low corrosion resistance.	Aircraft skins, aircraft structures, ballistic armor, fittings, truck wheels and frames, and forged and machined components.
3xxx	Non-heat-treatable medium-strength alloy, good formability and corrosion properties.	Chemical equipment, heat exchangers, storage tanks, and pressure vessels.
4xxx	High fluidity and castability.	Welding electrodes, for example, 4043.
5xxx	Non-heat-treatable medium-strength alloy, good formability and corrosion resistance in marine environment. Good weldability.	Armor plate, marine components, auto aircraft cryogens, drilling rigs, transportation equipment, missle components, and pressure vessels. Good for salt water service.
6xxx	Medium to high strength when heat treated, good corrosion resistance and weldability.	Heavy-duty structures requiring good corrosion resistance, truck and marine, railroad cars, exterior trim, door and window frames, piping, and structural components.
7xxx	Very high strength, susceptible to stress corrosion.	Aircraft and other structures, Forgings.
8xxx	Very high strength, relatively low density due to lithium additions.	Aircraft and aerospace structures, foil, defense.

Aluminum has a density of 2.7 g/cm³, approximately one-third that of steel (7.83 g/cm³), copper (8.93 g/cm³), or brass (8.53 g/cm³). It has very good corrosion resistance in most environments, including atmosphere, water (including salt water), petrochemicals, and many chemical systems. Corrosion resistance can be improved by the use of chemical conversion coatings (chem-film) and anodizing. Also, many alloys are available as "clad," with a pure aluminum coating to improve corrosion resistance.

When called upon to perform conductivity checks on aluminum plates and sheets, NDT personnel should be alert for clad materials. Since the electrical conductivities of the base metal and the cladding are invariably different, the conductivity measurement may include some combination of the two conductivities.

As evident from Table 4.9, wrought aluminum alloys can have tensile strength very close to 620 MPa (90 psi). Because of the ease of fabrication, good weldability, good corrosion resistance, high thermal and electrical conductivity, relatively low cost, and low density of aluminum (one third that of steel), their use in aerospace applications has been well accepted. Other uses include automotive, appliances, and electrical applications.

4.2.5 CAST ALUMINUM ALLOYS

Aluminum casting alloys have the following characteristics:
- Good fluidity, which helps in filling thin sections.
- Low melting point.
- Rapid heat transfer from the molten aluminum to the mold.
- Hydrogen is the only gas with appreciable solubility in aluminum and its alloys that can be controlled by processing methods.
- Many aluminum alloys are relatively free from hot-short cracking and tearing tendencies.
- Chemical stability.
- Good "as-cast" surface finish.
- Many casting alloys have good weldability.

Alloy and temper	Nominal Composition (%) (Major Elements)					Ultimate Tensile Strength		Tensile Yield Strength		Hardness (Brinell HB with 500 kg 10 mm ball)	Fatigue Endurance Limit		Modulus of Elasticity	
	Si	Cu	Mn	Mg	Other	MPa	ksi	MPa	ksi		MPa	ksi	GPa	10⁶ psi
1060-O	–	–	–	–	99.6 min Al	70	10	30	4	19	20	3	69	10.0
1100-O	–	0.12	–	–	99 min Al	90	13	35	5	23	35	5	69	10.0
2014-O	–	–	–	–	–	185	27	95	14	45	90	13	73	10.6
2014-T4, T451	0.8	4.4	0.8	0.5	–	425	62	290	42	105	140	20	73	10.6
2014-T6, T651	–	–	–	–	–	485	70	415	60	135	125	18	73	10.6
2024-O	–	–	–	–	–	185	27	75	11	47	90	13	73	10.6
2024-T3	–	4.4	0.6	1.5	–	485	70	345	50	120	140	20	73	10.6
2024-T4, T351	–	–	–	–	–	470	68	325	47	120	140	20	73	10.6
2219-O	–	–	–	–	–	175	25	75	11	–	–	–	73	10.6
2219-T42	–	6.3	0.30		0.06 Ti	360	52	185	27	–	–	–	73	10.6
2219-T62	–	–	–	–	–	415	60	290	42	–	105	15	73	10.6
3003-O	–	0.12	1.2		–	110	16	40	6	28	50	7	69	10.0
5052-O	–	–	–	2.5	0.25 Cr	195	28	90	13	47	110	16	70	10.2
5083-O	–	–	0.7	4.4	0.15 Cr	290	42	145	21	–	–	–	71	10.3
5456-O	–	–	0.8	5.1	0.12 Cr	310	45	160	23	–	–	–	71	10.3
6061-O	–	–	–	–	–	125	18	55	8	30	60	9	69	10.0
6061-T4, T451	0.6	0.28		1.0	0.20 Cr	240	35	145	21	65	95	14	69	10.0
6061-T6, T651	–	–	–	–	–	310	45	275	40	95	95	14	69	10.0
6063-O	–	–	–	–	–	90	13	50	7	25	55	8	69	10.0
6063-T1	–	–	–	–	–	150	22	90	13	42	60	9	69	10.0
6063-T4	0.40	–		0.7	–	170	25	90	13	–	–	–	69	10.0
6063-T5	–	–	–	–	–	185	27	145	21	60	70	10	69	10.0
6063-T6	–	–	–	–	–	240	35	215	31	73	70	10	67	10.0
7050-T73510, T73511	–	–	–	–	–	495	72	435	63	–	–	–	72	10.4
7050-T7451	–	2.3		2.2	6.2 Zn	525	76	470	68	–	–	–	72	10.4
7050-T7651	–	–	–	–	–	550	80	490	71	–	–	–	72	10.4
7075-O	–	–	–	–	–	230	33	105	15	60	–	–	72	10.4
7075-T6 T651	– –	– 1.6	– –	– 2.5	0.23 Cr 5.6 Zn	570	83	505	73	150	160	23	72	10.4
7075-T73 T7351	–	–	–	–	–	505	73	435	63	140	160	23	72	10.4

Table 4.9: Chemical compositions and typical mechanical properties of commonly used aluminum alloys.

Common aluminum casting alloys have high castability ratings. Aluminum castings are mostly produced by pressure-die, permanent-mold, green and dry-sand, investment, and plaster mold casting methods. Nominal chemical composition and typical mechanical properties of select casting alloys are shown in Table 4.10. Unless otherwise noted, these properties are obtained by heat treatment (solution heat treat and aging) and are from separately cast test bars. Table 4.10 shows common uses of these casting alloys.

Table 4.10: Typical chemical composition and mechanical properties of select aluminum casting alloys.

Alloy and Temper	Nominal Composition (%) (Major Elements)						Ultimate Tensile Strength		Tensile Yield Strength		Elongation in 50 mm
	Si	Fe	Cu	Mn	Mg	Other	MPa	ksi	MPa	ksi	(2 in.), %
A201.0-T7	0.10 (1)	0.15 (1)	4.6	0.35	0.35	0.25 Ti	485	70	435	60	4.5
A206.0-T7	0.10 (1)	0.15 (1)	4.6	0.35	0.25	0.10 Zn (1) 0.23 Ti	436	63	347	50	11.5
C355.0-T6 (2)	5.0	0.20 (1)	1.25	0.10 (1)	0.50	0.20 Ti (1)	240	35	170	25	3
A356.0-T6 (2)	7.0	0.20 (1)	0.20 (1)	0.10 (1)	0.35	0.20 Ti (1)	228	33	165	24	3.5
A357.0-T62 (3)	7.0	0.20 (1)	0.20 (1)	0.10 (1)	0.55	0.12 Ti 0.04-0.07 Be	360	52	290	42	8
A380.0 (4)	8.5	1.3 (1)	3.50	0.50	0.10 (1)	0.5 Ni (1) 3.0 Zn (1) 0.35 Sn (1)	325	47	160	23	4
712.0 (F or T5)	0.30	0.50	0.25	0.10	0.6	0.5 Cr 5.8 Zn 0.2 Ti	240	35	170	25	5

(1) Maximum
(2) Mechanical properties shown are for sand castings
(3) A357.0 is no longer available in the U.S. because it contains 0.04 to 07% beryllium, which is considered a health hazard. It has been replaced by F357.0
(4) Die castings

Table 4.11: Typical uses of common casting alloys.

Alloy	Typical Use
A201.0	Cylinder heads, pistons, pumps, and aerospace housings.
A206.0	Automotive, aerospace, gear housings, and truck spring hangar castings.
C355.0	Aerospace, fuel-pump bodies, air-compressor pistons, cylinder heads, water jackets, and blower housings.
A356.0	Aircraft pump components, fittings and control parts, automotive transmission cases, and water cooled cylinder blocks.
A357.0	Critical aerospace and defense applications where high strength and good toughness are required. Typically used as a permanent mold and investment casting alloy.
A380.0	Most widely used aluminum die casting alloy. Vaccum cleaners, floor polishers, automotive parts, and electrical industries.
721.0	Applications where good mechanical properties are required without heat treatment. Offers good dimensional stability and corrosion. No distortion due to heat treatment.

4.3 COPPER

4.3.1 PROPERTIES AND USE

Copper is one of the heavier structural metals with a density about 10% greater than that of steel. Tensile strengths range from 210 to 880 MPa (30 000 to 125 000 psi), depending on alloy content, degree of work hardening, and heat treatment. The ductility is excellent, and most alloys are easy to work by deformation processes, either hot or cold. The machinability ranges from only fair for some of the cast materials to excellent for some of the wrought materials. The most machinable are those containing lead or tin additives for the purpose of improving machinability.

Copper Has Excellent Thermal and Electrical Properties. If the preceding properties were the only properties of note that copper had, it would probably be little used. However, copper has outstanding electrical and thermal conductivity and excellent corrosion resistance, particularly when compared to ferrous metals. As noted before, three-fourths of the copper produced is used in pure form because of its conductivity. While aluminum has higher conductivity than copper on a weight basis and is displacing copper for some electrical applications, copper continues to be the principal metal for electrical use. This is particularly due to the higher strength-to-weight ratio of copper in pure-drawn form as is generally used for electrical conductors.

Corrosion Resistance to Some Environments Good. For other than electrical use, copper and its alloys compete with steel primarily because of better corrosion resistance. Copper alloys have excellent resistance to atmospheric corrosion, particularly under marine conditions. The combination of corrosion resistance and high thermal conductivity makes them useful for radiators and other heat exchangers.

4.3.2 COPPER ALLOYS

While the total tonnage of copper has not decreased, the importance of this metal relative to ferrous metals and to other nonferrous metals has decreased throughout recent history. However, copper is the metal that has been of greatest importance during the longest period of human history. The Bronze Age refers to the period of history during which humans fashioned tools from copper and copper alloys as they were found to occur naturally in the free state. The copper used today is reduced from ores as are other metals, and the continued use depends on the properties that make it useful as either a pure or an alloyed metal.

4.4 NICKEL AND NICKEL ALLOYS

4.4.1 PROPERTIES AND USE

Considerable Nickel Used as an Alloy in Steel. Nickel and manganese are metals that have mechanical characteristics similar to those of iron. However, neither is subject to alloying with carbon and control of hardness by heat treatment as is steel. Also, the ores of both metals are much less plentiful than iron ore, and the price is therefore higher. While manganese is little used except as an alloying element, nickel has sufficiently better corrosion and heat resistance than iron or steel to justify its use when these qualities are of enough importance. Nearly three-quarters of all the nickel produced is used either as a plating material for corrosion resistance or as an alloying element in steel. However, its use in steel has decreased in recent years with the discovery that other elements in lower percentages may have the same effects as nickel.

4.4.2 HIGH-TEMPERATURE NICKEL-CHROMIUM ALLOYS

Nickel-based alloys form a second group of high-temperature materials. They normally contain chromium or cobalt as the principal alloying element and smaller amounts of aluminum, titanium, molybdenum, and iron. These alloys have better properties at high temperatures than the stainless steel types but cost more and are even more difficult to process.

4.4.3 CORROSION-RESISTANT NICKEL ALLOY

Most Important Property Is Corrosion Resistance. As a structural metal by itself, or as the basis of alloys, the properties of nickel and its alloys are indicated in Table 4.12. Nickel and copper are completely soluble in the solid state, and many different compositions are available. Those richer in copper compete with brass but have higher cost, corrosion resistance, and temperature resistance. Those richer in nickel have superior heat and corrosion resistance at even higher cost and are used in many applications in which stainless steel is used. The composition of Monel® metal is determined largely by the composition of the ores found in the Sudbury district of Canada.

4.5 COBALT ALLOYS

Alloys having cobalt as the principal element form another group. They are generally referred to as *cobalt-based alloys,* although they may not contain as much as 50% of any single element. Other elements are generally nickel, chromium, tungsten, columbium, manganese, molybdenum, and carbon. Alloys of this type are useful structurally at temperatures as high as 1000 °C (1832 °F), at which they have good corrosion resistance and tensile strengths as great as 90 MPa (13 000 psi).

	Table 4.12: Properties of some nickel alloys.						
Name	**Composition Balance Nickel**				**Ten. St. 1000 psi (6.9 x 10⁶ Pa)**	**Percent Elong.**	**Characteristics and Uses**
	Mn	**Fe**	**Cu**	**Other**			
A nickel	0.25	0.15	0.05		55-130	55-2	Corrosion-resistant at high temperature. Vaccum tube parts, springs, chemical equipment.
Monel®	0.90	1.35	31.5		70-140	50-2	Good corrosion resistance combined with high strength at normal and medium temperatures. Pump shafts, valves, springs, food-handling equipment.
Inconel™	0.20	7.20	0.10	Cr 15	80-170	55-2	Similar to nickel-copper alloys but better high-temperature strength.
Nickel 36		64.0			70-90	36-20	Corrosion-resistant to atmospheres and to salt water. Low termal expansion.
Cast Monel®	0.75	1.5	32.0	Si 1.6	65-90	50-20	Good corrosion resistance to salt water and most acids. Valve seats, turbine blades, exhaust manifolds.

4.6 IRON ALLOYS

Nonferrous Metals Used for Alloying with Iron. Although iron is the most frequently used magnet material, having high permeability and low magnetic hysteresis, pure iron is a poor permanent magnet material. The best permanent magnets are alloys high in nickel, aluminum, and cobalt. Silver, copper, and aluminum have much greater electrical and thermal conductivities than any ferrous materials and are usually used instead of steel when these properties are important.

4.7 MAGNESIUM AND ITS ALLOYS

4.7.1 PROPERTIES AND USE

Although beryllium is the lightest metal available, its extremely high cost restricts its use to very special applications. Magnesium is therefore the lightest metal commercially available, with a density two-thirds that of aluminum. Magnesium alloys have good strength, ranging up to 350 MPa (50 000 psi) for wrought alloys and up to 280 MPa (40 000 psi) for cast alloys. Corrosion resistance is good in ordinary atmosphere, but for more severe conditions, including marine atmospheres, some surface protection is necessary.

Wrought and cast alloys have similar compositions. Aluminum, zinc, and manganese improve strength and forming properties. With 8% or more aluminum, a solution-precipitation hardening treatment is possible. Thorium, zirconium, and certain rare earth elements produce alloys useful at temperatures up to 480 °C (900 °F).

4.7.2 MAGNESIUM ALLOYS

Magnesium Alloys Work Harden Easily. The principal drawbacks of magnesium, other than the relatively high cost of recovery from seawater, are related to its crystalline structure. Magnesium is one of the few important metals having a close-packed hexagonal structure. Characteristic of these metals is a high rate of strain hardening. This property has two practical consequences. The amount of cold working that can be done without recrystallization is quite limited so that most forming operations must be done hot. This causes no great difficulty in rolling, forging, and extrusion operations that are normally performed hot with any metal, but secondary press operations on flat sheet may require heating of the dies and magnesium sheet. Most pressworking equipment is not designed for this type of operation.

Stress Levels High at Notches and Imperfections. The high rate of strain hardening also results in the fault called *notch sensitivity*. At a stress concentration point, such as the base of the notch in an impact test specimen, the load-carrying ability of a material depends on its ability to permit some plastic flow to enlarge the radius and relieve the stress concentration. The high rate of strain hardening in magnesium lessens its ability to do this and thus lowers its impact test values, and makes it subject to failure at such imperfections as grinding marks, small shrinkage cracks from welding or casting, or sharp internal corners permitted as part of a design. For this reason, magnesium components used in aircraft and similar applications are inspected nondestructively, usually by radiography for internal discontinuities and by penetrant testing for surface discontinuities.

Fine or Thin Magnesium Can Burn Readily in Air. Some problems are introduced in the processing of magnesium because of its inflammability. Reasonable care is necessary to prevent the accumulation of dust or fine chips where they might be subject to ignition from sparks, flames, or high temperatures.

4.8 TITANIUM AND TITANIUM ALLOYS

Titanium alloys are characterized by high strength, moderate density (half the density of steel and 70% higher than aluminum), and excellent corrosion resistance. Titanium alloys have high strength, ranging from 175 MPa (25,000 psi) for commercially pure titanium up to 1380 MPa (200 000 psi) for more complex wrought alloys. Corrosion resistance is excellent in oxidizing conditions, such as general atmosphere, marine, and biological environments, but titanium alloys are generally not resistant to attack from reducing acids, such as sulfuric, hydrochloric, and phosphoric acids. Oxidation resistance is effective up to a working temperature of 480 °C (900 °F), but higher thermal exposure will lead to the growth of a brittle surface oxide, known as "alpha case," which can be detrimental to mechanical properties.

Wrought and cast titanium alloys have similar compositions. Typically, two or more metallic elements—the list includes aluminum, vanadium, molybdenum, iron, zirconium, chromium, silicon, and tin—are alloyed with titanium, along with small amounts of oxygen, nitrogen, and carbon, to improve strength, fatigue (cyclic loading), and fracture toughness properties. Typical applications of titanium alloys include aircraft engine rotating components, aircraft primary structure, land-based turbine components, chemical processing equipment, and medical implants.

4.8.1 PROPERTIES AND USE

Characterized by its corrosion resistance and high strength and low density, titanium could easily be the most important nonferrous metal. However, it is also characterized by the high costs associated with its fabrication, which makes it less attractive when compared to other metals that can attain properties to make them just as useful but at a lower cost.

The strength of titanium is comparable to that of steel, and because of the additional properties of its relative light weight, combined with corrosion and heat resistance, it has been a prime metal for aerospace applications. These properties also foster its uses in military armor as well as sports applications such as high-end bicycles and golf clubs. The medical industry has also benefited from the low-weight/high-strength properties of titanium in products including surgical instruments and patient-assist products, such as wheelchairs. Another property that is invaluable is its biocompatibility. This enables the metal to be readily available for implants as it will not be rejected by the body.

In many applications, the high costs and more precise controls required during manufacturing can outweigh the benefits of titanium. As industries develop and technologies grow, the uses of titanium have been slightly reduced because of those factors. Metals such as aluminum and composite materials have replaced titanium in some applications primarily due to costs.

4.8.2 TITANIUM ALLOYS

Titanium is one of the most common elements and is found in the Earth's crust. It is the ninth most abundant element and the seventh most abundant metal. Titanium alloys usually consist of titanium mixed with small quantities of other metals, which help to provide improved properties over pure titanium, such as corrosion resistance, shapability, stability, and strength at elevated temperatures. The most typical alloy mix is 90% titanium, 6% aluminum, and 4% vanadium, commonly known as Ti-6AL-4V. This alloy is stable in elevated temperatures in excess of 370 °C (700° F).

There are several other grades of titanium alloys with different values of different metals mixed with the parent metal to achieve specific qualities based on the application or use. Small quantities of palladium, vanadium, aluminum, and tin are some of the metals that may be added for the alloy. The overall goal is to take advantage of its steel-like strength and corrosion-resistant, lightweight properties so the alloy mix will be designed to increase either one of those properties while trying to balance the stability and shapability of the metal.

Titanium Alloys Work Harden Easily. The principal challenges of titanium, other than the relatively high cost of refining the pure metal from titanium oxide–bearing ores, are related to its crystalline structure. Titanium, like magnesium and zirconium, is one of the few industrial metals having a close-packed hexagonal crystallographic structure. Characteristic of these metals is a high rate of strain hardening, which limits the amount of cold working that can be done without a recrystallization heat treatment. Titanium alloys are typically produced in wrought form by rolling, forging, and extruding at elevated temperatures in the range of 730 °C to 1150 °C (1350 °F to 2100 °F), although some specialty applications, such as golf clubs and turbine engine blades, are produced as castings.

Stress Levels High at Notches and Discontinuities. The high rate of strain hardening also results in the discontinuity called *notch sensitivity*. At a stress concentration point, such as the base of the notch in an impact test specimen, the load-carrying ability of a material depends on its ability to permit some plastic flow to enlarge the radius and relieve the stress concentration. Although titanium alloys have good bulk ductility, the high rate of strain hardening during local plastic deformation lowers its impact test values and makes it subject to failure at such discontinuities as grinding marks, small shrinkage cracks from welding or casting, or sharp internal corners permitted as part of a design. For this reason, titanium alloy components used in critical applications are inspected nondestructively usually by radiographic or ultrasonic methods for internal discontinuities and by penetrant inspection or eddy current for surface discontinuities.

4.9 SPECIAL-USE METALS

4.9.1 HEAT- AND CORROSION-RESISTANT ALLOYS

Several different groups of materials, including certain ferrous alloys, have traditionally been grouped on the basis of property requirements rather than base metal or alloy content. Of special importance are alloys designed for use under high-stress conditions at elevated temperatures in such applications as jet turbine engines, high-temperature steam piping and boilers, and rocket combustion chambers and nozzles. The efficiency of many such devices depends on the maximum temperature at which they can be operated, and they frequently involve highly oxidizing, corrosive, or erosive conditions.

Manufacturing Cost High. Most special materials that have been developed for these uses are difficult to process into usable products by some or all of the standard procedures. The high cost of such products is due both to the generally high cost of the materials themselves (rarity and cost of refining) and the cost of special processing. Hot working involves extra-high temperatures with high forces, which results in short equipment life; casting frequently must be done by investment or other high-cost techniques; cold working is difficult or impossible; welding involves elaborate procedures to avoid contamination and nondestructive testing to ensure reliability; and machining requires low cutting speeds with short tool life even under the best conditions.

Stainless Steels. Stainless steels, which were discussed earlier, have better strength and corrosion resistance than plain carbon or low alloy steels at temperatures higher than 649 °C (1200 °F). A number of alloys of the same general composition as standard stainless steels have been developed with larger amounts of nickel and generally larger amounts of the stabilizing elements such as titanium or molybdenum for better high-temperature properties. Aluminum or copper may be used to provide a precipitation reaction that makes the alloys hardenable by heat treatment. Such heat treatment usually involves solution temperatures higher than 1000 °C (1832 °F) and artificial aging at temperatures higher than 700 °C (1292 °F).

4.9.2 OTHER NONFERROUS METALS

Of the many other potential base metals, most are used under special conditions. Many of these metals have properties that are equal to or better than those of iron and the more common nonferrous metals, but their use is restricted by economic consideration. Gold, platinum, and other noble metals have high chemical inertness, but their rarity and high cost restrict their use. Beryllium has the highest strength-to-weight ratio of any known metal, but the difficulty of obtaining the pure metal and the rarity of the ore make the cost almost as high as that of gold. Titanium ores are abundant and titanium has extremely useful properties, but the cost of reduction is approximately one hundred times that of iron. Titanium could easily be the most important nonferrous metal if low-cost production methods could be developed. Table 4.13 gives the principal characteristics and uses for most nonferrous metals that are available commercially.

Table 4.13: Characteristics of most nonferrous metals.

		Applications	
Metal	**Principal Characteristics**	**Pure or as Base Metal**	**As Alloying Constituent**
Antimony	Hard, brittle	None	1% – 12% hardens lead fusible alloys.
Beryllium	Lightest structural metal; high strength/weight ratio; brittle, transparent to X-rays	Aircraft and rocket structure, X-ray tube windows	2% hardens copper
Bismuth	Soft, brittle, high negative coefficient of resistivity	Use restricted by cost; special resistance elements	Fusible alloys
Cadmium	Higher temperature strength than tin or lead-based alloy, corrosion resistant	Plating, especially on steel; bearing alloys; solders	Bearing alloys, solders
Cerium	Soft, malleable, ductile	Rare	Lighter flints, nodular iron
Cobalt	Weak, brittle, high corrosion resistant	Rare	High-temperature alloys, permanent magnets, hard facing tool steels
Columbium (Niobium)	High melting point, corrosion resistant	Nuclear reactors, missles, rockets, electron tubes	High-temperature alloys, stainless steels, nitriding steels
Germanium	Brittle, corrosion resistant, semiconductor	Diodes, transitors	Rare
Gold	Ductile, malleable, weak, corrosion resistant	Monetary standard, plating, jewelry, dental work, electrical contacts	Rare

Table 4.13 (continued): Characteristics of most nonferrous metals.			
		Applications	
Metal	**Principal Characteristics**	**Pure or as Base Metal**	**As Alloying Constituent**
Indium	Soft, low melting point	None	Hardener for silver and lead, corrosion resistance in bearings
Iridium	Most corrosion-resistant metal	None	Hardener for platinum jewelry, contact alloys
Lead	Weak, soft, malleable, corrosion resistant	Chemical equipment, storage batteries, roof flashing, plumbing	Improves machinability of steel and most nonferrous alloys, solders, bearing alloys
Manganese	Moderate strength, ductile	Rare	To 2% low alloy steels, 12% abrasion-resistant steel, stainless steels
Mercury	Liquid at room temperature	Thermometers, switches	Low melting point alloys, amalgam with silver for dental use
Molybdenum	High melting point, high strength at elevated temperature, oxidizes rapidly at high temperature	High-temperature wire, structural use with surface protection, mercury switch contacts	Low alloy steels, high-temperature alloys, stainless steel, tool steels
Palladium	Ductile, corrosion resistant	Chemical catalyst, electrical contacts	Jewelry, dental alloys
Rhodium	High reflectivity, free from oxidation films, chemically inert	Mirrors, plating	With platnium and palladium
Selenium	Special electrical and optical properties	Rectifiers, photocells	Machinability of stainless steel
Silver	Highest electrical conductivity, corrosion resistance to nonsulfur atmospheres	Coinage, jewelry, tableware, eletrical contacts, plating, catalyst reflectors	Brazing and soldering alloys, bearing alloys
Silicon	Semiconductor, special electrical and optical properties	Rectifiers, transistors, photocells	Electrical steel, cast iron, cast nonferrous
Tantalum	High melting point, ductile, corrosion resistant	Surgical implants, capacitors, chemical hardware, electronic tubes	Tantalum carbide cutting tools
Tin	Soft, weak, malleable, corrosion resistant	Plating, collapsible tubes	Bronzes, solders, bearing alloys
Titanium	Density between steel and light alloys, high strength, corrosion resistant	Marine, chemical, food-processing equipment	High-temperature alloys, stainless steel, aluminum alloys, titanium, carbide tools
Tungsten	Highest melting point of metals, strong, high modulus of elasticity, corrosion resistant	Lamp filiments, contacts, X-ray targets, nuclear reactors	Alloy steels, tool steels, high-temperature alloys, tungsten carbide tools
Vanadium	Moderate strength, ductile	Rare	Alloy steel, tool steel, nonferrous deoxidizer
Zirconium	Moderate strength, ductile, corrosion resistant	Structural parts in nuclear reactors	Stainless steels

5 Polymers, Ceramics, and Composites

5.1 POLYMERS: PROPERTIES AND USES

For some time, the fastest growing field of materials has been the group called *plastics*. Plastics are made up of small units of molecules bonded together into long chains called *polymers*. Any thorough treatment of plastics and polymers, especially concerning the chemistry of the materials, would require a number of volumes. On the other hand, plastics and polymers cannot properly be ignored in any treatment of materials and manufacturing processes because they are in direct competition with most metals. A greater tonnage of plastics is produced annually than of all non-ferrous metals combined.

Many Materials with Wide Range of Properties. A study of plastics is complicated by the tremendous number of material variations possible. There are roughly as many important families of plastics as there are commercially important metals. While it is true that many of the metals are alloyed to different combinations, the number is relatively small when compared with the number of distinct plastics possible in each family. Furthermore, while for metals the hardness and strength seldom exceed a ratio of perhaps 10:1 for any particular alloy group, many plastics that are under a single name are produced with properties ranging from liquids that are used as adhesives or finishes to rigid solids whose hardness and strength compare favorably with metals.

"There are roughly as many important families of plastics as there are commercially important metals."

Definition Difficult. The word *plastic* is derived from the Greek word *plastikos*, which means "fit for molding." Many of the materials called plastics today, such as finishes and adhesives, are not molded at all; moreover, many materials are molded that are not called plastics. Many metals and most ceramics are molded at times. Plastics might best be defined as a group of large-molecule organic compounds, primarily produced as a chemical product and susceptible to shaping under combinations of pressure and heat. To include all the plastics, the term organic must be expanded to include silicone-based as well as carbon-based materials.

Major Development Recent. Historically, the development of plastics has occurred in two general periods. Chemists in France, Germany, and England, during the period from 1830 to 1900, isolated and named many materials that are called plastics today. The actual commercial production of most of these materials was delayed until production methods and facilities became available that permitted them to compete with the more traditional materials. The second period of even more rapid developments has been in the U.S., particularly since 1940. Many new methods of manufacture and treatment as well as new plastic materials have been developed.

5.1.1 POLYMERIZATION REACTION

Plastic Structure. Chemically, plastics are all polymers. The smallest unit structure, or molecule, that identifies the chemical involved is called a *monomer*. By various means, including heat, light, pressure, and agitation, these monomers may be made to join and grow into much larger molecules by the process of *polymerization*. In general, the first polymerization involves the connecting of the monomers into long chains, usually with a progressive degree of solidification or an increase in viscosity as the polymerization proceeds. For most plastics, the properties depend on the degree of polymerization, which explains to a large degree the wide range of properties available. For the group of plastics known as *thermosetting*, a second type of polymerization takes place in which cross-linking occurs between adjacent chains. This thermosetting reaction frequently results in greatly increased rigidity. These two broad groups of plastics are based originally on their reaction to heat but more properly on the type of polymerization involved.

5.1.1.1 THERMOPLASTIC POLYMERS

Long Chain Polymers. Plastics that are called *thermoplastic* have the degree of polymerization controlled in the initial manufacture of the plastic raw material or resin. These materials soften with increasing temperature and regain rigidity as the temperature is decreased. The process is essentially reversible, but in some cases, chemical changes that may cause some deterioration of properties are produced by heating.

5.1.1.2 THERMOSETTING POLYMERS

Thermosetting Plastics—Gross-Linked Polymers. As noted before, the thermosetting plastics undergo a further cross-linking type of polymerization, which for the early plastics was initiated by the application of heat, but which for many modern thermosetting plastics may be initiated by other means. In the fabrication by molding of thermosetting plastics, an initial thermoplastic stage is followed by the thermosetting reaction at higher temperatures or with prolonged heating. Thermoplastics may be resoftened by reheating, but the thermosetting reaction is chemical in nature and irreversible so that once it has taken place, further heating results only in gradual charring and deterioration.

The origin of the resin distinguishes a number of different types of plastics. Some true plastics are found in nature and used essentially "as is." These include shellac, used most frequently as a finish for wood and as an adhesive constituent, and asphalt, used as a binder in road materials, as a constituent in some finishes, and, with fibrous filling materials, as a molding compound.

Some Plastics—Natural Materials. A number of plastics are natural materials that have undergone some chemical modification but retain the general chemical characteristics of the natural material. Cellulose may be produced as paper with slight modification, as vulcanized fiber with a slightly greater modification, and as cellulose acetate with even more modification. Wood in its natural state has thermoplastic properties that are used in some manufacturing processes. Rubber latex, as found in nature, is a thermoplastic material but is generally modified by chemical additions to act as a thermosetting material.

Most Plastics—Synthetic. The greatest number of plastics are most properly called *synthetic plastics*. While many of them make use of some particular natural material, such as petroleum, as the principal constituent, the chemistry of the raw material and the chemistry of the finished plastic have no direct connection. The raw material may be thought of simply as the source of elements and compounds for the manufacture of the plastic.

5.1.2 ALTERING POLYMER PROPERTIES

Tables 5.1 and 5.2 give the principal characteristics and typical uses for most of the plastics in common use. No such list can be complete because new plastics are constantly being introduced, and the timespan from discovery of a useful plastic to commercial use is decreasing. The cellulose plastics among the thermoplastics and phenol formaldehyde (a phenolic) among thermosetting plastics were the first plastics to be developed and are still in wide use today.

General Property Comparisons. Some comments may be made about the charts, keeping in mind that most general rules have exceptions. As a group, thermoplastics are somewhat lower in strength and hardness but higher in toughness than thermosetting materials. The thermosetting plastics generally have better moisture and chemical resistance than the thermoplastics. The terms *high* and *low*, when used for strengths, service temperatures, and other characteristics, are only relative and apply to plastics as a total group.

None of the plastics has a useful service temperature as high as that of most metals, and the modulus of elasticity of all plastics is low compared to most metals. While the ultimate strengths of many metals are greater than that available with plastics, some specific plastics offer favorable comparisons. Nylon, for example, is one of a few plastics that, being truly crystalline, may be hardened by working. Drawn nylon filaments may have a tensile strength of 345 MPa (50 000 psi), which is actually greater than some low-strength steels. Plastics excel in some applications as insulators or where chemical resistance is important. The greatest tonnage, however, is used in direct competition with other materials where plastics may be favored because of their low fabrication costs in large quantities, light weight, and easy colorability.

5.1.3 PLASTIC PROCESSING

Closed Die Molding Similar to Die Casting. In a general way, the forming of sheets of plastic may be compared to the presswork of metals, as many of the techniques are similar. Most of the casting methods used with plastics are similar to permanent mold casting of metals. The most important area of plastic processing is *matched die molding*.

Table 5.1: A summary of the principal characteristics and uses of thermoplastic plastics.

Resin Type	Principal Characteristics	Forms Produced	Typical Uses	Relative Cost
ABS	High strength, toughness, colorability	Injection moldings, extrusions, formable sheet	Pipe, appliance cabinets, football helmets, handles	50-60
Acetal	High strength, colorability, high fatigue life, low friction, solvent resistance	Injection moldings, extrusions	Gears, impellers, plumbing hardware	80
Acrylic	High strength, colorability, optical clarity, low service temperature	Injection moldings, extrusions, castings, formable sheet, fiber	Transparent canopies, windows, lenses, edge-lighted signs. mirrors, high-quality molded parts	45-55
Cellulose acetate	Moderate strength, toughness, colorability, optical clarity, wide hardness range, low service temperature	Injection moldings extrusions, formable, sheet, film, fiber	Toys, shoe heels, buttons, packaging, tape	36-58
Cellulose acetate butyrate	Moderate strength, high toughness, good weatherability colorability, optical clarity, low service temperature	Injection moldings, extrusions, formable sheet, film	Telephone handsets, steering wheels, appliance housings, outdoor signs, pipe	40-62
Cellulose propionate	Moderate strength, high toughness, good weatherability, colorability, optical clarity, low service temperature	Injection moldings, extrusions, formable sheet, film	Radio cabinets, pen and pencil barrels, automobile parts	40-62
Ethyl cellulose	Moderate strength, high toughness, flexibility, colorability, moisture resistance, better electric properties than other cellulostics, low service temperature	Injection moldings, extrusions, film	Refrigerator parts, aircraft parts, flashlight housings, door rollers	65-75
Cellulose nitrate	Toughest of all the thermoplastics, good formability, poor aging, high flammability, low service temperature	Extrusions, formable sheet	Ping-pong balls, hollow articles	70-200
Chlorinated polyether	High chemical resistance, moderate strength	Injection moldings, extrusions, sheet	Valves, pump parts in corrosive environments	250
TFE (tetrafluoro-ethylene)	Chemical inertness, high service temperature, low friction, low creep strength, high weatherability	Sintered shapes, extrusions, formable sheet, film, fiber	Pipe, pump parts, electronic parts, nonlubricated bearings, gaskets, anti-adhesive coatings	350-550
CFE (chlorotri-fluoroethylene)	Higher strength than TFE, lower chemical resistance than TFE, high service temperature, high weatherability	Injection moldings, extrusions, formable sheet, film	Coil forms, pipe, tank lining, valve diaphrams	700-800
Nylon (polyamide)	High strength, toughness, work hardenability, low friction, good dielectric properties	Injections moldings, extrusions, formable sheet, film, fiber	Gears, cams, bearings, pump parts, coil forms, slide fasteners, gaskets, high-pressure tubing	100-200
Polycarbonate	High strength, toughess, chemical resistance, weatherability, high service temperature	Injection moldings, extrusions	Gears, hydraulic fittings, coil forms, appliance parts, electronic components	150

Table 5.1 (continued): A summary of the principal characteristics and uses of thermoplastic plastics.				
Resin Type	**Principal Characteristics**	**Forms Produced**	**Typical Uses**	**Relative Cost**
Polyethylene	Moderate strength, high toughness, good dielectric properties, low friction, chemical resistance, flexibility	Injection moldings, extrusions, formable sheet, fim, fiber, rigid foam	Housewares, pipe, pipe fittings, squeeze bottles, sports goods, electrical insulation	32-38
Polystyrene	High strength, low impact resistance, high dielectric strength, colorability, optical clarity, low service temperature	Injection moldings, extrusions, formable sheet, film, foam	Toys, electrical parts, battery cases, light fixtures, rigid conduits	22-43
Vinyl	Wide range of properties, strength,toughness, abrasion resistance, colorability, low service temperature	Compression moldings, extrusions, castings, formable sheet, film, fiber, foam	Electrical insulation, floor tile, water hose, raincoats	24-43

Table 5.2: A summary of the principal characteristics and uses of thermosetting plastics.				
Resin Type	**Principal Characteristics**	**Forms Produced**	**Typical uses**	**Relative Cost**
Epoxy	Moderate strength, high dielectric strength, chemical resistance, weatherability, colorability, high service temperature, strong adhesive qualities	Casting, reinforced moldings, laminates, rigid foam, filament wound structures	Chemical tanks, pipe, printed circuit bases, short-run dies, randomes, pressure vessels	45-80
Melamine	Hardest plastic, high dielectric strength, moderate service temperature, colorability, dimensional stability	Compression and transfer moldings, reinforced moldings, laminates	Dinnerware, electrical components, table and counter tops	42-45
Phenolics	Moderately high strength, high service temperature, dimensional stability, color restrictions	Compression and transfer moldings, castings, reinforced moldings, laminates, cold moldings, rigid foam	Electrical hardware, poker chips, toys, buttons, appliance cabinets, thermal insulation, table and counter tops, ablative structural shapes	20-45
Polyester (including alkyds)	Moderately high strength, dimensional stability, fast cure, easy handling, good electrical properties, high service temperature, chemical resistance	Castings, reinforced moldings, laminates, film, fiber, compression and transfer moldings	Electrical parts, automobile ignition parts, heater ducts, trays, tote boxes, laundry tubs, boats, automobile bodies, buttons	31-60
Silicon	Highest service temperatures, low friction, high dielectric strength, flexible, moderate strength, high moisture resistance	Compression and transfer moldings, rienforced moldings, laminates, rigid foam	High-temperature electrical insulation, high-temperature laminates, gaskets, bushings, seals, spacers	275-540
Urea	Moderately high strength, colorability, high dielectric strength, water resistance, low service temperature	Compression and transfer moldings	Colored electrical parts, buttons, dinnerware	19-34
Urethane	Moderate strength, high toughness, very flexible, colorable, good weatherbility, excellent wear resistance, low service temperatures	Injection moldings, extrusions, blow moldings, foam	Gears, bearings, O-rings, footwear, upholstery foam	50-100

In this area, *compression molding* and *cold molding* are like forging and powder metallurgy in that the material is introduced into an open die, and the forming pressure is applied by the closing of the dies. *Transfer molding* is essentially cold chamber die casting, and *injection molding* is quite like hot chamber die casting. In fact, the equipment used for these processes is usually similar in appearance. Extrusion of plastics is directly comparable to the extrusion of metals.

Plastic Type Limits Processing. Many of the procedures have been developed because of the nature of the plastic groups, particularly because of the difference between thermosetting and thermoplastic materials. While the initial treatment of these two types is similar, and both soften during initial heating, this ductile stage of thermosetting plastics is of limited duration, and the setting reaction proceeds with time, particularly at elevated temperature. Thermoplastic materials, however, may be held in the softened condition for prolonged periods of time with little or no chemical change.

5.1.3.1 COMPRESSION MOLDING

Mold Closing Provides Pressure. The oldest and simplest of plastic molding processes is compression molding, shown in Figure 5.1. Material in powder, granule, pill, or preformed shape is first introduced into the mold, followed by the application of pressure and heat. With thermosetting plastics, for which the process is normally used, the first effect of the heat is to soften the material to a thermoplastic stage in which the particles coalesce and flow under pressure to fill the mold cavity. With prolonged application of heat, the thermosetting reaction takes place, and the material becomes permanently rigid. The mold may be opened while still hot and the finished part removed, although partial cooling is sometimes beneficial to the dimensional stability of the product. The setting time varies from a few seconds to several minutes, depending on material, temperature, heating method, and section thicknesses. It is possible to compression mold thermoplastics, but, after the pressure and heating portion of the cycle, the mold must be cooled before removal of the part.

Advantages and Limitations of Compression Molding. Compared with other molding techniques, a number of advantages and limitations are associated with compression molding. Size restrictions are relatively few, and the largest molded articles are generally made by this method. There is no waste material and little erosion of the dies because the material does not flow under high pressure from outside the mold. Because of the short, multidirectional flow of material within the mold, distortions and internal stresses within the mold may be minimized. On the other hand, undercuts and small holes are not practical, and the nature of the process requires that the shape of the article be such that the two halves of the mold can fit telescopically together to ensure filling. The high pressures required, together with the low viscosity of most thermosetting materials in the plastic state, result in filling clearances between mold parts even when they are on the order of 0.025 mm (0.001 in.). Thus, not only will removal of flash from the part be required but also cleaning of the mold parts between successive cycles will frequently be necessary.

5.1.3.2 CLOSED DIE MOLDING

By far, the most important molding processes used are those that introduce the plastic into closed dies by some external pressure system. The principal difference between these methods and the die casting used in the foundry is the softened plastic condition of the material rather than the liquid state of the metals. Because of the similarities, the terminology is mostly the same as that used in the foundry.

Transfer Molding—Thermosetting Plastics. The variations are due principally to the differences between thermoplastics and thermosetting materials. *Transfer molding,* used with the latter and shown in Figure 5.2, is like cold chamber die casting in all important respects. A predetermined quantity of molding compound, always including some excess, is introduced into the transfer chamber. This material is usually preformed and may be preheated. Sufficient heat is supplied to the material in the transfer chamber to bring the plastic to the softened state. Pressure is applied to force, or transfer, the charge to the die cavity. Additional heat is supplied to the die for the thermosetting reaction. The excess material in the transfer chamber, as well as the sprue and runner system, also set, resulting in a *cull* that must be removed at the completion of the cycle. This cull is scrap because the thermosetting reaction may not be reversed.

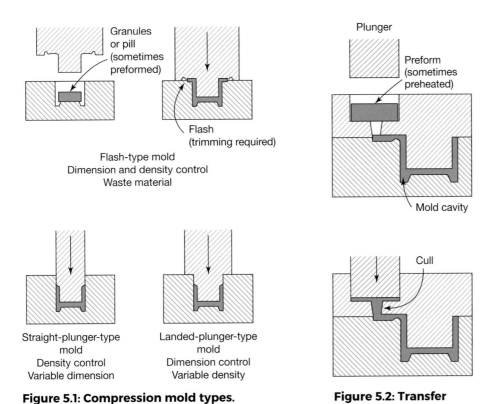

Figure 5.1: Compression mold types.

Figure 5.2: Transfer molding.

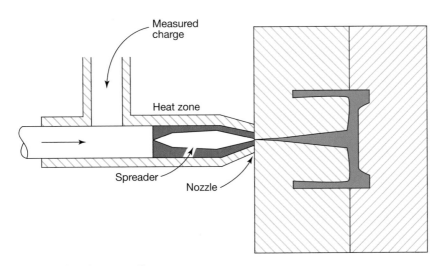

Figure 5.3: Injection molding.

Injection Molding—Thermoplastic Materials. For thermoplastic materials, the transfer process is simplified because of the nature of the material. The term injection molding is used to describe the process. Prolonged heating is not necessary or desirable, and the material may be forced into a cool die where the material becomes rigid as a result of cooling rather than chemical change. As indicated in Figure 5.3, a measured charge of raw material is introduced when the plunger is withdrawn, and, on the working stroke of the machine, the material is forced around the spreader where heat is supplied. Material for four to eight working strokes, or shots, is normally kept in the heating chamber. Temperatures are controlled so that the sprue separates at the nozzle when the parts are removed, with the material in the nozzle remaining heated sufficiently to be injected on the next cycle without the cull losses normally expected in transfer molding of thermosetting plastics.

Some injection molding of thermosetting materials is done, but precise temperature and time controls are necessary to prevent premature setting of the material in the injection chamber. When used for these materials, the process is known as *jet, flow,* or *offset molding.*

5.1.3.3 CASTING

With the exception of acrylic rod and sheet materials, which are cast against glass, and some protective coatings applied by dipping, casting of plastics is primarily a low tooling cost procedure restricted to thermosetting resins and used for low production of jewelry, novelty items, laboratory specimens, and similar parts. Polyesters, epoxies, and phenolics are most frequently used in syrupy or liquid form, with hardening promoted by chemical catalysts or by prolonged heating at low temperatures.

5.1.3.4 EXTRUSION

Most plastics that are finished as sheets, tubes, rods, filaments, films, and other shapes of uniform cross section are produced by *extrusion*. With some plastics that have a high degree of crystallinity, higher strengths may be developed by stretch deforming the material after extrusion.

Thin Plastic Films. Two methods are used for producing film. In one, the film is extruded through a slit of appropriate size. In the other, the material is extruded as a tube that is then expanded by air pressure and either slit or passed between heated rollers where it is welded into a single sheet. By the expanded tube method, films of less than 0.025 mm (0.001 in.) thickness are produced in large quantities for food wrapping and other packaging.

5.1.3.5 REINFORCED PLASTIC MOLDING

One of the fastest growing fields in recent years has been the production of relatively large plastic articles with filler in the form of reinforcing fibers in loose, woven, or sheet form. The principle is old; plywood is an example, although the early adhesives used for plywood were not considered to be plastics, and the wood fibers were not fully saturated with resin as is common with most molding of this type now.

Fibrous Fillers—Thermosetting Resins. Glass fibers and paper are the most common filler materials used. Wood and fabric in various forms also have some applications. At present, the process is limited to thermosetting materials because of both the nature of the processing used and the higher strengths available. Phenolics, polyesters, melamines, and epoxies predominate.

In nearly all variations of the process, the filler and resin are brought together in the process itself, and the thickness of the molded parts is established more by the placement of the filler material than by mold pressures.

Contact Layup—Filler, Resin. The simplest procedure is *contact layup,* in which successive layers of manually placed filler material are brushed or sprayed with resin as they are applied to the mold, which may have either a concave or a convex shape. The mold may be of almost any material that can be properly shaped, including wood, plaster, concrete, metal, or plastic, and there are almost no size limitations. The resins used may incorporate catalysts that promote setting at room temperatures, or heating may be required. In either case, because no pressure is applied, the ratio of resin to filler must be high to ensure complete saturation of the fibers. One of the more interesting applications involves the use of glass filaments, coated with resin, that are wound on mandrels into the shape of spheres or cylinders. With proper winding techniques, the filaments may be orientated to make most efficient use of the longitudinal strength of the fibers; tensile strengths up to 1000 MPa (150 000 psi) have been reported for structures produced by this method.

Contact Layup Variations. The commonest variations of the contact layup method, *vacuum bag* molding, *expanded bag* molding, and *autoclave* molding, are all methods for developing some pressure on the surface of the molding to permit a lower resin-to-filler ratio. Vacuum bag molding is identical with the contact layup method except that a sheet of vinyl plastic film is placed over the mold after the layers are built up and the mold is evacuated to cause atmospheric pressure to be applied. In the expanded bag process, pressures up to 0.35 MPa (50 psi) may be provided by blowing up a bag that conforms to and is held in contact with the molding. The autoclave method is similar to the expanded bag method except that heat and pressure are supplied by steam in a closed chamber.

Compression Process for Sheet Material. In a direct variation of compression molding, matched metal dies are used to form reinforced products. This process is used most for flat sheet manufactured for table and countertops but is also used for curved shapes, such as chairs, trays, and sinks. For the curved shapes, filler materials are generally preformed before molding. The use of matched metal dies is the only way to produce good finishes on both sides of the finished part, and the high pressures used permit as much as 90% filler and result in higher strengths than would otherwise be possible.

Reinforced Plastics Convenient. The success of fiberglass boats, automobile bodies, and similar large shapes attests to the value of reinforced plastics. The simplicity of tooling and equipment required (even for amateur home building projects) makes the contact method ideal for low-quantity production and permits rapid design changes when desired. Strength and shock resistance are generally quite high but depend primarily on the type and proportion of filler material.

5.1.3.6 POSTFORMING

Secondary Operations by Many Methods. Two general classes of operations are performed on plastics after the initial shape has been produced by one of the methods already discussed. Conventional material removal processes, including sawing, shearing, dinking, and blanking, are possible with any plastic but are most frequently used for the preparation of sheet stock prior to a further hot-forming operation. Machining is possible but is generally practical for small quantities only, and other processes are usually cheaper for large quantities. Cutting speeds for thermoplastics must be kept low to prevent heating and softening of the material.

Thermoplastics Often Reheated to Soften. The widest use of postforming operations is made on thermoplastics in sheet form that are heated and made to conform to a single surface mold or pattern by pressure or vacuum. Variations are based primarily on the method of applying pressure and include *draping,* where gravity only is used; *drawing* and *stretch forming,* which are identical to the same operations performed on metal; *blow-dieing,* which is a combined drawing and air-bulging operation; and *vacuum forming,* which is similar to vacuum molding of reinforced plastics except that no external film is used. Some small, relatively flat items, such as brush handles and buttons, are shaped by forging heated sheet stock in closed dies.

5.1.4 DESIGN CONSIDERATIONS

Plastics and Metals Often Competitive. The choice of plastic materials involves the same considerations that apply in choosing metals to fulfill a need. In fact, the two classes of materials are frequently in direct competition with each other. A number of different materials will usually satisfy the functional requirements of a part or product, and the choice depends primarily on the economics of manufacturing for which the material, fabrication, and finishing costs must all be considered. Many plastics require no finishing at all. Often a single plastic molding can replace an assembly of parts made of metal with resulting cost decrease, although the material cost alone may be higher.

Properties of Metals Usually Higher. The stability of properties and the durability of the appearance of plastics are usually poorer than those of metals.

They are generally better for thermosetting materials than for thermoplastics, but the thermosetting plastics are usually slower to process and more expensive. The dimensional stability for plastics ranges from poor to excellent. The low rigidity and thermal conductivity, when compared to metals, may be either advantageous or disadvantageous, depending on the application.

Plastic strengths are generally lower than metal strengths. Most plastics have tensile strengths below 69 MPa (10 000 psi), but some of the reinforced materials have extremely high strength-to-weight ratios, at higher cost. Many plastic articles compete successfully with metals only through the use of metal inserts for bearings, threads, and fastenings.

Most plastics excel in corrosion resistance to ordinary environments. This is true to the extent that many metals are coated with plastic films for protection.

5.2 CERAMICS AND CEMENTS

5.2.1 ENGINEERING CERAMICS

Some composites are random mixtures of several materials. The properties of such composites may be varied widely by varying the ratios and kinds of constituents used.

Ceramics are produced in a wide variety of types. The majority of ceramics are constructed from clays (compounds of silica and alumina) mixed with water, shaped to proper form, and then fired at a fusing temperature in a kiln. Products range from fine china to tile and brick. Ceramics are poor conductors of both heat and electricity. Those that are used in electrical application may require NDT to find cracks and crazes, which could hold foreign material and moisture to destroy the insulating property.

Another kind of ceramic, such as used for cutting tool inserts, is made of almost pure alumina (aluminum oxide) assembled from fine particles to a hard rigid block by powder metallurgy methods.

5.2.2 CEMENTS

Concrete. A mixture of gravel, sand, and portland cement when combined with enough water to form a thick paste will harden with passage of time into concrete. Concrete is normally used to support compressive loads; However, since almost any application—such as the bridge columns and beams of Figure 5.4—is subject to some bending loads (compression and tension), steel reinforcing wires, rods, or structural shapes are nearly always inserted in the material when it is cast.

Cement. Portland cement is about 80% carbonate of lime and 20% clay. Additives of various kinds may be added during cement manufacturing to develop special properties. The strength of concrete increases with time. Solidity may occur from a few hours to a few days, but what is defined as 100% strength requires 28 days for standard concrete. Actually, strength continues to increase and after one year may reach 150% or more. Most tests performed on concrete are destructive, so it is important that proper procedures be used during mixing and pouring.

5.3 COMPOSITES

Composite Material. The term *composite material* denotes a wide range of materials, some of which predate the Roman Empire and others that are still under development in materials research laboratories. Examples include the straw-reinforced mud used in brickmaking in the ninth century BCE; steel-reinforced concrete; doped fabric on vintage aircraft; fabric-reinforced phenolics; plastics reinforced with fibers of glass, boron, graphite, or aramids (class of heat-resistant and strong synthetic materials, for example, Kevlar®); ceramics containing boron fibers; and metals impregnated with boron fibers. Aircraft tires, automobile tires, and even plywood are composite materials. As can be seen from the above examples, a broad range of materials falls under the heading of composite material.

Composite material can be defined as an engineered material consisting of one or more reinforcing agents and a matrix binder acting together as a physical unit while

Figure 5.4: Bridge structures often appear to be all concrete. Both the columns and beams are internally reinforced to carry any tension loads—usually the tension component of a bending load.

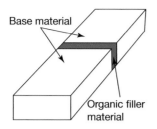

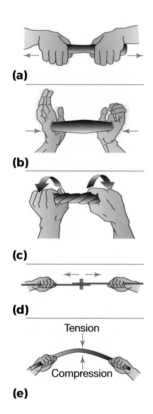

retaining their identities. The reinforcing agents are generally in the form of fiber, whiskers, or particles. The matrix binder (at least in the aerospace environment) is usually some type of resin. Normally, the interface between the reinforcing material and the matrix binder is physically identifiable. In other words, the components of the composite material remain distinct.

5.3.1 GENERAL PROPERTIES AND APPLICATIONS

Composites consist of mixtures of two or more materials that maintain their own identities but are attached together in such ways as to reinforce the properties of each by adhesive forces, by their respective positions, or frequently by both. Composites may be made up of all metals, combinations of metals and nonmetals, or all nonmetals. The most typical reason for the development of composites has been light weight with high strength, tailored stress, and sometimes the additional feature of withstanding some unusual environmental condition.

Adhesives. An adhesive is most commonly considered to be a material with some "tackiness" or "stickiness," and the animal glues used almost exclusively up to the current century met this requirement. Modern adhesives, however, have a wider range in this respect. Contact cements have sufficient tackiness that bonding with considerable strength occurs immediately, under only moderate pressure. Some thermosetting plastic compounds have little or no tackiness as applied and develop strength only after the setting reaction has been promoted by heat, pressure, or chemical reaction with the parts held in place (for example, iron-on clothing patches). The elements of an *adhesive bond* are shown in Figure 5.5. Oxides usually remain on surfaces. Resin solvents may provide some cleaning action.

Improvement of Properties. Reinforcing agents are most noted for their ability to contribute to the strength, stiffness, and impact resistance of the composite material. They have a wide range of form types: fibrous, whiskered, crystalline, and spherical (as in powders). Metals, ceramics, organics, and inorganics are represented among the reinforcing agents. The fibrous form type, usually consisting of glass, aramid, graphite/carbon, or boron, dominate the aerospace applications field. Besides aerospace, the field of applications for composite materials and structures is enormous, including boat hulls, furniture, skis, golf clubs, prosthetic limbs, and many, many more.

In some situations, composites can be considered an enabling technology, in that they make possible designs or applications that are otherwise not feasible or economical. Through proper design of ply orientations, it is possible to tailor filamentary composites to meet specific loading requirements involving stress. Five types of stress on structural members of aircraft components are shown in Figure 5.6. As an

Figure 5.5: Adhesive bond.

Figure 5.6: Stresses in aircraft structures:
(a) tension;
(b) compression;
(c) torsion;
(d) shear;
(e) bending.

Figure 5.7: Grumman X-29.

example, the various advantages of a forward-swept wing were known as far back as WWII when the Germans developed the Junkers 287 bomber. Among those advantages, the tips on a forward-swept wing design will stall last, maintaining roll control, a significant advantage. Unfortunately, forward-swept wings can experience dangerous flexing effects compared to aft-swept wings that can negate the tip stall advantage. If the wing is not sufficiently stiff, these flexing effects will cause the wing to "diverge." That is, they will bend upward until the wing breaks off. Prior to composite materials and structures being available, the necessary stiffness required a considerable amount of additional metal, which brought a significant weight penalty.

The Grumman X-29 (Figure 5.7) was an experimental technology demonstration project designed to test the forward-swept wing for enhanced maneuverability in 1984. The larger sweep suitable for high-speed aircraft, like fighters, was generally impossible until the introduction of the ability to tailor the load-carrying ability of the structure and of fly-by-wire systems that could react quickly enough to damp out the inherent instabilities.

Variety of Composite Structures. Composite structures come in an almost infinite variety. Figure 5.8 provides schematics of the stages of development of fixed wing assemblies using composites.

In addition to this are *sandwich panels* utilizing either a foam or honeycomb between two skins. A further level of complication is seen when all these elements are combined in hybrid reinforcement, such as the helicopter rotor blade shown in Figure 5.9. These can include carbon unidirectional tape, carbon woven fabric, a phenolic paper honeycomb core, fiberglass, adhesives, fillers, and more. As can be seen, composite structures provide numerous difficulties for NDT inspections. These include laminates that may be as thin as 0.127 to 0.254 mm (0.005 in. to 0.010 in.), very thick honeycomb or primary structure laminates, low densities, numerous discontinuity types and orientations, multiple anisotropic interfaces, and high attenuation.

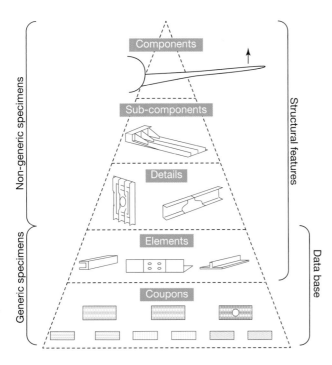

Figure 5.8: Schematics of building blocks involved in composite construction of a fixed wing.

Figure 5.9: Hybrid reinforcement.

5.3.2 METAL BONDING

Adherence as Common Factor. No clear distinction can be made among the terms *glue, cement,* and *adhesive.* Common to all of them, however, is the property of *adherence* to a surface, and this property is not essentially different from the metallic bond established between metallic surfaces brought into close contact. The surface to which an adhesive adheres or one of the bodies held to another by an adhesive is known as an *adherend.* At least four mechanisms may be responsible for adherence. *Electrostatic* bonds and *covalent* bonds result from the sharing of electrons by different atoms and account for the formation of most common chemical compounds. Even after bonds of these types are established, the positive and negative charges of most atoms are not completely neutralized, and *van der waals forces* provide additional bonding between the atoms. While not strictly an adherence phenomenon, *mechanical interlocking* may take part in the action of some adhesives, although this action appears to be secondary to true adhesion.

Close Contact Necessary. As in welding of metals, the proper performance of an adhesive requires that intimate contact, in addition to adherend cleanliness, be established between the adhesive and the surfaces to be joined. Different means are used to provide closeness. An adhesive can be applied as a solution in a volatile liquid. Evaporation of the solvent is necessary for the adhesive to develop the desired properties, and, as evaporation proceeds, the adhesive is drawn to the bare material surfaces. Adhesives of this type are useful for porous materials, such as wood, paper, and fabrics, into which the vapors can penetrate. For nonporous materials, extremely long drying times may be required because only the joint's edge is exposed for evaporation.

Some materials are normally solid but become liquid with application of pressure, then resolidify when the pressure is released. Other adhesives are purely thermoplastic in nature, softening or liquefying from heat and hardening on cooling.

Important adhesives for the bonding of metals are *thermosetting compounds* applied as liquids, pastes, or powders, then polymerized in place through the action of catalysts, heat, or pressure. The materials most used include epoxy, phenolic, polyester, and urea resins.

In addition to the importance of the traditional uses of adhesives in the manufacture of plywood and in the assembly of wood parts, there is considerable growth in the use of adhesives in the bonding of metal structures. These uses are becoming more important as higher strength materials are developed. Adhesives with tensile strengths above 70 MPa (10 000 psi) and shear strengths above 30 MPa (4000 psi) are available for bonding metals. Many new applications of joining of dissimilar metals, such as rubber to metal, are appearing.

5.3.3 REINFORCEMENTS

5.3.3.1 MATERIALS USED IN REINFORCEMENT

Composites are generally made up of a *matrix* and *reinforcement.* Many different forms of synthetic fibers are used in composite laminates. Both continuous and discontinuous fibers are used. *Continuous fiber* is a yarn or strand in which each of the filaments is the same unbroken length as the strand. *Discontinuous fiber* is a random assortment of fixed length or chopped random length fiber yarns, which are bound together on a flat mat. Discontinuous fibers may also be mixed with a resin and sprayed on a mold surface. Woven fabrics that are used in composites can be grouped as two-dimensional (2-D) and three-dimensional (3-D) structures. 2-D weaving is a relatively high-speed, economical process. However, woven fabrics have an inherent crimp or waviness in the interlaced fibers, which is undesirable for maximum composite properties. In 2-D structures, fibers are laid in a plane and the thickness of the fabric is small compared to its in-plane dimensions. In 3-D structures, the thickness or Z-direction dimension is considerable relative to the X and Y dimensions. Fibers or yarns are intertwined, interlaced, or intermeshed in the X, Y, and Z directions. For 3-D structures, there may be an endless number of possibilities for fiber placement.

5.3.3.2 TYPES OF FIBERS

Glass fiber is used in over 90% of composites. Glass is an attractive reinforcing agent because of its high tensile strength and its resistance to heat, fire, moisture, and chemicals. It doesn't conduct electricity and has a small coefficient of thermal linear expansion. In addition, it is an inexpensive material. There are several types of glass fiber. *E-glass*, a low alkali fiberglass originally named for enhanced electrical resistance, is noted for its excellent electrical insulation characteristics. *S-glass*, a magnesium aluminosilicate fiberglass named because of its stiffness, is a material with high tensile strength. Although glasses have several very desirable properties from an aerospace applications viewpoint, they have a low modulus of elasticity. Hence, glass fibers are not suitable where stiffness is the key parameter. Consequently, fiberglass composites have been widely used in fairings, radomes, and other secondary aerospace structures. Chopped fiber, or chopped strand mat, is the most common form of roll stock glass fiber material. It is used primarily in the marine and industrial composites industries.

Aramid fibers exhibit extreme tensile strength, impact resistance, and vibration dampening. Aramid fibers are yellow in color and can be dyed black, red, orange, green, and blue as optional colors (www.dupont.com). They are highly moisture sensitive and very sensitive to ultraviolet light. Color change may be the minor effect of UV exposure, and loss of strength and the formation of surface cracks may be worse effects (ieeexplore.ieee.org).

Carbon fibers have very high tensile strength and make very stiff, lightweight structures. They also have high compressive strength and a negative coefficient of thermal expansion. It is common practice to use the terms "graphite" and "carbon" as synonyms, although, strictly speaking, there are differences. *Carbon fibers*, when compared to *graphite fibers* have lower degrees of preferred orientation among the carbon atoms, a hexagonal structure, and lower tensile modulus of elasticity. In addition, carbon fibers have a lower carbon content (80-95%) than graphite fibers (>99%).

Ceramic fibers are used for very high-temperature applications including jet engine heat shields and exhaust deflectors, and electrical high-temperature heat shielding.

5.3.4 RESIN MATRIX SYSTEMS

Monomer as Smallest Structural Unit. Chemically, plastics are all polymers. The smallest unit structure, or molecule, that identifies the chemical involved is called a *monomer*. By various means, including heat, light, pressure, and agitation, these monomers may be made to join and grow into much larger molecules by the process of polymerization. In general, the first polymerization involves the connecting of the monomers into long chains, usually with a progressive degree of solidification or an increase in viscosity as the polymerization proceeds. For most plastics, the properties depend on the degree of polymerization, which explains to a large degree the wide range of properties available. For the group of plastics known as *thermosetting*, a second type of polymerization takes place in which cross-linking occurs between adjacent chains. This thermosetting reaction frequently results in greatly increased rigidity.

Thermoplastics and Thermosets. The resin matrix transfers loads to the reinforcement and protects the reinforcement from environmental effects. As described in section 5.1, there are two basic family groups of resin matrix systems: *thermoplastics* and *thermosets*. The most commonly used thermoset resins used in composite applications are polyester, vinyl ester, epoxy, and polyurethane. The less common resins used more in aerospace applications requiring high temperature and self-extinguishing fire properties include phenolic, silicone, polyimide, and bis-maleimide.

As a group, thermoplastics are somewhat lower in strength and hardness but higher in toughness than thermosetting materials. The thermosetting plastics generally have better moisture and chemical resistance than the thermoplastics. The terms *high* and *low*, when used for strengths, service temperatures, and other characteristics, are only relative and apply to plastics as a total group.

None of the plastics has a useful service temperature as high as that of most metals, and the elastic moduli of all plastics is low compared to most metals. While the ultimate strengths of many metals are greater than that available with plastics, some specific plastics offer favorable comparisons. Nylon, for example, is one of a few plastics that, being truly crystalline, may be hardened by working. Drawn nylon filaments may have a tensile strength of 345 MPa (50 000 psi), which is actually greater than some low-strength steels. Plastics excel in some applications as insulators or where chemical resistance is important. The greatest tonnage, however, is used in direct competition with other materials where plastics may be favored because of their low fabrication costs in large quantities, light weight, and easy colorability.

5.3.5 CORE MATERIALS

The *core material* is normally low-strength material, but its higher thickness provides the sandwich composite with high bending stiffness with overall low density. Open- and closed-cell-structured foams such as polyvinylchloride, polyurethane, polyethylene, or polystyrene foams, as well as balsa wood, syntactic foams, cork, and honeycombs, are commonly used core materials. Each type of core has different physical and mechanical properties due to chemical or structural differences, but all are used for the same function: to lighten, stiffen, and strengthen by utilizing the *sandwich principle*. In order for the sandwich to function correctly, the adhesive layers between the skins and the core must be able to transfer the loads and thereby be at least as strong as the core material. Without a proper bond, the three entities work as separate beams/plates and the stiffness is compromised.

5.3.6 FABRICATION

Fabrication is the process of by which the reinforcing agent and the matrix agent are integrated to form a composite material and, when necessary, subsequently processed to form a useful structure. Fabrication can be generally divided into two types, *primary* and *secondary*.

5.3.6.1 PRIMARY FABRICATION

Primary fabrication is the process by which the reinforcing agent and the matrix agent are integrated to form a cured composite material. Primary fabrication involves the construction and stacking or continuous fiber pre-impregnated (pre-preg) plies in a specific pattern. A *ply* is a single layer of unidirectional or woven fibers. Frequently, the specified ply width exceeds the width of the ply layup material (for example, pre-preg tape). In these cases, tapes are carefully laid side by side with the same fiber orientation until the required width is achieved. Each ply is worked to remove trapped air and wrinkles, ensuring intimate contact with the previously laid ply.

The basic steps in the primary fabrication of continuous fiber composites are (1) layup and (2) curing, the process of physically consolidating, densifying, and chemically transforming the composite's constituents through the application of heat and pressure. A variety of techniques are used to layup and cure composite materials.

Layup. *Layup* refers to the positioning of the uncured composite material in or on the mold, mandrel, fixture, or tool that provides the shape to the part. Layup can be done manually or by machines operating in semiautomatic or automatic modes. Manual, or hand layup, refers to the placement of layer after layer of pre-preg tape or broadgoods in a prescribed orientation on separate ply templates with subsequent stacking of the plies. Templates are also used as patterns for cutting pre-preg tapes and broadgoods. Machines, some fully automated, have been developed to layup composites. As a group, the machines are capable of using several layup processes such as braiding, filament winding, ply winding, and ply on ply.

Pre-preg materials are a fiber material (either unidirectional or woven) that has been pre-impregnated, or wetted out, with a resin system. It contains a controlled amount of matrix material and is workable for laminating at room temperature. Pre-pregs are manufactured by depositing a precise amount of resin onto the unidirectional fibers or fabric or as it passes through a series of rollers that serve to wet out the fabric and apply the carrier (parting or backing film). It also must have a controlled heat source applied to initiate exothermic reaction and final cure. It is expensive and not the best choice for every application.

Pre-preg Advantages and Disadvantages. The benefits of pre-preg include a precise resin ratio content, easy handling, partially cured matrix allowing for easy placement and alignment of fibers, lower weight of the finished product by eliminating excess resin through human error, and extended assembly time because the matrix does not have a limited pot life. Because of these properties, pre-preg is often used for repairs. The disadvantages of pre-preg include special handling and storage, storage in

Figure 5.10: Warping resulting from residual stress due to incompatible CTEs.

a frozen condition to prevent slow curing, and the necessity to thaw out in sealed bags before use to prevent moisture contamination. In addition, some have a limited "out time" from the freezer before the matrix becomes too hard to use. All of these disadvantages add to its expense. Terms that apply to pre-pregs include *tack*, which is the sticky-to-the-touch quality of fresh matrix, and *out-time*, the cumulative time that a pre-preg has been exposed to temperatures above that of the storage temperature.

Serious problems can result if the differing *coefficients of thermal expansion* (CTEs) for the various components of a structure are not carefully considered. After cure, these can result in residual stresses that can warp a part or component as shown in Figure 5.10.

Curing. Once layup has been completed, the unconsolidated laminate is prepared for the curing process and then cured. There are several methods by which to form the composite's constituents into a unified single construction. Most continuous fiber composites are consolidated and densified, or debulked, by three bag-molding methods: *vacuum bag molding, pressure bag molding*, and *autoclave molding*. Consolidation refers to the bonding of pre-preg plies and other adherends (the faying surfaces of two bodies) into a unified mass. Densification, or debulking, occurs when voids and excessive resins are removed from the stacked plies. In each method, pressure differentials are used to produce the desired results. Trapped air, volatile products from the curing laminate, and excessive resin are bled out of the stacked plies. Although most cures are done by using electric or gas heaters to elevate temperatures above ambient, cures can be done using induction, ultraviolet, electron beam, gamma ray, xenon flash, dielectric, and microwave techniques.

5.3.6.2 SECONDARY FABRICATION

Secondary fabrication involves the machining and joining of structural materials to produce useful structures. As used here, secondary fabrication involves the mating of composite substructures to other substructures, including those made from, but not limited to, composite materials.

The *machining* of composites can be broken into several basic operations: drilling, trimming (or profiling), and finishing. The specific methods and techniques employed relate to the physical and mechanical properties of the composite and its constituents. Some organic fibers are very tough. This can lead to excessive wear on tool cutting edges. The cured resinous matrix can burn or soften when excessive temperatures are reached during machining operations. Delamination may occur during drilling if adequate support is not provided to the back surface of a laminate. Tools used to machine composites range from ordinary scissors to lasers.

Joining. Fiber-reinforced composites are normally joined by two methods: mechanical and adhesive. Sometimes a combination of the two methods is used. Mechanical joining methods include bolting, riveting, and pinning. The mechanical joining procedure for composites is similar to that for metals. The adherends are drilled, countersunk, and then joined with a specific type of fastener. Noble metal fasteners (for example, titanium and stainless steel) are normally used to join graphite or carbon-reinforced composites to minimize the potential for galvanic corrosion.

Adhesive bonding is the process through which the adherends are bonded by an adhesive material. Adhesive bond strength is related to two factors: *cohesion* and *adhesion*. Cohesion refers to the ability of the adhesive to hold itself together. Adhesion refers to the ability of the adhesive layer to attach itself to the adherend. Adhesion forces always exceed cohesion forces in good bonds. That is, the adhesive is the weak link. The strength of a freshly made adhesive bond is related to many factors, including formulation and form of the adhesive, bonding method, cure cycle parameters, adherend surface conditions, and the physical and chemical characteristics of the adherends.

Forms of Adhesive Bonding. Two forms of adhesive bonding are commonly used: secondary bonding and co-cure bonding. Secondary bonding refers to the process of bonding pre-cured composite substructures together and/or to other structural components to form a useful component. Co-curing involves the simultaneous layup and curing of a structure's several components. Normally, adhesive films are not inserted between substructures. Rather, the excess resin from uncured adjacent substructures melds to form a bond during the curing process. It is applicable to all-composite reinforced shells (for example, skins reinforced with hat section stiffeners) and honeycomb structural sandwiches. Provision must be made for the uniform application of autoclave pressure to all surfaces and for the removal of tooling from confined areas. The process is attractive because it eliminates the cost and fit-up problems associated with secondary bonding.

5.3.7 TYPES OF DAMAGE

Shock, impact, or repeated cyclic or environmental stresses can cause the laminate to separate at the interface between two layers, a condition known as *delamination*. Individual fibers can separate from the matrix, referred to as *fiber pull-out*.

5.3.7.1 IMPACT DAMAGE

Impact damage can come from a variety of sources including dropped tools and tool boxes, hail, debris, birds, ballistic shells, forklifts, and heels of shoes. Polymer matrix composites tend to be brittle. The amount of damage done to a composite structure by the impact of a foreign object depends on several factors. These include the energy and shape of the impacting object, the laminate's mechanical properties and thickness, and the impact location relative to support or attachment points. Impact damage can be divided into two types: low- and high-velocity impact damage.

Low-velocity impact damage is a consequence of impacts by objects such as dropped tools, hail, runway debris, and catering trucks and other ramp vehicles in aviation. There is an energy threshold below which no damage is done to a given composite material or structure. However, immediately above this threshold is an energy range in which external damage occurs without visual indications at the surface. Figure 5.11a shows the external side of a representative composite fuselage sec-

(a)   (b)

Figure 5.11: Representative composite fuselage: (a) external view; (b) internal view with significant damage.

tion that has experienced a low-velocity, high-mass impact similar to what might be seen from a catering truck. No damage is evident visually. Figure 5.11b illustrates significant internal damage including delaminations and separation of various elements.

If not detected, this damage may lead to a premature failure of the structure for no apparent reason. Thin laminate skins, whether backed by stiffeners or honeycomb core, are very susceptible to low-velocity impact damage. Because of its brittle but elastic nature, the composite may spring back to its original shape leaving little, if any, external evidence of damage that can be sensed by the human eye. However, internal damage as evidenced by broken fibers and cracks in the matrix may be present. Even if there is damage that is visible on the external surface, the damage may have much greater extent internally. Figure 5.12 also illustrates this issue quite clearly. This is a carbon control rod with visual, external damage. The outlined area represents the actual extent of delamination internally.

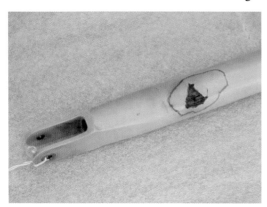

Figure 5.12: Carbon control rod showing actual damage (circled area) extending well beyond visible damage.

Damage to Honeycomb Panel. Another situation that is difficult to detect is an impact on a honeycomb panel that compresses the skin, which in turn crushes the core. As illustrated in Figure 5.13, the skin then springs back to its original shape, leaving the distorted core no longer bonded to the skin.

High-velocity impact damage can be represented by the impact of ballistic projectiles, for example, a car or truck into a bridge. A non-explosive projectile, for example, over a relatively short period of time, imparts some or all of its energy to a composite structure. In a high-velocity impact, fracture often occurs in an impacted zone where compression is dominant. Mechanical and thermal shock waves propagate through the structure.

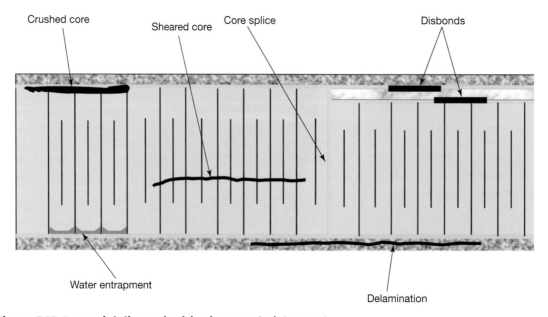

Figure 5.13. Potential discontinuities in a sandwich panel.

5.3.7.2 MATRIX AND FIBER DAMAGE

Cracking. *Matrix cracking* is the first type of failure, usually caused by low-velocity impact. Matrix cracks can be either parallel to the plies or perpendicular to them depending on the layup structure. *Shear cracking* (inclination of 45°) and *bending cracking* (vertical inclination) are examples of matrix cracking. It is the initial damage that affects the structure but cannot be seen by the naked eye. The impact response of the structure is not affected by matrix cracking. It can decrease the interlaminar shear and compression strength properties on the resin or the fiber/resin interface. Micro-cracking can have a significant effect on a high-temperature resin's properties.

Delamination. In a low-velocity impact, the most critical damage mechanism in composites is *delamination*. Delamination forms between the layers in the laminate. It may be initiated by matrix cracks when the threshold energy has been reached or from low-energy impact. Delamination can dramatically reduce the post-impact compressive strength of the laminate. Bending cracks and shear cracks are also responsible for delaminations. Delaminations are frequently generated in composite laminates due to out-of-plane impacts, and many experiments and analytical studies on low-velocity impact damage have been conducted assuming tool drops.

Fiber Damage. *Fiber pull out and fiber breakage* are the most common failures under low-velocity impact testing. Fiber failure occurs because of the high stress field and indentation effects. In destructive testing, the impactor—a pendulum in a charpy test machine with a notched specimen or a mass at a known height in drop-weight impact testing —induces a shear force and high bending stresses in the non-impacted side of the specimen.

5.3.7.3 DISBOND

Disbond damage can be of two kinds. *Adhesive fracture* (sometimes referred to as *interfacial fracture*) is when disbonding occurs between the adhesive and the adherend, whereas a *cohesive fracture* is obtained if a crack propagates in the bulk polymer that constitutes the adhesive. In this case, the surfaces of both adherends after disbonding will be covered by fractured adhesive. The crack may propagate in the center of the layer or near an interface. In the case of honeycomb, the adhesive wicks down the cell walls and creates a fillet near the adhesive layer. In this case, the core can totally come out of the adhesive (as will a contaminated core that does not stick) leaving the fillet shape with no core inside, or the core itself can fail, leaving pieces of aluminum in the adhesive.

5.3.7.4 ENVIRONMENTAL DAMAGE

Problems with Moisture. *Moisture* can create problems when a composite structure requires repair. The pressure resulting from the expansion of liquid water to ice can cause mechanical damage. At the other extreme, elevated temperatures can transform the water into the vapor state, resulting in elevated pressures within the structure. Practices have evolved to minimize moisture ingress during repairs. These include surface coatings, sealing of machined edges, and reducing the use of machining to the lowest levels practical. Organic coatings are not particularly effective in protecting carbon/epoxy materials from moisture expansion.

Moisture in all its physical states (gas or vapor, liquid, and solid) has the potential to degrade composite materials and structures. Moisture in the vapor state is capable of penetrating the polymer matrix through a diffusion-controlled process until an equilibrium concentration is reached. It acts like a resin plasticizer, softening the polymer matrix and lowering its glass transition temperature (T_g). The net result is lowering the composite's mechanical properties. This degradation process is of potential concern in aerospace applications where the inservice temperature environment could exceed the resulting lower T_g.

Influence of Temperature. *Temperature limits* placed on a composite are largely a result of the matrix constituent. At low temperatures, polymers generally retain their desired stiffness and strength characteristics. However, they are less flexible and, therefore, more susceptible to mechanical load fatigue. As temperature increases, the composite's mechanical properties remain relatively unchanged until the matrix begins to soften. If or when the glass transition temperature is reached, the matrix changes from a glass-like to a rubber-like state and the matrix suffers substantial losses in its mechanical properties. Although this elevated temperature normally has little impact on the reinforcement, the serious loss in the matrix's mechanical properties leads to a serious degradation in the composite's mechanical properties. Thermal cycling with its accompanying material expansions and contractions can result in thermal fatigue.

Water Pressure. Water in the liquid state is capable of degrading some composite structures through two modes: galvanic corrosion and change in physical state. The pressure resulting from the expansion of liquid water to ice can cause mechanical damage. At the other extreme, elevated temperatures can transform the water into the vapor state, resulting in elevated pressures within the structure. In composite skinned honeycomb sandwich structures, this may result in a "blown core" and disbonding of the skin from the core material. Moisture can both degrade the inservice performance of composites and also create problems when a composite structure requires repair.

Corrosion. Polymer matrix composites are inherently corrosion resistant. However, under certain conditions, some composites will undergo galvanic corrosion, which can occur when certain composites and metals (for example, carbon skins and metal fasteners, edge members, cores, and so on) are in direct contact with each other in the presence of moisture. Isolation is normally used to prevent this galvanic corrosion between composites and metals that have such a tendency. Nonconductive materials (for example, aramid or fiberglass plies and primer) are applied to the faying surfaces during the fabrication process, and care must be taken that they remain in place and effective during repairs.

Erosion. The rate of particulate erosion is dependent on several factors including the particle's physical characteristics, its quantity and velocity, and of course, the physical and mechanical properties of the composite material. It is a standard practice to provide composites exposed to such an environment with erosion protection. Conventional paint finishes and lightning protection materials are frequently used to provide erosion protection for composite structures. Elastomeric materials such as polyurethanes, neoprenes, and fluorocarbons are also used for erosion protection. In cases of extremely high erosion potential, such as the leading edge of composite propeller blades, a titanium or nickel cap may be used for protection.

Fire. Polymer composites range widely in flammability. Some are highly flammable; others burn with great difficulty. Aramid fibers, graphite fibers, and boron filaments are inherently resistant to flame. Cured graphite/epoxy and boron/epoxy are rated as self-extinguishing. However, when composites do burn, such as in an aircraft crash, extreme care must be taken to be aware of the gases given off as they can be extremely toxic.

Lightning strikes can cause damage to composite structures, although composite structures are less likely to attract a lightning strike than similar structures made of metal. In high hazard situations, it is common practice to equip the composite with a lightning protection system. Numerous protection systems have been devised. One common method consists of a metal wire screen (for instance, made of aluminum or bronze) bonded one or two plies deep in the laminate. Another system consists of a metal-coated, glass-fiber fabric that can be impregnated with the same polymer as the laminate and then co-cured. Some lightning protection systems also provide protection against precipitation static (P-static) charge by bleeding off static charges before they accumulate to unacceptable levels.

5.3.7.5 INSERVICE DAMAGE

Chemical fluids found in the maintenance and inservice environments (including fuel vapors, oils, hydraulic fluids, anti-icing fluids, solvents, cleaners, and paint strippers) pose a risk to composite materials and structures. Low void content composite laminates have low permeability rates and an inherent resistance to many fluids. In addition, finished components are normally equipped with protective coatings. However, the organic components of polymer composites may be degraded when exposed to these fluids. Exposed cut edges of laminates, or matrix cracks, may result in the wicking of fluids into the laminate. Long-term exposure to some fluids may affect the bond strength of composite or titanium patches over damaged areas. To avoid degradation of a composite structure when providing maintenance or repair involving the application of a chemical fluid (such as paint stripper), only authorized fluids must be selected. Strict adherence to prescribed concentration levels and procedural matters is of great importance.

Proper Training Neccessary to Prevent Damage. Training, or lack thereof, is also a major source of damage. Composites can be damaged by using typical metalworking techniques, such as drilling out fasteners. Mechanics must be properly trained in the concerns associated with the maintenance and repair of composites, including proper selection of cutting tools and processes. Not replacing drill bits often enough can result in increased speed and pressure, which can cause delamination or matrix softening. Mechanics must also be aware of isolation methods used to prevent galvanic corrosion and be sure that if they are damaged or removed that they be properly reapplied. Figure 5.14 illustrates the results of improper drilling when removing rivets. Because the mechanic was not familiar with the potential problems, every other hole was delaminated in the same direction, indicative of how the drill was held.

Figures 5.13 and 5.15 illustrates just some of the potential discontinuities that can be encountered in composite components. They also illustrate the importance of an NDT technician having proper drawings and standards before evaluating such panels. It is common practice for a technician to set up on a "known good area" and then evaluate the damage. Without knowledge of the underlying substructure, it is

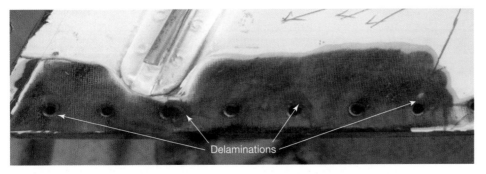

Figure 5.14: Delaminations due to improper drilling identified with red wax pencil marks where ultrasonic testing found indications.

not possible to know if one is setting up on an area that is configured the same as the area to be evaluated. This can result in completely erroneous results.

5.3.8 REPAIR TECHNIQUES

The repair method selected to restore a damaged composite structure is a result of a long chain of decisions that weigh many factors—for example, types and severity of damage, availability of facilities, tools, equipment, materials, qualified personnel, and operational demands.

5.3.8.1 DAMAGE ASSESSMENT

Damage assessment comprises three distinct steps: discontinuity detection/location, discontinuity assessment, and defect removal assessment. Discontinuity detection/location uses one or two of several NDT techniques. Once the discontinuity is located and mapped, an assessment must be made regarding type, size and relevance of the indication(s). Engineer-developed accept/reject criteria are applied to determine the appropriate condition category: negligible, repairable, not repairable, or beyond economical repair. In the case of repair procedures designed to eliminate the defect by removing composite material, it is necessary to re-inspect the structure after removing all the apparent damage. Delaminations for example, can mask or hide deeper damage. In addition, some discontinuities may propagate during removal operations. Thus, it is common practice to inspect the material surrounding the discontinuity's location for additional damage incurred during the removal operation. From the repair viewpoint, specific types of damage include surface damage, delaminations, disbonds, inclusions, laminate penetration, sandwich penetration, stiffener damage, and attachment hole damage.

5.3.8.2 REPAIR MATERIALS

Repair joints are basically bolted, bonded, or a combination of these. Bolted joints (Figure 5.16) usually use metal sheet and plate for the patch material. Titanium is often preferred, but aluminum and sometimes stainless steels are also used. Aluminum patches must be isolated from graphite or carbon to prevent galvanic corrosion. Bonded joints (Figure 5.17) are usually recommended over bolted joints because the former have up to twice the load-distributing efficiency of mechanically fastened joints. The repair technician has a variety of materials available for repairing structural damage including adhesives (films, paste, foams), injection resins, potting compounds, sealants, and aerodynamic smoothers. Research findings indicate

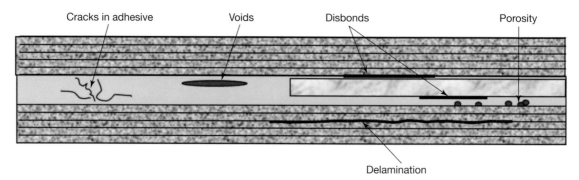

Figure 5.15. Potential discontinuities in a structure with monolithic skins and aluminum stiffener flange.

that resin injection for delamination, including edge delamination, does not result in structural improvement. Rather, it is a nonstructural repair, only suitable for sealing and cosmetic improvement. Also, some of these materials are effective absorbers of ultrasonic energy and can lead to interpretation problems for the NDT technician.

5.3.8.3 REPAIR PROCEDURES AND OPERATIONS

Research is continually ongoing to develop more efficient, less costly, stronger, more durable repairs for composite materials and structures. When a repair situation arises, it is standard practice to work in accordance with specific maintenance manuals or other authorized repair guides. The general objective of the material, methods,

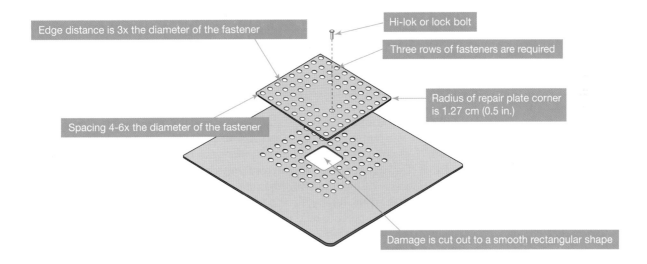

Figure 5.16: Repair layout for the bolted repair of a composite structure.

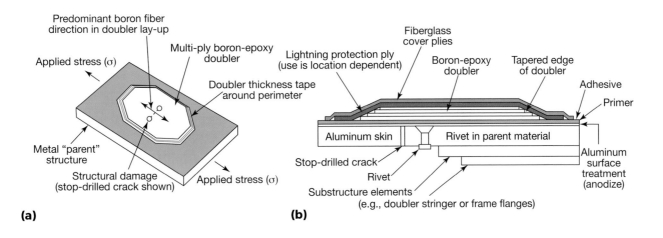

Figure 5.17: Bonded composite doubler installation on an aluminum skin: (a) schematic; (b) isometric view.

and procedures is to restore the composite structure's physical and mechanical properties to its original levels. However, repaired structures are rarely as strong as the original. Depending on many details, the repaired structure is typically 60% to 80% as strong as the original structure. Maintenance manuals normally provide limits (for example, damage size, weight, balance, and repair proximity) based on the criticality of specific parts. In cases where specific instructions are unavailable or cannot be followed, the responsible engineering authority must be consulted. Only the responsible engineering authority is empowered to authorize deviations or substitutions in repair design (including materials, methods, and procedures) and repair criteria. Several operations are common to most types of repair.

Coatings. Paint and other coatings prevent good bonding of faying surfaces. Most coatings also reduce friction in mechanically fastened joints. Normally, it is highly desirable to remove these coatings. Chemical paint strippers are not satisfactory for the removal of paint from composite materials. Paint removal is frequently accomplished by carefully controlled mechanical abrasion.

Drying. Resin matrix composites, especially epoxies, are normally dried before making repairs involving structural bonding. Drying is especially important if the laminate's temperature will exceed 93 °C (200 °F). Failure to properly dry the composite structure may lead to blistering of the laminate, bondline porosity, blown core, and blown skins. In addition, the presence of liquid water in voids and cracks may adversely affect ultrasonic inspection efforts.

Removal Operations. Removal of damaged material is necessary if a good repair is to be made. The removal operation may involve sawing, drilling, routing, peeling, and cutting. Careless operation of the equipment can result in additional damage to the structure. Damage removal may involve only the removal of a few skin plies in the case of a surface discontinuity. In the case of skin penetration or damage to the core of a sandwich panel, it may involve the removal of composite skin or the removal of both skin and core material.

Scarfing involves tapering the edges of the remaining material in order to establish high-strength joints and return the original external contour. An assortment of tools can be used to produce scarfs, such as drum sanders and routers. In the case of

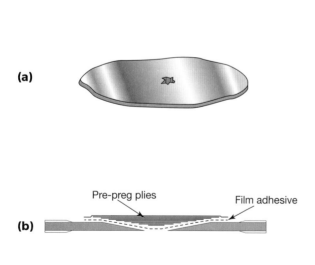

Figure 5.18. Straight scarf repair: (a) damaged laminate; (b) cutaway view of repair technique.

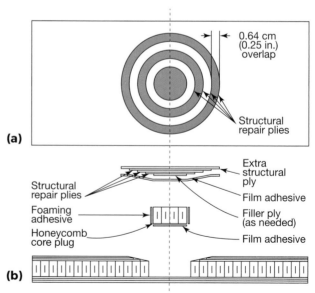

Figure 5.19: Step scarf repair: (a) top view; (b) side view.

skin penetration damage, the cutting is done until the scarf intersects with the far side of the laminate. The technique of *straight scarfing* exposes each ply over a gradual slope, as shown in Figure 5.18. Repair plies of fiber do not always overlap on the original laminate plies with the fibers oriented in the exact same direction. This does not allow for direct transfer of loads through each ply as per the original design. Because of this indirect load transfer, the *step scarf* as shown in Figure 5.19 is stronger than the straight scarf because it provides overlap of repair plies over the remaining original plies.

In the case of a honeycomb sandwich panel, skin penetration or impact damage to the skin frequently results in damage to the core also. As a result, core removal and replacement may be required. When necessary, core material is removed and replaced with a core plug. If the damaged core area is small, the core is sometimes potted (that is, reinforced with a polymer matrix) rather than replaced.

Patches. In general, the patches used to make bonded joint repairs on laminate skins are built from pre-preg composite tape. Ready-made, procured patches are available as are kits or pre-pregs that the repair technician can use to fabricate a patch specifically tailored for the restoration. It is a common practice to make the repair using a pre-preg patch to which a co-cure adhesive film has been applied.

Because of the potential for galvanic corrosion when employing certain combinations of composites and metals, nonconductive materials (for example, aramid or fiberglass plies, primer, and so on) are applied to the faying surfaces during the fabrication process, and care must be taken that it remains in place and effective during repairs.

Once the patch has been properly oriented, it is pressed to the surface of the item being repaired. Elevated temperatures and pressures are normally required to cure both the patch and the adhesive bonding of the patch to the parent material. If a pre-cured patch is used, the temperature and pressure requirements relate to curing the adhesive. This is accomplished by bagging the repair. A bag is placed over the repair and its edges sealed to the parent material. Provisions are made in the bag to allow the movement of fluids out of the repair area. The removal of air from the bag causes the atmosphere to exert pressure on the repair during the cure process. The heat required for the cure is supplied by a heat blanket. Once the cure is completed, all bagging material is removed and the repair is inspected in accordance with approved procedures. If the structural repair is accepted, all nonstructural repairs are completed and protective coatings reapplied as necessary.

5.3.9 HEALTH AND SAFETY

Technicians performing inspections or repairs on damaged composite structures must be aware of potential health and safety hazards associated with those activities. Strict compliance with all relevant warnings, cautions, and notes found in the repair and inspection documentation is a must. Working with composites undergoing repair may affect the skin, eyes, and/or lungs if compliance is lax.

Damaged composite structures may be hazardous to human health. The ends of exposed fibers (for example, carbon or fiberglass) can easily penetrate bare skin, break off, and remain lodged in the skin or subcutaneous tissue. The removal process is similar to that used to remove small cactus needles from the skin. It is a slow, uncomfortable procedure generally requiring a magnifier and tweezers.

Repair operations involving cutting, sanding, drilling, and grinding can create a potential health risk if procedures to control removed material are not followed. The potential risk arises from exposure to the fibers themselves and also from materials that may cling to the fibers. These materials can be of a sensitizing type, having the potential to cause allergic dermatitis. Airborne carbon fibers may also damage some metals and electrical/electronic gear. Carbon in contact with aluminum or aluminum alloys can lead to galvanic corrosion. Infiltration of the tiny fibers into unprotected electrical/electronic equipment may result in corrosion, shorts, and other forms of damage.

The cleaning agents, solvents, adhesives, and matrix constituents (for example, hardeners and epoxies) used to prepare faying surfaces and to lay up or bond composite patches can irritate the skin and eyes. Some of these materials have the potential to cause allergic dermatitis from exposure to their vapors. The curing process can produce vapors with the potential to irritate eyes and produce allergies. Repair operations also frequently involve the use of flammable materials or require elevated temperatures and pressures, underscoring the need for health and safety precautions.

MANUFACTURING
PROCESSES

CONTENTS

6 Casting

6.1 INTRODUCTION

Casting is the process of causing liquid metal to fill a cavity and solidify into a useful shape. It is a basic method of producing shapes. With the exception of a very small volume of a few metals produced by electrolytic or pure chemical methods, all material used in metal manufacturing is cast at some stage in its processing. Castings of all kinds of metals, in sizes from a fraction of an ounce up to many tons, are used directly with or without further shape processing for many items of manufacture. Even those materials considered to be wrought start out as cast ingots before deformation work in the solid state puts them into their final condition.

A vast majority of castings, from a tonnage standpoint, are made from cast iron. A relatively small number of these are subjected to NDT. In most cases they are designed for noncritical applications with principally compressive loading and oversize dimensions to eliminate the problematic effect of the innumerable discontinuities inherent in the material. However, some of these castings and many others made of different material may be used in such a way that careful inspection is essential for satisfactory service. Penetrant or magnetic particle testing may be in order for surface examination. Radiographic or ultrasonic testing may be needed to detect internal discontinuities regardless of the material or type of casting.

"Casting is the process of causing liquid metal to fill a cavity and solidify into a useful shape."

Radiography is the most widely used method for this purpose. It can be difficult to accomplish complete coverage of complex castings. Image evaluation is usually by comparison to standard reference images for various types of discontinuities. Ultrasonic techniques are difficult to use with some castings because of noise created by grain structure. The rough surfaces of many castings also can produce problems in transducer coupling, but ultrasonic testing is used extensively in the examination of critical coolant passages in turbine engine blades to measure thickness. Electromagnetic (eddy current) and penetrant methods are also used to detect leading and trailing edge cracks before and during service of turbine blades. Neutron radiography is sometimes used to detect residual waste in internal passages of turbine blades and other parts made by the lost wax casting process.

Process Starts with a Pattern. The casting, or founding, process consists of a series of sequential steps performed in a definite order, as shown in Figure 6.1. First, a pattern to represent the finished product must be chosen or constructed. Patterns can be of a number of different styles but are always the shape of the finished part and roughly the same size as the finished part with slightly oversized dimensions to allow for shrinkage and additional allowances on surfaces that are to be machined. In some casting processes, mainly those performed with metal molds, the actual pattern may be only a design consideration with the mold fulfilling the function of a negative of the pattern as all molds do. Examples would be molds for ingots, die casting, and permanent mold castings. Most plastic parts are made in molds of this type, but with plastics, the process is often called *molding* rather than casting. The following information applies generally to sand casting or casting with sand molds. Specific differences in other casting methods are described individually.

A Mold Is Constructed from the Pattern. In some casting processes, the second step is to build a mold of material that can be made to flow into close contact with the pattern and that has sufficient strength to maintain that position. The mold is designed in such a way that it can be opened for removal of the pattern. The pattern

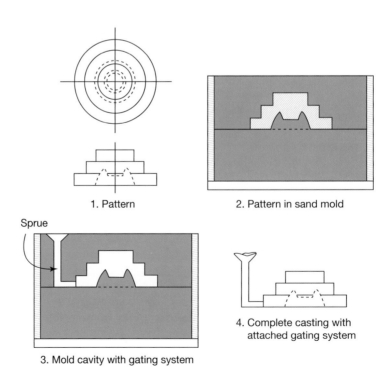

1. Pattern

2. Pattern in sand mold

3. Mold cavity with gating system

4. Complete casting with attached gating system

Sprue

Figure 6.1: Casting steps for pulley blank.

may have attachments that make grooves in the mold to serve as channels for flow of material into the cavity. If not, these channels, or *runners,* must be cut in the mold material. In either case, an opening to the outside of the mold, called a *sprue,* must be cut or formed.

Mold Cavity Filled with Molten Material. Liquid metal is poured through the channels to fill the cavity completely. After time has been allowed for solidification to occur, the mold is opened. The product is then ready for removing the excess metal that has solidified in the runners, cleaning for removal of any remaining mold material, and inspecting to determine if discontinuities have been formed by the process. The casting thus produced is a finished product of the foundry. This product occasionally may be used in this form but more often than not needs further processing, such as machining, to improve surface qualities and dimensions. Therefore, it becomes raw material for another processing area.

6.1.1 IMPORTANT PARAMETERS IN THE CASTING PROCESS

6.1.1.1 CASTING DESIGN

The first consideration that must be given to obtain good castings is to casting design. Although volumetric shrinkage of the liquid is thought of as being replaced by extra metal poured into the mold and by hydraulic pressure from elevated parts of the casting system, this can be true only if no parts of the casting freeze off before replacement takes place. Except for the small pockets completely enclosed by solid metal in the development of dendritic structures, the shrinkage of solidification can be compensated for if liquid metal can be progressively supplied to the freezing face as it advances.

Progressive versus Directional Solidification. The term *progressive solidification,* the freezing of a liquid from the outside toward the center, is different from *directional solidification.* Rather than from the surface to the center of the mass, *directional solidification* is used to describe the freezing from one part of a casting to another, such as from one end to the other end, as shown in Figure 6.2. The direction of freezing is extremely important to the quality of a casting because of the need for liquid metal to compensate for the contraction of the liquid during solidification. Casting design and procedure should cause the metal farthest from the point of entry to freeze first with solidification moving toward a *feed head,* which may be at the point where metal is poured into the mold or can be located at other points where liquid can be stored to feed into the casting proper.

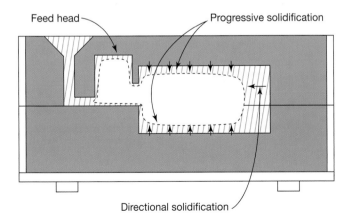

Figure 6.2: Progressive and directional solidification.

Hot Spots Are Focal Points for Solidification. The highest temperature areas immediately after pouring are called *hot spots* and should be located as near as possible to sources of feed metal. If isolated by sections that freeze early, they may disturb good directional solidification with the result that shrinks, porosity, cracks, ruptures, or warping will harm the casting quality. It is not always necessary to completely inspect some castings when the vulnerable spots can be determined by visual inspection. Discontinuities are most likely at hot spots created by section changes or geometry of the part and where gates and risers have been connected to the casting.

Control of Hot Spots Usually by Proper Design. Hot spots are usually located at points of greatest sectional dimensions. Bosses (protruding feature of a casting used for attachment points or bearing surfaces), raised letters, nonuniform section thicknesses, and intersecting members are often troublemakers in the production of high-quality castings. Solutions to the problem involve changing the design, as shown in Figure 6.3, or pouring the casting in such a way that these spots cease to be sources of trouble. Changing the design might include coring a boss to make it a thin-walled cylinder, relieving raised letters or pads on the backside, proportioning section thicknesses to uniform change of dimensions, using a thin-ribbed design instead of heavy sections, spreading and alternating intersection members, and making other changes that will not affect the function of the part but will decrease the degree of section change.

Uniform Section Thicknesses Desirable. As a general rule, section changes should be minimized as much as possible in order to approach uniform cooling rates and reduce discontinuities. When iron is poured, heavy sections tend to solidify as gray iron with precipitated graphite. Thin sections of the same material cooling at higher rates tend to hold the carbon in the combined state as iron carbide with the result that these sections turn out to be hard, brittle white iron. Since it is clearly impossible to design practical shapes without section changes, the usual procedure calls for gradual section size changes and the use of liberal fillets and rounds. Some section changes are compared in Figure 6.4.

6.1.1.2 POURING

Most Pouring Done from Ladles. Pouring is usually performed by using ladles to transport the hot metal from the melting equipment to the molds. Most molds are heavy and could be easily damaged by jolts and jars received in moving them from

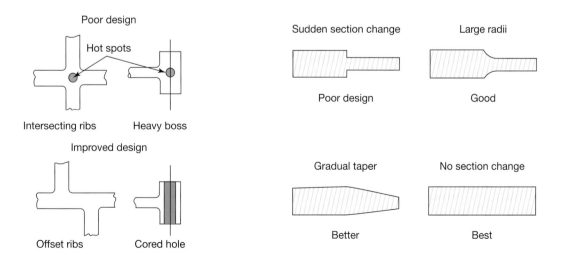

Figure 6.3: Hot spot elimination.   **Figure 6.4: Section changes in casting design.**

one place to another. Exceptions exist with small molds or with heavier molds, with which special equipment is used, that can be conveyorized and moved to a central pouring station. Even with these, the hot metal is usually poured from a ladle, though some high-production setups make use of an automatic pouring station where spouts are positioned over the mold and release the correct amount of metal to fill the cavity.

Turbulent Flow Harmful. Casting quality can be significantly influenced by pouring procedure. Turbulent flow, which is caused by pouring from too great a height or by excessive rates of flow into the mold, should be avoided. Turbulence will cause gas to be picked up that may appear as cavities or pockets in the finished casting and may also oxidize the hot metal to form metallic oxide inclusions. Rough, fast flow of liquid metal may erode the mold and result in loss of shape or detail in the cavity and inclusion of sand particles in the metal. *Cold shots* are also a result of turbulent flow. Drops of splashing metal lose heat, freeze, and are then entrapped as globules that do not join completely with the metal. A *cold shot* is different from a cold shut, which is described below.

Pouring Rate. The pouring rate used in filling a mold is critical. If metal enters the cavity too slowly, it may freeze before the mold is filled. Thin sections that cool too rapidly in contact with the mold walls may freeze off before the metal travels its complete path, or metal flowing in one direction may solidify and then be met by metal flowing through another path to form a discontinuity known as a *cold shut*. Even though the mold is completely filled, the cold shut shows the seam on the surface of the casting, indicating the metal is not solidly joined and is therefore subject to easy breakage.

If the pouring rate is too high, it will cause erosion of the mold walls with the resulting sand inclusions and loss of detail in the casting. High thermal shock to the mold may result in cracks and buckling. The rate of pouring is controlled by the mold design and the pouring basin, sprue, runner, and gate dimensions. The gating system should be designed so that when the pouring basin is kept full, the rest of the system will be completely filled with a uniform flow of metal.

6.1.1.3 THE GATING SYSTEM

Metal is fed into the cavity that shapes the casting through a gating system consisting of a *pouring basin,* a *down sprue, runners,* and *ingates.* Typical systems are shown in Figure 6.5. There are many special designs and terminology connected with these

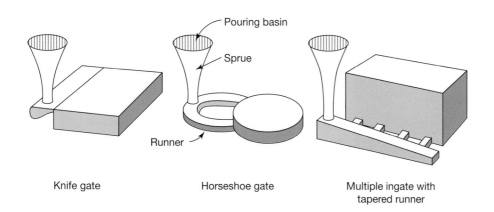

Figure 6.5: Typical gating systems.

channels and openings whose purpose is that of improving casting quality. Special features of a gating system are often necessary to reduce turbulence and air entrapment, reduce velocity and erosion of sand, and remove foreign matter or dross. Unfortunately, no universal design is satisfactory for all castings or materials. There are no rules that can be universally depended upon, and experimentation is commonly a requirement for good casting production.

The location of the connection for the gate, or gates, can usually be determined visually. These spots are possible concentration points for discontinuities.

6.1.1.4 RISERS

Risers Are Multipurpose. *Risers, feeders,* or *feed heads* serve as wells of material attached outside the casting proper to supply liquid metal as needed to compensate for shrinkage before solidification is complete. Although most liquid contraction is taken care of during pouring, a riser may supply replacement for some of this contraction after parts of the casting have frozen solid, as shown in Figure 6.6. However, the principal purposes of risers are to replace the contraction of solidification and to promote good directional solidification. The need for risers varies with the casting shape and the metal being poured.

6.1.1.5 CHILLS

Chills Initiate Solidification. Help in directional solidification can also be obtained in a reverse manner by the use of *chills*, which are heat-absorbing devices inserted in the mold near the cavity (Figure 6.7). To absorb heat rapidly, chills are usually made of steel, cast iron, or copper and designed to conform to the casting size and shape. Because chills must be dry to avoid blowhole formation from gases, it is sometimes necessary to pour a mold soon after it has been made, before the chills have time to collect moisture from condensation. In addition to helping with directional solidification, chills may also improve physical properties. Fast cooling during and after solidification retards grain growth and thus produces a harder, stronger structure.

Choice of Internal Chills Critical. Internal chills that become an integral part of the casting are occasionally used to speed solidification in areas where external chills cannot be applied. The design and use of internal chills is critical. Usually this type of chill is made of the same material as the casting. The chill must be of such size

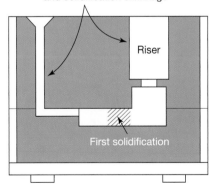

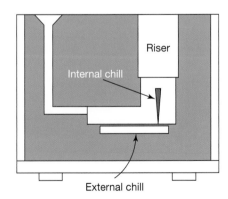

Figure 6.6: Risers for shrinkage control.

Figure 6.7: Chills as an aid to directional solidification.

that it functions as a cooling device, but at the same time it must be heated enough that it fuses with the poured material to become an integral and equally strong part of the casting.

Radiography is often used to detect unfused internal chills and adjacent discontinuities that may be caused by the change in cooling rate created by the presence of the chill.

6.1.1.6 FOUNDRY TECHNOLOGY

Although the casting process can be used to shape almost any metal, it has been necessary to develop a number of different methods to accommodate different materials and satisfy different requirements. Each method has certain advantages over the others, but all have limitations. Some are restricted to a few special applications.

6.1.2 FLUID FLOW AND HEAT TRANSFER

6.1.2.1 SOLIDIFICATION OF METALS

The casting process involves a change of state of material from liquid to solid with control of shapes being established during the change of state. The problems associated with the process, then, are primarily those connected with changes of physical state and changes of properties as they may be influenced by temperature variation. The solution to many casting problems can only be attained with an understanding of the solidification process and the effects of temperature on materials.

6.1.2.2 SHRINKAGE

Shrinkage Occurs in Three Stages. Some of the most important problems connected with the casting process are those of shrinkage. The amount of shrinkage that occurs will, of course, vary with the material being cast, but it is also influenced by the casting procedure and techniques. The three stages of contraction that occur as the temperature decreases from the temperature of the molten metal to room temperature are illustrated in Figure 6.8.

First Stage—Shrinkage in the Liquid. In the melting procedure, preparatory to pouring castings, the metal is always heated well above the melting temperature. The additional heat above that necessary for melting is called *superheat*. It is necessary to provide fluidity of the liquid to permit cold additives to be mixed with the metal before pouring. Superheat allows the metal to be transferred and to contact cold equipment without starting to freeze, and ensures that sufficient time will elapse before freezing occurs to allow disposal of the material. Some superheat is

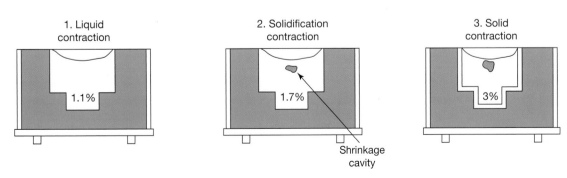

Shrink percentages approximate only for cast iron

Figure 6.8: Three stages of metal contraction.

lost during transfer of the liquid metal from the melting equipment to the mold. However, as the metal is poured into the mold, some superheat must remain to ensure that the mold will fill. Loss of superheat results in contraction and increased density but is not likely to cause serious problems in casting. The volume change can be compensated for by pouring additional material into the mold cavity as the superheat is lost. An exception exists when the cavity is of such design that part of it may freeze off and prevent the flow of the liquid metal for shrinkage replacement.

Solidification Shrinkage. The second stage of shrinkage occurs during the transformation from liquid to solid. Water is an exception to the rule, but most materials are denser as solids than as liquids. Metals contract as they change from liquid to solid. The approximate volumetric solidification shrinkage for some common metals is shown in Table 6.1. Contraction at this stage can be partially replaced because the

Table 6.1: Approximate solidification shrinkage of some common metals.				
Metal	Gray iron	Steel	Aluminum	Copper
Volumetric shrinkage	0-2%	2.5-4%	6.6%	4.9%

entire metal is not yet frozen. If a suitable path can be kept open, liquid metal can flow from the hot zones to replace most of the shrinkage. However, in the formation of a dendritic grain structure, small pockets have been left completely enclosed with solid material. Depending upon the characteristics of the material and the size of the liquid enclosures, localized shrinking will develop minute random voids referred to as *microporosity* or *microshrinkage* (Figure 6.9). Microporosity causes a reduction in density and tends to reduce the apparent shrinkage that can be seen on the surface of a casting.

The shrinkage that occurs during solidification and the microporosity that often accompanies it are minimized in materials that are near eutectic composition (that is, a mixture of substances that solidifies at a temperature below that of the separate constituents). This seems to be due to more uniform freezing with lower temperature gradients and more random nucleation producing finer grain structure. Microshrinkage is often a problem in aluminum or magnesium castings.

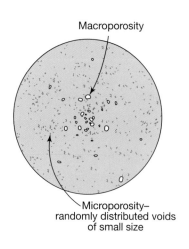

Figure 6.9: Porosity.

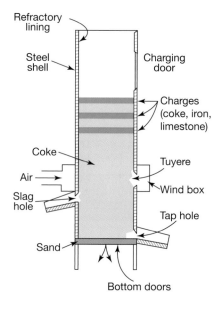

Figure 6.10: Cupola.

Macroporosity. The porosity of a casting may be amplified by the evolution of gas before and during solidification. Gas may form pockets or bubbles of its own or may enter the voids of microporosity to enlarge them. The evolved gas is usually hydrogen, which may combine with dissolved oxygen to form water vapor. These randomly dispersed openings of large size in the solid metal are referred to as *macroporosity*.

Contraction in the Solid State. The third stage of shrinkage is that occurring after solidification takes place and is the primary cause of dimensional change to a size different from that of the pattern used to make the cavity in the mold. Although contraction of solidification may contribute in some cases, the solid metal contraction is the main element of *patternmaker's shrinkage,* which must be allowed for by making the pattern oversized.

6.1.3 ECONOMY OF CASTING

Casting Is a Large Industry. The tonnage output of foundries throughout the U.S. is very large. According to the American Foundry Society (AFS), total tonnage of castings produced in the U.S. in 2012 was 10.9 million metric tons (12 million tons). Furthermore, the U.S. is the global leader in applications and second in production. On average, according to AFS, if you live in the U.S., you are likely within 3 m (10 ft) of a metal casting at all times. Foundries are scattered all over the U.S., but are concentrated primarily in the eastern part of the nation with a secondary concentration on the West Coast in the two areas where the main manufacturing work is carried on.

Foundries Tend to Specialize. Because of differences in the problems and equipment connected with casting different materials, most foundries specialize in producing either ferrous or nonferrous castings. Relatively few cast both kinds of materials in appreciable quantities in the same foundry.

A few foundries are large in size, employing several thousand workers, but the majority are small, with only one to 100 employees. Most large foundries are captive foundries, owned by parent manufacturing companies that use all, or nearly all, of the foundry's output. More of the small foundries are independently owned and contract with a number of different manufacturers for the sale of their castings. Some foundries, more often the larger ones, may produce a product in sufficient demand that their entire facility is devoted to the making of the product with a continuous production-type operation. Most, however, operate as job shops that produce a number of different parts at one time and are continually changing from one product to another, although the duplication for some parts may run into the thousands.

6.2 CASTING PRACTICES

Melting Equipment. The volume of metal needed at any one time for casting varies from a few pounds for simple castings to several tons in a batch-type operation with a continuous supply, usually of iron, being required by some large production foundries. The quantity of available metal can be varied by the size and type of melting equipment as well as the number of units in operation. The required melting temperature, which varies from about 200 °C (390 °F) for lead and bismuth to as high as 1540 °C (2400 °F) for some steels, also influences the type of melting equipment that will serve best.

Cupola. A considerable amount of cast iron is melted in a special chimney-like furnace called a *cupola*. It is similar to a blast furnace (described in Chapter 4) used for refining iron ore. The cupola (Figure 6.10) is charged through a door above the melting zone with layers of coke, iron, and limestone and may be operated continuously by taking off melted iron as it accumulates in the well at the bottom.

Crucible Furnaces. Melting of small quantities (0.45 to 45 kg [1 to 100 lb]) of nonferrous materials for small-volume work is often performed in lift-out crucibles constructed of graphite, silicon carbide, or other refractory material. Gas or oil is combined with an air blast around the crucible to produce the melting heat. Unless a cover is placed on the crucible, the melt is exposed to products of combustion and is susceptible to contamination that may reduce the quality of the final castings. This is true of all the natural-fuel-fired furnaces.

Pot Furnaces. Quantities of nonferrous materials to several hundred kilograms (pounds) may be melted in pot furnaces that contain a permanently placed crucible. Metal is ladled directly from the crucible, or, in the larger size equipment, the entire furnace is tilted to pour the molten metal into a transporting ladle.

Reverberatory Furnaces. Some of the largest foundries melt nonferrous metals in reverberatory furnaces that play a gas-air or oil-air flame through nozzles in the sidewalls of a brick structure, directly on the surface of the charged material. Gas absorption from products of combustion is high, but the large capacity available and high melting rate provide economics that help compensate for this fault. Smaller tilting-type reverberating furnaces are also available for fast melting of smaller quantities of metal.

Electric Arc Furnaces. The electric arc provides a high-intensity heat source that can be used to melt any metal that is commonly cast. Since there are no products of combustion and since oxygen can be largely excluded from contact with the melt, the quality of the resulting cast metal is usually high. The arc may be *direct* (between an electrode and the charged metal) or *indirect* (between two electrodes above the charge).

Induction Furnaces. Induction furnaces melt materials with the heat dissipated from eddy currents. Coils built into the furnace walls set up a high-frequency alternating magnetic field, which in turn causes internal eddy currents that heat the charge to its melting point. Rapid heating and high quality resulting from the absence of combustion products help offset the high cost of the equipment and power consumed.

Foundry Mechanization. The preceding discussion briefly describes the most common foundry techniques for producing castings. Most are performed largely by manual effort, resulting in relatively slow production. However, at any time the production quantities justify the needed expenditure for equipment, these same techniques are subject to almost complete mechanization, resulting in higher production rates and improved consistency.

Metal Mold and Special Processes. Metal patterns and metal core boxes are used in connections with molding whenever the quantities manufactured justify the additional expense of the longer wearing patterns. The metal mold process refers not to the pattern equipment but to a reusable metal mold that is in itself a reverse pattern in which the casting is made directly.

Special Processes Receive Limited Use. In addition to the metal mold processes, there are special processes involving either single-use or reusable molds. Their use is limited to a comparatively small number of applications in which the processes, even though more costly, show distinct advantages over the more commonly used methods.

6.2.1 CONTINUOUS CASTING

Although only a small tonnage of castings is produced by continuous casting, it is possible to produce two-dimensional shapes in an elongated bar by drawing solidified metal from a water-cooled mold.

Special Equipment and Skills Required. As shown schematically in Figure 6.11, molten metal enters one end of the mold, and solid metal is drawn from the other. Control of the mold temperature and the speed of drawing are essential for satisfactory results.

Good Quality Castings Possible. Exclusion of contact with oxygen, while molten and during solidification, produces high-quality metal. Gears and other shapes in small sizes can be cast in bar form and later sliced into multiple parts.

An automotive manufacturer makes use of the concept as a salvage procedure for saving bar ends of alloy steel. The waste material is melted and drawn through the mold in bar form. Subsequently, the bars are cut into billets that are suitable for processing into various automotive parts.

6.2.2 SAND CASTING, PATTERN, CORES, AND MOLD DESIGN

6.2.2.1 SAND MOLDING

Sand is the most commonly used material for construction of molds. A variety of sand grain sizes, combined and mixed with a number of other materials and processed in different ways, causes sand to exhibit characteristics that make it suitable for several applications in mold making. A greater tonnage of castings is produced by sand molding than by all other methods combined.

Procedure for Sand Molding. The following requirements are basic to sand molding, and most of them also apply to the construction of other types of molds.

- **Sand:** to serve as the main structural material for the mold.
- **Pattern:** To form a properly shaped and sized cavity in the sand.
- **Flask:** to contain the sand around the pattern and to provide a means of removing the pattern after the mold is made.
- **Ramming method:** to compact the sand around the pattern for accurate transfer of size and shape.
- **Core:** to form internal surfaces on the part (usually not required for castings without cavities or holes).
- **Mold grating system:** to provide a means of filling the mold cavity with metal at the proper rate and to supply liquid metal to the mold cavity as the casting contracts during cooling and solidification.

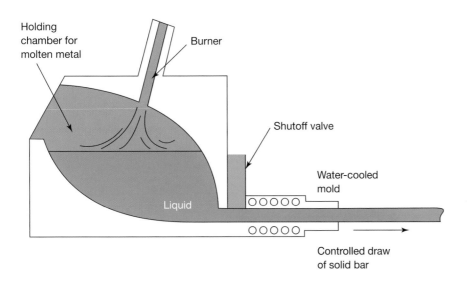

Figure 6.11: Schematic diagram of continuous casting process.

The usual procedure for making a simple green sand casting starts with placing the pattern to be copied on a *pattern,* or *follower, board* inside one-half of the flask, as shown in Figure 6.12. Sand is then packed around the pattern and between the walls of the flask. After striking off excess sand, a *bottom board* is held against the flask and sand, and the assembly turned over. Removal of the pattern board exposes the other side of the pattern. A thin layer of *parting* compound (dry nonabsorbent particles) is dusted on the pattern and sand to prevent adhesion. Addition of the upper half of the flask allows sand to be packed against the pattern.

After the sprue is cut to the parting line depth, the upper half of the mold can be removed, the pattern withdrawn, and the gating system completed. Reassembly of the mold halves completes the task, and the mold is ready for pouring.

6.2.2.2 GREEN SAND

The Term *Green* Refers to Moisture. The majority of castings are poured in molds of *green sand,* which is a mixture of sand, clay, and moisture. The materials are available in large quantities, relatively inexpensive, and, except for some losses that must be replaced, reusable. The proportions of the mixture and the types of sand and clay may be varied to change the properties of the molds to suit the material being poured. To produce good work consistently, it is important that advantage be taken of the properties that can be controlled by varying the constituents of the sand mixture.

Sand Grains Held Together by Clay. In a mold, the sand particles are bound together by clay that is combined with a suitable quantity of water. The most commonly accepted theory of bonding is that as pressure is applied to the molding sand,

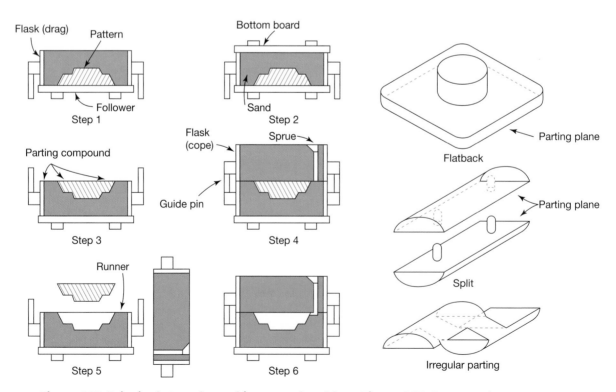

Figure 6.12: Principal steps for making a sand mold.   **Figure 6.13: Common loose pattern types.**

the clay, which coats each sand particle, deforms and flows to wedge and lock the particles in place. The clay content can be varied from as little as 2% or 3% to as high as 50%, but the best results seem to be obtained when the amount of clay is just sufficient to coat completely each of the sand grains.

Water Conditions the Clay. Water is the third requisite for green sand molding. The optimum quantity will vary from about 2% to 8% by weight, depending largely upon the type and quantity of clay present. Thin films of water, several molecules in thickness, are absorbed around the clay crystals. This water is held in fixed relationship to the clay by atomic attraction and is described as rigid water, or tempering water. The clays that have the greatest ability to hold this water film provide the greatest bonding strength. Water in excess of that needed to temper the molding sand does not contribute to strength but will improve the flowability that permits the sand to be compacted around the pattern.

6.2.2.3 PATTERNS

By most procedures, *patterns* are essential for producing castings. In occasional emergency situations, an original part, even a broken or worn part, may be used as a pattern for making a replacement, but considerable care and skill are necessary when this is done.

Patterns are made of various materials: principally wood, metal, plastic, or plaster, depending on the shape, size, intricacy, and amount of expected use. They are constructed slightly larger than the expected resulting part to allow for shrinkage of the liquid metal, during and after solidification, to room-temperature size. Extra material is also left on surfaces to be machined or finished to provide removal material on the casting. Patterns also must be constructed with suitable *draft* angles to facilitate their removal from the mold medium. Patterns may be designated as *flatback*, where the largest two dimensions are in a single plane; *split*, which effectively separates to form flatback patterns; or *irregular parting*, which requires separation along two or more planes for removal of the pattern to produce the casting cavity. Any of these pattern types can be mounted on a matchplate for improved accuracy and faster production if justified by the needed quantity of castings. Pattern types of the loose variety are shown in Figure 6.13.

6.2.2.4 FLASKS

Flasks are open-faced containers that hold the molten medium as it is packed around the pattern. They are usually constructed in two parts: the upper-half *cope* and the lower-half *drag* (refer back to Figure 6.12), which are aligned by guide pins to ensure accurate positioning. The separation between the cope and drag establishes the parting line and when open permits removal of the pattern to leave the cavity whose walls form the casting when liquified material solidifies against it.

Some flasks, used most for small-quantity casting, are *permanent* and remain around the sand until after pouring has been completed. Others used for higher production quantities are removable and can be used over and over for construction of a number of molds before pouring is required. The removable flasks are of three styles: *snap* flasks, having hinged corners, that can be unwrapped from the mold; *pop-off* flasks that can be expanded on two diagonal corners to increase the length and width to allow removal; and *slip* flasks that are made with movable sand strips that project inside to obstruct sliding of the mold medium until they are withdrawn to permit removal of the flask from the mold. When molds are constructed with removable flasks, *jackets* are placed over them to maintain alignment during pouring.

6.2.2.5 SAND COMPACTION

Casting Quality Dependent on Proper Compaction. *Compaction, packing,* or *ramming* of sand into place in a mold is one of the greater labor-intensive and time-consuming phases of making castings. It also has considerable influence on the quality of the finished castings produced. Sand that is packed too lightly will be weak and may fall out of the mold, buckle, or crack, which will cause casting discontinuities. Loosely packed grains at the surface of the cavity may wash with the metal flow or may permit metal penetration with a resulting rough finish on the casting. Sand that is too tightly compacted will lack permeability, restrict gas flow, and be a source of blowholes, or may even prevent the cavity from completely filling. Too tightly packed sand may also lack collapsability so that as solidification occurs, cracks and tears in the casting may be caused by the inability of the sand to get out of the way of the shrinking metal. Each of the several available methods for compacting sand has advantages over the others and limitations that restrict its use.

Manual Ramming. Peen and butt rammers may be used on a bench or on the floor by manual operation, or, in the case of large molds, the work may be done with pneumatic rammers similar to an air hammer. *Peen* ramming involves the use of a rib-shaped edge to develop high-impact pressure and is used principally to pack sand between narrow vertical walls and around the edges of the flask. *Butt* ramming is done with a broader-faced tool for more uniform compaction of the sand throughout the mold.

Jolting and Squeezing Use Mechanical Energy. Most production work and a large part of work done in small quantities is performed by use of molding machines whose principal duty is that of sand compaction. They are designed to compact sand by either *jolting* or *squeezing,* or both methods may be combined in a single machine.

Jolt compaction involves the lifting of the table carrying the mold and dropping it against a solid obstruction. With the sudden stop, inertia forces cause the sand particles to compress together. Jolt compaction tends to pack the sand more tightly near the parting surface. For this reason, it is usually not too satisfactory when used alone with patterns that are high and project close to the mold surface.

On the other hand, *squeeze compaction,* applied by pushing a squeeze plate against the outside of the sand, tends to pack the sand more tightly at the surface. The combination of jolting and squeezing is frequently used to take advantages of each method, although when both the cope and drag are being made on the same machine, it may be impossible to jolt the cope half (the second half constructed) without damage to the drag.

Sand Slinging Limited to Large Molds. Foundries that manufacture quantities of large castings often use sand *slingers* to fill and compact the sand in large floor molds. The sand is thrown with high velocity in a steady stream by a rotating impeller and is compacted by impact as it fills up in the mold. Figure 6.14 illustrates common compaction methods.

6.2.2.6 CORES

Cores are bodies of mold material, usually in the form of inserts that exclude metal flow to form internal surfaces in a casting. The body is considered to be a core when made of green sand only if it extends through the cavity to form a hole in the casting. Green sand cores are formed in the pattern with the regular molding procedure.

Cores Need Strength for Handling. The vast majority of cores are made of dry sand and contain little or no clay. A nearly pure sand is combined with additives that burn out after pouring to promote collapsability and with binders to hold the particles together until after solidification takes place.

Final Core Properties Very Important. The properties needed in core sand are similar to those required for molding sand, with some taking on greater importance because of differences in the cores' position and use. Most cores are baked for drying and development of dry strength, but they must also have sufficient green strength to be handled before baking.

The *dry strength* of a finished core must be sufficient enough to withstand its own weight without sagging in the mold, and it must be strong enough so that its own buoyancy, as liquid metal rises around it, will not cause it to break or shift.

Permeability is important with all molding sands but is especially so with core sand because cores are often almost completely surrounded by metal, and a relatively free passage is essential for the gases to escape through core prints or other small areas.

Collapsability is likewise important because of this metal enclosure. Ideally, a core should collapse immediately after metal solidification takes place. In addition to not interfering with shrinkage of the casting, it is important in many cases that cores collapse completely before final cooling so that they can be removed from inside castings in which they are almost totally enclosed. For example, cores used to form the channels in a hot-water radiator or the water openings in an internal combustion engine would be almost impossible to remove unless they lost their strength and became free sand grains. The casting metal must supply the heat for the final burning out of the additives and the binding material.

When a substantial portion of a core is enclosed in a casting, radiography is frequently used to determine whether or not the core shifted during casting, or to be certain that all the core material has been successfully removed after casting.

Chaplets. Very large or long, slender cores that might give way under pressure of the flowing metal are sometimes given additional support by the use of *chaplets*. Chaplets are small metal supports with broad-surfaced ends, usually made of the same metal as that to be poured, that can be set between the mold cavity and the core. Chaplets become part of the casting after they have served their function of supporting cores while the metal is liquid.

NDT may be necessary for castings requiring the use of chaplets. One potential problem is that the chaplets may not fuse with the base metal due to the unsuitability of the material to do so. In addition, shrink cavities may form during cooling, porosity may form from moisture condensation, and nonfusing may occur from too low a pouring temperature to melt the surface of the chaplet. Radiography of the finished casting can reveal discontinuities surrounding chaplet regions and can indicate whether the chaplets completely fused with the base metal.

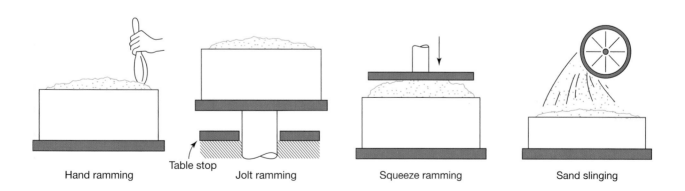

Hand ramming   Table stop   Jolt ramming   Squeeze ramming   Sand slinging

Figure 6.14: Common sand-compaction methods.

6.2.2.7 GREEN SAND ADVANTAGES AND LIMITATIONS

Green Sand Process Extremely Flexible. For most metals and most sizes and shapes of castings, *green sand molding* is the most economical of all the molding processes. Green sand can be worked manually or mechanically and, because very little special equipment is necessary, can be easily and cheaply used for a great variety of products. The sand is reusable with only slight additions necessary to correct its composition. In terms of cost, the green sand process can be outdone only when the quantity of identical castings is large enough that reduced operational costs for some other process will compensate for a higher intitial investment or when the limitations of the green sand process prevent consistent meeting of required qualities.

Green Sand Not Universally Applicable. One of the limitations of green sand is its low strength in thin sections. It is not satisfactory for casting thin fins or long, thin projections. Green sand also tends to crush and shift under the weight of very heavy sections. This same weakness makes the casting of intricate shapes difficult also. The moisture present in green sand produces steam when contacted by hot metal. Inability of the steam and other gases to escape causes problems with some casting designs, resulting in blowhole damage. The dimensional accuracy of green sand castings is limited. Even with small castings, it is seldom that dimensions can be held closer together than ± 0.5 mm (0.02 in.); with large castings, ±3 mm (1/8 in.) or greater tolerances are necessary.

6.2.2.8 DRY SAND MOLDS

Elimination of Moisture Reduces Casting Discontinuities. Improvement in casting qualities can sometimes be obtained by use of *dry sand molds*. The molds are made of green sand modified to favor the dry properties and then dried in an oven. The absence of moisture eliminates the formation of water vapor and reduces the type of casting discontinuities that are due to gas formation. The cost of heat, the time required for drying the mold, and the difficulty of handling heavy molds without damage make the process expensive compared to green sand molding, and it is used mostly when steam formation from the moisture present would be a serious problem.

Skin Drying—Substitute for Oven Drying. Most of the benefits of dry sand molds can be obtained by *skin drying* molds to depths from a fraction of a centimeter (inch) to 2.5 cm (1 in.). With the mold open, the inside surfaces are subjected to heat from torches, radiant lamps, hot dry air, or electric heating elements to form a dry insulating skin around the mold cavity. Skin-dried molds can be stored only for short periods of time before pouring, since the water in the main body of the mold will redistribute itself and remoisturize the inside skin.

6.2.2.9 FLOOR AND PIT MOLDS

Large Molds Difficult to Handle. Although the number of extremely large castings is relatively small, molds must be constructed for one, five, ten, and occasionally, even as much as several hundred metric ton castings. Such molds cannot be moved about, and the high hydrostatic pressures established by high columns of liquid metal require special mold construction stronger than that used for small castings. Floor molds made in the pouring position are built in large flasks. The mold can be opened by lifting the cope with an overhead crane, but the cope flask usually must be constructed with special support bars to prevent the mold material from dropping free when it is lifted.

Drag of Pit Molds Below Floor Level. Pit molds use the four walls of a pit as a flask for the drag section. The cope may be an assembly of core sand or may be made in a large flask similar to that used for a floor mold. The mold material for these large sizes is usually loam—50% sand and 50% clay—plus water. The mold structure is often strengthened by inserting bricks or other ceramic material as a large part of its substance.

6.2.2.10 SHELL MOLDS

Shell molding is a fairly recent development that, as far as casting is concerned, can be considered a precision process. Dimensions can be held within a few hundredths of a millimeter (thousandths of an inch) in many cases to eliminate or reduce machining that might be necessary otherwise and to decrease the overall cost of manufacturing. The cost of the process itself, however, is relatively high, and large quantities are necessary for economical operation.

Sand Bonded with Thermosetting Plastic. The mold is made by covering a heated metal pattern with sand that is mixed with small particles of a thermosetting plastic. The heat of the pattern causes the mixture to adhere and semicures the plastic for a short depth. The thin shell thus made is baked in place or stripped from the pattern, further cured by baking at 300 °C (572 °F), and then cemented to its mating half to complete the mold proper. Because the shell is thin, approximately 3 mm (0.1 in.), its resistance to springing apart is low; it may be necessary to back it up with loose sand or shot to take the pressures set up by filling with liquid metal. The sand particles are tightly held in the plastic bond. As erosion and metal penetration are minor problems, high-quality surface finishes, in addition to good dimensional control, are obtained from shell molding.

6.2.3 EXPENDABLE PLASTER MOLD CASTING

Molds made of plaster of paris with additives, such as talc, asbestos, silica flour, sand, and other materials to vary the mold properties, are used only for casting nonferrous metals. Plaster molds will produce good quality finish and good dimensional accuracy as well as intricate detail. The procedure is similar to that used in dry sand molding. The plaster material must be given time to solidify after being coated over the pattern and is completely oven dried after removal before it is poured.

Casting Cools Slowly. The dry mold is a good insulator, which is an advantage but has a disadvantage. The insulating property permits lower pouring rates with less superheat in the liquid metal. These contribute to less shrinkage, less gas entrapment from turbulence, and greater opportunity for evolved gases to escape from the metal before solidification. On the other hand, because of slow cooling, plaster molds should not be used for applications in which large grain growth is a serious problem.

6.2.4 INVESTMENT (LOST WAX) CASTING

The Working Pattern Is Destroyed During Investment Casting. *Investment casting* (Figure 6.15) is also known as *precision casting* and as the *lost wax process*. The process has been used for at least 3500 years for making small ornamental objects. In modern times, the process has been used in dentistry and jewelry making. A new wax pattern is needed for every piece cast. For single-piece casting, the wax pattern may be made directly by impressions as in dentistry, by molding or sculpturing as in the making of statuary, or by any method that will shape the wax to the form desired in the casting. Shrinkage allowances must be made for the wax, if it is done hot, and for the contraction of the metal that will be poured in the cavity formed by the wax. Reentrant angles in the casting are possible because the wax will not be removed from the cavity in solid form. Variations of this process involve the use of frozen mercury or low-melting-point thermoplastics for the pattern.

Duplicate Parts Start with a Master Pattern. Multiple production requires starting with a master pattern about which a metal die is made. The metal die can be used for making any number of wax patterns. A gating system must be part of the wax pattern and may be produced in the metal die or attached after removal from

1. Wax pattern

2. Coat with refractory slurry

3. Reinforce with plaster backing (investment)

4. Oven dry to liquify or vaporize pattern and dry mold

5. Pour and metal

6. Remove investment material

Figure 6.15: Steps for investment casting.

the die. For precision parts, the wax patterns are carefully finished by highly skilled workers. When complete, the wax pattern is dipped in a slurry of fine refractory material and then encased in the investment material (plaster of paris or mixtures of ceramic materials with high refractory properties). The wax is then removed from the mold by heating to liquify the wax and cause it to run out to be reclaimed. Investment molds are preheated to suitable temperatures for pouring, usually between 600 °C and 1100 °C (1112 °F and 2012 °F), depending upon the metal that is to fill the mold. After pouring and solidification, the investment is broken away to free the casting for removal of the gating system and final cleaning.

Process Limited to Small Castings. Most investment castings are small castings, usually not over 4 kg (8.8 lb) in weight, but many foundries are capable of making parts in the 9 to 54 kg (20 to 120 lb) range. The largest part known to have been made by the lost wax method is about 454 kg (1000 lb). The principal advantage of the process is its ability to produce intricate castings with close dimensional tolerances. High-melting-temperature materials that are difficult to cast by other methods can be cast this way because the investment material of the mold can be chosen for refractory properties that can withstand these higher temperatures. In many cases, pressure is applied to the molten metal to improve flow and densities so that very thin sections can be poured by this method.

High Quality versus High Cost. It can easily be realized, by examination of the procedures that must be followed for investment molding and casting, that the costs of this process are high. Accuracy of the finished product, which may eliminate or reduce machining problems, can more than compensate for the high casting cost with some materials and for some applications.

A number of important parts, some of new or exotic materials, are presently manufactured by investment casting. Many of these, such as high-strength alloy turbine buckets for gas turbines, require NDT inspection by radiographic and penetrant methods to ensure that only parts of high quality get into service.

6.2.5 LOST FOAM CASTING

The lost foam casting process was invented in 1964. However, the first product actually produced by the process, a cylinder head for 4.3 L V-6 diesel engine, wasn't made until 1981. Lost foam is similar to lost wax. A foam such as polystyrene is used instead of wax. Molten metal vaporizes the foam so there is no need to melt it out of the mold as is done with wax. In a variation called *foamcast*, the polystyrene is fully burned out of the mold before metal is poured. Because polystyrene is 92% carbon by weight, the original lost foam procedure should not be used for ultra-low carbon stainless steels and other materials where carbon pickup would be unacceptable.

For small castings, this process can typically achieve tolerances of ±0.125 to 0.25 mm (0.005 to 0.010 in.), compared to ±0.75 mm (0.030 in.) for green sand casting and ±0.075 mm (0.003 to 0.005 in.) for lost wax castings. Tolerances increase with increasing size of the part.

6.2.6 DIE CASTING

Die casting differs from permanent mold casting in that pressure is applied to the liquid metal to cause it to flow rapidly and uniformly into the cavity of the mold or die. The die is similar to that used for permanent molding. It is made of metal, again usually cast iron or steel; has parting lines along which it can be opened for extraction of the casting; and is constructed with small draft angles on the walls to reduce the work of extraction and extend the life of the die. Vents, in the form of grooves or small holes, also are present to permit the escape of air as metal fills the die.

Hot Chamber Die Casting. The machines in which the dies are used, however, are quite different because, in addition to closing and opening the die parts, they must supply liquid metal under pressure to fill the cavity. The *hot chamber die-casting process*, shown in Figure 6.16, keeps metal melted in a chamber through which a piston moves into a cylinder to build up pressure, forcing the metal into the die.

Machines Limited to Low Pressures. Because the piston and the portions subjected to pressure are heated to the melting temperature of the casting metal, hot chamber machines are restricted to lower pressures than those with lower operating temperatures. Although it is a high-speed, low-cost process, the low pressures do not produce the high-density, high-quality castings often desired. In addition, iron absorbed by aluminum in a hot chamber machine would be detrimental to its properties. Pressures as high as 14 MPa (2000 psi) are used in the hot chamber process to force-fill the mold.

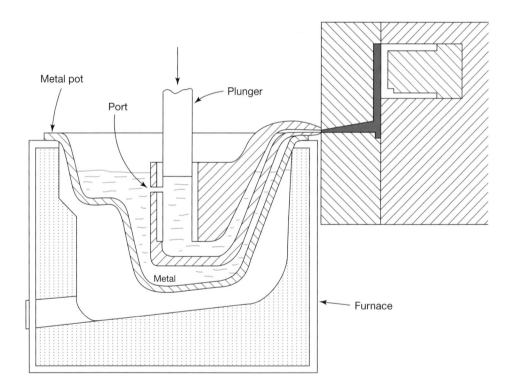

Figure 6.16: Hot chamber die casting.

Cold Chamber Die Casting. With the *cold chamber die-casting process*, as shown in Figure 6.17, molten metal is poured into the shot chamber, and the piston advances to force the metal into the die. Aluminum, copper, and magnesium alloys are die cast by this method with liquid pressures as high as 210 MPa (30 000 psi).

Casting Quality High. Sections as thin as 0.4 mm (0.016 in.) with tolerances as small as 2.05 mm (0.002 in.) can be cast with very good surface finish by this pressure process. The material properties are likely to be high because the pressure improves the metal density (fewer voids), and fast cooling by the metal molds produces good strength properties. Other than high initial cost, the principal limiting feature of die casting is that it cannot be used for very high-strength materials. However, low-temperature alloys are continually being developed, and, with their improvement, die casting is being used more and more.

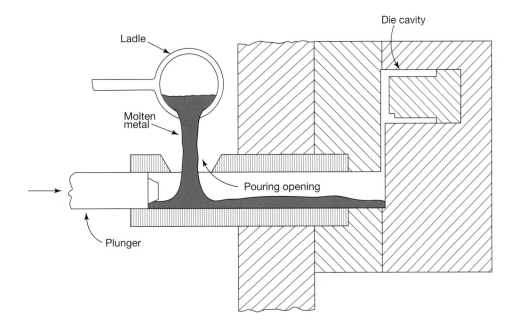

Figure 6.17: Cold chamber die casting.

6.2.7 CASTING USING CENTRIFUGAL FORCE

Several procedures are classed as *centrifugal casting* (Figure 6.18). All of the procedures make use of a rotating mold to develop centrifugal force acting on the metal to improve its density toward the outside of the mold.

True Centrifugal Casting—Hollow Product. The true centrifugal casting process shapes the outside of the product with a mold but depends upon centrifugal force developed by spinning the mold to form the inside surface by forcing the liquid metal to assume a cylindrical shape symmetric about the mold axis. At one time the principal product was cast iron sewer pipe, but uses of centrifugal castings include shafts for large turbines, propeller shafts for ships, and high-pressure piping. Because of the critical nature of some applications, NDT may be necessary to check the wall thickness and quality of the product material. The columnar grain structure may produce problems in applying nondestructive tests.

Semicentrifugal Casting—Solid Product. A similar process, which may be termed *semicentrifugal casting*, consists of revolving a symmetric mold about the axis of the mold's cavity and pouring that cavity full. The density of a casting made in this way will vary, with dense, strong metal around the outside and more porous, weaker metal at the center. The variation in density is not great, but the fast filling of the external portion of the mold cavity produces particularly sound metal. Wheels, pulleys, gear blanks, and other shapes of this kind may be made in this way to obtain maximum metal properties near the outside periphery.

Centrifuge Casting—Multiple Product. A third type of casting using centrifugal force can be termed *centrifuge casting*. In this process, a number of equally spaced mold cavities are arranged in a circle about a central pouring sprue. The mold may

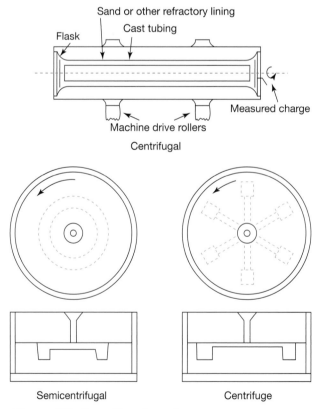

Figure 6.18: Centrifugal casting.

be single or stacked with a number of layers arranged vertically about a common sprue. The mold is revolved with the sprue as an axis, and, when poured, centrifugal force helps the normal hydrostatic pressure force metal into the spinning mold cavities. Gases tend to be forced out of the metal, which improves metal quality.

6.2.8 OTHER PERMANENT-MOLD CASTING PROCESSES

Metal Molds Used Mostly for Low-Melting-Point Alloys. *Permanent molds* may be reused many times. Their life will depend, to a large extent, upon the intricacy of the casting design and the temperature of the metal that is poured into the mold. Cast iron and steel are the most common materials with which the mold is made. Permanent mold casting is used most for the shaping of aluminum, copper, magnesium, and zinc alloys. Cast iron is occasionally poured in permanent molds that have much lower mold life because of the higher operating temperature. Satisfactory results require operation of the process with a uniform cycle time to maintain the operating temperature within a small range. Initial use of new molds often demands experimentation to determine the most suitable pouring and operating temperatures as well as to correct the position and size of the small vent grooves cut at the mold parting line to allow the escape of gases.

High Accuracies and Good Finishes. The cost of the molds, sometimes referred to as dies, and the operating mechanism by which they are opened and closed is high, but permanent mold casting has several advantages over sand casting for high-quantity production. Dimensional tolerances are more consistent and can he held to approximately ±0.25 mm (0.1 in.). The higher conductance of heat through the metal mold causes a chilling action, producing finer grain structure and harder, stronger castings.

The minimum practical section thickness for permanent molding is about 3 mm (1/8 in.). The majority of castings are less than 300 mm (12 in.) in diameter and 10 kg (22 lb) in weight. The process is used in the manufacture of automobile cylinder heads, automobile pistons, low-horsepower engine connecting rods, and many other nonferrous alloy castings needed in large quantity.

6.3 OTHER SOLIDIFICATION PROCESSES

6.3.1 SINGLE CRYSTAL PRODUCTION

Used to Produce Silicon Wafers. The best-known application for single crystal production is probably silicon wafers for semiconductors. There are a few single crystal industrial products that might be subject to NDT.

Various proprietary fabrication techniques are used. All involve very carefully controlled heating and cooling so that the material solidifies progressively such that there are no grain boundaries. The resulting structure is not as strong as a polycrystalline version of the same composition and dimensions, but it is exceptionally stable over a wide temperature range and very resistant to high-temperature creep. It is also possible to control the directional mechanical properties of a part by growing the crystal with a desired grain orientation. The process is used for small components that must be very stable while operating at extreme temperatures.

6.3.2 RAPID SOLIDIFICATION

Energy in the form of heat added to a metal changes the force system that ties the atoms together. Eventually, as heat is added, the ties that bind the atoms are broken, and the atoms are free to move about as a liquid. Solidification is a reverse procedure, as shown in Figure 6.19, and heat given up by the molten material must be dissipated. If consideration is being given evenly to a pure metal, the freezing point occurs at a single temperature for the entire liquid. As the temperature goes down, the atoms become less and less mobile and finally assume their position with other atoms in the space lattice of the unit cell, which grows into a crystal.

Crystal Growth Starts at the Surface. In the case of a casting, the heat is being given up to the mold material in contact with the outside of the molten mass. The first portion of the material to cool to the freezing temperature will be the outside of the liquid, and a large number of these unit cells may form simultaneously around the interface surface. Each unit cell becomes a point of nucleation for the growth of a metal crystal, and, as the other atoms cool, they will assume their proper position in the space lattice and add to the unit cell. As the crystals form, the heat of fusion is released and thereby increases the amount of heat that must be dissipated. Before further freezing can occur, temperature gradients are reduced and the freezing process retarded. The size of crystal growth will be limited by interference with other crystals because of the large umber of unit cell nuclei produced at one time with random orientation. The first grains to form in the skin of a solidifying casting are likely to be of a fine equiaxed type with random orientation and shapes.

Second Phase Slower. After formation of the solid skin, grain growth is likely to be more orderly, providing the section thickness and mass are large enough to cause a significant difference in freezing time between the outside shell and the interior metal. Points of nucleation will continue to form around the outside of the liquid as the temperature is decreased. The rate of decrease, however, continues to get lower for a number of reasons: the heat of fusion is added; the heat must flow through the already formed solid metal; the mold mass has been heated and has less temperature differential with the metal; or the mold may have become dried out to the point that it acts as an insulating blanket around the casting.

Second Phase Also Directional. Crystal growth will have the least interference from other growing crystals in a direction toward the hot zone. The crystals, therefore, grow in a columnar shape toward the center of the heavy sections of the casting.

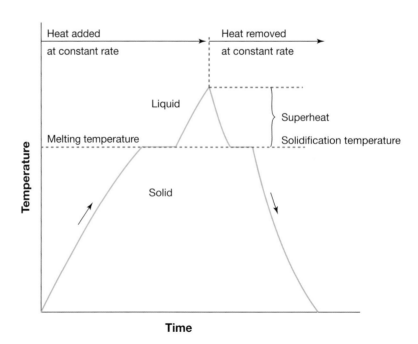

Figure 6.19: Heating and cooling curves for temperature increase above the melting point for a metal.

With the temperature gradient being small, growth may occur on the sides of these columns, producing structures known as *dendrites* (Figure 6.20). This pine-tree-shaped first solidification seals off small pockets of liquid to freeze later. Evidence of this kind of crystal growth is often difficult to find when dealing with pure metals but can readily be detected with most alloy metals.

Third Phase. As the wall thickness of frozen metal increases, the cooling rate of the remaining liquid decreases even further, and the temperature of the remaining material tends to equalize. Relatively uniform temperature distribution and slow cooling permit random nucleation at fewer points than occurs with rapid cooling, and the grains grow to large sizes.

Grain Characteristics Influenced by Cooling Rates. As shown in Figures 6.21 and 6.22, it would be expected in castings of heavy sections that the first grains to form around the outside would be fine equiaxed. Columnar and dendritic structure would be present in directions toward the last portions to cool for distances, depending upon the material and the cooling rate under which it is solidified. Finally, the center of the heavy sections would be the weakest structure, made up of large equiaxed grains. Changes in this grain-growth

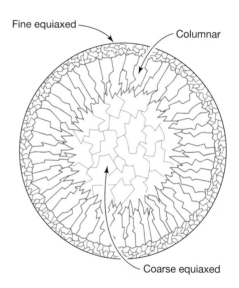

Figure 6.21: Typical grain structure from solidification of a heavy section.

Figure 6.20: Schematic sketch of dendritic growth.

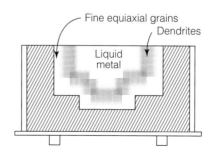

Figure 6.22: Grain formation in a heavy sand casting.

pattern can be caused by a number of factors affecting the cooling rate. Thin sections that cool very quickly will develop neither the columnar nor the coarse structure. Variable section sizes and changes of size and shape may cause interference and variations of the grain-structure pattern. Different casting procedures and the use of different mold materials can affect grain size and shape through their influence on the cooling rate.

Results of NDT for internal discontinuities may be difficult to analyze because of effects from variable grain size in massive castings. Large grains cause diffraction effects with radiographic methods, and reflection from grain boundaries causes problems with ultrasonic testing. Special techniques that minimize these effects may be necessary to test large-grained castings.

Eutectics Similar to Pure Metals. Eutectic alloys freeze in much the same manner as pure metal. By definition, a *eutectic alloy* is one for which solidification takes place at a single temperature that is lower than that for the individual components of the alloy. The grain size produced with a eutectic alloy is smaller than the grain size of a pure metal under the same conditions. It is believed that this is due to a smaller temperature gradient and the formation of a greater number of nucleation points for the start of grains.

Noneutectics Freeze through a Temperature Range. The majority of products are made from *noneutectic alloys*. Instead of freezing at a single temperature, as do pure metals and eutectic alloys, noneutectic alloys freeze over a temperature range. As the temperature of the molten material is decreased, solidification starts at the surface and progresses toward the interior where the metal is cooling more slowly. Partial solidification may progress for some distance before the temperature at the surface is reduced low enough for full solidification to take place. The material at temperatures between those at which solidification begins and ends is partially frozen with pockets of liquid remaining to produce a mixture that is of mushy consistency and relatively low strength. Figure 6.23 is a graphic representation of this kind of freezing. The duration of this condition and the dimensions of the space

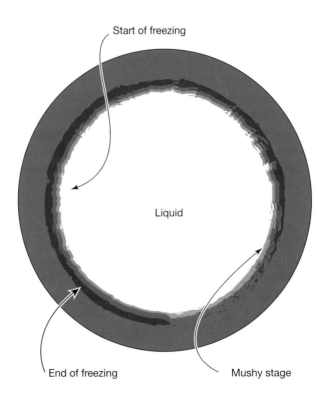

Figure 6.23: Process of freezing.

between the start and finish of freezing are functions of the solidification temperature range of the alloy material and the thermal gradient. The greater the solidification temperature range (in most cases meaning the greater the variation away from the eutectic composition) and the smaller the temperature gradient, the greater the size and duration of this mushy stage.

Segregation. Dendritic grain growth is much more evident in the noneutectic alloy metals than in pure metal. When more than one element is present, segregation of two types occurs during solidification. The first solids to freeze will be richer in one component than the average composition. The change caused by this *ingot-type segregation* is small, but, as the first solids rob the remaining material, a gradual change of composition occurs as freezing progresses to the center. The other type of segregation is more localized and makes the dendritic structure easy to detect in alloy materials. The small liquid pockets, enclosed by the first dendritic solid, supply more than their share of one component to the already frozen material. This difference in composition shows up readily by difference in chemical reaction if the material is polished and etched for grain examination.

6.4 QUALITY OF THE CASTING PRODUCT

6.4.1 COMPARISON OF QUALITY OF DIFFERENT CASTING PRACTICES

"Quality" means different things to different people and in different situations. One definition is "conformance to specifications." One technician might define quality as tighter dimensional tolerances for one casting, increased strength for another, and increased corrosion resistance for a third. The variety of casting methods and techniques in use today has come about because of the divergent needs of a wide variety of customers. Some new practices have made it possible to produce parts that actually could not have been made previously. Others have been developed to reduce manufacturing costs by replacing several components with a single casting. Sand casting cannot match the dimensional tolerances and surface finish of lost wax casting, but it is still clearly better for making some parts. Often there are two or even three possible methods for making a particular casting. Choosing the best one requires a careful study of requirements, the experience of potential vendors, initial investment, planned length of production run and quantities required, and NDT needed to ensure surface and internal discontinuities are within required limits.

6.4.2 SURFACE FINISH AND INTERNAL QUALITY OF CASTINGS

As mentioned earlier, metals are superheated above their melting temperature to increase their fluidity and to allow for heat losses before they are in their final position in the mold. For good castings, the metal must be at the correct superheat at the time it is poured into the mold. If the temperature is too low, misruns and cold shuts will show up as discontinuities in the casting, or the metal may even freeze in the ladle. If the temperature at pouring is too high, the metal may penetrate the sand and cause very rough finishes on the casting. Pouring temperatures that are too high may cause excessive porosity or increased gas development, leading to voids and increased shrinkage from thermal gradients that disrupt proper directional solidification. A high pouring temperature increases the mold temperature, decreases the temperature differential, and reduces the rate at which the casting cools. More time at high temperature allows greater gain growth so that the casting will cool with a weaker, coarser grain structure.

Typical discontinuities found in castings are shown by number in Figure 6.24 and are defined as follows:

1. **Porosity:** usually caused by the release of dissolved gases as the molten metal cools, creating bubbles or pores. Pores are generally small in diameter with smooth surfaces. Multiple pores in one area are called cluster porosity, and if the porosity is moving as the metal cools, the porosity may form an elongated void commonly called piping or wormhole porosity, as shown.

2. **Gas holes:** created in the same manner as porosity but are larger in diameter and generally tend to be isolated or limited in the number found in any one area.

3. **Inclusions:** areas where nonmetallic materials such as slag or sand are trapped in the material as the metal cools.

4. **Hot tears:** cracklike tears that occur when the material starts to contract during the initial cooling phase, just below the solidification temperature. If the hardening material is restrained by the mold at that point, the material may tear, usually at changes in section where a stress riser already exists.

5. **Cracks:** irregularly shaped, linear discontinuities (fractures) that can be caused when internal stresses exceed the strength of the material. In the casting process, stress cracks can occur due to contraction, residual stress, and shock, or due to inservice stresses.

6. **Shrinkage cavities:** occur when the liquid metal contracts and solidifies during cooling. If there is not enough molten metal to offset the resulting contraction, the metal may pull apart, creating a void or cavity in the solidified material. These typically occur where additional molten metal cannot be fed in quickly enough to offset the contraction or where there are variations in section thickness.

7. **Air pockets:** occur when the air in the unfilled mold cannot escape as the molten metal is added. These generally are found just beneath the top surface of the object.

8. **Cold shuts:** areas where part of the filler material solidifies before the mold cavity is completely filled. As additional molten material reaches the already cooled section of metal, it may not fuse together, forming a tight line of disbond between the two segments of metal. In the welding process, this would be considered lack of fusion.

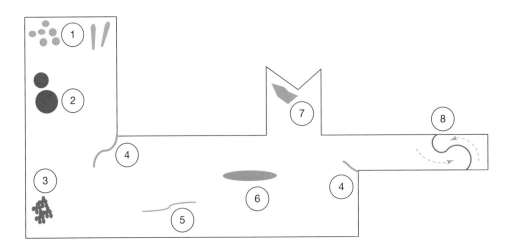

Figure 6.24: Casting discontinuities.

6.5 THE FUTURE OF CASTINGS

Continuous Improvement. There are ongoing improvements in most types of castings methods. Much research and development is directed toward saving costs by replacing multi-component welded assemblies with single castings to reduce weight and labor costs. Aluminum castings are replacing some steel forgings in automobiles to help reach future fuel economy goals. Improvement in dimensional tolerances of castings receives a great deal of attention. These developments are resulting in more complex castings with more restrictive internal quality requirements, providing a double challenge for NDT.

7 Metal Forming

7.1 INTRODUCTION TO FORMING

Manufacturing consists of converting some raw material, which may be in rough, unrefined shape, into a usable product. The selection of the material and the processes to be used seldom can be separated. Although in a few cases some unusual property requirements dictate a specific material, generally a wide choice exists in the combination of material and processing that will satisfy the product requirements. The choice usually becomes one of economic comparison. In any case, a material is usually selected first, sometimes rather arbitrarily, and a process must then be chosen. Processing consists of one or many separate steps producing changes in shape, properties, or both.

7.1.1 PLASTIC DEFORMATION

Shape Changes. Shape changing of most materials can be accomplished with the material in one of several different forms or states: liquid, solid, or plastic. Melting of a material and control of its shape while it solidifies is referred to as *casting*. Reshaping of the material in the plastic or semisolid form is accomplished by molding, forging, pressworking, rolling, or extruding. Shaping by metal removal or

"Shape changing of most materials can be accomplished with the material in one of several different forms or states ..."

separation in the solid state is commonly performed to produce product shapes. If the removed material is in chip form, the process is machining. The joining of solid parts by welding usually involves small, localized areas that are allowed to solidify to produce a complete union between solid parts.

7.1.2 EFFECT ON TEMPERATURE AND DEFORMATION RATE

Energy Form. The material condition and the energy form used to effect shape changes may vary. As noted, the material may be in a liquid, solid, or plastic form. The energy may be supplied in the form of heat, mechanical power, chemical reaction, electrical energy, or, as in one of the newest procedures, light. In nearly every instance, one principal objective is change of shape, but usually part of the energy is consumed in property changes, particularly in those processes involving state changes or solid deformation. Different materials react differently to the same energy system, and the same materials react differently to different energy systems.

Process Effect on Properties. Many concepts and fundamentals in reference to materials are common to different kinds of processes. When studied in connection with the material, these concepts, then, can be applied regardless of the kind of process by which the material is treated. For example, the metallurgical changes that take place during solidification during casting are of the same nature as those that take place in fusion welding.

7.1.3 NET SHAPE MANUFACTURING

Auxiliary Steps. The completion of a product for final use generally includes the various finishing procedures apart from basic shape-changing processes. The dimensions and properties that are produced by any process are subject to variation, and, in practically all cases, some nondestructive inspection is necessary for controlling the process and for ensuring that the final product meets certain specifications as to size and other properties. As one of the final steps, or sometimes as an intermediate step, control of properties by *heat treatment* or other means may be necessary. The final steps may also require surface changes for appearance, wear properties, corrosion protection, or other uses. These steps may involve only the base material or may require the addition of paints, platings, or other coatings.

Few finished products are constructed of single pieces of material because of the impracticality of producing them at a reasonable cost. Also, it is frequently necessary that properties that can be obtained only from different materials be combined into a single unit. The result is that most manufactured articles consist of *assemblies* of a number of separate parts. The joining of these parts can be accomplished in many ways, with the best method being dependent on the factors of shape, size, and material properties involved in the particular design.

7.2 BULK DEFORMATION PROCESSES

Although some of the softer metals that can be found in a relatively ductile condition in nature, such as copper, lead, gold, and silver, were originally wrought by hammering methods, most shaping of metal articles in the early days of manufacturing was performed by casting processes. As indicated in Chapter 6, casting is still an important shaping process and is frequently the cheapest and most satisfactory method for producing a useful shape from some materials.

Some Serious Limitations in Casting Processes. Some limitations exist, however, that discourage universal use of cast metal products. Picture, for instance, the problems associated with casting thin sheets of large area in any kind of material. Even with thicknesses of 25 mm (1 in.) or more, the problems of obtaining uniform thickness and properties over large areas are enormous. Unfortunately, many of the materials that have the best castability have other properties that are unsatisfactory for many applications. Porosity and associated problems reduce strength. Increased brittleness, leakiness, and poor appearance are faults commonly associated with cast materials.

Deformation Improves Properties. With many metals, the internal structure to provide the best properties can be developed only by deforming the material in the solid state, usually by a process involving cold working. The deformation processes, cold or hot, can often be used to provide the double benefits of property improvement and shape changing at the same time.

Even with higher costs, the value of improved properties is so great that approximately 80% of iron-based metals are finish processed as wrought material. Although nearly all metals are and can be cast in the making of some products, a situation similar to that for iron-based metals exists for aluminum-based, copper-based, and other metallic materials, and large percentages of each are deformation worked for improvement of their shapes, dimensions, and properties.

Most Output Requires Further Processing. Most of the output of the mill is in shapes that become raw material for further processing in smaller quantities at some specific user's plant. Typical products of this class include foil for packaging operations, cold-rolled sheet for pressworking operations, bar stock for machined parts, and rough-rolled billets for forging operations.

End Product by Secondary Deformation. The second group of deformation operations involves those that are product oriented and are usually performed on a smaller scale in plants fabricating finished products. For practically all of these operations, the raw material is bar or sheet stock that is produced in large quantities as a mill operation. For example, the most convenient raw material for a drop-forging operation might be a 150 mm (6 in.) length of 13 cm² (2 in.²) hot-rolled steel. This would be cut from a long length of 13 cm² (2 in.²) hot-rolled bar. The same size hot-rolled bar might be the most convenient size for other fabricators for forgings, for parts that are to be machined, or for welded assemblies. It is often economical to apply NDT to products intended for secondary operations in order to ensure that prior processing discontinuities are not carried forward into secondary processing. The discontinuities might include seams, cracks, and other internal discontinuities of significant size.

Few Mills—Many Fabricators. These smaller fabricators are much greater in number than are producers of mill products. The equipment for the secondary operations is lighter, the initial cost of the equipment is generally less, and the total tonnage of metals used by any individual fabricator is small compared to the output of a mill.

7.2.1 FORGING AND ALLIED OPERATIONS

With the exception of some tube-making operations and some cold-finish rolling and extrusion, especially on ferrous metals, the operations so far described are all performed almost exclusively in large mills. Mill products usually represent only an intermediate stage of manufacture with no specific finished product in mind. Of the remaining deformation operations, those performed primarily on flat sheet metal will be discussed later in this chapter.

Forging Is Three-Dimensional. In mill operations, the primary shape control is over the uniform cross-sectional shape of a product. In press operations on sheet metal, the thickness of the metal is not directly controlled by the operation. *Forging* operations exhibit three-dimensional control of the shape. For most of these operations, the final shape of the product is forged, and further finishing operations are necessary only because of accuracy limitations of the process.

Forging Dies May Be Open or Closed. The purpose of forging is to confine the metal under sufficient pressure to cause plastic flow. In *open die forging,* the metal is alternately confined in different directions with the final result that three-dimensional control is gained. With *closed impression dies,* the work material is fully confined at least at the completion of the operation in a manner similar to casting except for the state of the material. As in metal mold casting, draft angles are required, and there are similar shape restrictions based on removing the part from the die.

High Compressive Loads Required. The load requirements for forging have led to several means for applying the pressure. In those forging methods in which the metal is worked throughout at the same time, the flow can be produced by constant squeezing pressure or by impact. Because of the large amounts of work energy required and the need to exceed the yield strength throughout the material at the same time, these operations are frequently done hot, and even then the equipment is massive compared to the size of the workpiece, particularly when constant pressure is supplied. For localized flow, the yield strength must generally be exceeded only on small areas at a time, either because of the progressive nature of some rolling-type operations or because of the need to reorient the workpiece periodically to present new areas to be loaded, as in hammer forging or rotary swaging.

7.2.1.1 NDT OF FORGINGS

Because large volumes of metal are deformed and moved during any forging process, the probability of discontinuity formation can be relatively high. Forgings done at improper temperatures or excessive pressures can exhibit a variety of discontinuities, both surface and subsurface. Because of the improvement in properties and controlled directionality offered by forgings, they are often used in lightweight critical structures such as aircraft and missiles. Even in less demanding applications, forgings are generally selected where high strength and/or directionality is used to advantage.

With the capabilities of NDT to aid in the assurance of high quality, safety, and reliability, forgings are frequently inspected by various methods of NDT. Ultrasonic testing is used principally for detection of internal discontinuities, while magnetic particle and penetrant methods are used for detecting surface discontinuities. Since many forging discontinuities can be tightly closed and in many cases lie in unexpected orientations due to the large deformations typical in forgings, much care and attention to technique must be applied in the NDT of forgings. Forgings often present challenging NDT problems because of the odd shapes and varying cross sections commonly encountered. Personnel responsible for developing and directing the NDT of forgings must have knowledge of the forging process in considerable detail if reliable inspection is expected.

7.2.1.2 OPEN DIE FORGING

Blacksmithing—A Manual Operation. When the quantity of parts to be manufactured is small and the cost of tooling must be kept low, *blacksmith* or *hammer* forging may be used to alter the shape of the material. One of the simplest examples is the manufacture of a horseshoe from bar stock by using a hammer and anvil with manual power and manipulation. While the village blacksmith is no longer prevalent, this method still finds wide use industrially for the manufacture of special tools and low-quantity products that are often of an experimental nature. Accuracy and shape of the product are greatly dependent on the operator's skill. Because of the close association with the human element, duplication accuracy is limited, and large quantities can seldom be economically produced. The manual operation of black-smith forging can therefore be used only for relatively light work and is almost always performed hot.

Power Assist for Heavy Work. Hammer forging is an extension of blacksmithing for larger workpieces in which power is supplied by pneumatic, hydraulic, or mechanical hammers. The operator is still responsible for positioning the work under the hammer but may lay special tools over the hammer faces for producing some shapes. For very heavy workpieces, mechanical supports and handling devices are frequently used as aids.

7.2.1.3 CLOSED DIE FORGING

Closed Dies Expensive. Most forging was done with flat-faced hammers until just prior to the Civil War when matched metal dies were developed. The process was first used in the production of firearms. With flat-faced hammers and simple groov-ing tools, no particular connection exists between the tooling and a specific product, and it is feasible to forge even a single part. Matched metal dies, like patterns for castings, must be made for each shape to be forged and become feasible only when the tooling investment can be divided among a sufficiently large number of parts.

Forging and Casting Competitive. To some extent, forging and casting are com-petitive, even where different materials are involved with each process. As a general rule, the tooling investment is higher for forging than for casting. Thus, the use of forging tends to be restricted to applications in which the higher material properties of steel compared to cast iron or the higher properties of wrought steel compared to cast steel can be made use of in the design. Because forgings compete best in high-strength applications, most producers take particular care in raw material selection and inspection. In many cases, either forgings or castings may have adequate proper-ties, and one process has no clear economic advantage over the other.

Material Quality Improved. Proper design for forgings must capitalize on the improvement in properties in certain directions that occurs with metal flow. Voids tend to close and be welded shut under the high heat and pressure, and inclusions are elongated to the degree that they have little effect on the strength in some directions.

Sequential Steps Necessary. In forging, a suitable quantity of metal is placed or held between the halves of the die while they are open, then forced to conform to the shape of the die by pressure from the dies themselves as they are closed. In *drop* and *press forging*, the dies are not completely closed until the forging is completed, with the consequence that, as the dies are closed, the metal may be squeezed to the part-ing line and be forced out of the die in some places before the closing is completed. To overcome this difficulty, two steps are taken. For most forgings, some preshaping operations are used to ensure that approximately the right quantity of metal is already at the proper place in the dies before they are closed. These operations are frequently similar to open die or hammer forging and include:

- **Upsetting:** enlarging the cross section by pressure from the end.
- **Drawing:** reducing the cross section of stock throughout.
- **Fullering:** reducing the cross section of stock between the ends.
- **Edging:** distributing the metal to the general contour of the finished stock.
- **Blocking:** shaping to rough-finished form without detail.

Excess Metal Ensures Die Filling. Even with the preshaping operations, it is nec-essary to provide some excess metal to ensure that all parts of the final die cavity are filled. The dies are constructed so that in the closed position a space is left at the parting line through which this excess metal is forced into a *gutter*. The excess metal, called *flash,* is actually part of the forging and must be removed in a secondary operation, generally by trimming in a shearing type of die.

The basic closed die forging principle is shown in Figure 7.1. Note the grain flow in the test object (arrows in the right figure) as the metal is compressed to fill the die. As with the other forming processes, inherent discontinuities will be stretched and flattened in the direction in which the metal moves.

Steel Drop Forged—Nonferrous Materials Press Forged. Theoretically, any metal with enough ductility could be either press forged or drop (impact) forged. In practice, steel is almost exclusively drop forged because of the large capacity presses that would be required for press forging and because the die life would be shortened by the longer time of contact between the die and the heated steel. Most nonferrous metals are press forged. The slow squeezing action in press forging permits deeper flow of the metal than in drop forging, and the dies may have somewhat less draft.

Fast and Accurate but High Setup Cost. Machine forging provides high production rates with little or no material loss and is thus close to an ideal process, providing that tolerances are acceptable, quantities are large enough to cover tooling costs, and the deformation ratios are permissible.

Most common machine forged parts made in very large quantities, such as bolts, rivets, nails, small gear blanks, and great numbers of small automotive fittings, require very little inspection of any kind after the process is in operation. Tool life is long and consistency of product is extremely good. One precaution to be observed is that suitable material continues to be fed into the machines.

7.2.1.4 FORGING WITH PROGRESSIVE APPLICATION OF PRESSURE

In any closed die forging operation, it is necessary to provide, either by constantly applied pressure or by impact, a great enough load that the compressive strength of the material is exceeded throughout the material for the forging to be completed. Even for forgings of a few kilograms (pounds), this requires heavy, massive equipment. For a

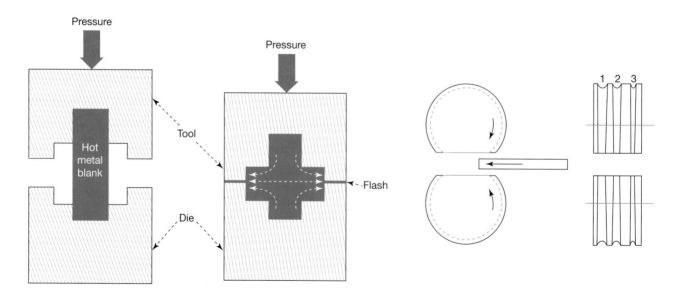

Figure 7.1: Basic forging process.

Figure 7.2: Roll forging.

few particular shapes, processes have been developed by which the material is worked only locally with light loads being required, and the area being worked progresses by a rolling action to other parts of the workpiece.

Roll Forging Progressively Reduces Cross Section. Roll forging, illustrated in Figure 7.2, is particularly useful when a cylindrical part is to be elongated throughout part of its length. The drawn section may be tapered, but the process is not capable of upsetting or enlarging the original diameter. In operation, the heated workpiece is placed between the first groove (1), and the rolls are energized to make one turn (2), after which the workpiece is moved to the next groove (3), and the operation repeated.

7.2.2 ROLLING OPERATIONS

7.2.2.1 HOT ROLLING

Hot Rolling Is the Common Initial Operation. The chart of Figure 7.3 is typical of steel mills and also applies to most nonferrous mills, although emphasis on the operations will vary for different metals. One of the most common mill operations is the rolling of metal into flat and two dimensionally formed shapes. This is accomplished by passing the material between flat or shaped rollers to set up forces that squeeze the material and cause it to flow to an elongated form while the cross-sectional dimensions are being reduced. For those materials that have little ductility and for large changes of section in any material, the work is usually done hot to reduce the energy requirements and to permit ductility recovery by recrystallization as deformation occurs. Some materials must be worked at elevated temperatures in order to attain adequate stability and ductility to preclude fractures during deformation.

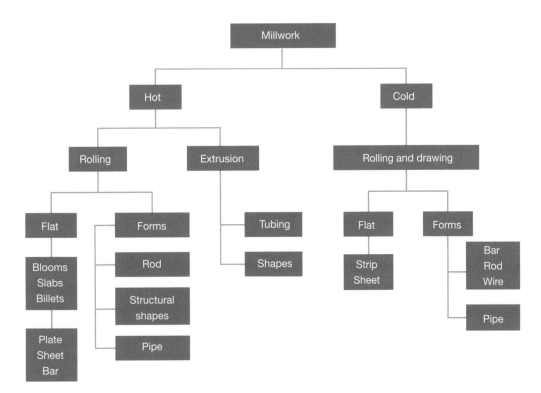

Figure 7.3: Processes and product types of primary mills.

Blooms, Slabs, and Billets. Following reduction of the ore or, in the case of steel, following carbon reduction, most materials start as cast ingots that are rolled initially into blooms, slabs, or billets. Blooms and billets are approximately square cross sections of large and small size, respectively, and slabs are rectangular shapes. All are destined for further deformation work by rolling, forging, or extrusion, usually at the same mill but sometimes at an individual fabricator's plant.

Thickness Reduction by Compression. Mill rolling is done by passing the material through rolling stands where rollers, arranged as shown in Figure 7.4, apply pressure to reduce the section thickness and elongate the metal. The major portion of stress is compressive and is in such direction that the effect on width dimensions is minor compared to the others.

Blooming Mill Reversible. At the blooming mill where the first deformation work is done on the material, the cast ingot is rolled back and forth between rolls or continuously through sets of stands as the rolls are brought closer together to control the rate of reduction and establish new dimensions. Mechanical manipulators are used to turn the block, or additional vertical rolls are used for making an approximately square cross section bloom or rectangular slab that may be as much as 18 or 21 m (60 or 70 ft) long.

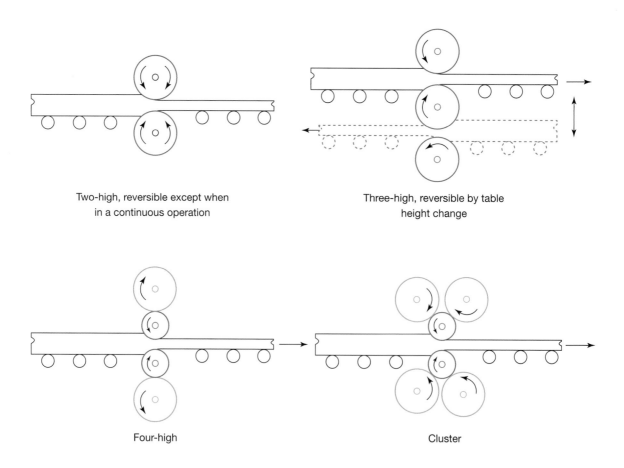

Two-high, reversible except when in a continuous operation

Three-high, reversible by table height change

Four-high

Cluster

Figure 7.4: Various arrangements of rolls in rolling stands; backup rolls (yellow) add support to contact rolls (purple).

Cast Ingot Discontinuities Removed. As much as one-third of the bloom may be *cropped* (cut away) to eliminate a major portion of the impurities, shrink, and poor quality metal originating in the ingot. Near-surface discontinuities caused by ingot or rolling faults are removed during or following primary rolling by chipping, grinding, or *scarfing* (oxygen torch burning). These long blooms are then sheared to lengths convenient to handle and suitable for the anticipated final material form.

Continuous Casting Eliminates Ingots. Increasing use is being made of continuous casting as a step in steelmaking. Although the cost of changeover is high, the installation eliminates the making of ingots and their breakdown in the blooming mill. The continuous casting is made in a heavy slab or plate form that can be introduced directly into the hot-roll stands. Another advantage gained is the elimination of ingot cropping.

Billets Smaller than Blooms. Blooms are frequently reduced to billet size, with maximum cross section of 232 cm² (36 in.²), in a similar stand with reversing features, although some installations have been set up with a number of rolling stands in sequence so that billets can be formed by continuous passage through the series.

Hammer Forging for Special Cases. Some demand exists for small quantities of wrought materials in large shapes not adaptable to rolling. These may be of variable section size, for example, a large steam turbine shaft, or sizes not ordinarily produced by the rolling mill. In these cases, the ingot may be worked to the desired shape by a forging operation, usually between flat-faced hammers.

Continuous Hot Rolling. Following the primary reduction operations in the blooming or slabbing mill, the sections are usually further rolled in some secondary operation, still at the mill. Plate, sheet, and rod shapes are in sufficient demand that many mills produce them in continuous mills. The material proceeds directly from one rolling stand to the next, with progressive reduction and shaping of the cross section and simultaneous elongation along the direction of rolling. Scale-breaking rolls are followed by high-pressure water or steam sprays for removal of scale. Both the roughing and finishing operations are done in continuous mills consisting of a number of strands in sequence. Some hot-rolled strips are used directly as they come from the hot-rolling mill for the making of finished goods such as railway cars, pressure vessels, and boats. Most of the flat hot-rolled steel is further processed by cold rolling.

Surface Oxidation a Problem. As pointed out earlier, the mechanical properties of hot-worked material are affected by the heat to which it is subjected. Working at high temperature permits maximum deformation, but for those materials for which the working temperature is above the oxidation temperature for some of the constituents, burning and scale result, and adverse effects on finish occur. Before use as a product in the hot-rolled state, or before cold-finishing operations are performed, surface cleaning is required. Cleaning is often done by immersing the material in acid baths (pickling) that attack the scale at higher rates than the base metal.

Limited Accuracy in Hot Rolling. Because of differences in working temperatures affecting shrinkage, differences in oxidation depths, and more rapid wear on the rolls, dimensions are more difficult to hold in hot-rolling processes than when finishing is done cold. Tolerances depend to some extent on the shape and the material. For hot-rolled round bars of low carbon steel, they range from ±0.1 mm (0.004 in.) for material up to 10 mm (0.4 in.) in diameter to ±1 mm (0.040 in.) for bars 10 cm (4 in.) in diameter.

7.2.2.2 COLD FINISHING

Properties Changed by Cold Working. While most steel is shipped from the mill in the hot-rolled condition, much of the material is cold finished by additional rolling in the cold state or by drawing through dies. The forces set up by either procedure are similar and result in reduction of cross-sectional area. Materials that are treated in this way must have sufficient ductility at the beginning, but that ductility is reduced as the hardness, yield strength, and tensile strength are increased as the deformation progresses.

Flat Products. The flat products of a steel mill are called *strip, sheet, plate,* or *bar,* depending on the relative widths and thicknesses, and most are cold finished by rolling. For this work, the rolling stands are of the four-high type illustrated in Figure 7.5 or the cluster type that performs the same function of permitting small-diameter work rolls to be in contact with the material. Figure 7.6 shows typical arrangements of stands for cold-rolling strip or sheet. The tandem mill, with a higher initial investment, is a higher production method but has less flexibility than the single-stand reversing mill. Power for reduction may be supplied by the reels alone, by the rolls alone, or by driving both the reels and the rolls. Sheet is normally kept in tension as it passes through the stands.

Since cold-rolled strip and sheet are usually produced with highly accurate thickness requirements, some mills are equipped with online ultrasonic or radiation thickness gages. In some sophisticated systems, the output from the thickness gage is fed back to provide roll spacing and tension adjustments while rolling is in process.

A Variety of Bar Shapes Rolled. Bar material can be in the form of square, rectangular, round, hexagonal, and other shapes. In the rolling of strip and sheet, the edges are not confined, and the final width of the sheet may vary. Subsequent to shipping from the mill, the material is normally trimmed to correct width by rotary shears. Most bar shapes are not adaptable to close dimensional control in cold rolling and are therefore finished by drawing through hardened dies. The operation is performed in a machine called a drawbench, a schematic of which is shown in Figure 7.7. The end of the oversized hot-rolled bar is first pointed by swaging or forging, then inserted through the die and gripped in the draw head. Connection of the draw-head hook to a moving chain provides the power to draw the material through the die. Reductions generally range from 0.5 to 3 mm (1/64 to 1/8 in.). Round stock may also be cold finished by rolling between skewed rollers in a process called *turning* or centerless ground for highest accuracy.

7.2.2.3 TUBE AND PIPE MAKING

The terms *pipe* and *tube* have no strict distinctions, but in most common use, the term *pipe* refers to a hollow product used to conduct fluids. Except for some relatively thin-walled welded products, tubing is generally seamless.

Pipe and Tubing—Mill Products. Most pipe and tubing products are produced in mills, frequently along with sheet, strip, and bar products. The manufacture of tubular products involves both hot and cold working, in the same order as for other mill

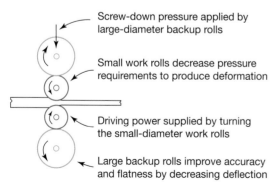

Figure 7.5: Arrangement of conventional four-high rolling stand.

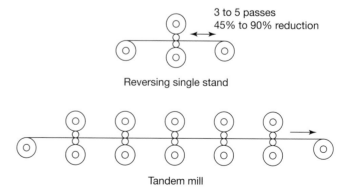

Figure 7.6: Cold reduction methods.

products, with hot working being used in the rough forming stages and cold working in the finishing and sizing operations. Most pipe made by welding processes is steel. Some steel and nearly all nonferrous tubular products are made by seamless processes. Regardless of the process, NDT is nearly always used at some stage in the processing of pipe and tubing if the product is to be used in high-pressure applications.

Pipe by Welding Bell. One of the oldest but still much-used processes for making steel pipe consists of drawing heated bevel-edged *skelp* in lengths of 6 to 12 m (20 to 40 ft) through a welding bell such as pictured in Figure 7.8. Skelp is the term for wrought iron or steel that has been rolled or forged into narrow strips for pipe or tubing. The skelp is gripped by tongs and drawn through the bell where it is formed to tubular shape and the edges pressed together to form a butt-welded joint. Power is supplied by a drawbench as in drawing bar stock.

Pipe by Roll Welding. Figure 7.9 illustrates the method used for *butt-welding* pipe in a continuous manner. Skelp from a reel passes through a furnace and is drawn through forming rolls where it is shaped. Welding rolls then apply pressure to establish the butt-welded joint. Following the welding station, rollers squeeze the pipe to smaller size after which it is cut to length by a flying saw. Both types of butt-welded pipe may require some cold-finishing operations, such as sizing between rollers and straightening by stretching or cross rolling, before being cut to exact length and finished by facing or threading operations. Pipe is produced by pressure butt welding, either short lengths or continuously, in sizes up to 102 mm (4 in.) in nominal diameter.

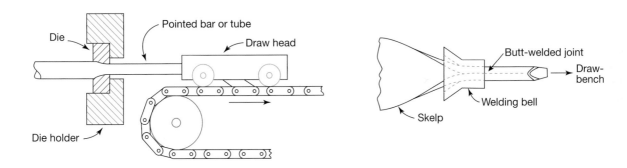

Figure 7.7: Drawbench for cold reduction of bar or tubing.

Figure 7.8: Shaping and welding of pipe in a welding bell.

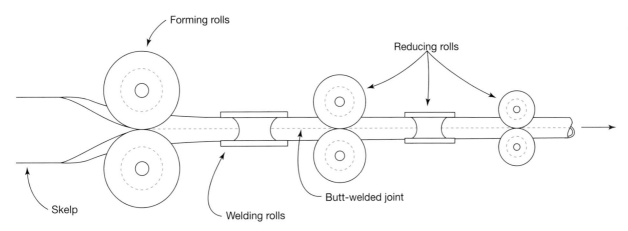

Figure 7.9: Continuous process of butt-welding pipe.

Resistance-Welded Tubing. Light-gage steel tubing in sizes up to 40 cm (16 in.) in diameter may be produced by *resistance welding* of stock that has been formed cold by rolls, which progressively shape the material from flat strip to tubular form. The general arrangement is shown in Figure 7.10. After forming, the tube passes between electrodes, through which welding current is supplied, and pressure rolls that maintain pressure in the weld area. Because the material is heated only locally, the pressure produces flash on both the inside and outside of the tube. The outside flash is removed by a form cutter immediately following the welding operation. The inside flash may be reduced by a rolling or forging action against a mandrel, depending on size. Because this process uses rolls of strip stock as raw material and is best operated continuously, a flying saw is required to cut the tubing to correct length. Resistance butt welding may be done in a mill, but because of the relatively light equipment needed, it frequently is performed as a secondary operation in a fabricator's plant.

Some Pipe Welded with Filler Metal. For large sizes from about 15 cm (6 in.) to an unlimited upper limit that are needed in relatively small quantities, pipe may be manufactured by forming of plate or sheet and welding by any of the fusion processes. In practice, the *submerged-arc method*, discussed in Chapter 8, is often the most economical welding procedure. After the edges of the plate have been properly prepared by shearing or machining, the steps shown in Figure 7.11 are followed in forming the pipe.

A relatively small quantity of larger pipe, from about 4 to 75 cm (1.5 to 30 in.) in diameter, is *lap welded*. For this process, the skelp is beveled on the edges as it emerges from the furnace. It is then formed to cylindrical shape with overlapping edges. While at elevated temperature for welding, the tube is passed between a pressure roller and a mandrel for the establishment of welding pressure.

Spiral-Welded Pipe. The making of light-gage pipe or tubing as pictured in Figure 7.12 can be accomplished by resistance welding of a continuous spiral butt or lap joint. A principal advantage of the process is the light equipment required and the flexibility in changing from one size or one material to another. Any material that can be welded can be fabricated into pipe by this method.

Seamless Tubing. In practice, the term *seamless tubing* refers to a tubular product that is made without welding. The most common method used for steel involves *piercing* of round billets of relatively large cross section and short length, with subsequent deformation operations to control the final diameter, wall thickness, and length. Figure 7.13 shows the most common type of piercing mill used. The skew rollers both flatten and advance the billet with a helical motion. High shear stresses are developed at the center of the billet, at which point the material is forced over a bullet-shaped mandrel.

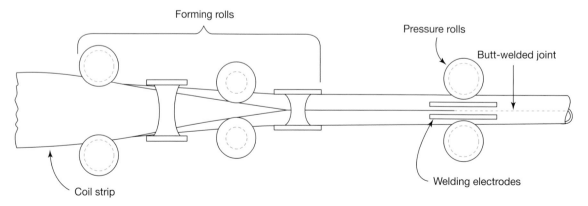

Figure 7.10: Resistance welding of tubing.

Sizing of Seamless Tubing. Subsequent operations include *reeling* and *rotary rolling,* which are similar to piercing and permit the inside diameter to be further enlarged with a reduction of wall thickness. Rolling between grooved rollers reduces both the outside and inside diameter with elongation along the axis of the tube. Much seamless tubing is finished cold by rolling or drawing through dies with the advantages of improved tolerances, surface finish, and mechanical properties. Squares, ovals, and other noncircular shapes may be produced by drawing through special dies and over special mandrels.

Seamless Tubing Useful for Machine Parts. Seamless steel tubing is manufactured from nearly all the common grades of steel, including plain carbon up to 1.5% AISI alloy steels, and stainless steels of most types. In addition to use for fluid conduction, seamless tubing is also much used as a raw material for many machined parts, such as antifriction bearing races, where considerable material and machine-time savings may be made.

Some Tubing Made by Press Operation. In *cupping* operations, seamless tubing is produced by a press-type operation similar to shell drawing, which is discussed below. A heated circular disc is forced through a die by a punch to form a closed-bottom cylinder. The cylinder may be further processed into a pressure container, or the bottom may be cut off and the tube processed into standard tube types.

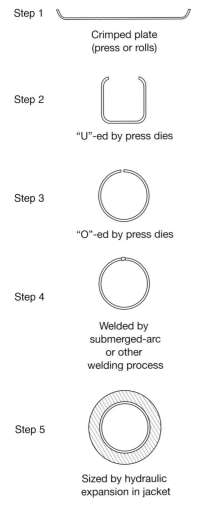

Step 1

Crimped plate
(press or rolls)

Step 2

"U"-ed by press dies

Step 3

"O"-ed by press dies

Step 4

Welded by
submerged-arc
or other
welding process

Step 5

Sized by hydraulic
expansion in jacket

Figure 7.11: Electric welding of large pipe.

Figure 7.12: Spiral welded pipe.

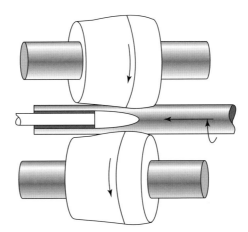

Figure 7.13: Roll piercing of round bar material.

NDT of Seamless Tubing. Since the production of seamless tubing can cause tears and other cracklike discontinuities and irregularities in sizing and wall thickness, electromagnetic testing utilizing encircling coils is frequently applied. By such methods, seamless tubing can be automatically inspected at rates up to several hundred meters (feet) per minute.

Perfect Welds Difficult. It is possible to produce welded tubular products that effectively are seamless. The weld area can have the same properties as the rest of the pipe or tube and may in fact be undetectable after welding. However, this degree of perfection might require heat treatment after welding and additional deformation or machining to produce uniform thickness. In addition, it would be very difficult to produce perfect welds in higher-alloy steels, especially in heavy sections. Both radiological and ultrasonic tests are used for inspection of the welds in pipe produced using a welding process. Fluoroscopic techniques have been widely applied for rapid inspection of the welds. A few ultrasonic systems have been designed to provide pipe weld inspection online. Some small-diameter seamless pipes are inspected by electromagnetic testing techniques, such as eddy current, that are capable of detecting not only weld discontinuities but discontinuities in the stock material as well.

7.2.3 EXTRUSION

Figure 7.14 shows various extrusion methods. Tubing may be extruded by direct or indirect methods with mandrels as shown. Indirect, or reverse, extrusion requires lower loads but complicates handling of the extruded shape. Lead-sheathed electrical cable is produced by extruding the lead around the cable as it passes through the die.

Extrusion a High-Energy Process. The high degree of deformation required for extrusion leads to a number of limitations. Most metals are ductile enough for extensive extrusion only at high temperatures. Even then, the loads are very high and require large, heavy equipment and large amounts of power. Die materials must be able to withstand the high loads and temperatures without excessive wear. This presents a particularly serious problem with steel, which usually must be heated to about 1250 °C (2192 °F) to have sufficient ductility for extrusion.

Steel may be extruded hot with glass as a lubricant, but die life is short; the process is used primarily for steel sections produced in such low quantity that the cost of special rolls could not be justified, and for some high-alloy steels that are difficult to forge or roll.

Used Extensively for Nonferrous Materials. The extrusion process is used primarily for forming shapes of aluminum, copper, lead alloys, and plastics. In fact, except for flat stock that may be more economically rolled, extrusion is the principal process used for producing parts having uniform cross sections from these materials. Many metals may be extruded at room temperature. For lead, tin, and zinc, this actually means hot working because the recrystallization temperatures are at or below room temperature, and some heating of the metal occurs as a result of deformation work energy being converted to heat.

Flexible Process but Limited to Uniform Cross Sections. Theoretically, extruded parts have no size restrictions. In practice, the size of the equipment limits the size of the extrusion that can be produced. Dimensional tolerances depend on the material involved, the temperature, and the size of the extrusion. In hot extrusion, the die tends to expand as the material passes through, resulting in a taper to the extruded part. The principal error is in straightness, and most extrusions require straightening. This is accomplished automatically when the extrusion is cold finished by die drawing.

The principal shape limitations are concerned with maintaining uniform cross-sectional thicknesses. Otherwise, the extrusion process is quite flexible; odd and hollow shapes are possible that would be impossible or uneconomical to roll. As previously mentioned, electromagnetic testing techniques are most commonly applied to testing tubular products that are intended for high-pressure applications or high-strength structural applications.

7.2.4 DRAWING

Drawing Involves Multiple Stresses. The most complex press operation, from the standpoint of the stresses involved, is *drawing.* In simple bending, a single axis exists about which all the deformation occurs, and the surface area of the material is not significantly altered. Drawing involves not only bending but also stretching and

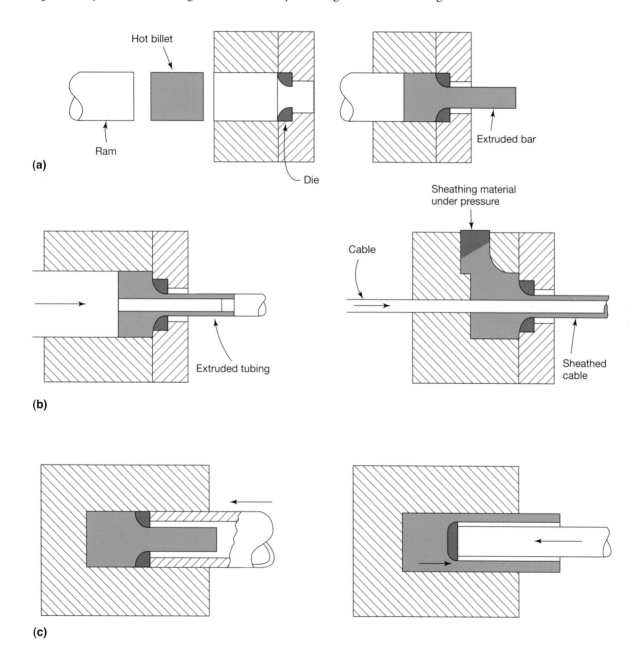

Figure 7.14: Common extrusion methods: (a) basic extrusion process; (b) examples of direct extrusion; (c) examples of reverse extrusion.

compression of the metal over wide areas. Examples of drawing are many and include such items as automobile fenders and other body parts, aircraft wing and fuselage panels, kitchenware, and square or rectangular box shapes. However, the simplest illustration is *shell drawing* in which a flat circular blank is pushed through a round die to form a closed-ended cup or shell, as shown in Figure 7.15.

In many cases, the dimensions of the required shell are such that it cannot be completed in a single step. A series of two or more dies, each smaller in diameter than the previous, is then used to produce the final product dimensions.

Recrystallization May Reduce Number of Steps. An operation might be accomplished with a single redraw if the part were reheated for recrystallization after the first draw to restore the original ductility and permit a greater reduction in the first redrawing operation. The actual choice of a single draw and two redraws as opposed to a single draw, recrystallization, and one redraw would depend on the economics of the particular situation and would involve consideration of quantities, equipment, and other factors.

Single Form Used in Stretch Forming. Figure 7.16 illustrates the short-run method known as *stretch forming*. The sheet to be formed is held under tension with sufficient force to exceed the yield point and pulled down over, or wrapped around, the single form block. Considerable trimming allowance must be left along the edges of the part, and the process is restricted to shallow shapes with no reentrant angles. However, the method is capable of forming operations on large parts and has been used mostly in the aircraft industry for large wing and body sections.

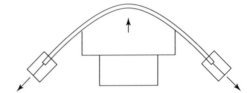

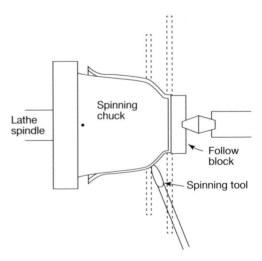

Figure 7.16: Stretch forming.

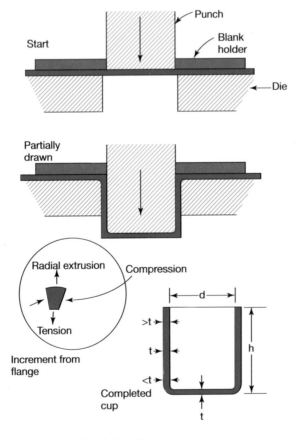

Figure 7.15: Shell drawing.

Figure 7.17: Spinning.

Spinning—Versatile, Low-Cost, but Low-Quantity, Process. One of the oldest production methods for cylindrical drawn shapes is *spinning,* shown in Figure 7.17. Prior to the manufacture of automobiles and other consumer goods in mass quantities after 1900, spinning was the predominant method for forming deep-drawn shapes and is still used to a considerable extent when low quantities are produced. Most spinning is done cold, but for heavy materials or materials without sufficient ductility at room temperature, elevated temperatures are used. Typical parts include pressure tank ends, kitchenware of a special design and in special metals, and many experimental parts that will, in production, be produced by conventional deep drawing in steel dies.

Tooling is generally low cost and, for light-gage ductile materials, wood is the most common form material. Shapes produced may be shallow or deep, and bulging operations are possible with special setups. Nearly all metals may be spun, most of them cold. Limitations include the operation time involved and the skill required of the operator because the spinning tool is held and manipulated manually except in highly automatic setups where the process loses its low tooling cost advantage. Usually, some thinning of the metal occurs. The problems of wrinkling and tearing are present as in conventional drawing operations, particularly with thinner materials.

7.2.5 SWAGING

Rotary Swaging. A rotary swaging machine, as shown in Figure 7.18, is constructed like a straight roller bearing with the inner race replaced by a powered spindle carrying shaped dies in slots. As the spindle rotates, the backs of the dies are forced inward as they pass each roller. Machines of this type are used most frequently for reducing the ends of bar, tube, or wire stock so that it may be started through a die for a drawing operation. Rotary forging may be done either hot or cold, in many cases the choice being determined by the requirements of the drawing operation that follows the forging. In addition to the pointing of stock for drawing purposes, the process is used for the closing or necking of cylinders and for overall reduction of tubular products.

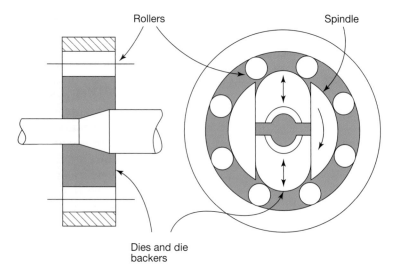

Figure 7.18: Rotary swaging.

7.3 SHEET-METAL FORMING PROCESSES

Since its inception about 1850, the working of sheet metal has grown constantly in importance and today is perhaps the most important method of fabricating metal parts. About 30% of steel mill output is in the form of sheet and plate. Most of this material is further processed by individual fabricators by various pressworking operations that involve deformation, usually cold, and shearing operations in which metal is removed.

Most Metal Consumer Goods Pressworked. The importance of this form of processing to the economy is especially apparent from an examination of mass-produced metal consumer goods, such as automobiles, home appliances, housings, and office equipment. In addition to exterior housings, many functional parts are made from sheet metal; for business machines and other equipment made in large quantity, the percentage of parts made by this process may approach 100%.

7.3.1 SHEET-METAL CHARACTERISTICS

Ductility Essential. Two prerequisites to this type of processing are (1) sufficient quantities to justify the high tooling cost that is required and (2) the presence of enough ductility in the material to permit the plastic flow necessary for the particular type of operation being considered. Shearing operations, in which plastic flow is not required, are possible on nearly all sheet materials, even brittle materials such as glass and some plastics. All other pressworking operations are deformation operations, and the degree of processing permissible is dependent on the ductility present in the particular material. Some metals may be cold worked to completion with material as it comes from the mill, some metals require intermediate recrystallization between cold-working operations, and some require heating for more than shearing or minimum deformation operations.

Applied Loads Cause Material Failure. Pressworking operations, whether shearing or deformation, involve the failure of the metal by controlled loading. In shearing operations, the metal is loaded in a manner to cause fracture. In bending, drawing, and other deformation operations, the metal is loaded past the elastic limit to cause plastic flow only, usually by application of tension or bending loads. Unlike most forging operations in which the metal is totally confined, the final thickness of the metal depends on the original thickness and the nature of the operation.

Special Tools—High Cost. The majority of pressworking operations require special tooling. In most cases, the cutting or forming tools are attached to a standardized die set that is mounted in the press. Figure 7.19 shows a simple die set for shearing a round hole or producing a round disc.

Tooling Aligned in Die Set. When mounted in a press, the punch shoe is attached to the ram of the press and the die shoe to the bolster plate, which is the fixed member corresponding to the anvil of a forging press. The guide posts ensure proper alignment of the punch and die and simplify the setup because the entire die set may be removed from the press and replaced later without any critical adjustments to be made. In some complex dies, there may be confusion as to which is the die and which is the punch; in normal use, however, the tool member with a recess, hole, or depression is called the die, and the punch is the member that enters the hole or depression of the die. In most cases, stock feeding and handling problems are simplified by mounting the punch on the top and the die on the bottom of the die set.

7.3.2 SHEARING

Shearing Is a Cutting Operation. The term *shearing*, as used in pressworking, applies specifically to the operation of loading to fracture with opposed edges. Shear stress applies to an internal load condition tending to slide one plane on another, and various amounts of shear stress occur with practically all loading systems. In a shearing operation, material is actually loaded by a combination of compressive and bending loads, and the internal stress condition is quite complex. Of real importance is the fact that when the external loads become great enough, the internal stresses will exceed critical values for the material and rupture will occur. The rupture may or may not be preceded by plastic flow, depending on the properties of the particular material.

Shearing Used for a Variety of Purposes. A number of different shearing operations exist with some confusion in names. One of the many ways of classifying these operations is by the purpose of the process. The purpose may be to

- produce an external shape, which may be either a finished shape or the raw material for some other operation;
- remove part of the material or cut it in such a way that an opening or indentation is produced; or
- remove material that was necessarily left on the part from some other operation.

Categories. Shearing operations may be grouped into three categories.

1. Stock preparation and blank-producing operations:
- Shearing
- Slitting
- Cutoff
- Parting
- Dinking
- Blanking

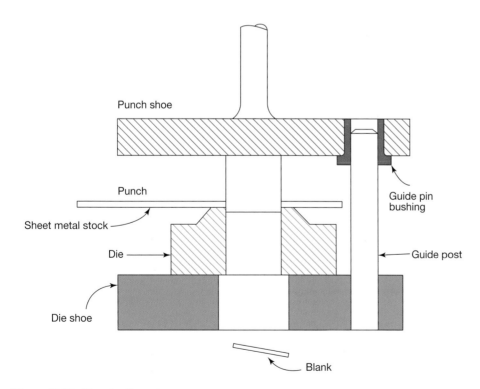

Figure 7.19: Simple die set.

2. Hole-making operations:
- Punching
- Slotting
- Perforating
- Semi-notching
- Notching
- Lancing
- Piercing

3. Finishing operations:
- Trimming
- Shaving

Straight-Line Shearing. The term *shearing* generally refers to straight-line cutting performed on a squaring shear that has permanently mounted, opposed straight blades. The upper blade is set at an angle to give progressive engagement and reduce the maximum force required. Squaring shears may be used to reduce large sheet or coil stock to smaller size for handling purposes or to produce parts with finished or semifinished shapes, as indicated in Figure 7.20.

Slitting. Figure 7.21 shows *rotary slitting*, which is used primarily for reducing coil stock to narrower widths. Slitting is usually a mill or warehouse operation, but occasionally is done by an individual fabricator.

7.3.3 BENDING OF SHEET AND PLATE

In shearing operations, any plastic flow that occurs along the edge is incidental because the purpose of shearing is to cause separation of the metal without any deformation in the sheet itself. Bending is intended to cause localized plastic flow about one or more linear axes in the material without causing fracture.

Ductility Required for Bending. Bending is accomplished by loading the material so as to set up stresses that exceed the yield point of the material and cause permanent

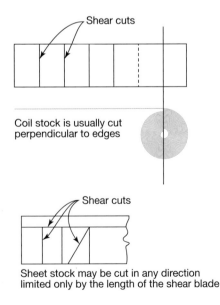

Figure 7.20: Shearing.

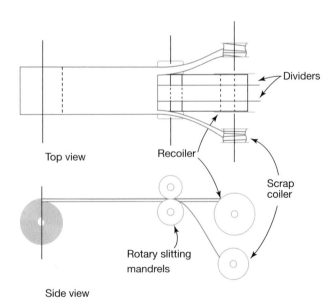

Figure 7.21: Slitting.

deformation. Shearing is possible on materials having very low ductility as well as on those having high ductility. Bending is possible only on materials having sufficient ductility to permit the required amount of plastic flow. The severity of bends possible will depend on the ductility. While the degree of bending possible cannot be determined directly from a standard tensile test, this test gives useful comparative data. For two materials, the one showing the greatest percentage of elongation in the tensile test may be bent more severely than the other.

Outside Radius Distorted. Figure 7.22 indicates the nature of the deformation taking place in a bend. The metal on the inside of the radius (r) is subject to high compressive stresses that may cause an increase in width for material that is nearly square in cross section. With any cross section, and regardless of how the operation is performed, the high tensile stresses on the outside of the bend cause thinning of the metal. The degree of thinning will depend on the ratio of bend radius to metal thickness (t). In practice, the distortion must be considered for two reasons. Unless the metal is actually squeezed at the completion of the bend with sufficient force to cause forging, the outside shape of the bend will not be a true radius and is uncontrolled. On part drawings, the inside radius only should be specified because this radius can be controlled by the tooling.

Forming. By a strict definition, bending would include only operations in which the plastic flow is confined to a narrow straight-line region where the bend is made. It is not possible to perform a bend along a curved axis without plastic flow occurring in the material away from the line of the bend. This type of operation would more strictly be called *drawing*. In practice, however, a number of operations are considered bending that do include some drawing. The term *forming* is sometimes used in a broad sense to include simple bending, multiple bends made along more than one axis, operations that are primarily bending but include some drawing, and some operations that are basically drawing in nature but are of shallow depth or confined to a small area of the workpiece.

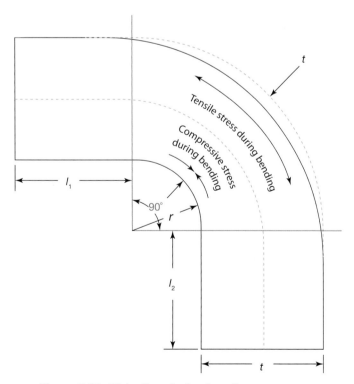

Figure 7.22: Distortion during bending.

Roll Forming—Alternative to Conventional Bending. *Roll forming*, illustrated in Figure 7.10 in connection with tube making, is not a press operation, but the metal is shaped by means of a continuous bending action. While the completed shape can be produced by bending only, some stretching occurs during the actual forming as the strip changes from flat to formed. Roll forming is used for making tubing, architectural trim, and other similar parts in which a uniform cross section of relatively long length is necessary. The choice between roll forming or shaping by conventional press tooling requires economic analysis. Short parts are frequently made by cutting roll-formed stock to correct length.

7.3.4 MISCELLANEOUS SHEET METAL FORMING PROCESSES

Most new developments in this area have at least two features in common. Like the processes just discussed, most are low-tooling-cost methods, useful for low production quantities, and most make use of a single forming surface instead of matching dies. All of them use nonconventional energy sources, usually some system that releases large amounts of energy in a short time. This feature has led to the use of the term *high energy rate forming* (HERF).

Explosive Forming. The most highly developed of these methods is *explosive forming*, shown in Figure 7.23a. Two general methods have been used. In the first, sheet metal structures are sized or formed by drawing; high explosives detonated in air or in water at some predetermined distance from the workpiece are used. Pressures as high as 27 579 mPa (4 000 000 psi) are developed by the explosion, which creates a shock wave in the fluid medium that transmits the energy to the workpiece. In the second method (Figure 7.23b), a closed die is used, and lower pressures of about 275 MPa (40 000 psi) are developed by slower-burning propellants or gas mixtures. This system is particularly useful for bulging operations. In either case, a number of advantages exist when the process is compared to conventional press forming. The capital investment is low compared to conventional press equipment, tooling is simple and inexpensive, and sizes can be shaped that would be impractical with conventional equipment. The principal restriction is long production time so that the processes cannot be economically used for quantity production. There has been some indication that greater amounts of deformation may be achieved by explosive forming than by conventional press forming.

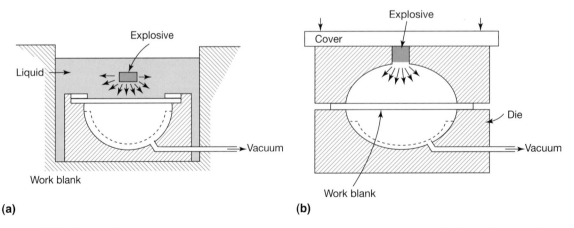

(a)   **(b)**

Figure 7.23: Two methods of explosive forming: (a) explosive removed from workpiece; (b) explosive within closed die.

Electrical Energy Methods. Similar methods are based on the sudden release of electrical energy stored in banks of condensers. In one method, a spark is created between two electrodes while they are submerged in water or air near the workpiece. In a second method, a high current discharged through a relatively small-diameter wire results in vaporization of the wire. In either case, a shockwave is created that transfers energy to the workpiece.

One of the newer methods involves the release of stored electrical energy through a coil near the workpiece, as shown in Figure 7.24. The rapidly created magnetic field induces eddy currents within a conductive (though not necessarily ferromagnetic) workpiece, which sets up fields that interact with the coil fields to create high forces. With properly designed coils, tubular shapes may be expanded into a die or compressed onto a mandrel or various inserts. Flat workpieces may be forced into a shallow drawing die. One of the principal uses has been in assembly of tubular components with end fittings. The system has been called either *electromagnetic forming* or *inductive-repulsive forming.* It is not limited to low production as are most other high-energy-rate techniques.

7.4 POWDER TECHNOLOGY

7.4.1 POWDER METALLURGY

The definition for the term *powder metallurgy,* as provided by the Committee for Powder Metallurgy of ASM International (formerly, the American Society for Metals) is: "The art of producing metal powders and objects shaped from individual, mixed, or alloyed metal powders, with or without the inclusion of nonmetallic constituents, by pressing or molding objects which may be simultaneously or subsequently heated to produce a coherent mass, either without fusion, or with the fusion of a low melting constituent only."

Originally Developed as a Step in Refining. References to the granulation of gold and silver and subsequent shaping into solid shapes go back as far as 1574. It is also noteworthy that in the 19th century more metallic elements were produced in powder form than in any other form. For the most part, these were all precious or rare metals for which powder metallurgy was the only practical method of

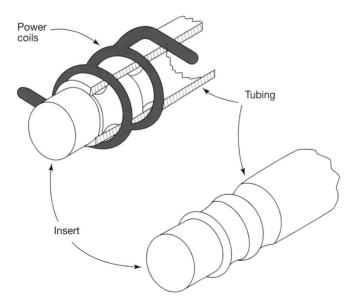

Figure 7.24: Electromagnetic forming.

manufacture. However, beginning in the 1930s, this process has become competitive with more conventional processes in the manufacture of articles from iron, copper, aluminum, and other common metals.

Two Unique Advantages. Early developments in powder metallurgy were based on two factors. During the production of platinum, tantalum, osmium, tungsten, and similar refractory metals, reduction was purely a chemical process from which the reduced metal was obtained as a precipitate in flake or powder form. Because furnaces and techniques were not available for complete melting of these materials, the only procedure for producing them in solid form was to press them into coherent masses and sinter at temperatures below the melting point. This procedure still applies in the production of some metals, especially tungsten. A second major advantage of the process, which led to early use and is still applied today, is in the production of porous shapes obtained with lighter pressing pressures or lower sintering temperatures. Materials in this form are useful as chemical catalysts, filtering elements, and bearings.

Process Involves a Series of Steps. Figure 7.25 shows the steps ordinarily required in the production of a part by the powder metallurgy process. Suitable powder must first be produced. While theoretically any crystalline material may be fabricated by powder metallurgy, the production of suitable powder has presented restrictions in many cases, either because of difficulty in obtaining adequate purity or because of economic reasons. After selection and blending of the powder and manufacture of a die for the shape to be produced, the powder is pressed to size and shape. The application of heat results in crystalline growth and the production of a homogeneous body.

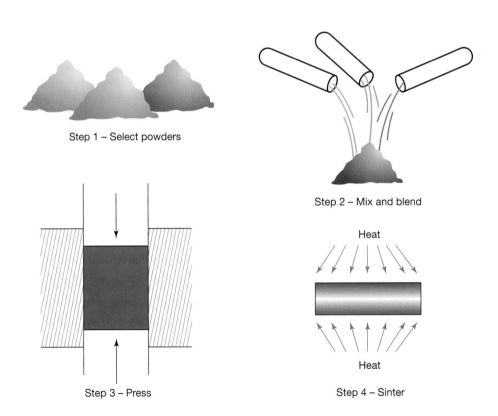

Step 1 – Select powders

Step 2 – Mix and blend

Step 3 – Press

Step 4 – Sinter

Figure 7.25: Elements of powder metallurgy.

Little Opportunity for NDT during Processing. Most NDT on powdered metal products is performed after the parts have completed the sintering process. Parts produced from sintered metal powders are nominally inspected as though they were produced by either casting or a deformation process or combination of both. Inclusions, cracks, voids, and density variations can result from improper processing. Since net or near-net shapes are commonly produced by powder metallurgy, NDT is most often called upon to inspect for both surface and subsurface discontinuities. Radiography is useful to reveal internal voids, cracks, and inclusions, and to provide a qualitative assessment of compaction consistency. Conventional penetrant methods are used to detect surface-connected discontinuities, such as porosity and cracks.

Properties Influenced by Heat-Pressure Cycle. Various combinations of heat and pressure may be used. Some sintering takes place under high pressure at room temperature. However, cold pressing is usually followed by sintering at a temperature somewhat below the lowest melting point of any of the constituents. An intermediate elevated temperature may be used during pressing; then the shape is removed from the press and subjected to higher temperature. In hot pressing, the final sintering temperature is applied simultaneously with the pressure.

Mixing Important to Product Quality. Mixing is required for even a single metal powder to promote homogeneity with a random dispersion of particle sizes and shapes. Single materials are often mixed from a variety of sources to develop improved properties. The mixing and blending is even more important for combinations of materials that depend on uniform alloying to develop final properties. Small amounts of organic materials may be added to reduce segregation. Other materials, both organic and inorganic, may be added to act as lubricants during pressing or sometimes in the final product.

7.4.2 COMPACTION OF METAL POWDER

Mechanical and Atomic Bonds Established. The bond that is established between particles in powder metallurgy varies all the way from mechanical interlocking to the growing of new, common crystals across the borders of the initial particles. Every atom is surrounded by a force field that is effective at up to a few atom diameters. Proper bonding thus depends primarily on bringing adjacent particles close enough together that these atomic forces can be effective. The effective closeness is dependent on both particle size and particle shape. Mixed sizes and shapes, at least with random packing, provide the maximum closeness and the greatest number of contact points.

Deformation Increases Contact Area. Most metals can be plastically deformed, and, with these, pressure can be applied to cause the contact points to grow into relatively large areas. Face-centered cubic metals such as nickel, copper, and lead do not work harden readily and can be deformed with comparatively low pressures. The metals that work harden easily and that are also usually harder and stronger to begin with, such as the body-centered cubic structures of iron, tungsten, and vanadium, require much higher pressures to establish suitable contact areas.

High Temperature Accelerates Bonding. Surface atoms are rearranged both by plastic flow and by mutual attraction with atoms of the adjacent surface. Increasing temperature aids both of these mechanisms by decreasing resistance to plastic flow and by increasing the energy of the atom. Particles that have been severely work-hardened as a result of the plastic flow may recrystallize at elevated temperatures, and the new crystals may actually cross the original particle boundary to establish complete atomic bonds.

Multidirectional Forces Desirable. Compacting of metallic powders ideally would be done by applying pressure in all directions at one time. This is usually impractical for commercial use, and most compaction is done along a single axis. Pressure is sometimes applied from one direction only, but in other cases opposing motions are used to reduce the effect of sidewall friction. Figure 7.26 shows the effect of sidewall friction on the density of a compact. The effectiveness of pressing is most often evaluated by measuring the density of the material and expressing it as a percentage of the theoretical density for solid metal of the type being treated. Densities depend on the particle size and shape, the material, the pressure, the time, and the temperature. The figure illustrates the variation in density as the distance from the source of pressure increases. This variation depends primarily on the length-to-width or -diameter ratio of the compact and ranges from as little as 3% for a ratio of one-fourth to as much as 25% for a ratio of 2.

Uniform Density Difficult with Complex Shapes. The density variation problem is further complicated by shapes that are other than simple cylinders. Partial solution to this density variation problem may be accomplished by prepressing or the use of multiple punches, as shown in Figure 7.27. Development of pressure by centrifuging may produce more uniform density because each particle of material supplies a force of its own. Rods of various cross-sectional shapes may be extruded with relatively uniform density throughout their length. Thin coatings of powdered materials may be applied to rigid backings by rolling. This procedure is especially useful for various bearing materials.

7.4.3 SINTERING

The term *sintering* is used to identify the mechanism by which solid particles are bonded by application of pressure or heat, or both. In its broadest sense, the process includes such procedures as welding, brazing, soldering, firing of ceramics, and union of plastic flakes or granules. Each of the procedures other than those involving metal in powder form are important enough and of such wide usage as to have developed their own language and technology.

Sintering a Nonmelting Procedure. Sintering can be accomplished at room temperature with pressure alone but is most often performed at elevated temperatures, either at the same time or after pressure has been applied. With some multiple-constituent compositions, some of the low-temperature-melting materials may be melted, but in most cases sintering is a fully solid-state process. The two most common sintering procedures are (1) application of heat and pressure together, called *hot pressing*, and (2) application of heat after the particles have been closely packed, by *cold pressing*.

Densities Improved with Hot Pressing. In hot pressing, the plasticity of the particles is greater, and they recrystallize more readily, thus permitting high densities to be achieved with lower pressures than would be necessary at lower temperatures. For some materials, densities high enough to provide acceptable properties in the finished product are possible only by hot pressing. However, a number of problems are

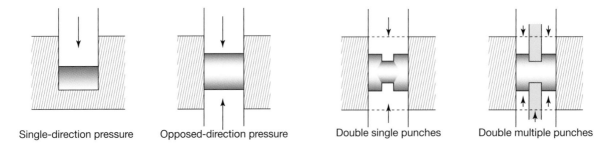

Single-direction pressure　　Opposed-direction pressure　　Double single punches　　Double multiple punches

Figure 7.26: Density variation from sidewall friction.　　**Figure 7.27: Multiple punch for density control.**

involved. The high temperatures—above 1370 °C (2500 °F) for some materials—require expensive die materials whose life may be very short. For some materials, a graphite die is used for each part pressed. Gas that is evolved may be trapped within the material, which leads to porosity discontinuities as in castings.

Protective Atmosphere Desirable. Cold-pressed parts that are subsequently sintered may be heated in a conventional manner by being placed in ordinary furnaces or salt baths. In those cases where heat is supplied by convection or radiation, it is usually necessary to provide a protective atmosphere of inert or reducing gas to protect the part from corrosion or chemical change.

7.4.4 SHAPING, SIZING, AND POSTSINTERING TREATMENTS

Properties Improved by Deformation. Because of variations of density and other factors, shrinkage of powder metallurgy products during sintering is difficult to control. Parts that require close tolerances must nearly always be finished by some dimensional treatment. Cold working may be used for minor changes of dimensions, but this procedure is limited by the lack of ductility common to powder metallurgy products. *Repressing*, sometimes referred to as *coining*, improves the density, strength, and ductility of the material. Even with this process, it is seldom that these properties are equal to those of a similar material produced by fusion. Most commercial deformation working is done by hot working or by cold working with frequent interruptions for recrystallization.

Conventional Heat Treatments Possible. Powder metallurgy products may be heat treated in the same ways as other materials of similar chemical composition, but the treatments are usually not as effective as for the fusion-produced metals, mainly because of the porous structure restricting the heat conductivity. Many of the voids within powder metallurgy products are stress concentration points that not only limit service loads but also increase the stresses arising from thermal gradients during heat treatment. Treatments include resintering for stabilization and homogeneity, annealing for softness, grain refinement for improved ductility, and hardening for improved wear resistance. Hardening processes may be *quench hardening* of carbon steels, *precipitation hardening* of nonferrous materials, or *surface hardening* by carburizing, cyaniding, and nitriding.

Machined When Necessary. The machinability of sintered materials is usually poor, but machining is sometimes necessary to provide final control of dimensions or to establish shapes that are not practical for the powder metallurgy process. With some types of products, such as the cemented carbides, grinding is the common finishing process both to control size and shape and, in many cases, to eliminate the surface produced in the sintering process. The original surfaces may contain faults or inclusions damaging to the use of the product.

7.5 QUALITY OF PRODUCTS

7.5.1 QUALITY AND IMPERFECTION OF SHEET-METAL PRODUCTS

Limitations of NDT Applications. Most products using sheet metal seldom require extensive NDT of the sheet-metal components. For example, while large quantities of sheet metal are used in aircraft, most of the NDT performed on aircraft during manufacturing is devoted to substructures, such as frames, beams, and spars, or heavier structures, such as landing gear and engine components. There are exceptions, however, and at some time the NDT specialist is likely to be asked to provide inspection of sheet metal.

While sheet-metal inspections are most likely to occur during the service lifetime of the structure to which the sheet metal is integral, some thin metals are used in rockets, some ordnance devices, marine and transportation structures, and pressure vessels. Therefore, some knowledge of the common manufacturing processes for sheet metals will be needed if inspection and NDT is called for. One example of an important application of NDT to thin metals is in thickness control and measurement. Ultrasonic and electromagnetic testing methods can both provide highly accurate means for thickness measurement and are particularly useful where access is limited to only one surface of a thin metal structure. Products made from bending, drawing, spinning, and other forming operations may also require NDT to ensure freedom from discontinuities that can result from the large deformations that such operations produce. Ultrasonic, penetrant, and electromagnetic tests are generally most suitable for detecting tears and cracks that can result from irregularities in the materials or processes used.

7.5.2 POROSITY AND IMPERFECTION OF PRODUCTS MADE FROM POWDERS

Properties Improved by Impregnation. One important finishing step is that of *impregnation*. Inorganic materials, such as oils or waxes, may be impregnated into porous metal products for purposes of lubrication. An entirely different kind of product can be produced by impregnating high-melting-temperature metals with low-melting-temperature metals. The principal use of this technique is in the production of cemented steels. A porous, skeleton iron compact, which may be produced from low-cost iron powder, is impregnated with molten copper. The resulting product has better strength, ductility, and machinability than conventional powder metallurgy parts and may be more readily plated or joined by brazing. Sintered iron has also been impregnated with lead alloys to improve antifriction properties for use as bearings.

Conventional film radiography and fluoroscopy have been effectively utilized on metal/metal impregnations to determine the adequacy of the impregnation. Most often, the material used to impregnate is of much different density than the host compacted material. Unimpregnated voids can be readily seen as can the extent of migration of the impregnating metal.

8 Joining and Fastening

8.1 INTRODUCTION TO JOINING

Engineering structures rarely start out as a single part, so joining is often a key process in the manufacture of devices or assemblies or the erection of structures. The purpose of the joint is to keep the component parts of assemblies or structures together while maintaining the designed arrangement, orientation, and alignment to allow the overall assembly or structure to perform its intended function(s) while resisting imposed loads. This can be accomplished by several means, and most will be discussed in this chapter.

Welding is a *joining* procedure in which shape changes are only minor in character and local in effect. Welding may be defined as "the permanent union of metallic surfaces by establishing atom-to-atom bonds between the surfaces." In practice, some distinction is usually made between *true welding*, on the one hand, and *brazing* and *soldering* on the other. In true welding, the filler material has a composition similar to that of the base metal(s). In brazing and soldering, however, the filler is a metal with a lower melting point than the base metal(s). *Adhesive joining*, which is sometimes performed as a true welding process with certain plastics, usually makes use of organic adhesives, often containing plastic filters and inorganic solvents that fuse the surfaces of the plastic and adhesive together. With some plastics, a sound

"The purpose of the joint is to keep the component parts of assemblies or structures together ..."

plastic-to-plastic joint can be formed by only introducing a volatile solvent, which "melts" the plastic-to-plastic interface, essentially welding the parts together.

Development of Welding Relatively Recent. Welding is both an ancient and a new art. Evidence indicates that prehistoric humans, finding native metals in small pieces and being unable to melt them, built up larger pieces by heating and then welding by hammering or forging. On the other hand, arc welding was first used in 1880 and oxyacetylene welding in 1895. Even after these developments, welding remained a minor process, used primarily as a last resort in maintenance and repair, until about 1930. After this date, the increased knowledge of metallurgy and testing and the development of improved techniques led to increased confidence and use, so that today welding may be considered a basic shape-producing method in direct competition with forging, casting, machining, and other processes.

Versatility Provides Many Applications. While it is true that welding itself does not change the shape of the individual components, the finished *weldment*, or assembly of parts, constitutes a unified structure that functionally has the properties of a solid part. In some cases, particularly with spot welding, welding is purely an assembly procedure and competes with mechanical fastening, such as riveting or bolting. In other cases, the goal in welding is to provide a joint that has the same structure, strength, and other properties as the base metal so that the weld area itself would be undetectable. This goal is approached in producing some pipe and high-pressure vessels but usually requires elaborate precautions to prevent contamination, heat treatment of the entire weldment after welding, and thorough testing, usually by radiography. In most cases, these procedures would not be practical or economical; consequently, some reinforcement of the welded area is provided by designing with reinforcing plates or gussets.

Often Replaces Bolting and Riveting. With the exception of some of the special purpose techniques in other areas, welding is in a greater period of growth than any of the other manufacturing procedures. Welding has largely replaced riveting and bolting in structural steel work for bridges and buildings. In the manufacture of automobiles and home appliances from sheet metal, most of the joining of large shapes is by welding, and in many cases these welds are not even apparent in the finished product. A typical automobile, for example, has over 4500 spot welds in addition to other welding.

8.1.1 COMPARISON OF VARIOUS JOINING PROCESSES

The most common method of joining two parts together is by mechanically fastening them using hardware such as screws and nuts. A localized clamping force is applied about the screw head or washer equal to the preload placed on the screw by torquing the screw or nut as shown in Figure 8.1. Wooden structures are often nailed together. The friction between the nail and wood prevents the nail from backing out as it is hammered in. Other methods of mechanically joining components together usually require a skilled operator for proper execution. Figure 8.2 presents a chart that categorizes the different welding processes, which include soldering and brazing.

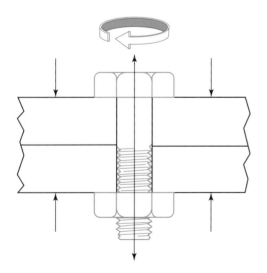

Figure 8.1: Mechanical fastening of parts.

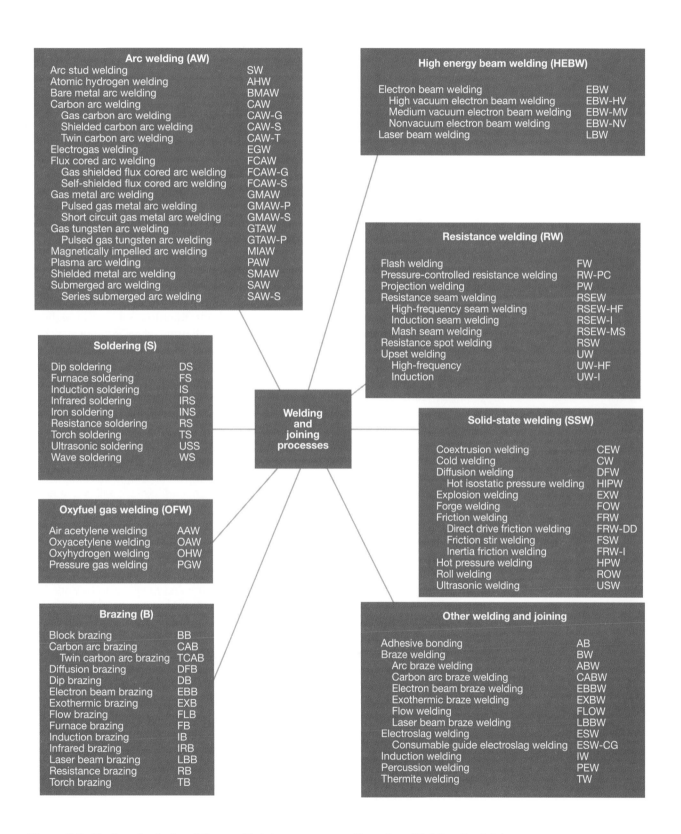

Figure 8.2: Master chart of welding and joining processes (American Welding Society).

8.1.2 NATURE OF BONDING

Atomic Bonding Essential. Most welding definitions include some reference to heat and pressure, and in practice most welding processes do make use of heat or pressure or both. However, neither of these is theoretically necessary. If two perfectly matched clean surfaces are brought together within suitable atomic spacing, atomic bonds will automatically be established between the surfaces, and the surfaces will, in fact, be welded. The essential features are not so easy to realize, however.

Atomic Cleanliness and Closeness. *Atomic cleanliness* requires that atoms exposed on the surfaces actually be the atoms of the materials to be joined. Even if this condition is set up on a surface, exposure to the atmosphere results in almost immediate formation of oxide or sulfide films on most metals. *Atomic closeness* requires that the distances between atoms brought into contact be that at which atoms are normally spaced in the crystalline structure of a metal. Normally, when two surfaces are brought into contact, this condition will occur only at a number of points because surfaces of even the best quality have a finite roughness of a much larger order than atomic distances.

Melting Common but Not Essential. Various means may be used to establish these two essential conditions of atomic cleanliness and closeness. Cleanliness may be established by *chemical cleaning (fluxing)*, providing the products of the cleaning operation may be removed from the surface by *melting* the surface area so that the surface films float to the surface of the molten material or by *fragmentation* as a result of plastic deformation of the base metal. Atomic closeness may be established by filling with a liquid metal, as in brazing and soldering, without actually melting the joined metals, by elastically or plastically deforming the surfaces until contact is established, or by actually destroying the surfaces by melting and allowing molten base metal or melted filler material to resolidify in contact with the unmelted base metal.

Welding may be accomplished as a result of any combination of conditions that establishes the two essential elements of atomic cleanliness and atomic closeness.

8.1.2.1 FUSION BONDING

Most important welding processes, particularly those in which high strengths are a principal goal, make use of *fusion bonds* in which the surfaces of the pieces to be joined (*parent* or *base* metal) are completely melted, as shown in Figure 8.3. Liquid metal then flows together to form the union, and cleanliness is established as the impurities float to the surface. No pressure is necessary, and the parts to be joined need only be located and held in proper relationship to each other.

Metallurgical Effects Like Casting. The resolidification of the metal results in a localized casting for which the unmelted base metal serves as a mold. It can then be expected that the same metallurgical changes and effects, such as grain-size variation and shrinkage, that occur in casting will occur in fusion welding. It is also implied that simply heating an entire structure that is to be fusion bonded would not be satisfactory because the entire structure would reach the melting temperature at the same time. The heat must be supplied locally to the area to be melted, and the rate of heat input must be great enough to prevent overheating of the adjacent areas. This requirement leads to some difficulties in welding aluminum, copper, and other metals having very high thermal conductivities. Hence, nondestructive testing (NDT) for weldments is similar to that for castings. The same kinds of discontinuities are likely to be found and similar NDT methods may be effective. In most cases there is no advantage in inspecting the entire weldment because the weld discontinuities will be concentrated in the weld itself or in the heat-affected zone (HAZ) of the weld.

Filler Sometimes Added. In fusion welding, at least the surface of the parts being welded is always melted, and this amount of molten metal may be sufficient to form the weld. In the more used fusion-welding processes, however, additional molten metal (*filler*) is supplied, usually by continuously melting a rod or wire. The use of filler is nearly always necessary in welding sheet and structural shapes more than 3 mm (1/8 in.) in thickness and, in many cases, permits more freedom in joint design by making possible the filling and buildup of gaps and cavities.

Welded Joint Strength. The strength of fusion-welded joints depends on the composition and metallurgical structure of the filler material and base metal, on any structural changes that take place in heated areas of the base metal adjacent to the weld, on the perfection with which the desired geometry of the weld is established, on residual stresses built up as a result of the differential heating and cooling, and on the presence or absence of impurities in the weld. It is at least theoretically possible to produce 100% efficiency in a fusion weld as compared to unwelded base metal.

8.1.2.2 PRESSURE BONDING

Heat Aids Cleanliness and Closeness. The term *pressure bonding* or *pressure welding* is somewhat misleading in that some heating is involved in the process. Pressure alone may be sufficient to form a bond, but heat is used for two principal reasons. The close union required is established by plastic flow, as indicated in Figure 8.4, and, in general, metals become more plastic and strengths are lower as the temperature is raised. Pressure and flow cause some fragmentation of the oxides on the surface because most are quite brittle and cannot maintain a continuous film as the metal flows plastically.

Of even greater importance are the two effects heat has on this oxide layer, which must be removed or dispersed before bonding can be effective. First, the fragments tend to assume spherical shapes as their total energy is raised. Spherical shapes disrupt a lower percentage of the surface areas to be joined, allowing greater contact between exposed base materials. This same type of spheroidization accounts for the malleabilizing of cast iron and for the effect on the cementite particles in the prolonged heating of high carbon steels. The second heat effect is that the solubility of oxygen in the base metals is raised with increased temperature, and some dissociation of the oxides occurs with the oxygen being diffused into the base metal.

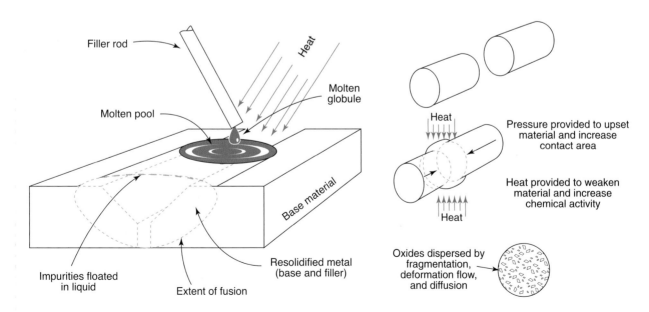

Figure 8.3: Fusion bond.

Figure 8.4: Pressure bond.

Overall Joint Efficiency High. While a small amount of fusion of the base metal may occur in some pressure bonds, it is incidental. No pronounced solidification shrinkage occurs as it does with fusion welds. Consequently, distortion after welding is usually very slight. The efficiency of pressure bonds, based on the original area, may be as high as 95%. Even though some inclusions are in the weld area, lowering unit strength, pressure-welded joints may actually be stronger than the original cross section as a result of the enlargement that occurs with plastic flow. This is especially true in butt-welding procedures as used in the manufacture of some chain links and fittings.

8.1.2.3 FLOW BONDING

Base Material Not Melted. When a filler material of different composition and lower melting temperature than the base metal is used, the mechanism is described as *flow bonding* (Figure 8.5). While some fusion of the base metal may occur, it is not essential to the process and is usually undesirable. The closeness necessary for bonding is established by the molten filler metal conforming to the surface of the base metal. The required cleanliness is produced by use of fluxes, ordinarily metal halides, or borax, which dissolve the surface oxides and float them out of the joint.

Joint Defined by Temperature and Spacing. Three different operations using flow bonds have been named: *braze welding*, *brazing*, and *soldering*. In braze welding, the filler material is a metal or alloy having a melting point above 449 °C (840 °F) and a composition significantly different from the base metal. In practice, the commonest alloys used as filler are copper or silver based. Occasionally, pure copper is used for braze welding steel. The filler is usually in rod form, and the procedures are similar to those employed in some fusion welding except that only the filler material is melted. Fluxes are heated on the joint surfaces for cleaning. Braze welding is used mainly for joining and repairing cast iron but is being replaced by fusion welding in many cases. The joint strength is limited to that of the filler material in cast form.

8.1.3 SOLDERING AND BRAZING

Both brazing and soldering are common and relatively economical methods of mechanically joining both similar and dissimilar metals with filler material. These processes require contact between mating surfaces as the filler material, when heated to slightly above its melting temperature, is drawn into the microscopic voids

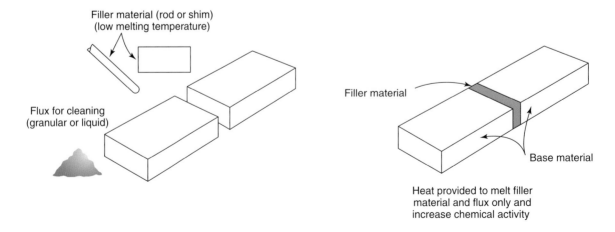

Figure 8.5: Flow bond.

between the surfaces by capillary action. A flux is required to promote wetting of the surfaces to allow for the capillary action to occur. Preparation of the surfaces by mechanically removing any oils, particulates, and oxides is crucial for the joint to be free of any voids and unwanted inclusions.

8.1.3.1 SOLDERING

Soldering actually includes application similar to both braze welding and brazing. The essential difference is in the melting temperature of the filler metal. Soldering occurs at temperatures below 449 °C (840 °F). Traditionally, soldering uses several compositions of tin-lead alloys with melting points from 185 °C (361 °F) to slightly above 315 °C (600 °F). The mechanical strengths of soldered joints, particularly built-up joints of the braze-weld type, are low, and the greatest use for soldering is for providing fluid tightness, for electrical connections, and for sheet metal joint filling in automotive assembly work.

Soldering Operations. Formulations of solder have been introduced where silver (or some other metal) replaces the lead to eliminate toxicity. Soldering operations for single components are typically performed using a hot iron or torch fueled by propane or methyl acetylene-propadiene propane (MAPP) gas. In the electronic industry, a large number of components (often small in size) have to be connected together or attached to plastic printed wire boards. The connections have to be free of impurities to provide good electrical conductivity. This is done most often by two methods:

- Dipping the component in the solder pot to cover the leads with solder and placing them on the solder patches deposited on the printed wire boards. The leads and patches are cleaned using fluxes. The connections are then heated to reflow the solder and form the joint.
- Using a *solder-wave machine*. In this procedure, a revolving impeller, immersed in a pot of molten solder, produces a vertical wave of solder between two parallel surfaces, so that the height of the wave, depending upon the impeller speed, is above the normal level of solder. Components that have to be soldered are inserted into through-plated holes on the printed circuit boards, and flux is applied to the surfaces where contacts have to be established. The assembled and fluxed board then passes over a relatively clean wave of solder, which is in slight motion at its surface.

8.1.3.2 BRAZING

Brazing is done at temperatures above 449 °C (840 °F). Brazing uses several varieties of filler material, which is chosen based on its application. Brazing operations involve the use of a combination of either MAPP gas or acetylene and oxygen due to the need for higher temperatures.

The word *brazing,* when used alone, designates the use of filler materials similar to those used in braze welding but applied to a close-fitting joint by preplacement or by capillary action. Filler material may be rod, wire, foil, slug, or powder, and fluxes similar to those used in braze welding are necessary. Heat may be furnished by torch, furnace, or induction, and, in production quantities, by dipping in molten salts, which may also provide the fluxing action.

Brazing quality depends upon the proper combination of base metal properties and joint preparation, filler metal properties, brazing temperature, and time at temperature. All factors in this combination are significant to provide for melting the braze filler metal, causing it to flow, fill, wet the joint, and diffuse into the surface layers of the atomic structure of the base metal.

Joint Thickness Critical to Strength. Figure 8.6 shows the importance of thickness to the strength of a brazed joint. The low strength of very thin joints is due to the formation of "capillary dams" caused by uneven surfaces that prevent complete filling. This fault can be overcome to some extent by use of special techniques, such as application of ultrasonic vibration while brazing. The fact that the strength of the joint can be higher than that of cast filler is due to the differences in modulus of elasticity between the filler and the base material. The filler metal is prevented from yielding by the more rigid base metal; the result is high shear stresses normal to the direction of the load in the filler material. These shear stresses generate tensile stresses in such direction that when they are combined vectorially with the direct tensile stresses caused by the load, a lower stress value is produced on the plane normal to the load than would occur in a homogeneous material. When the joint becomes thicker, there is less restraint in the center of the filler layer, the shear stresses are lower, and their effect in compensating for direct load stresses is reduced.

Brazing is frequently used to join parts together, particularly when one or more of those parts would be subject to changes from exposure to high temperature (above that needed for brazing). If the joint strength is critical or if leakage is a factor, NDT might well be used to establish that the necessary joint quality exists. The worst possible fault (assuming the braze itself is complete) would be wide spacing, either total or partial, due to poor preparation, angular geometry, or wide positioning. Sloppy fit-up of joints can also cause the molten braze filler to fail to completely fill the joint. Obviously, such conditions also produce joints of very low strength. Porosity and inclusions are other possible discontinuities. In critical applications, either ultrasonic or radiographic tests may be used to check the joint quality. Radiography readily reveals unfilled joints and porosity. However, unwetted and undiffused joints can seldom be revealed by radiography. If such conditions are suggested, ultrasonic techniques should be used; ultrasonic transmission characteristics through a properly wetted and diffused joint are significantly different from those through an inadequate joint.

8.1.4 DIFFUSION BONDING

Another method of joining similar and dissimilar metals, *diffusion bonding* literally diffuses the mating surfaces with the application of immense pressure and heat. Atomically, diffusion is where relatively small atoms squeeze into the spaces between the regular lattice atoms as discussed in Chapter 2. The part usually comprises several plates. These plates—think of them as cross sections—are stacked and fused

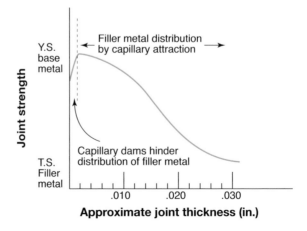

Figure 8.6: Strength of brazed joints (Y.S. = yield strength; T.S. = tensile strength).

together to form the overall part. No flux or filler material is required; however, mating surfaces must be prepped to where machining may be required. Due to the processes involved, this method can be quite costly.

Solid-state processes of joining metals were the earliest used and antedate the fusion processes. Revived interest in the principles of the solid-state processes, however, has recurred with increased theoretical knowledge of solid-state bonding. The result is development of diffusion welding.

Pressure, Temperature, Time-Independent Variables. The diffusion welding process involves the establishment of a smooth, clean surface that must be maintained until the weld is made. This often means protecting the surfaces in an inert gas environment for a few seconds to a number of minutes. Low to moderate pressure is applied to the surfaces to be joined at the same time the temperature is raised. The welding temperature is somewhat dependent on other conditions but usually falls someplace between the recrystallization temperature and the melting temperature of the material.

Present Use Limited. Diffusion welding does not seem to be economically competitive with other processes when these other processes can produce satisfactory results. The main use has been in welding new materials to avoid metallurgical, corrosion, and physical problems sometimes associated with older welding techniques. The process has been used most for joining special alloys in aerospace and atomic energy applications.

8.1.5 ADHESIVE BONDING

Often grouped as epoxies, *adhesive bonding*, with a few exceptions, is a quick and affordable method of joining both similar and dissimilar metals along with other materials. In terms of strength, structural adhesives, when applied correctly, are on par with some cast irons. However, the adhesive does not necessarily need to be as brittle. The underlying mechanism responsible for adhesion is *surface adsorption*. Surface adsorption involves the formation of relatively weak secondary bonds. Because of this principal mechanism for adhesion, successful adhesive bonding requires the joining of large surface areas.

Through different formulations of resins, hardeners, catalysts, and fillers, various properties can be achieved. Many composites use this method to create very strong structures, such as honeycomb panels. With this method, plies of carbon fiber impregnated with resins and hardeners create the high-performance carbon fiber panels used in racing and aerospace industries.

8.1.6 DESIGN OF JOINTS

Since the typical function of a joint is to transmit or distribute forces from one part to another throughout an assembly, the design of the joint is determined primarily from the type of service loading yet remains cost effective to produce. Joints also must be designed to reduce stress concentration. Sharp changes in part geometry near the joint tend to increase stress concentration or notch effects. Smooth contours and rounded corners tend to reduce stress-concentration effects. Joint design aspects, such as the size, length, and orientation of the joint, are based on stress calculations that take into consideration the service loads, material properties, section properties, and appropriate structural design requirements.

Joints must allow proper access or they can reduce overall quality and productivity, depending on the method of joining. As an example, arc-welded joint designs employ bevel angles and root openings to enhance accessibility to the welding torch (or electrode) and provide adequate weld penetration. The best bevel angles provide adequate accessibility while reducing the amount of weld metal required to complete the joint.

8.1.7 QUALITY AND INSPECTION OF JOINTS

A chain is only as strong as its weakest link, and that is also true for any part or assembly. Therefore, it is crucial to design and implement the proper joint such that it will meet or exceed its intended service life. Depending on the application, many typically used joining methods are employed, several of which are categorized as industry standards and are subject to quality inspections. Inspection techniques may vary and are chosen per designer or customer request. Traditional methods include destructive testing of a coupon made from the same batch as the part and/or assembly. On a typical lap joint, the joint can be mechanically tested for its shear strength by applying the tensile test on a coupon, which is representative of the actual part. Nondestructive testing has made use of radiographic and ultrasonic techniques to detect imperfections in a joint.

8.2 WELDING

Welding may fulfill either one of two basically different design concepts. As a shape-producing means, welding competes with other processes, especially forging and casting. The individual parts making up a weldment are most frequently cut from rolled sections that are produced in high quantities at low cost. Ideally, the finished weldment may be thought of as a homogeneous structure equivalent to a single part. Even with less than 100% joint efficiency, the single-piece concept may still be used in design if the maximum permissible stresses are considered and joint areas are increased where necessary.

   Unitized Product. The single-piece concept is used in many applications. For example, in much welded pipe, the weld is undetectable without critical examination; a drill or reamer shank is continuous with the body of the tool, even though they are of different materials. In modern welded structural steel assemblies, the joints may be stressed as continuations of the beams involved, although strengthening plates are sometimes necessary. In many instances, welding permits the single-piece concept to be applied to designs that would not otherwise be possible.

   Assembly Fastening. The second concept of welding is as an assembly means in competition with mechanical fastenings. The welded assembly is generally permanent, but the individual parts retain their identity, and the strength of the structure is frequently governed by the strength of the joints. The use of spot, seam, and projection welding is normally in this class. In many cases, not only are the mechanical fasteners eliminated but also preparation by drilling or punching holes is unnecessary and gaskets are not needed for sealing. Fitting of parts together may be simplified because alignment of holes is not required. The parts may be merely positioned with proper relationship to each other.

8.2.1 DESIGN OF WELDED JOINTS

Design of an appropriate weld joint can help reduce distortion caused by the welding process. Fusion welding processes employ localized melting and solidification to join parts. This can result in excessive thermal strains, which are dependent on the type of material, the welding process, and the welding procedure. Reducing the overall length of the weld or the amount of weld metal that needs to be deposited to complete a joint reduces both residual stresses and distortion. For example, intermittent welding versus continuous welding reduces the overall length of a weld. When making a fillet weld using an arc welding process, if thicknesses of the members are not greatly different, directing the arc toward the thicker member may produce acceptable penetration. However, special designs for joining will be required when large differences in section thicknesses result in large differences in heat-dissipating capacities.

8.2.1.1 JOINTS

The terminology applied to the shapes of welded joints is somewhat loose. The type of joint and the type of weld are two different considerations. Two flat plates, for example, may have their edges butted together, one may be lapped over the other, or they may be placed at right angles to each other. The configuration adopted would be referred to as the type of *joint*. Although some joints are more conveniently welded by some processes than by others, and some processes are restricted to certain types of joints, the specification of a joint type does not automatically specify the welding process or the manner in which filler material is to be placed.

Weld Type Usually Distinguished from Joint Type. The actual shape of the bonded area or the cross-sectional shape of the filler material, frequently governed by the preparation given the edges of the part to be welded, is known as the *type of weld*. In the lapped position, the plates might be joined by building up fillets along the edges, filling in holes or slots in one plate with weld metal, spot welding, or seam welding. Frequently, a close connection exists between the type of weld and the process that may be used. Either term, *joint* or *weld*, is sometimes used to refer to both the relative positions of the parts to be welded and the type of weld.

Figure 8.7 shows the weld types that may be produced by fusion welding. Following the name is the drawing symbol for each type. *Bead welds* are often used for building up metal on a surface where joining is not needed. The type of groove

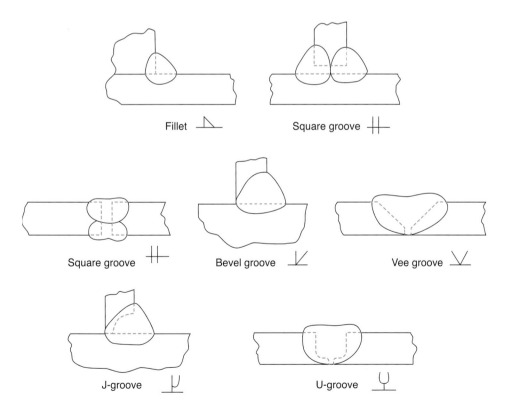

Figure 8.7: Fusion weld types.

weld used will have considerable influence on the penetration into the base metal necessary for good bonding and on the amount of distortion encountered. A vee or bevel weld requires simpler preparation than a U- or J-weld but results in greater distortion because much more heat is present at the opening of the vee than at the bottom. The heat difference is not so great in a U-weld. Where access is available to both sides of the members, many groove welds are made in double form, especially for heavy members. Adequate penetration with square grooves is generally possible only by welding from both sides. The weld types shown also apply to braze welding, except that in this application no melting of the base metal would occur, and the dotted lines in the figure would be the extent of fusion.

Configuration Determines Joint Type. Five basic types of joints are used for welding. These are shown in Figures 8.8 through 8.12. The types of welds that may be used with each and the standard weld symbols that apply are shown.

8.2.1.2 DESIGN CONSIDERATIONS

It has been fully realized in recent years that welding is a unique process and that all of the design rules applied to other processes do not necessarily apply to

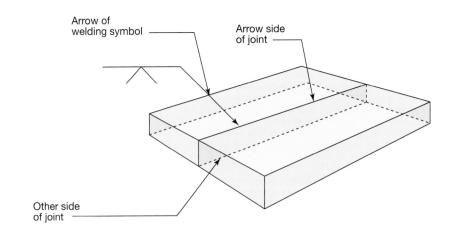

Figure 8.8: Butt joint.

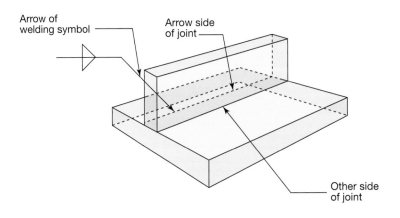

Figure 8.9: Tee joint.

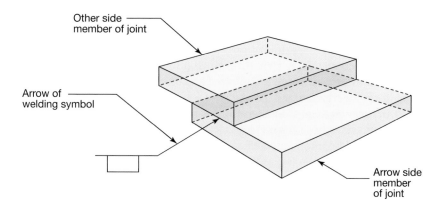

Figure 8.10: Lap joint.

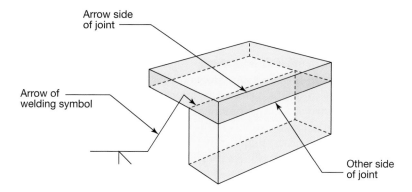

Figure 8.11: Corner joint.

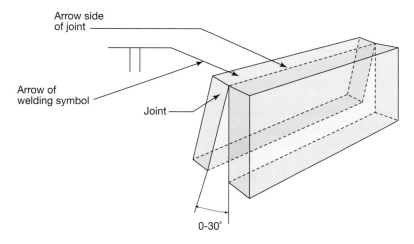

Figure 8.12: Edge joint.

welding. Welding started as a repair method and developed primarily as a substitute for other methods of *joining*. When it is used strictly as a joining method, particularly by spot welding, little trouble is experienced. However, when parts are fully joined to form rigid, one-piece structures, designers have not always realized that such structures do not respond to loading in the same way as a bolted or riveted structure. Many structures must allow for yielding or shifting in service that might be permitted by a bolted structure but not by a weldment, unless the design were changed.

Unit Structure—Special Consideration. A number of failures of welded ships and storage tanks have been traced to cracks that can grow to a large size in a welded structure but would be interrupted by a mechanically fastened joint. Monolithic welded structures have been found to be somewhat more notch sensitive with a corresponding drop in impact strength, especially at low temperatures.

On the other hand, designers have not always taken full advantage of the potential joint strengths offered by welding. Welding can produce rigid joints that improve beam strengths. The material would be used inefficiently if a welded structural steel assembly were designed according to rules that permit freedom in the joints as is generally assumed for bolting or riveting. Large improvements in joint strength and ductility have resulted from improved methods for preventing contamination of the weld metal as the metallurgical changes that take place in a weld have become fully understood.

8.2.2 WELDABILITY

Weldability is generally defined as (a) a metal's capability to be welded into a specific structure within certain specific properties and characteristics, and (b) the ability of the welded structure to satisfactorily meet service requirements. As might be expected, weldability involves a large number of variables, thus making generalizations difficult. Material characteristics, such as alloying elements, impurities, inclusions, grain structure, and processing history of the base metal and filler metal are all important. Other factors that influence weldability are properties such as strength, toughness, ductility, notch sensitivity, elastic modulus, specific heat, melting point, thermal expansion, surface tension characteristics of the molten metal, and corrosion.

Preparation of surfaces for welding is important, as are the nature and properties of surface oxide films and absorbed gases. The welding process employed significantly affects the temperatures developed and their distribution in the weld zone. Additional factors that influence weldability are shielding gases, fluxes, moisture content of the coatings on electrodes, welding speed, welding position, cooling rate, preheating, and postwelding techniques, such as stress relieving and heat treating.

Weldability Varies with Material. The relative ease with which a sound union may be produced between two parts by welding is knows as the *weldability* of a metal. A number of factors must be considered. Some metals may be more easily contaminated than others. The contamination may consist of gross oxide inclusions or voids that would be very apparent in a cross section of the weld, or of micro-contamination that results in structural changes detectable only by examining the metallurgical structure. Gross discontinuities not only reduce the actual cross section of the weld but also introduce stress concentrations that are particularly harmful in a metal with low ductility. The principal effect of structural changes is reduced ductility. Contamination can be controlled by providing the correct environment for the molten metal.

Hardenability. Especially important for steels is consideration of the hardenability of the metal. It will be remembered that this term is related to the cooling rate necessary to form a structure of given hardness in a steel. Again remembering that as hardness is increased, ductility decreases, the effect of hardenability on weldability can be predicted. In all the important welding processes, the metal is heated near or above the melting temperature, and cracking or high residual stresses as the metal cools differentially can be prevented only by yielding of the metal in the weld area. With few exceptions, any element that is added to pure iron increases its hardenability and therefore decreases its weldability by reducing ductility and increasing the possibility of cracks or high residual stresses. Therefore, increased welding difficulty can be expected as carbon or alloy content is increased in any steel. The major exception to this rule is the addition of vanadium, which reduces hardenability.

Thermal Conductivity. Another factor affecting weldability is the thermal conductivity of the metal. If a metal has infinitely high thermal conductivity, it cannot be fusion welded at all because it cannot be locally melted. Aluminum, for example, has such high conductivity that high rates of heat input are required to prevent excessive melting of the base metal. On the other hand, stainless steels have low conductivity, which results in hot spots, and very high temperature gradients in the weld zone, which results in increase of the stresses developed on cooling.

Composition. Composition can have other effects than those on hardenability. Stainless steels may not be hardenable to martensite at all but may develop higher stress on cooling than carbon steels of equivalent strength at room temperature because stainless steels have higher yield strengths at elevated temperatures. The chromium in stainless steel is especially subject to oxidation, and chromium oxide does not separate out easily from the molten weld pool. Many nonferrous alloy constituents are subject to segregation when cooled rapidly.

Recrystallization. Heat produces other effects on structure than those of quench hardening of steels. Material that has been cold worked is automatically recrystallized during welding, usually for a considerable distance away from the actual weld. Most aluminum alloys begin to recrystallize at about 150 °C (300 °F) so that a weldment made from work-hardened aluminum may actually be more ductile in the HAZ than in the unheated base metal but only with an accompanying reduction of strength. Grain growth will follow recrystallization, and even subsequent heat treatment cannot restore a desirably small grain size in most nonferrous metals.

Corrosion Resistance. The corrosion resistance of stainless steels may be especially affected by welding. At low cooling rates, small amounts of carbon can combine with chromium and reduce the corrosion resistance. Nearly all cooling rates will exist somewhere in the weld area; consequently, corrosion resistance will likely be lowered in some spots. Post-heat treating of stainless steel weldments is nearly always required to restore maximum corrosion resistance.

In addition to the structure effects, heat causes other changes. The surface of practically all metals is oxidized at welding temperatures. While surface oxidation may not directly affect strength, it does affect appearance and may produce surface imperfections that lead to fatigue failures or serve as focal points for intergranular corrosion.

Distortion. Even when the residual stresses do not lead to actual failures, they cause other difficulties. The dimensions of a weldment are usually different before and after welding, and machining is nearly always necessary for close dimensional control. The machining itself may release residual stresses to cause further dimensional change. When close tolerances must be held, stress relief prior to machining is usually required.

A number of precautions and corrections can alleviate the problems caused by stresses and distortions. If the amount of distortion can be predicted, the parts to be welded may be purposely off-positioned before welding to compensate. This procedure is somewhat like overbending sheet metal to compensate for springback. Some automatic compensation will occur in a double-groove weld made from both sides of a joint, but the first side welded usually will have the greatest effect. When a number of welds are to be made at a number of locations in a weldment, distortion may be controlled by choosing the proper sequence for making the welds.

Pre-Heat and Post-Heat Treatment. The most universal solutions to the problems of stresses and distortion are pre- and post-heat treatment of weldments. Pre-heat treatment does not eliminate shrinkage and yielding that lead to stresses, but by lowering the yield strength of the base metal, it provides greater volume through which the shrinkage may be distributed, and by lowering the thermal gradients in the weld zone, it reduces the size of the stresses by distributing them over greater areas. Post-heat treatment relieves stresses by permitting yielding to occur at reduced stress levels; it can also help restore a uniform structure with an improved grain size, particularly in steel.

When materials have sufficient ductility, correct dimensions can be established by straightening. This may involve pressing operations in fixtures or localized heating with torches.

The factors that lead to residual stresses and distortion generally have an adverse effect on the strength of welded metals. Inclusions or voids not only reduce area but also are stress concentration points. Composition changes in the weld area may either increase or decrease strength with a corresponding change in ductility. In some nonferrous alloys, brittle intermetallic compounds may form that have a serious effect on ductility.

Weld Penetration. The efficiency of a fusion-welded joint may depend on the amount of penetration achieved. Although melting of the base metal is not absolutely necessary for bonding, and, in any case, proper bonding requires only that the surface of the base metal be melted, practical joint shapes cannot generally be heated to melting only on the surface. To obtain proper bonding at the bottom of a square-groove weld with most heat sources, it is necessary to melt a considerable amount of base metal. Heat sources differ in their ability to penetrate, that is, in the depth-to-width ratio of the molten zone that may be produced, dependent largely on the degree of heat concentration.

8.2.3 SYMBOLS USED IN WELDING

The Welding Symbol. Figure 8.13 illustrates the elements of a welding symbol as recognized by the American Welding Society. The symbol is used on drawings to designate the details of a weld. Any part of the symbol that is not needed for clarity may be omitted. Figure 8.14 shows the manner in which the symbol would be used to describe a welded corner joint together with the result of following these specifications. The joint is to have a 6 mm (1/4 in.) unfinished fillet weld on the inside of the corner (opposite side) and a 6 mm (1/4 in.) back weld on the outside (near, or arrow side) that is to be ground flat. The shielded metal arc welding process is to be used. It is to be a continuous weld along the corner because no pitch or spacing is designated. A range of welding symbols is presented in Figures 8.15 and 8.16. (Note that Figure 8.13 is an enlarged view of the diagram located in the bottom right-hand portion of Figure 8.15.)

Weld Testing Symbols. A testing symbol is very much like the welding symbol used to specify welding types and procedures. As with the welding symbol, the placement of the basic test symbol below the reference line means testing is to be performed from the side to which the arrow points. Figure 8.17 shows the testing symbol that carries a tail only if some special reference is to be indicated and may at times be combined with the welding symbol for the same joint by carrying two reference lines. In this case, the symbol indicates that a vee-groove butt weld is to be inspected with both magnetic particle testing (MT) and radiographic testing (RT) from the opposite side.

8.2.4 OXYFUEL GAS WELDING

In *oxyfuel gas welding* (OFW), a combination of oxygen and fuel (usually acetylene) flows through specially designed nozzles to create a flame, with temperatures of about 3500 °C (6330 °F), well capable of melting almost any metal. For comparison, the *Modern Welding* textbook states that a temperature of about 3087 °C (5589 °F) is ideal for oxyacetylene welding (OAW) of steel and cast iron. This temperature produces a neutral flame combination of acetylene and oxygen. The weld pool is protected from the contaminating atmosphere due to the high flow of superheated gases. The flow of both fuel and oxygen can be varied to create the optimal flame for the application. A filler metal, available in differing sizes and alloys, is used to add material to the weld pool. Unlike soldering and brazing operations, no flux is required during the welding process. However, surface preparation is crucial for a high-quality weld. The same gases and process are used in *torch cutting* except the process involves a sudden increase in fuel and oxygen flow once the weld pool stabilizes. This increase of super-heated gases literally "blows away" the molten material. The same fuel and oxygen combination is also used to braze components as discussed previously.

Oxyacetylene. The oldest and still most used source of heat based on a chemical reaction is the burning of acetylene (C_2H_2) and pure oxygen. A reducing or carbur-izing flame prevents or reduces decarburization and causes less oxidation of steel. An excess of oxygen produces a strongly oxiding flame that has only limited use but yields maximum temperatures. With three parts oxygen to one part acetylene, the temperature is 3482 °C (6300 °F). Other temperatures range from 815 °C (1500 °F) at the tip of the inner cone of a neutral flame (one-to-one proportions of oxygen and acetylene) to about 3300 °C (5972 °F) in the hottest portions of the outer envelope.

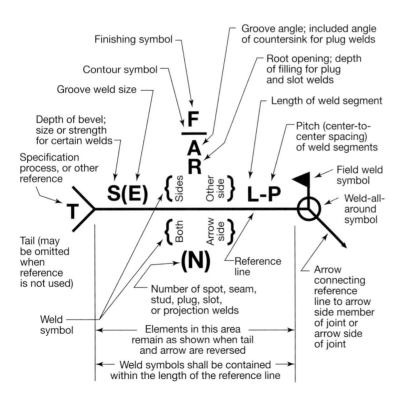

Figure 8.13: Elements of a welding symbol (American Welding Society).

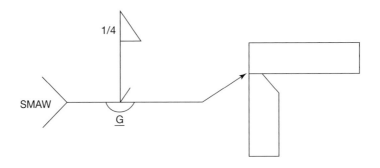

Figure 8.14: Example of a welding symbol in use.

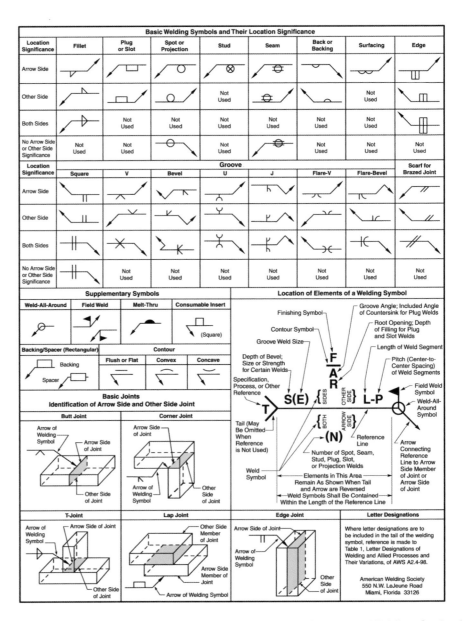

Figure 8.15: Basic welding symbols and configurations (American Welding Society).

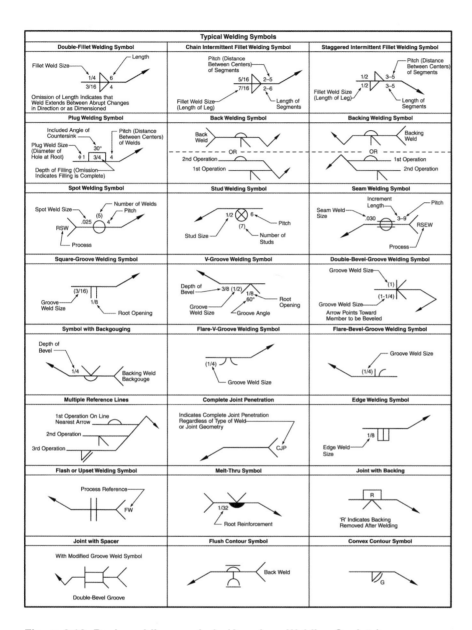

Figure 8.16: Basic welding symbols (American Welding Society).

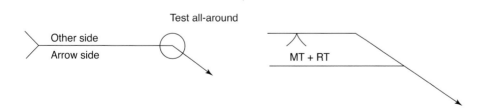

Figure 8.17: Weld testing symbol: (a) general form; (b) combined with welding symbol.

Portability an Important Advantage. Oxyacetylene has advantages of portability, low initial cost, and flexibility. With relatively simple equipment, operations ranging from brazing and soldering to flame cutting may be performed. For fixed installations and high production processes, the electric arc is used more than oxyacetylene because of the greater heat input that may be obtained and the lower cost of electrical energy.

Other Gases Less Used. Other gases burning with oxygen are also used but to a much more limited degree. Oxyhydrogen can provide a strongly reducing flame without the soot associated with oxyacetylene and is used for welding aluminum and lead. Natural gas, propane, or butane, burned with oxygen, are used for preheating and for brazing and soldering but have limited temperatures, making them less useful than oxyacetylene for fusion welding.

8.2.5 ARC WELDING PROCESSES: CONSUMABLE ELECTRODE

Gas metal arc welding (GMAW), formerly referred to as *metal inert gas* (MIG) welding, *flux core welding,* and *shielded metal arc welding* (SMAW), or *stick welding,* are all examples of the welding process where the welding electrode is consumed. The electrical arc current flows through the electrode as it is fed into the weld pool, adding material to the joint. These processes are usually "dirtier" in the sense that a break in the current causes splattering where small amounts of molten material are flung around the weld. With the correct execution, this can be avoided and a relatively clean weld can be obtained.

Stick welding and flux core welding processes leave a protective cover of slag over the weld, preventing oxidation from occurring, while the molten pool solidifies underneath. This must be removed post welding or the surface will quickly begin to corrode. Since the electrode is being added into the weld and becoming part of the joint, the material of the electrode must be taken into consideration. Depending on the weld bead size desired, the feed and correct gage must be used or the weld quality will suffer. GMAW and flux core welding processes utilize a "gun," which feeds the wire electrode into the weld. GMAW welding typically uses an inert gas, usually argon and/or helium, to locally provide a protective environment around the molten weld pool to prevent oxidation from occurring and contaminating the weld. Inert gases are used because they do not react with the molten weld pool. However, active gas may also be used with this process, making MIG terminology no longer accurate.

With *flux core welding,* as the name suggests, flux core spools contain the protective flux inside the wire. As the wire electrode is fed into the weld, the filler metal is melted within the arc column and transferred into the weld pool. The flux melts and pools to the surface of the weld bead, leaving the protective slag that needs to be removed post weld.

8.2.5.1 THE ELECTRIC ARC

Practically all production welding today makes use of electricity as an energy source. The first application was the electric arc, developed about 1880 (Figure 8.18) but restricted in use until the development of coated electrodes. The electric arc is one of the hottest sources of energy available except for nuclear reactions. Arc column temperatures are near 6090 °C (11 000 °F), which is well above the melting points of common metals and alloys. With typical arc-welding conditions of 25 V at 300 A, the total energy supplied would be 6550 kilocalories (26 000 BTU) per hour.

Ionization Establishes Current Path. Most gases, including those in the atmosphere, are very poor conductors at room temperature, and the voltage necessary to maintain an arc over any practical distance would be very high.

However, gas molecules at arc temperatures have such high velocities that they ionize (lose some electrons by collision) in numbers sufficient to make the gas highly conductive for electric current. When the arc is extinguished, it cools and loses its ionization in the order of one thousandth of a second, and re-ionization must occur before the arc can be reestablished.

The temperature of the arc is essentially constant throughout the length and diameter of the arc column. The electrical characteristics, including the voltage drop in the arc and at the surfaces at which the arc terminates, are determined by the composition and length of the arc. With long arcs and highly conductive gases such as hydrogen, higher inputs are required to maintain the arc.

The Work Frequently Serves as One Electrode. The arc usually exists between the work and a metal rod, which may progressively melt and serve as filler material or may be nonconsumable.

Some Metal Lost during Transfer. Welding arcs with consumable electrodes transfer this metal in molten form to the weld pool on the work. Transfer may be by fine metal spray or by relatively large globules and rivulets that may even short circuit the arc temporarily. The rate of electrode burn-off is almost directly proportional to the welding current for any given rod diameter. However, the range of currents that may be used with any electrode to obtain a balance between burn-off and heating of the base metal is limited. From 10% to 30% of the melted rod is normally lost through vaporization and spattering outside the molten pool.

Gas Shielding Improves Quality. During transfer across the arc gap, the molten metal is shielded by protective gases from oxidation and other reactions with the arc atmosphere. These gases may be provided by the burning of coatings on the welding rod itself, by flux powders beneath which the arc burns, or by a flow of shielding gas from an external source.

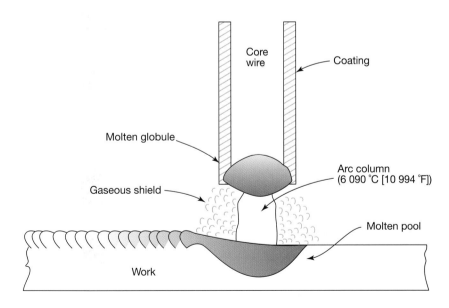

Figure 8.18: Welding arc.

Straight Polarity—Welding Rod Negative. With certain welding rods, the polarity of the rod with respect to the work exerts a measurable influence on burn-off rate and the amount of spattering. When the rod is negative, the setup is called *straight polarity*. When the rod is positive, the setup is called *reverse polarity*. Manufacturers designate the preferred polarities for most rods.

Arc Welding Versatile and Important. Arc welding has developed into the most versatile of all welding processes. Power supplies of almost unlimited capacity are available, and deposition rates in excess of 45 kg (100 lbs) per hour are used with the faster procedures. Many production processes have been developed, most with automatic regulation of current, rod feed, and speed of travel along the proper path. With proper shielding, most metals and alloys may be arc welded. Products that are regularly arc welded include tanks and other pressure vessels, structural steel, large diameter steel pipes, ship hulls and fittings, large machinery frames, and aircraft structures.

Percussive Welding. One other use of the electric arc is in *percussive welding*, a process more closely associated with pressure than fusion methods and used only for making butt joints between the flat ends of workpieces without filler material. The workpieces are connected to a large capacitor charged to about 3000 V, then driven toward each other by high spring or air pressure. Before contact can take place, arcs with current on the order of 50 000 to 100 000 A are established. These high currents quickly heat the surfaces of the work to vaporization temperatures. The vapor holds the workpieces apart until the capacitor is nearly discharged, at which time the pressure completes the contact against a thin film of clean molten metal. Equipment costs are high and applications are limited, but percussive welding may be used for joining widely dissimilar materials. Heat effects in the base material are limited in extent.

Stud Welding. A further variation in the use of an arc for welding is in the process called *stud welding*, developed in the shipbuilding industry for attaching steel studs to the steel deck of a ship. These studs are then used for holding the wood overdeck. The stud is supported in a special gun and forms the electrode in much the same manner as the filler material in conventional arc welding. It is then moved to the work until an arc is established, drawn back, then forced into the work—after a short period of arc heating—with sufficient pressure to cause some upsetting of the end of the stud. The process is used primarily for attaching threaded fastening devices in applications similar to that described above.

8.2.5.2 WELDING EQUIPMENT AND PROCEDURES

Most of the basic shape-producing methods make use of a relatively small number of equipment types for each of the individual processes. For both practical and economic reasons, the majority of welding processes make use of heat to establish the conditions necessary for welding. Most heating means are used at one time or another, so that the equipment design varies over a wide range. Welding is still in an earlier stage of development than casting, forging, pressworking, or machining, and new techniques with associated equipment are constantly being developed.

8.2.5.3 ARC WELDING ELECTRODES

Coatings Provide Protective Atmosphere. Early welding rods were bare iron wires, with which it was difficult to maintain stable welding arcs; the deposited metal was frequently porous or contained oxides and other inclusions. Modern welding rods for manual use are usually heavily coated with constituents that alleviate these problems. The first function of the coating is to provide a gaseous shield that flushes away the atmospheric gases to prevent oxidation and other gaseous contamination of molten metal during transfer from the rod and after deposition in the molten pool. The gaseous shield generally also contains ionizing constituents that assist in ionizing the arc atmosphere by reducing the effective ionization potential so that the arc may burn with lower applied voltage. Sodium salts are commonly used for direct-current welding rods. Potassium salts are used for alternating-current welding rods for which arcs are more difficult to maintain because the current passes through zero 120 times each second (twice for each cycle of 60 Hz current).

Slag Protects Hot Metal. In addition, the coating may provide slag blanket-forming materials, which form a protective layer over the deposited weld metal. The insulating coating reduces the rate of cooling by heat loss to the atmosphere and protects the hot metal from atmospheric oxidation and gas absorption at the higher temperatures at which gases are readily soluble in the metal. For welding on vertical and overhead surfaces, special coatings with high slag viscosities are needed to prevent the slag from running off the surface of the metal during the period when the slag itself is molten.

Coating May Add Filler. In high-deposition-rate rods for flat position welding, extremely heavy coatings may be employed to carry powdered iron or iron oxide materials that combine with the deposited metal to add to the deposition rate. Contact electrodes are designed with coatings that burn off slowly enough to support the rod at a proper distance above the work for good arc length with less operator skill than demanded by the usual manual procedure. The operator merely drags the electrode over the work, yet maintains a good arc position as the coating burns away in unison with the melting of the metallic material.

8.2.5.4 MODIFICATION OF ARC WELDING FOR SPECIAL PURPOSES

Manual Procedures Very Versatile. Many installations are for manual welding. Most use coated electrodes of consumable types; shielding of the arc is provided by burning of the electrode coating. The core wire provides the deposited metal. These electrodes are manufactured in stick form with core wires of various diameters and coatings for various welding purposes.

Manual Welding Economical for Small Quantities. Manual welding is costly in terms of time and labor as compared to automatic production processes but requires little or no setup time. Speed of manual welding is increased, where feasible, by using *work positioners*. These permit welding on complex shapes to be carried out in optimum welding positions, flat or horizontal if possible. In this way, high-deposition-rate electrodes may be employed to speed the work and lower its cost.

Certain applications, such as repair and maintenance welding, construction of bridges and structures, and welding of cross-country pipelines, do not permit positioning of the work. Even so, welding often proves to be far cheaper and produces more reliable structures than other fabrication processes.

Quality and Speed Improved with Modifications. When manual arc welding with stick rods cannot provide welds of high enough quality or when the nature of the work, especially the amount of welding to be done, permits higher setup and equipment costs with reduced operating labor time, a number of modifications are available.

Wire Electrode May Supply Filler. Several variations of *gas metal-arc welding* (GMAW), shown in Figure 8.19, have been developed. Processes of this type have in common the use of a filler material in wire form, which is continuously fed into the weld metal pool, and a shielding gas, or mixture of gases, to provide the protective atmosphere. Filler-wire diameter may range from 0.5 to 30 mm (0.020 to 0.125 in.), and currents may range from 90 to 800 A. Equipment is available for both handheld and machine-guided operation.

Several Gases Used as Shields. Argon, helium, or mixtures of argon and helium are the commonest shielding gases, particularly for high-alloy steels and nonferrous metals, because of their complete chemical inertness. However, the gas mixture has considerable effect on the depth of penetration, the contour of the weld surface, and the arc voltage. Oxygen from 0.5% to 5% is sometimes added to improve the weld contour. Carbon dioxide gas is frequently used when welding mild steel; even then it is difficult to avoid porosity in the weld. Weld quality may be improved by providing a small amount of dry flux as a magnetic powder that either clings to the rod as it emerges from the holder or is contained in the center of hollow filler wire. Similar improvement may be obtained by using two shielding gases: a small amount of inert gas such as argon or helium near the rod and a larger flow of cheaper carbon dioxide surrounding the inert gas.

8.2.6 ARC WELDING PROCESSES: NONCONSUMABLE ELECTRODE

Gas tungsten arc welding (GTAW), makes use of a "torch," which houses a nonconsumable tungsten electrode. The process also makes use of an inert gas, typically argon or helium, to provide a protective environment around the weld pool. (See Figure 8.20.) This process is the most controlled and preferred of the arc welding processes due to the variety of weld beads possible. Once a controlled molten weld pool is established, a filler material may or may not be manually added as required by a particular application. The tungsten electrode never contacts the weld pool but remains within proximity to establish and maintain an arc. Tungsten electrodes vary in composition and are created to perform better for certain metals. Filler materials come in a multitude of sizes and alloys affecting the overall quality and strength of the weld.

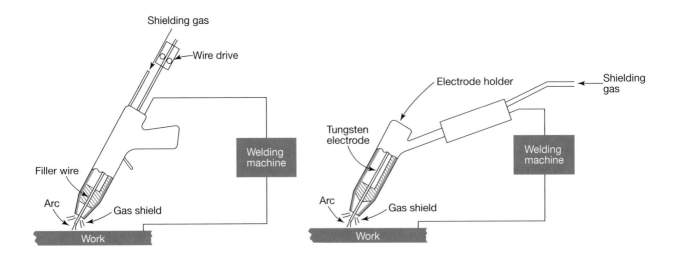

Figure 8.19: Schematic of gas metal arc welding.   **Figure 8.20: Schematic of gas tungsten arc welding.**

Welding of many modern metals and alloys, such as magnesium, titanium, stainless steels, and others is done with GTAW. This method has been well developed and finds many applications today, particularly for welding of difficult materials. In the past, this nonconsumable process has been referred to as *tungsten inert gas* (TIG) welding.

Automatic Welding. Almost all electric arc processes, except those using covered electrode wire, are amenable to a certain amount of automatic or machine control. Those using gas metal arc and/or flux core wire with a gas shield are sometimes adapted for automatic operation. Usually, a constant voltage power supply and adjustment of current flow permit the burn-off rate to maintain an approximately uniform arc length regardless of the rate of wire feed.

A great amount of automatic welding is performed by the GTAW method because the nonconsumable tungsten electrode provides for a heat source with good stability. Most automatic GTAW machines are applied with electronic controls that automatically move the electrode holder upward or downward to maintain a constant arc length. The possible compactness of the electrode holder permits use of the method in locations where a human operator could not see or manipulate. Much of the development work was performed in submarines for successfully welding pipe in inaccessible areas.

The method is widely used for pipe welding both in the field and in the shop. In some cases, welds without filler wire are produced—most on relatively thin sheet metal products. In other cases, cold filler wire is fed into the weld puddle or, in still other cases, preheated filler wire is fed to promote faster welding. *Pulsed-arc power supplies* are capable of providing various pulse characteristics to the arc. Such controls impart high-frequency agitation of the matter puddle, in effect stirring the oxides and evolved gases out of the weld.

Automatic Welding under Flux. A high production process in wide use is *submerged arc welding* (SAW), shown in Figure 8.21. The power supply and feeding arrangement are similar to those that would be used with GMAW, but shielding is provided by a granular flux fed from a hopper to surround the arc completely. Part of the flux is fused by the heat of the arc to provide a glassy slag blanket that protects the molten metal and the solidified weld as it cools. In addition, the normally nonconductive flux becomes conductive when fused and permits very high current densities that give deep penetration. Because of the greater penetration with a saving of filler material and a higher welding speed for a given current, smaller grooves may be used for joint preparation with this process than with others. It is basically a shop process.

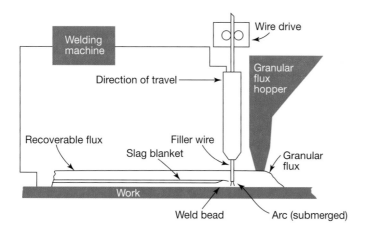

Figure 8.21: Schematic of submerged arc welding.

8.2.7 HIGH ENERGY BEAM WELDING

With *high energy beam welding*, a flow of electrons from an electron source/gun or photons from a laser beam is focused to power densities large enough to melt and vaporize the metals being joined. High-quality, deep-penetrating welds with small heat-affected zones and minimized distortion can be produced. In certain applications, high-energy beam welds can offer both high quality and cost effectiveness when compared to other welding methods. The field of additive manufacturing has benefited greatly from this technology. Several processes, such as *selective laser sintering* (SLS), weld thin layers of powder from the material. This process also opens the field of *micro-joining* when weld dimensions are less than a millimeter and where spot size, beam control, and part manipulation become more challenging. This process is typically used in manufacturing microelectronics and integrated circuits. At these sizes, joint preparation and cleanliness are critical for a high-quality weld; however, not all of the materials with differing thermal expansion rates are weldable.

Electron beam welding (EBW) is valuable for welding beryllium, molybdenum, zirconium, hafnium, and other refractory metals difficult to weld by other methods. The process uses high-cost equipment, and the total amount of heat available is small.

Electron Beam Gun. Energy for heating may be made available in many forms. In the *electron beam gun* (Figure 8.22), a stream of high-energy electrons is focused electrically toward a spot on the surface to be heated. Rapid localized heating takes place with the possibility of melting for welding or of complete vaporization for removing metal. The process is carried out in a vacuum so that no products of combustion and no contamination or oxidation of the heated work occur. The boiling of the molten metal at the high temperatures removes impurities that may be present, and the resulting weld may be of higher quality than the base metal. The high rate of heating restricts the HAZ, and there is minimum distortion and alteration of physical properties. A ratio of fusion depth to width of as much as 20 is possible.

8.2.8 LASER WELDING

Laser beam welding (LBW) uses a highly focused laser with spot sizes typically ranging from 0.2 mm to 13 mm (0.008 in. to 0.5 in.). (See Figure 8.23.) The laser

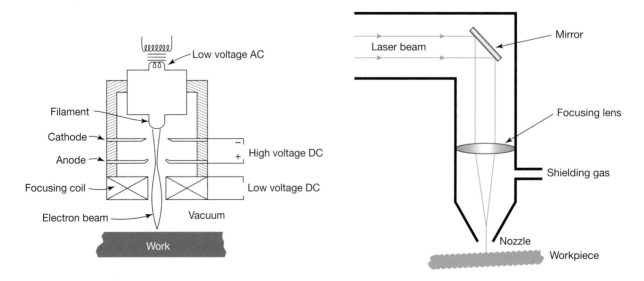

Figure 8.22: Schematic of a simple electron beam gun.   **Figure 8.23: Schematic of laser beam welding.**

beam has high-power density and typically creates a narrow weld seam and small HAZ. The laser beam can be continuous or pulsed for different applications. Because of the high production rate, LBW is particularly dominant in the auto-motive industry.

8.2.9 PLASMA ARC WELDING

Plasma is a gas that has been heated to such a temperature that the gas is ionized. A reduction in temperature results in the recombination of atoms to the molecular form and the release of energy as heat. The gas column in arc welding is ionized, but in this case, it is a relatively small, stationary quantity of gas that is involved.

In the *plasma arc process*, a stream of gas is ionized by heat as it is passed through an electric arc by one of the two methods shown in Figure 8.24. Thermal expansion of the gas stream causes it to flow at supersonic speeds as its diameter is restricted by the magnetic properties of the arc. The drop in temperatures caused by contact with the relatively cool work surface results in loss of ionization and the release of large amounts of heat directly at the surface to be heated. The process has a high intensity and a high rate of heat transfer, which makes it useful for welding high-conductivity metals such as aluminum.

8.2.10 FORGE WELDING

Forge welding (FOW) is a solid state process in which the workpieces are heated to the welding temperature and then applied with loads sufficient to cause permanent deformation at the faying surfaces. Pressure is typically applied by hammering,

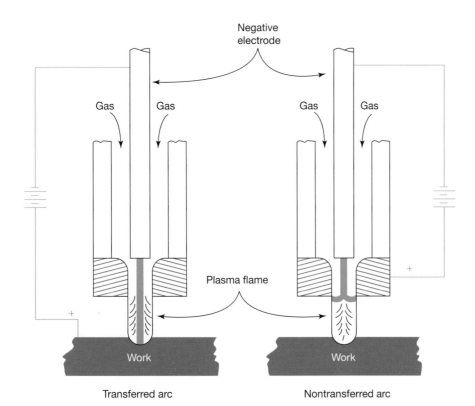

Figure 8.24: Plasma arcs.

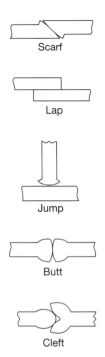

Figure 8.25: Forge welding joints.

rolling, or extruding through dies. It is most commonly applied to the butt welding of steels at temperatures of 80% to 90% of the melting temperature (T_m) or about 1125 °C (2060 °F) for carbon and low-alloy steels. The forge welding process generally requires post-heat treatment along with preheating to avoiding such metallurgical problems as embrittlement, sensitization, and excessive grain coarsening.

Typical joint designs used in manual forge welding operations are shown in Figure 8.25. The joint surfaces are slightly rounded or crowned to ensure that the centerline region of the components joined will be welded first to force any contaminants (for example, slag, dirt, oil, and/or oxide) present on the surfaces out of the joint.

Flux must be added when forge welding certain metals to prevent the formation of oxide scale. Silica sand and borax are two fluxes commonly used on steels. For example, because of its low fusion point, borax is sprinkled on the workpiece while it is in the process of being heated for use in the forge welding of high-carbon steels. However, the oxides of very low-carbon steels (iron ingots) and wrought irons do not require fluxes because of their low melting points.

8.2.11 COLD WELDING

In *cold welding*, tremendous compressive forces diffuse the contacting surfaces to join the material together, as shown in Figure 8.26. The weld or metallurgical bond is affected by the re-formation of the atoms of the material. One method uses hydraulics to axially compress the workpieces together. Another method is where tubes are drawn together through a die and mandrel.

Theory of Cold Bonding. The currently accepted hypothesis that accounts for a cold pressure weld taking place is basically that the atoms of metals are held together by the "metallic bond," so called because it is peculiar to metallic substances. The bond can be described as a "cloud" of free negatively charged electrons, enveloping

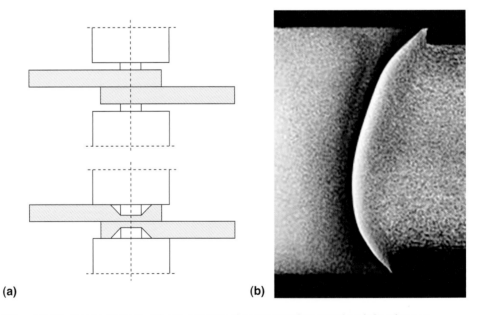

(a)   (b)

Figure 8.26: Cold welding: (a) schematic of compression used to join pieces; (b) cross section of cold-welded area showing 8 mm (0.315 in.) diameter copper rod joined to 9.5 mm (0.374 in.) diameter aluminum rod.

ionized, positively charged atoms into a unit as a result of attractive forces. Thus, if two metallic surfaces are brought together with a space of only a few angstroms separation and there are 300 million angstroms (Å) to one centimeter (1 cm), interaction between the free electrons and ionized atoms can occur. This will eliminate the potential barrier, allowing the electron cloud to become common. This now effects a bond and therefore a weld. A more simplified explanation is that if two surfaces, when considered on an atomic scale, are atomically flat and atomically clean and they are put together, a bond is effected equal to that of the parent metal.

Contact Area Increased. In practice, welds are made by squeezing the metal between two punch faces that cause metal flow normal to the direction of load (Figure 8.27). As the area of contact is increased, the brittle surface oxides fragment and cover a smaller percentage of the area, exposing clean metal-to-metal contacts. The greatest success is with copper and aluminum base metals.

8.2.12 ULTRASONIC WELDING

One of the principal limitations on cold bonds is the excessive deformation required to provide enough fragmentation of the oxide layers on the contacting surfaces. Cold bonding may be performed with less deformation by applying high-frequency mechanical energy in the process called *ultrasonic welding* (USW). In USW, small, quickly oscillating motions through a transducer shear mating surfaces together while a small axial load is applied. The friction between the parts melts the surfaces together, fusing the parts. Many products with plastic housings commonly use this technique to weld the pieces that make up the housing unit.

Vibration Aids Cleaning. The vibrations that introduce shearing forces assist in the fragmentation; as a result, more than 50% clean-metal contact may be established. Both spot and seam welds may be made, and the widest use has been for metals difficult to join by conventional processes. These include stainless steel, molybdenum, zirconium, various bimetal combinations, and thin foil or sheet aluminum. The upper limit is about 2.54 mm (0.1 in.), although thin sheets may be welded to thicker sections. USW is also an important assembly method for plastics.

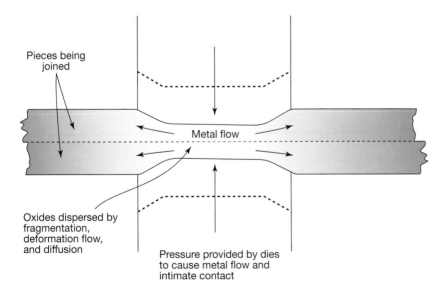

Figure 8.27: Cold bond.

8.2.13 FRICTION WELDING

In ultrasonic welding, mechanical energy is supplied to facilitate fragmentation. In *friction welding* (Figure 8.28), mechanical energy is supplied not only to facilitate fragmentation but also to develop heat. In this process, used almost exclusively for making butt welds in heavy round sections, the bars or tubes are brought together with high force while one is rotated. The friction develops sufficient heat to make the metal plastic and to permit cleaning and closeness to be achieved in much the same manner as in resistance butt welding.

Friction between mating surfaces creates enough heat to weld the surfaces together. Typically, a stationary part is held against its rotating or reciprocating counterpart until the point of seizure. Properly fixturing both parts is critical for a proper joint, adding to the difficulty and cost of both part and process. In this case, material parameters such as ductility are more representative of its weldability. However, due to the nature of the process, large loads are imparted on the part, making this process unsuitable for many load-sensitive parts.

8.2.14 ELECTROSLAG WELDING

Slag Protects the Heated Metal. The principle of *electroslag welding* is illustrated in Figure 8.29. The edges to be joined are placed in a vertical position with a gap between them. Water-cooled copper shoes or slides cover the gap where the welding is in process. Slag is first deposited in the gap and a wire electrode introduced to form an arc. Once the arc has melted the slag, the arc is automatically extinguished, and heat is produced by the passage of current through the molten slag. The electrode is fed into the slag as it melts, and, as the gap fills, the copper shoes and electrode guide are gradually raised. The process might well be defined as *continuous casting*, with the base metal and the copper slides forming a moving mold. The slag forms a protective layer for the weld pool and, in addition, forms a coating over the copper slides that protects them from the molten metal. By changing the rate of wire feed and the electrical input, the rate of deposition and the penetration into the base metal may be controlled.

Multiple Electrodes Needed for Heavy Sections. A single electrode is used for sections up to about 51 mm (2 in.) thick. For thicker sections, multiple electrodes may be used, and melting rates of up to 18 kg (40 lbs) per hour for each electrode are possible. While the principal applications have been for forming butt welds between plates and for producing heavy-walled cylinders rolled from flat plate, shaped rather than flat slides may be used for producing tee joints of special built-up shapes on the surface of a part. In a variation of the process, an arc is used continuously, without slag, but with a protective gas atmosphere fed through ports at the tops of the copper slides.

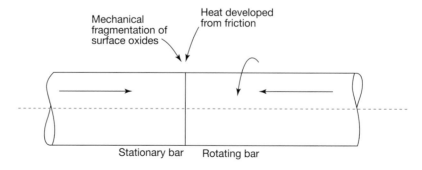

Figure 8.28: Friction welding.

8.2.15 RESISTANCE WELDING

Resistance welding (RW) is sometimes referred to as *spot* or *seam welding*. This process is commonly used in the automotive and pipe industries and relies on the resistance of the joining surfaces. The resistance impedes the flow of the current, causing the area to locally heat to the point where welding occurs. As an example, seamed tubing is manufactured by progressively rolling a continuous sheet in the form of a tube, then welding the seam as it passes through water-cooled welding electrode wheels. The resistance of the welded material to dissipating heat energy causes the tube to weld while the conductivity of the copper electrode wheels prevents the electrodes from being consumed.

Highest Resistance at Interfaces. The rate of power expenditure in any electrical circuit is given by:

(Eq. 8.1) $$P = I^2 R$$

where P is the power in watts; I, the current in amperes; and R, the resistance in ohms.

Heat is generated throughout the circuit, and resistance welding processes are based on the fact that the highest resistance occurs at the interfaces between metal surfaces where the contact is limited to a number of points of relatively small area. This condition occurs not only at the interface between the workpieces, where maximum heat is desired, but also at the contacts with the electrodes, for which the heating effect is minimized by using high-conductivity copper alloys with water cooling and high-pressure contact of formed surfaces.

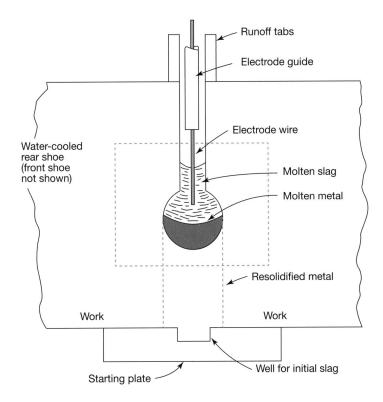

Figure 8.29: Electroslag welding.

Melting Incidental Only. As the contact points heat between the work surfaces, they become plastic, and the clean metal union is expanded by deformation and by the fragmentation, spheroidization, and diffusion of the oxides into the base metal. Some local melting may take place but is not necessary for the process to be successful. Even with the increased area of contact, the interface area remains the point of greatest heat generation because the resistance of the base metal rises as its temperature is increased. The duration of the current is controlled by a timer that in most cases regulates the periods of current flow by controlling the number of cycles of alternating current permitted to flow through the primary of the step-down transformer. The pressure is also timed, with an increase to cause plastic flow after heating has occurred.

Dissimilar Metals May Be Joined. Nearly all metals, as well as most combinations of different metals, may be resistance welded. Difficulties are sometimes encountered in welding high-conductivity metals, such as aluminum and copper, or in joining parts of different thicknesses. Experimentation to establish the best weld conditions will produce satisfactory welds for most applications.

Spot Welding for Joining Sheet Metal. The most important applications of resistance heating are for *spot welding* and its variations. Used primarily for lap joints between flat sheets, spot welds are obtained by concentrating the pressure and current flow with shaped electrodes, as shown in Figure 8.30. Accurate control is necessary to prevent burning of the electrodes and excessive heating of the base material, which would cause too much plastic flow under the pressure of the electrodes. Spot welding is sometimes facilitated by interrupting the current flow and using a series of short heating periods to provide a different heat distribution.

Modified Spot Welding. The two most common variations are *seam* and *projection welding*, shown in Figure 8.31. In seam welding, a series of overlapping spot welds produce a continuous joint used primarily where pressure or liquid tightness is a requirement, as in automotive gasoline tanks.

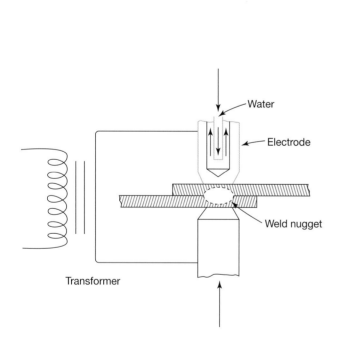

Figure 8.30: Spot welding.

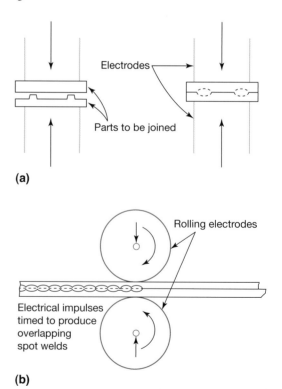

Figure 8.31: Variations of spot welding:
(a) projection welding; (b) seam welding.

In many cases, multiple spot welds or single spot welds of highly localized character may be made by confining the area of contact to projections on the surface of one or both workpieces. Large electrodes shaped to the contour of the work may be used so that the exterior of the part has little or no marking from the electrodes. Uses of projection welding include the joining of electrical contacts to relay and switch parts and the manufacture of fencing in which the projections are inherent in the product where the wires cross.

Spot Welding an Important Assembly Process. Spot welding and its variations are among the most used joining processes in the manufacture of high-quantity goods, such as automobiles, home appliances, office equipment, and kitchenware. Dissimilar metals and parts of different thicknesses may be lined. Little cleaning of the parts is necessary either before or after welding. The greatest limitations are the initial cost of equipment, the experimentation sometimes necessary with new applications, and the restrictions to joining relatively thin material except in the case of projection welding.

8.2.16 EXPLOSION WELDING

Explosion welding (EXW) is a solid state metal joining process that uses an explosive force to create an electron-sharing metallurgical bond between two metal components. Although the explosive detonation generates considerable heat, there is not enough time for the heat to transfer to the base metals, so temperature increase in the metals is minimal. Explosion welding is an effective joining method for virtually any combination of metals. The only metallurgical limitation is sufficient ductility and fracture toughness to undergo the rapid deformation of the process without fracture.

In recent years, explosion welding has developed into an important process particularly suited to joining large areas of two or more metals of different compositions. Standard explosive materials supply the energy to produce the weld, which may be made on flat or curved surfaces.

Progressive Cleaning and Welding. A uniform covering layer of explosive material is detonated to produce a shock wave that progresses uniformly across the material to be welded. The materials to be welded are originally spaced a small distance apart. The shock wave from the explosion closes the gap in such a way that surface impurities are pushed ahead and extremely high pressures establish the contact of clean metal for welding.

The greatest use for the procedure is in coating, or *cladding*, structural metal with a more expensive but more corrosion-resistant metal. The purpose may be to protect the metal from ordinary environmental exposure or to prevent damage from more intense exposure such as in chemical process containers.

8.3 DISCONTINUITIES IN WELDS

Most discontinuities in welds can be seen on the surface of the weld bead or detected by the size and shape of the weld bead itself. Several factors can lead to a poor-quality weld, and the root cause is almost always due to operator error. Therefore, proper execution of surface preparation, correct weld settings and equipment, proper operator technique, and careful workmanship are critical to ensure a high-quality weld. A mechanical destructive test is typically used on a sample to reveal the overall strength of the weld but is not able to tell if any internal imperfections exist and does not represent the actual weld on the part but only a typical sample. More advanced quality nondestructive testing (NDT) inspection methods can reveal the presence of internal cracks, inclusions, or pockets, and depth of penetration of the weld.

Several common discontinuities in poor-quality welds can be traced to poor surface preparation. Since metals react with the surrounding atmosphere, a thin oxide layer forms on the exposed surfaces. These oxides remain as the metal underneath becomes molten and gathers in the weld pool. Similar to oil and water, the surface tension of the molten metal and oxides prevents emulsification. As the weld cools and solidifies, pockets of the oxides are trapped in the weld. This can often be seen remaining on the surface if left post-weld.

Often, the inexperienced operator may not have allowed the weld pool to reach the proper fusion, allowing the weld pool to stabilize. This can be the result of too much filler material or not enough power and heat to stabilize the plasma arc and weld pool. The weld bead itself does not penetrate into the joining parts, so the added material just builds up on the surface. The opposite effect is also a typical reason for poor-quality welds. If the weld pool receives too much heat, not only is the surrounding material affected, the weld itself becomes highly brittle and becomes much more susceptible to surface cracking. This can be the result of too much power and heat applied to the weld pool or not enough filler material being added.

A common problem the operator may face is when a thick part is arc welded to a thin part. The heat or current needed to obtain proper penetration into the thick part can be too much for the thinner part, often resulting in undercutting the thin part and a poor weld. If the proper amount of current for the thin part is applied, the heat is insufficient for adequate fusion of the thick part, again resulting in a poor weld. Too little heat input can also cause underbead cracking in certain structural materials.

The general sources of weld discontinuities include improper design, poor joint preparation, defects in the parent material, improper welding technique, faulty solidification of molten metal, and heating or cooling effects on both the base metal and the weld metal. Some depreciating faults, such as decreased strength of cold-rolled steel due to recrystallization of the base metal in the HAZ, are inherent in the process and essentially pose design problems. If the somewhat broad assumption is made that the design is proper, many discontinuities are the result of improper welding technique. It follows then that an experienced, knowledgeable operator using care and good equipment should turn out the work containing the fewest discontinuities. Even under the best of conditions, however, perfect results should never be expected. There are too many possible reasons for discontinuities to occur. All critical welds require NDT for assurance of quality or as a means to enable repairs to be made.

8.3.1 DISCONTINUITIES IN FUSION WELDS

When welding is used during the manufacture of consumer products and for large structures, with the exception of resistance spot welding, a fusion arc welding process is most likely selected. The American Welding Society (AWS) categorizes weldment discontinuities in three general classes:

- Those associated with drawing or dimensional requirements.
- Those associated with structural discontinuities in the weld itself.
- Those associated with properties of weld metal or the welded joint.

8.3.2 DIMENSIONAL EFFECTS

Warping. Differential heating and cooling sets up unequal stresses in the weld area that must be absorbed by position shift (warping), deformation (plastic flow), or cracking if neither of the others can occur. For example, the angular distortion of a butt joint produced with single-vee preparation is shown in Figure 8.32. Although warping is inherent in the process, it can be minimized by proper welding control, including joint preparation. When necessary, fixtures may be used also to minimize distortion. In some cases, *peening* to produce localized deformation or *post-heating* to equalize residual stresses may be needed to prevent cracking.

Weld Dimensions and Profile. Usually the unit strength of weld material is weaker than the unit strength of the base material it joins. This is due not only to the chemical composition normally used but also to the possible discontinuities it may contain as a finished weld filler. When full strength is desired, welds are made slightly oversize with a given shape. If the convexity is too large, though, time and material are wasted and the chance of other discontinuities is increased.

Figure 8.33 shows three discontinuities in the profile of a fillet weld (b–d) compared with an ideal weld (a). As can be seen in Figure 8.34, the profiles of double-vee welds show discontinuities related to weld reinforcement in (b) and (c) compared with an ideal double-vee weld in (a).

Final Weldment Dimensions. All weldments are designed to meet dimensions necessary to function properly or unite with other parts. Welds, especially when multiple, must be carefully controlled regarding spacing for overall dimensions to be within usable range. Accumulation of weld size error affects overall dimensions and even when balancing may cause poor-quality welds.

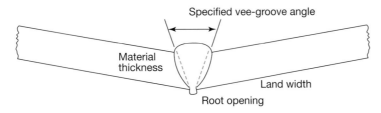

Figure 8.32: Warping in a single-vee butt joint.

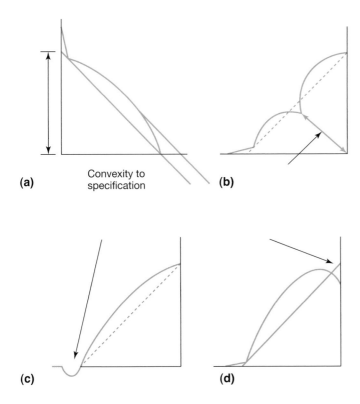

Figure 8.33: Profiles of fillet welds: (a) ideal; (b) insufficient throat; (c) undercut; (d) overlap.

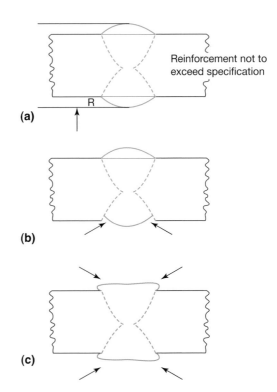

Figure 8.34: Profiles of double-vee welds: (a) ideal reinforcement; (b) undercut; (c) overlap.

8.3.3 STRUCTURAL DISCONTINUITIES

Porosity. The term *porosity* is used to describe pockets or voids that are the result of the same kind of chemical reactions that cause similar discontinuities in castings. Gases are produced or released at high temperatures and, when unable to escape, remain in the solidified metal. In welds made with an inert covering gas, inadequate fast flow or excess moisture in the gas can result in oxide and porosity formation. They may be microscopic in size or exist as large as 3.2 mm (1/8 in.) or more in diameter. It is seldom that porosity in welds can be eliminated completely but a few small, scattered pores may not create significant harm except in the most critical applications. As shown in the radiographs in Figure 8.35, porosity may exist as (a) scattered, tending to be uniform in size for a given condition; (b) clustered, often associated with some welding condition change; or (c) linear, occurring most often in the root pass of a multipass weld.

Inclusions. The most common inclusions that appear in welds are slag, metal oxides, and nonmetallic solids that are entrapped during welding. They are to some degree associated with certain types of welding but are most likely to be present when the weld metal temperature has not been high enough to permit their floating to the surface, when there is an undercut or recess over which welding is performed, or almost certainly when insufficient clearing has been performed on previous passes of multipass welds. Figure 8.36 shows possible locations of slag in a multiple-pass vee weld. In welds made by the fast tungsten-arc process, small bits of tungsten are occasionally dislodged from the electrode and enter the weld metal.

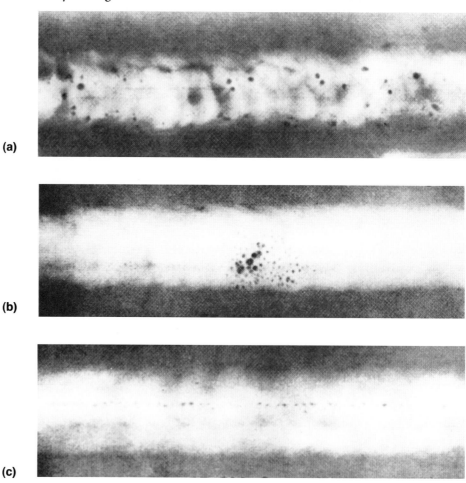

(a)

(b)

(c)

Figure 8.35: Three types of weld porosity: (a) scattered; (b) clustered; (c) linear.

Incomplete Fusion and Inadequate Joint Preparation. Incomplete fusion can occur in any location where the base metal, or previous pass weld metal, has not been brought up to fusion temperature. Inadequate joint penetration, when present, usually occurs in the root area of the weld and is caused by similar reasons, namely, sufficient heat for fusion does not reach the bottom of the groove. Either may be caused by welding operator error, but inadequate penetration may also be caused by too close fit-up or other improper joint preparation or design. Other contributing factors are too large an electrode, too fast travel, or too low welding current. Figures 8.37 and 8.38 show examples of poor fusion and incomplete penetration, respectively.

Undercut. Undercuts are the result of melting base metal and not replacing it with weld metal, leaving a notch or groove. When occurring on the last pass of a multiple-pass weld, or with single-pass welds, the groove, if deep, may be a serious discontinuity that should not be left. Undercuts, such as shown in Figure 8.39, are the result of operator technique in most cases but are also influenced by welding conditions.

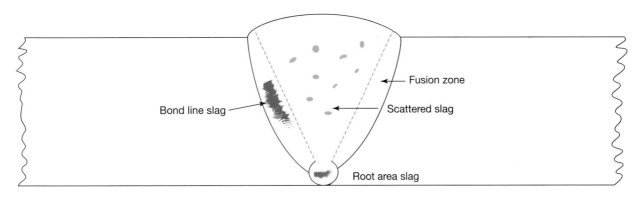

Figure 8.36: Types and locations of slag inclusions.

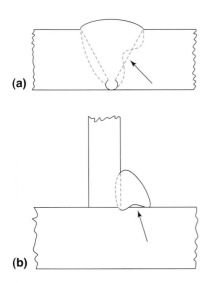

Figure 8.37: Incomplete fusion:
(a) vee groove; (b) fillet weld.

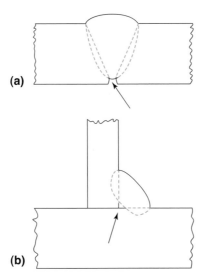

Figure 8.38: Incomplete penetration:
(a) vee groove; (b) fillet groove.

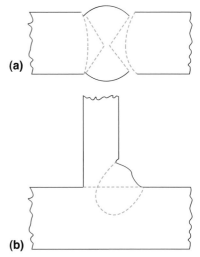

Figure 8.39: Undercuts:
(a) double-vee butt weld;
(b) horizontal fillet weld.

Cracks. The cracking of weld metal and base metal in or near the weld zone is usually caused by high stresses set up by localized dimensional changes. Such changes are caused by the large thermal gradients established during heating and cooling of a weld joint. Cracking may occur during welding, during cooling, or particularly with hard or brittle materials at some later time. Weld cracks are most likely to occur when weldments are of heavy sections, creating a faster quenching action.

Cracks may occur in many different orientations in the weld. The two most common types of cracks—longitudinal and transverse—are shown in Figure 8.40. A *longitudinal crack* forms along the weld axis, whereas a *transverse crack* is perpendicular to the weld axis. Sometimes the cracks are highly visible, sometimes magnification is required to see them, and at other times they can be detected only by NDT methods.

Crater cracks are small shrink cracks that can occur in the weld puddle at the end of a weld bead (crater) that has not been fully filled, as shown in Figure 8.41. This type of crack may be single or star-shaped multiple and form during shrinkage of the final weld pool. They may propagate into longitudinal cracks, or they may appear any place along a weld where welding has been stopped and restarted unless they are completely remelted in the process. Unless removed or fully remelted, cracks in the root of a weld are likely to propagate through all subsequent weld layers.

Cracks in the HAZ of base metal occur almost entirely only in metals that are heat-treat hardenable. Most are longitudinal in direction and sometimes may be extensions of bond-line cracks as shown in Figure 8.42. Crack discontinuities in fillet welds may appear in the weld or as longitudinal toe cracks or longitudinal root cracks, as illustrated in Figure 8.43.

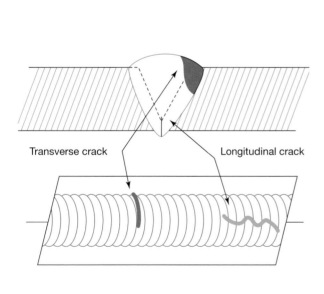

Figure 8.40: Types of cracks in weld metal.

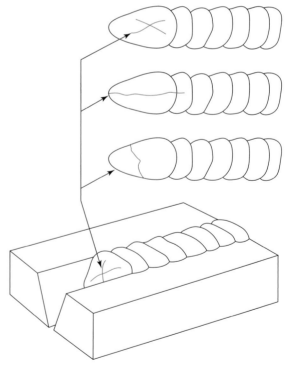

Figure 8.41: Location and typical appearance of crater cracks in a weld.

Surface Irregularities. Occasionally, surface irregularities and imperfections may be nuclei of future failure, but usually they have little significance in weld joint strength and utility. However, spatter, weld ripple, uniformity of bead, and other surface qualities are frequently covered by specification and may require inspection even if their only effect is on appearance.

8.3.4 RESIDUAL STRESSES AND HEAT-AFFECTED AREA

Complex thermal stresses occur in parts during welding due to the localized application of heat. *Residual stresses*, also referred to as *internal stresses*, caused from nonuniform temperature distributions, otherwise known as *thermal stresses*, lead to distortions that remain after the weld is completed. Residual stresses in metal structures occur for many reasons during various manufacturing stages, including casting, rolling, bending, flame cutting, forging, machining, and grinding. Heat treatments at various stages also influence residual stresses. For example, quenching treatments produce residual stresses, while stress-relieving heat treatments may reduce such stresses.

During welding, the weldment undergoes shrinkage and deformation. Transient thermal stresses, residual stresses, and distortion sometimes cause cracking and mismatching of joints. Under certain conditions, large tensile residual stresses in areas near the weld can cause premature failures. For example, a compressive load is applied to a welded pole on a base plate. Distortion and compressive residual stresses in the base plate can reduce the buckling strength of the pole subjected to compressive loading. This is because, along the axis of the pole, one side experiences tensile stresses while the other side undergoes compressive stresses. The added moment about the weld area also contributes to the increase in stress. The effect is understandably more dramatic as the scale diminishes. Correction of unacceptable distortion is costly and, in some cases, impossible.

8.3.4.1 DISTORTIONS AND STRESSES

A homogeneous unrestricted body may be heated to any temperature below its melting point without shape change. A volumetric expansion will occur with heating, but if this expansion occurs uniformly, no stresses will be introduced. As the body is cooled, the process reverses, and the final result will be the original unstrained state.

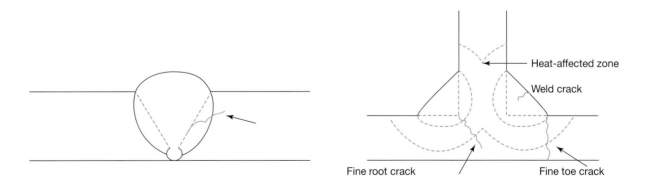

Figure 8.42: Bond-line crack extending into base metal.

Figure 8.43: Root and toe type cracks in base metal with fillet welds.

Restraints Create Stresses and Distortion. With restraint either on heating or cooling or with heating or cooling of localized areas at a more rapid rate than others (self-restraint), the picture will be changed. Many welds have a vee cross section, and the molten and heated areas will have a related shape. Furthermore, the heat input and higher temperatures occur on the open side of the vee. Figure 8.44 illustrates the result of cooling on this cross section for various weldments joined with vee welds. The greater shrinkage occurring on the wide side of the vee leads to angular distortion, as shown. The effect is amplified by multipass welds, in which a number of weld deposits are made along the length of a single vee. Each pass contributes to the distortion with the deposits from previous passes serving as a fulcrum for increased angular movement.

While a vee weld will always tend to distort angularly in the manner shown, the *lateral distortion* between members of a weldment may vary in direction and amount, depending on the size of the members compared to the weld, the number of passes made, the rate of heat input, and the speed of welding (Figure 8.45). As the weld proceeds along the groove, the heating of base metal along the edge of the groove but ahead of the actual weld leads to a spreading of the plates. On the other hand, the shrinkage accompanying the solidification and cooling of the completed weld tends to pull the plates together.

All Welds Create Residual Stresses. Practical weldments never have absolute restraint or absolute freedom, and the actual degree of restraint and temperature difference cannot always be predicted or measured. However, some degree of restraint always exists, at least in the parent metal adjacent to the weld zone, even for members that as a whole are free. Any fusion weld will contain some residual stresses when completed and cooled to room temperature. These stresses will be both tensile and compressive because a balance must exist for the member to be in equilibrium.

Stresses and Distortion Are Associated. Some results of *longitudinal distortion* are indicated in Figure 8.46. For a weld along the edge of a plate, the longitudinal shrinkage will cause curvature as indicated. Although the plate has no external restraint, it will be subject to stresses similar to those resulting from external loading that would cause equivalent curvature. In the case of the weldment, however, there will be two neutral axes with both edges in tension and the center under compression.

For a circular weld around a pipe, similar self-restraint exists. The shrinkage along the length of the weld results in a reduction in diameter that is resisted by the solid pipe adjacent to the weld. The result would be high tensile stresses in the weld and high compressive stresses in the pipe on both sides of the weld.

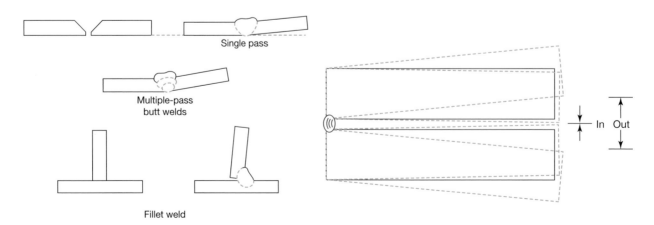

Single pass

Multiple-pass butt welds

Fillet weld

In Out

Figure 8.44: Angular distortions.   **Figure 8.45: Lateral distortion.**

Even when the welded members have no external restraint or apparent gross distortion, high residual stresses can exist. Figure 8.47 indicates the kind of stress distribution to be expected from a longitudinal butt weld between two plates.

Stresses Reduced by Post-heating. The most widely accepted method of reducing residual stresses in the weldments is based on two facts: (1) no stresses higher than the yield stress can exist in a material at any given temperature, and (2) if an entire unrestrained body is cooled uniformly from any given temperature, no increase in stress will occur. If a weldment is heated to an elevated temperature, yielding will occur and the stresses will be reduced. As the temperature is reduced, the entire weldment will shrink, but no new stresses will be introduced. Residual stresses cannot be completely eliminated by this method; however, as Figure 8.47 shows, the yield strength at elevated temperatures is quite low.

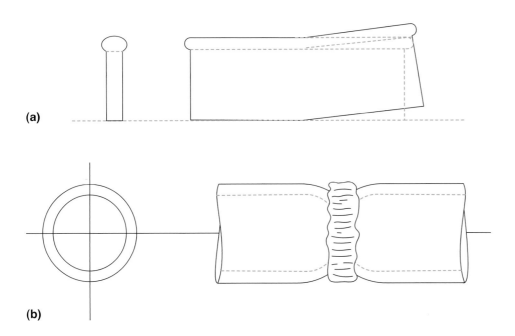

(a)

(b)

Figure 8.46: Longitudinal distortion: (a) edge weld; (b) butt pipe weld.

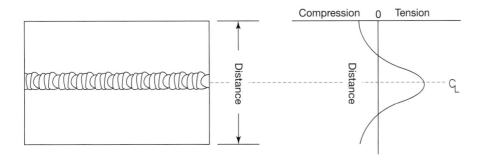

Figure 8.47: Longitudinal stress in a butt weld.

The stabilization of stresses in a weldment requires that the entire weldment reaches a uniform temperature and that all distortions permitted by its restraints take place. Time is required for each to happen, and even after stabilization some residual stresses may be very near critical levels. It is sometimes important that final inspection be delayed hours, or longer, to be certain that post-cracking will not occur shortly after an inspection has been made.

Grain Uniformity Requires Transformation. *Normalizing* provides stress relief and, in addition, increases the uniformity of the grain structure. Stress relieving of weldments is frequently performed by heating to about 650 °C (1200 °F). While grain refinement is not obtained at this temperature, the chances for distortion are less than those that might be introduced by the allotropic transformation, which occurs at higher temperatures.

8.3.4.2 EFFECTS ON GRAIN SIZE AND STRUCTURE

Cooling Rates Higher Than in Casting. Grain formation in fusion welds can best be understood by remembering that a fusion weld is a casting, and all the effects present in casting will be duplicated. However, the mold wall is not fixed, and the solidification and cooling rates are faster than normally occur in a casting (Figure 8.48). Fusion welds are subject to solidification and cooling shrinkage, as shown in Figure 8.49. The grain-size effects are not confined to the molten metal, because a

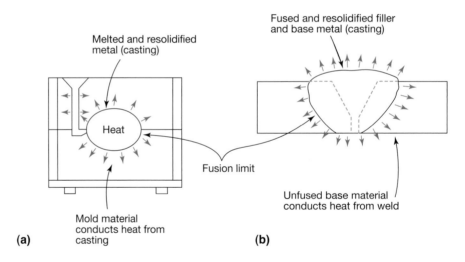

Figure 8.48: Comparison of (a) casting with (b) fusion weld.

Figure 8.49: Solidification of a bead weld.

temperature high enough to result in annealing, allotropic transformation, and recrystallization extends for some distance into the base metal, as shown in Figure 8.50. The fused material is cooled rapidly by the high thermal conductivity of the surrounding metal, and small grain size results.

Heat Affects Base Material. The zones indicated in Figure 8.50 do not have sharp dividing lines and represent only typical results. The results can vary from those shown, depending on the shape and size of the parts, the initial temperature of the base material, the rate of heat input, and the alloy content. In any case, for steels, an area immediately surrounding the molten metal will be heated above the transformation temperature, and some degree of austenitization can occur. Final results will depend on the time at temperature and the cooling rates, which cannot always be accurately predicted. Grain growth can proceed, and, for the metal heated near its melting temperature, the final grain size can be large. The metal heated only slightly above the transformation temperature is effectively normalized and will have a small final grain size, which can be smaller than that of the unheated base metal. Any heat-treat or cold-work hardening that existed in the area heated below the transformation temperature will be subject to tempering or recrystallization, depending on the actual temperature reached and the pre-weld condition.

When ultrasonic inspection is being performed on a weldment, it is important to recognize that the abrupt change in grain size can often be detected. The ultrasonic signal reflected from this HAZ may be misinterpreted in some cases as being lack of fusion or a variety of other discontinuities, depending on location.

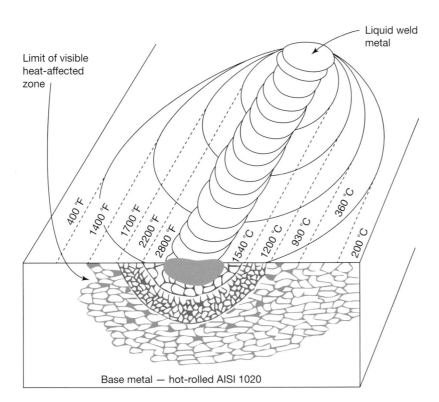

Figure 8.50: Grain structure in a fusion weld.

Multiple Cooling Rates. Again, depending on cooling rates induced and compositions involved, for the metal heated above the transformation temperature, the cooling may be equivalent to that required for annealing, normalizing, or actually quenching to martensite, provided enough carbon is present. Some of the latter nearly always occurs in unpreheated carbon steel weldments and, when combined with the uneven shrinkage that may be present, can result in brittle structures subject to cracking. Alloy rods or rods of different carbon content may be used for controlling some of the possible discontinuities. Low carbon filler material is often used in welding higher carbon steels to avoid the formation of excessive amounts of martensite. In the fusion zone where cooling rates are high, the composition would be near the composition of the filler material. Even with rapid cooling, the structure would consist mainly of ferrite with sufficient ductility to shrink without cracking.

Structure Varies with Cooling Rate. In the base material adjacent to the liquid metal, the cooling rate would be somewhat less but still sufficiently rapid to form fine pearlite and some martensite. It must be remembered that grain size and structure are two different considerations; in this region, grain size will be large because of the long time at high temperature, but structure will be fine because of the rapid cooling. At a greater distance from the molten zone but still within the area raised above the transformation temperature, the cooling rate will be nearer that usual with normalizing, and the resulting structure will be medium to coarse pearlite.

Preheating Lowers Cooling Rate. The cooling rate of the weld and the entire weld area is changed by preheating the base metal surrounding the area to be welded. At any given point in the weld area, the cooling rate will be reduced because of the reduced thermal gradient established. Average grain size will be larger because of the longer times at high temperature, but structures will be softer because of the reduced cooling rates.

Effects in Pressure Welding Reduced. Effects similar to those of fusion welding will be observed in pressure welding. With lower temperatures, and frequently higher thermal gradient, the HAZ will be smaller. Shrinkage problems are reduced because of little or no fusion and more uniformly welded cross sections.

Localized Heat Most Common. The most important welding processes make use of localized heating. For fusion welding, this is a necessity to prevent excessive melting and to restrict the HAZ in the base metal. The temperature differential in the weld area will depend not only on the rate of heat input and the degree of localization but also on the thermal properties of the base metal and the geometry of the weldment. Heat sources differ in the maximum temperature possibilities, the degree of concentration, and the maximum practical amount of energy that may be transferred.

8.3.5 DESTRUCTIVE TESTING OF WELDED JOINTS

Several organizations such as the American Welding Society (AWS) and ASTM International (formerly, the American Society for Testing and Materials) have standardized tests and procedures established for testing welded joints. *Longitudinal* and *transverse tension tests* are performed on specimens removed from actual welded joints and from the weld-metal area. *Stress-strain curves*, indicating the yield strength, ultimate tensile strength, and ductility (measured in terms of percentage elongation and reduction of area) of the welded joint in different locations and directions, are then obtained by the procedures described in Section 3.3. Tests of weld hardness may also be used to indicate weld strength and microstructural changes in the weld zone. Localized corrosion may occur due to differences in the composition and microstructure of the material in the weld zone.

Several bend tests can be used to determine the ductility and strength of welded joints. In a particular test, the welded specimen is bent around a fixture. If bent until complete failure, the area of failure is inspected to ensure the weld did not fail. Specimens in the tension-shear test are specially prepared to simulate actual welded joints and procedures. The specimens are then subjected to tension, and the shear strength of the weld metal and the location of fracture are determined. Fracture toughness tests commonly use impact testing techniques. V-notched specimens are prepared and tested for toughness, usually with a *drop-weight test* where a falling weight supplies the test energy. The *peel test* is commonly used when testing the strength of spot welds. In a peel test, the weld is broken apart by clamping one of the welded sheets in a vise and gripping the other welded sheet with pliers, pincers, or a roller tool. The weld is loaded with an application of force perpendicular to its original orientation, resulting in the weld being peeled open.

8.3.6 WELD METAL AND BASE METAL PROPERTIES

Weld Metal. The properties of the weld metal are controlled basically by the weld filler material and the way it is deposited. Most tests to determine its quality are destructive types and can be used only as spot checks. However, a weld inspector should observe and check that proper materials and methods are used and that the welding operator uses the techniques necessary to produce the desired quality.

Base Metal. Similar to weld metal tests, most tests for checking properties of base metal are destructive. Code colors and other methods are used to ensure that proper materials are being used. The inspector should also be fully aware at all times while performing nondestructive tests for weld quality that discontinuities in base material may be indicated. Discontinuities such as depicted in Figure 8.51 may have been missed in base material that was previously not inspected. Welds deposited over already existing discontinuities can cause the base metal discontinuities to enlarge or extend into the weld deposit. Such conditions found during weld inspections often indicate the need for more complete inspection of the base material prior to welding on subsequent weldments.

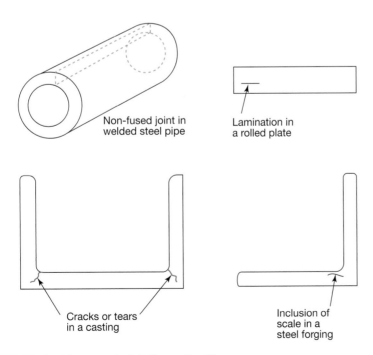

Figure 8.51: Typical base material discontinuities.

9 Material Removal Processes

9.1 MATERIAL REMOVAL

9.1.1 INTRODUCTION

Machining is the most universally used and the most important of all manufacturing processes. Machining is a shape-producing process in which a power-driven device causes material to be removed in *chip* form. Most machining is done with equipment that supports both the workpiece and the *cutting tool,* although, in some cases, portable equipment is used with unsupported workpieces.

    Low Setup Cost for Small Quantities. Machining has two applications in manufacturing. For casting, forging, and pressworking, each specific shape to be produced, even one part, nearly always has a high tooling cost. The shapes that may be produced by welding depend to a large degree on the shapes of raw material that are available. By making use of generally high-cost equipment but without special tooling, it is possible, by machining, to start with nearly any form of raw material, so long as the exterior dimensions are great enough, and produce any desired shape from any material. Therefore, machining is usually the preferred method for producing one or a few

"Machining is a shape-producing process in which a power-driven device causes material to be removed in chip form."

parts, even when the design of the part would logically lead to casting, forging, or pressworking if a high quantity were to be produced.

Close Accuracies, Good Finishes. The second application for machining is based on the high accuracies and surface finishes possible. Many of the parts machined in low quantities would be produced with lower but acceptable tolerances if produced in high quantities by some other process. On the other hand, many parts are given their general shapes by some high-quantity deformation process and machined only on selected surfaces where high accuracies are needed. Internal threads, for example, are seldom produced by any means other than machining, and small holes in press-worked parts are machined following the pressworking operations.

Tool Applies Controlled Loading to Cause Material Failure. Machining, as well as forging and pressworking, is based on the fact that one material can be harder and stronger than another. If the harder one is properly shaped, it can be called a *tool*; when the tool is brought into contact with a weaker workpiece with sufficient force, failure results in the workpiece. All deformation operations are based on the proper control of this failure. The loading is controlled in machining so as to produce only localized failure in the workpiece, which results in the removal of material in the form of chips without significant deformation in other parts of the workpiece.

Processes Differ Primarily in Energy Use. To understand better what is involved in machining, it might be well to consider what is involved in some of the other fabrication processes and then see how machining differs.

Casting—Heat Energy. In casting, energy is added in the form of heat so that the internal structure of the metal is changed and it becomes liquid. In this state, the metal is forced by pressure, which may consist of only the force of gravity, into a shaped cavity where it is allowed to solidify. The shape changing is therefore accomplished with the metal in such condition that the energy form is primarily that of heat, and little energy in the form of force is required.

Welding—Heat and Force Energy. Welding involves placing the metal in a molten or near-molten condition, again by the addition of heat, and effecting a union by fusion, which may involve pressure. Neither of these processes changes the shape of the metal while it is in its solid and strong state.

Deformation Processes—Mainly Force Energy over Large Areas. In forging, bending, drawing, rolling, and extruding operations, advantage is taken of the property of metals to deform plastically. In forging, rolling, and extrusion, pressure loading is applied so that the primary stresses produced in the metal are compression. In drawing operations, metal is pulled or drawn through a controlling die with a complex stress distribution involving tension and compression at the point of metal flow. The forces used to produce shapes by bending result in compressive stresses on one side of the material and tensile stresses on the other. All of these operations are basically the same in the sense that a given quantity of metal is placed in a new shape without any appreciable change in volume.

Machining—Localized Force Energy. To shape a product by material removal in machining, a fracture failure must be caused at the desired location. Loading of the material by relative motion of the tool causes plastic deformation of the material both before and after the chip formation. All materials, however brittle, undergo some plastic deformation in the machining process. In machining, the energy is in the form of a localized force that causes plastic deformation and fracture to produce a chip.

9.1.2 CHIP FORMATION

Some controversy exists over the theory that best explains the formation of a chip in metal cutting. The following, whether or not it is completely correct, is one of the more generally believed theories that serves a good purpose in helping provide a better understanding for tool design and use.

The Tool Is Simply a Loading Device. First, it should be understood that a cutting tool is merely a device for applying external loads to the work material. If a tool is strong enough that it will not fail and the work is rigid enough to resist deflection away from the tool, a chip will be produced by a relative motion between the two, regardless of the shape of the cutting tool edge in contact with the work. Although any shape of edge may cause a chip to be formed, certain shapes will be more efficient in use of work energy than others and will exhibit less tendency to set up forces of such magnitude that the tool or work will be damaged.

Forces Are Created by Tool Motion. Figure 9.1 shows a single-point tool moving into the work and subjecting it to compressive loading. The load may be broken down into two forces: a force perpendicular to the tool face, which is called the *normal force,* and, because this is a dynamic situation, a force along the tool face, which is the *friction force.* The two forces may be added vectorially to produce a resultant that, as is shown, projects downward into the work material. The direction and magnitude of the resultant are dependent on its two component forces and are influenced by the angle of the tool face and the coefficient of friction between the chip and tool face. Equal and opposite forces occur in the tool, but these are of little interest, providing the tool is strong enough to withstand the applied loads.

Stresses Cause Material Failure. An external force applied in a single direction may set up stresses in other directions within the material. Figure 9.2 shows that maximum shear stresses are induced at an angle of approximately 45° to the direction of the resultant and that the plane region extending from the tip of the cutting tool to the uncut surface of the work is subjected to these maximum shear stresses. Plastic flow occurs when the shear stresses reach a critical value for any material. As plastic flow occurs along this plane, work hardening will increase resistance to further flow, higher stresses will develop, and fracture failure near the tip of the tool will cause the separation of a chip that will ride over the face of the tool and thereby create the friction that causes one of the component forces acting on the work.

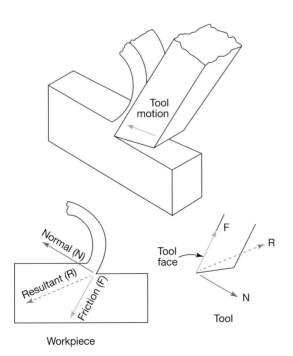

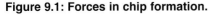

Figure 9.1: Forces in chip formation.

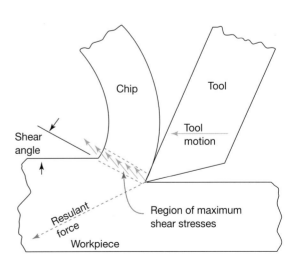

Figure 9.2: Shear stresses in chip formation.

Chip Form Dependent on Material and Force Direction. If the material is of brittle nature, it will be able to stand only a small amount of plastic deformation without fracture failure. If it is of ductile nature, the chip may hold together in a long continuous strip or ribbon, deforming considerably, but not fracturing except near the tool tip where it separates from the parent stock.

Figure 9.3 indicates the probable nature of the deformation in the chip, assuming a homogeneous work material with uniform round crystals. Because actual materials are not completely homogeneous, a single plane of maximum shear probably does not exist, but rather there is a shifting plane creating a region or zone in which plastic flow of the work material occurs. In this region, the material is deformed in such a way that the chip is always thicker and shorter than the material from which it is made. The amount of change in shape is dependent not only on the characteristics of the work material but also on the direction of the applied forces.

Chip Types. There are three distinct types of chips that are produced in machining depending primarily upon the machining qualities of the work material but also influenced by tool shape, cutting speed, and other factors.

- With brittle materials, the chips universally break into segments because of the inability of these materials to withstand the deformation of chip formation without fracture. Tool shape and use to create chips of small pitch (short segments) usually produce the best results concerning tool life and surface finish.
- When ductile materials are machined, the resulting chips tend to hold together, producing chips that are continuous or of relatively long length before breaking free. Ideally, all the material that breaks away from the base material will escape uniformly and continuously over the tool face, leaving a smooth work surface that has been disturbed to only a minimum degree.
- Unfortunately, most chips from ductile materials tend to form somewhat intermittently with some material adhering to the tip temporarily, then escaping both over and under the tool tip. This leads to fluctuating forces, which may cause machining vibrations referred to as *chatter*, and leaves partially removed particles on the work surface, affecting the finish and wear qualities.

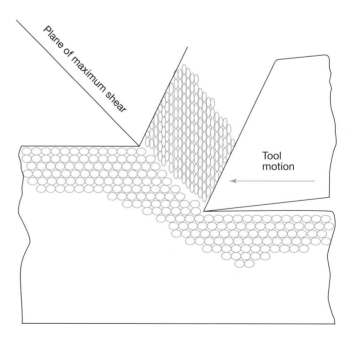

Figure 9.3: Deformation of chip material.

In addition to the above three identifiable types of chips, under many machining conditions, chips may have varying degrees of the qualities of each and cannot be categorized as a single type.

Surface Effects From Machining. Regardless of the type of chip produced during machining, force must be used and energy expended, resulting in material deformation and heat formation.

The force required to form the chip is in such a direction, as previously indicated in Figures 9.1 and 9.2, that it not only deforms the material of the chip but also applies high pressure to the newly created work surface that passes under the tool. With some materials, this deformation action may result in fine surface cracks.

Although machining is not normally a heat-dependent process, evidence of its presence is usually quite clear. Immediately after machining, a part will feel warm or hot, depending on the amount of material removed, or there may even be considerable radiant heat from the part or chips. In many chips, red heat can be observed at the tool tip as it cuts, and, in nearly all cases, chips show discoloration from being exposed to air at room temperature. Except for certain nonferrous materials, grinding displays sparks of burning materials as a result of cutting action.

In many cases, such as grinding or other high-cutting-speed operations, very high localized temperatures approaching the melting temperature of the work material may be generated. High temperature gradients can set up thermal stresses sufficient to cause small surface cracks that could be harmful. For critical parts, inspection by NDT may be required to detect these discontinuities and determine their frequency. It should be noted that these discontinuities are often disguised by *smear metal* wiped over the surface by the machining operation—even during some of the finest grinding work.

9.1.3 CUTTING TOOL MATERIALS

Tool materials have always played an important part in the economy of the world. In early history, stone was the principal tool material. As late as the 19th century, Native Americans used flint for arrow points, spearheads, knives, and other types of cutting edges. During the Bronze Age, copper alloys took the place of stone in more civilized areas. With the discovery of iron and steel, a tool material was found that has been used for hundreds of years and was added to only after the Industrial Revolution and the development of mass-production principles called for tool materials that could operate at higher speeds. Since the beginning of the 20th century, a number of new tool materials have been developed, and most of them play some part in current manufacturing.

Strength at Elevated Temperatures an Important Characteristic. The requirements for a satisfactory cutting tool material are that it be harder and stronger than the material it is to cut, that it be abrasion resistant to reduce wear, and that it be able to maintain these properties at the temperatures to which it will be exposed when cutting. The latter requirement has become increasingly important because of the development of work materials with superior properties and the need for operating at higher cutting speeds to increase production. The principal difference between the tool materials in common use is in their ability to maintain hardness and strength at elevated temperatures. Some of the tool materials with their principal characteristics are as follows:

- **Carbon Tool Steel:** A plain high carbon steel containing from 0.9% to 1.2% carbon. Machinable in its annealed condition. Heat-treat hardened and tempered after machined or forged to shape. Little used as a cutting tool material except for some special low-use tools.
- **High-Speed Steel (HSS):** An alloy steel that maintains cutting hardness and strength to about 550 °C (1000 °F), approximately twice that of carbon tool steel.

Used for many drills, reamers, milling cutters, and other cutting tools where the cutting speed has relatively small effect on the overall manufacturing cost.

- **Cast Nonferrous Alloys:** Alloys that are not normally machinable except by grinding. As a cutting tool, they are used to some degree for machining cast iron and malleable iron because of their high abrasion resistance. More commonly used as a structural material or coating because of their chemical and abrasion resistance.
- **Cemented Carbides:** A powder metallurgy product of tungsten, titanium, and/or tantalum carbides combined in various mixtures with cobalt or nickel to produce a variety of hardness and strength properties. The single most important industrial cutting tool group in manufacturing. Used mostly as a cutting tool tip or insert. Withstands temperatures over 1100 °C (2000 °F).
- **Ceramics or Cermets:** Another powder metallurgy product, the most successful of which has been made of almost pure aluminum oxide. Less shock resistant than most of the cemented carbides, but economical to use for removal of large amounts of material with uninterrupted cuts or for machining some hard materials that would otherwise require grinding.
- **Diamonds:** The hardest material known to humans, but brittle and subject to failure from thermal shock. Used in single-crystal or sintered polycrystal form for machining low-tensile-strength materials (aluminum, sintered bronze, graphite, and some plastics) with high-speed, shallow cuts producing hard quality finishes.
- **Coated Tool Materials:** Strong, shock-resistant tool bodies coated with hard, wear-resistant materials. An example is titanium carbide impregnated into the surface of high-speed steel to take advantage of the values of each.

9.1.4 MACHINABILITY

Many people have at some time used a pocketknife to whittle some shape from wood. While such an operation does not meet the full definition of machining, it is nevertheless a chip-forming operation that uses a hard and strong tool to cause localized failure in a workpiece. The whittler has doubtlessly also noticed that some woods are easier to shape than others. He or she is faced with an inherent difference in the "whittleability" of different kinds of wood. This ease of working is affected not only by the kind of wood but also by the moisture content and the state of seasoning.

A similar consideration arises in machining metals. Different metals may be cut at different rates, require different amounts of power, and obtain different finishes. These differences depend not only on the kind of metal or alloy but also on its prior history of processing, including deformation and heat-treating operations that affect its hardness, strength, and grain structure.

Machinability—an Inherent Material Quality. The term *machinability* is used to describe the relative ease with which any material may be machined. In one respect, the term is like the word *strength*, for a material can have tensile strength, shear strength, impact strength, fatigue strength, and compressive strength, all of which are measured in different ways and any one of which does not necessarily correlate with the others. That is, materials having equal tensile strengths do not always have the same impact strength or fatigue strength. Three different measurements—finish, power consumption, and tool life—may be considered in machinability. Unlike measurements of strength properties, these do not always give precise numerical information but are more often relative to some standard.

9.1.5 SURFACE FINISH

To have real meaning, any measurement of finish would have to be made with all the variables that might affect finish under strict control, and the values obtained would be reliable only for a particular set of machining conditions. The relative finishability of different materials has somewhat more reliability. For example, brass normally finishes better than steel under any given set of conditions.

Waviness—Broad Uniform Variations. The geometry of any surface is affected to different degrees by various factors. The gross conformance of a surface to its intended or theoretical shape is controlled by the accuracy of the machine tool motions, by vibrations or deflections of the machine tool or workpiece, and by deformations that may occur as the result of temperature change or the release of residual stresses. The term *waviness* is used to describe those variations of conformance that are relatively widely spaced or large in size.

Roughness—Fine Uniform Variations. The term *roughness* is used to refer to the relatively finely spaced surface irregularities, the height, width, and direction of which establish the predominant surface pattern. These irregularities are superimposed on the waviness. Roughness may be due to higher-frequency vibrations, to feed marks occurring as a result of the combination of tool shape and machine tool relative motions, or to the particles of built-up edge that have escaped under the cutting edge and been smeared on the finished surface.

Lay—Direction of Tool Mark Pattern. The *lay* of a surface is the direction of the predominant surface pattern. Lay is determined primarily by the direction of the cutting motion used to machine the surface and may be single direction, circular, or random in nature.

The exact classification of many surface irregularities frequently depends on the method of measurement. Most surface-finish measuring instruments may be adjusted to respond only to variations of less than some particular width so that feed marks, low-frequency vibration, or chatter may or may not be recorded in the measurement. Measurements of both waviness and surface roughness will generally be different when measured in a different direction because of the effect of the lay.

Imperfections Usually Random. Any surface may contain, in addition to roughness and waviness, randomly distributed discontinuities or imperfections. These are most often due to inherent faults, such as inclusions or voids in the material, which are exposed only when the outside surface is machined away. Scratches or marks caused by mishandling also fall in this category.

Finish Not Always Predictable. While surface finish depends on many variables and in many cases on the particular combination of all the variables, especially when vibration is encountered, it is possible to make some general statements about the effect of the more important factors. Table 9.1 shows the most likely effect on surface finish caused by increasing the more important machining variables from some standard set of conditions. The predicted results are intended to be qualitative only and even then apply only if one variable at a time is changed.

There are major exceptions when vibration is considered. Changing almost any condition can often stop vibration, even when the change is in the direction that would otherwise produce a poorer finish. Further exceptions occur at feed rates and depths of cut near zero. With either of these variables at very low values, finish is frequently poor, especially as tools become dull. With a very small depth of cut or feed

Table 9.1: Relation of machining variables to surface finish.	
Variable	**Finish Effect with Increase of Variable**
Cutting speed	Improvement
Feed	Deterioration (degree dependent on nose shape)
Depth of cut	Deterioration
True rake angle	Improvement
Relief angle	Little effect
Nose radius	Improvement
Work hardness	Improvement

and a worn tool, the *rake angle* (angle of the cutting face relative to the work) is decreased with increased forces and greater tendency for built-up edge.

Some compromise is frequently involved among finish, tool life, and machining time. Decreasing the depth of cut or feed may improve finish, but either change would increase machining time. Increasing cutting speed almost universally decreases tool life. Increasing the rake angle may make the tool subject to edge chipping or fracture failure or may induce chatter.

9.2 MACHINING PROCESSES

9.2.1 MACHINING TOOLS

Although there are many kinds of machines used in manufacturing and industry, the term *machine tools* has been assigned to that group of equipment designed to hold a cutting tool and a workpiece and establish a suitable set of motions between them to remove material from the work in chip form. There are two relative motions necessary for a controlled surface to be established. One is the *cutting motion*, which supplies the power for chip forming. The other motion, or sometimes motions, is the *feed motion* which presents new material to the cutting edge and, in combination with the cutting motion, establishes the shape being cut. The common available combination of motions is shown in Figure 9.4.

There are five basic types of machine tools that differ in the combination of cutting and feed motions they permit and in the usual kind of cutting tool for which they are designed:

- Turning and boring.
- Drilling
- Milling.
- Straight-line machines.
- Grinding.

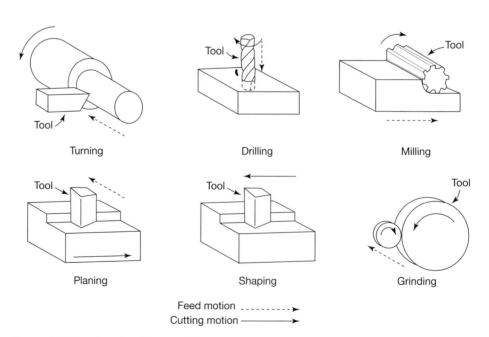

Figure 9.4: Feed and cutting motions.

Turning and Boring. These machines normally rotate the workpiece to produce the cutting motion and feed a single point tool parallel to the work axis or at some angle to it. External cylindrical machining is called *turning,* internal cylindrical machining is called *boring,* and making a flat surface by feeding the tool perpendicular to the axis of revolution is termed *facing.* Figures 9.5–9.8 show machines for turning and boring.

(a)

(b)

Figure 9.5: Fully manual bench lathe designed for light use: (a) full view; (b) another view showing 15 cm. (6 in.) three-jaw chuck (background), drill bit chuck (foreground), and tool post (left).

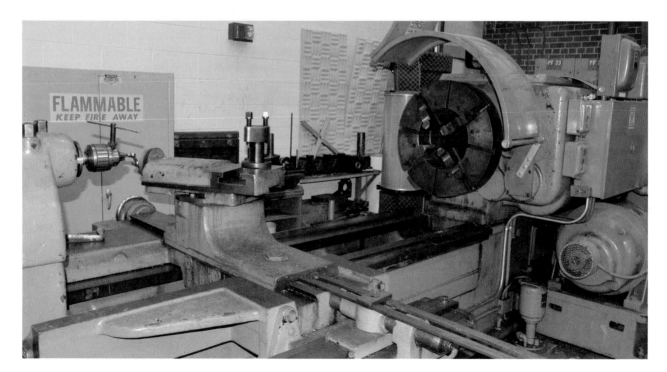

Figure 9.6: Large fully manual bench lathe.

Figure 9.7: Chips from a copper sample that was machined on a lathe (two views).

Figure 9.8: Large vertical turret lathe with 107 cm (42 in.) table (two views).

Drilling. A special fluted tool with two or more cutting lips on its exposed end is called a drill and is rotated and advanced axially into the workpiece by use of a *drill press.* The principal work is the making of, or enlarging of, cylindrical holes. Figures 9.9 and 9.10 show drilling machines.

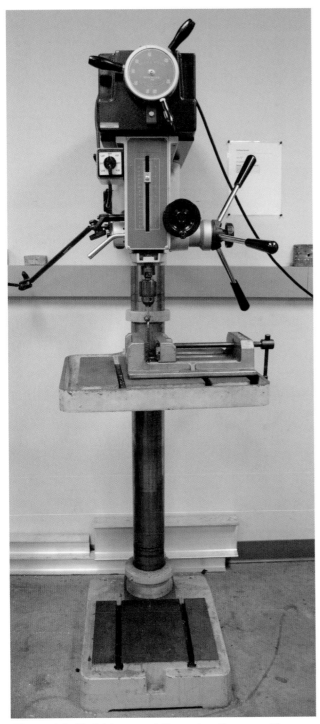

Figure 9.9: Variable speed floor-standing sensitive drill press.

(a)

(b)

Figure 9.10: Bits for industrial use: (a) typical tapered computer numerical control (CNC) tool holders equipped with various ball-end and square-end mills and drill bits; (b) collection of twist drills for use in a drilling machine.

Milling. There is a great variety of *milling machines*, which, like the drill press, employ special multi-edge cutters. Except for some special production-type milling machines, this equipment permits multidirection feeding and the cutters perform their principal cutting on their periphery edges. Milling machines are shown in Figures 9.11 – 9.13.

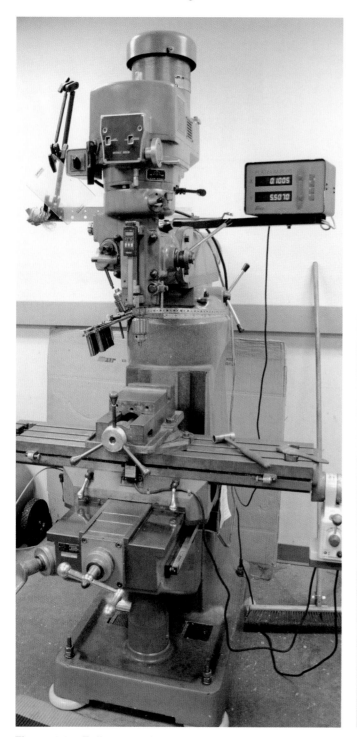

Figure 9.11: Fully manual vertical knee milling machine designed for light use.

Figure 9.12: Copper workpiece clamped for machining in a vertical knee milling machine during milling.

Figure 9.13: Fully manual horizontal knee milling machine.

Straight-Line Machines. One group of machine tools provides straight-line motion for its cutting action. This includes the *shaper* (straight-line motion of the cutter), the *planer* (straight-line motion of the workpiece), and the *broach* (straight-line motion of a special multitooth cutter). Because of the high cost of the special cutter, broaching is used only for production-quantity machining, but the shaper and planer are job-shop type machines. Types of straight-line machines are shown in Figures 9.14 and 9.15.

Grinding. Because any shape surface made by any other process or machine may require grinding as a finishing operation, there are a great number of *grinding machine* types. The machine drive rotates abrasive wheels at high cutting speed for the cutting motion and usually produces multiple feed motions simultaneously so the wheel contact may cover the desired surface. Machines used for grinding are shown in Figures 9.16 and 9.17.

Production Equipment. Machine tool types range from those that require complete attention and considerable operating skill from the operator to production types that are fully automatic. Companies manufacturing large quantities of similar products obtain their greatest economy using transfer-type machines connected together with automatic handling systems to move the product from one station to the next. These machines frequently include built-in output during continuous manufacturing. Production machines are shown in Figure 9.18.

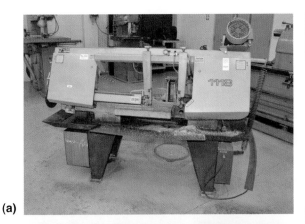

(a)

(b)

Figure 9.14: Manual horizontal bandsaw for cutting samples as large as 51 cm (20 in.) wide: (a) full view; (b) blade in fully down position with clamping vise.

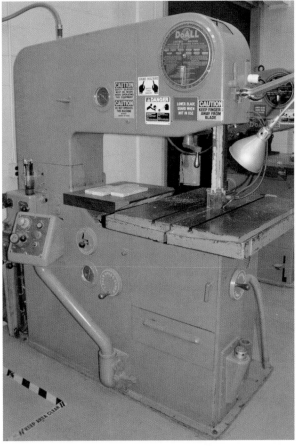

Figure 9.15: Contour vertical bandsaw.

Figure 9.16: Through-feed centerless grinder.

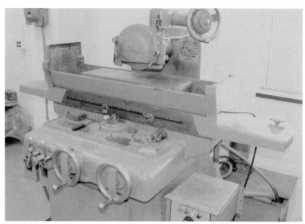

Figure 9.17: Two-axis hydraulic surface grinder.

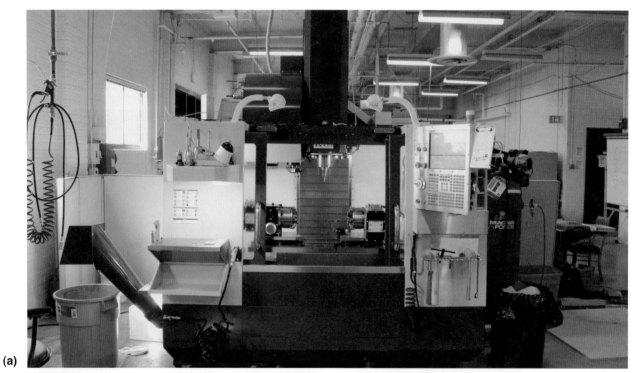

(a)

(b)

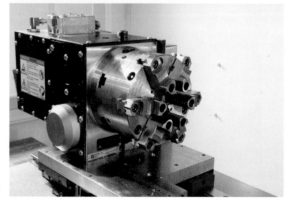

(c)

Figure 9.18: Modern CNC-controlled vertical machining center: (a) full view with automated tool changer (25 tool capacity) and as many as 5 axes of movement; (b) close-up of control panel; (c) view showing 15 cm (6 in.) six-jaw chuck mounted to a rotary table.

9.2.2 OTHER MACHINING PROCESSES

The following processes are "miscellaneous" only because they do not fit well in any of the established categories of casting, welding, deformation, or machining. For many applications, they are in direct competition with sawing and shearing for both straight-line and contour cutting.

9.2.2.1 TORCH CUTTING

This separation process depends on keeping the material being cut above its kindling temperature (800 °C [1500 °F] for pure iron) and supplying a stream of oxygen to promote fast oxidation. High temperature in the cutting zone is aided by the exothermic reaction of burning material.

Process Limited Mostly to Steels. Conditions for cutting are easily obtained with pure iron and low alloy steels but are different with many other metals. Reduced exothermic reaction and/or increased thermal conductivity reduce the practicality of using the process with cast iron, high-alloy steels including stainless, and most nonferrous alloys.

Easily Mechanized. Figure 9.19 shows a mechanized setup for making a straight-line cut in steel plate. Oxyacetylene flames are used to bring the steel to kindling temperature; then pure oxygen is supplied through a central orifice in the torch tip to burn a slot through the steel as the carriage moves along as its guide. The torch path may also be established by numerical control or may be guided by a line reader following the lines on a part drawing.

The process is very versatile, may be equipped with multiple torches for higher production, and produces accuracies similar to those obtained by sawing. This sheet may be cut singly or stacked. Steel over 1.5 m (5 ft) in thickness has been cut by this process, and *scarfing*—removal of discontinuities in large casting and forgings—is commonly practiced by use of flame cutting.

Arc Cutting Possible. Use of a steel wire electrode fed at high speed with gas shielding and very high currents can also be used for cutting. The thickness of the cut is much more limited than with the torch method, but materials difficult to cut with flame can be parted with the arc.

9.2.2.2 FRICTION SAWING

Friction sawing has limited but important use. This process also is used mostly for cutting steel.

High-Speed Rubbing Creates Heat. Localized heat is created in the workpiece by contact with the edge of a fast-moving blade or disc. Edge speeds are in the range of 3000 to 7500 m/min (10 000 to 25 000 ft/m). The tool may be smooth edged but usually has notches or teeth that help remove softened metal from the *kerf,* the slit or notch made by a saw or cutting torch.

The process is used mostly for cutoff work on bars and structural shapes in steel mill and warehouse operations. It may also be useful occasionally for cutting steel that is too hard to be cut by conventional means.

9.3 GRINDING AND FINISHING

9.3.1 ABRASIVES

The previously mentioned tool materials are used for single-point tools or for multi-point tools in which the cutting edges are carefully related to each other. Another group of materials known as *abrasives* are used as wheels, sticks, or stones, or in free form. In use, each abrasive grain, as it makes contact with the work, cuts by exactly

Figure 9.19: Oxyacetylene cutting.

the same mechanism as would a single point cutting tool. The random shape of the grains together with their random orientation creates a multitude of cutting conditions, which continually vary as tool wear occurs.

- **Aluminum Oxide:** A hard, strong grain, much larger than when used in a ceramic cutting tool, used for the vast majority of grinding tools and applications.
- **Silicon Oxide:** Harder and sharper grains than aluminum oxide but more brittle so they break easier in use. Used largely for tool grinding work and for grinding low-strength materials.
- **Diamond:** The same material used for single-point tools but in this case crushed, graded, and usually supported by a metal or ceramic backup material. Used to a great extent for finish grinding some of the harder cutting tools.
- **Boron Cubic Nitride:** Approaches the hardness of diamond. It has had some success as a lapping material and shows promise in wheels for tool grinding.

9.3.1.1 ABRASIVE BARREL FINISHING

A Low-Cost Cleaning and Finishing Method. When large numbers of small parts that do not need to have sharp detail or accurate dimensions require cleaning, the rotating barrel method may be very economical. Names used are *barrel finishing, rolling, tumbling,* and *rattling.* They are all similar, but various media may be combined with the work as indicated in Figure 9.20. High polish may be produced by tumbling with pieces of leather to wipe the surfaces smooth as in a strop-honing operation. In some cases, a number of hours may be required to produce the desired results, but since the finishing machines do not have to be tended by operators, the unit cost may be extremely low.

Machines with a vibratory motion and loaded with abrasive media are also used for similar-type cleaning and finishing work.

9.3.1.2 WIRE BRUSHING

A number of cleaning operations can be quickly and easily performed by use of a high-speed rotating wire brush. In addition to cleaning, the contact and rubbing of the wire ends across the work surface produce surface improvement by a burnishing-type action. Sharp edges and burrs can be removed. Scratches, rough spots, and similar mechanical imperfections can be improved primarily by plastic flow, which also tends to work-harden the surface material. Most wire brushing is done under manual control, but where the surfaces can be made accessible and the quantity to be treated is sufficiently large for economic feasibility, machines for automatic brushing can be set up. Common applications of wire brushing are the cleaning of castings, both ferrous and nonferrous; the cleaning of spatter and slag from weldments; and the removal of rust, corrosion, and paint from any object with a base material strong

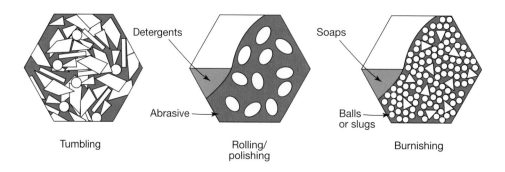

Figure 9.20: Barrel finishing.

enough to withstand the brushing. Wire brushing produces a distinctive pattern on the surface, and, in addition to cleaning, it sometimes is used to produce a decorative surface.

Problem of Surface Smearing. A precaution regarding surface discontinuity detection should be kept in mind. Any method of surface cleaning involving abrasion or rubbing may smear the surface material in such a way as to disguise or cover over surface discontinuities and prevent their detection by usual methods. Careful selection of a method may be necessary, or, in some cases, such drastic methods as etching may be needed. Machining, including fine grinding, also has similar effects to a lesser degree but should be remembered when small discontinuities could be serious regarding service life of the part under consideration. Penetrant tests are most severely affected and can be rendered practically useless if discontinuity openings have been smeared.

9.3.2 POLISHING

The term *polishing* may be interpreted to mean any nonprecision procedure providing a glossy surface but is most commonly used to refer to a surface finishing process using a flexible abrasive wheel. The wheels may be constructed of felt or rubber with an abrasive band, of multiple coated abrasive disks, of leaves of coated abrasive, of felt or fabric to which loose abrasive is added as needed, or of abrasives in a rubber matrix.

Polishing Is a Surface-Blending Process. These wheels differ from grinding wheels only by being flexible, which enables them to apply uniform pressure to the work surface and permits them to conform to the surface shape.

Polishing is usually done offhand except when the quantity is large. The process may have several objectives. Interest may be only in finish improvement for appearance. The surface finish may be important as an underlay for plating, which has only limited ability to improve surface quality over that of the surface on which it is placed. Polishing may also be important as a means of improving fatigue resistance for products subject to this kind of failure.

9.3.3 BUFFING

About the only difference between buffing and polishing is that, for buffing, a fine abrasive carried in wax or a similar substance is charged on the surface of a flexible wheel. The objectives are similar. With finer abrasive, buffing produces higher quality finish and luster but removes only minor amounts of metal. With both polishing and buffing, particularly of the softer metals, plastic flow permits filling of pores, scratches, and other surface discontinuities to improve both appearance and resistance to corrosion.

9.3.4 ELECTROPOLISHING

If a workpiece is suspended in an electrolyte and connected to the anode in an electrical circuit, it will supply metal to the electrolyte in a reverse plating process. Material will be removed faster from the high spots of the surface than from the depressions and will thereby increase the average smoothness. The cost of the process is prohibitive for very rough surfaces because larger amounts of metal must be removed to improve surface finish than would be necessary for the same degree of improvement by mechanical polishing. Electropolishing is economical only for improving a surface that is already good or for polishing complex and irregular shapes, the surfaces of which are not accessible to mechanical polishing and buffing equipment.

9.4 CHEMICAL, ELECTRICAL, AND HIGH-ENERGY BEAMS

9.4.1 METAL REMOVAL PROCESSES

Except for the introduction of new tool materials, more sophisticated design, and more highly powered machines, traditional machining has undergone no fundamental changes in the last century. On the other hand, some newer processes are referred to as *nontraditional* or *nonconventional* when compared to conventional machining because they do not necessarily use a high-strength tool to cause material failure by applying heavy localized loads to the workpiece.

Most Economically Feasible Only for Special Needs. None of these new methods can currently compete economically with conventional machining for shaping low- and moderate-strength materials when the surface to be machined is readily accessible and is composed of planes, cylinders, cones, or other simple geometric shapes. However, it is only under special circumstances that materials with hardnesses above about 50 Rockwell C can be machined with single-point cutting tools, and, even then, tool life is likely to be quite short. In addition, while few shapes are absolutely impossible to machine, many are especially difficult and particularly uneconomical in small quantities. It is toward solving these two problems—high material properties and difficult shapes—that most of these processes are directed. As with some of the newer low-tooling-cost pressworking processes, the aerospace industry has been the largest user of these metal-removing processes.

Sometimes Referred to as Chipless Machining. These processes are categorized as machining for several reasons. They all remove material, most of them slowly and in small amounts, although not necessarily in chip form. Most of the machines used still have the appearance and general design features of conventional machine tools because they must still provide for the proper positioning of a tool relative to the work and must still provide a geometrically controlled interference path between the tool and the work. The biggest difference occurs in the mechanisms used to produce material failure. With few exceptions, it is a chemical or a thermal, rather than a mechanical, failure.

9.4.2 CHEMICAL MILLING

Chemical milling is a process for shaping metals by chemical dissolution without electrical action. The name apparently originated from early applications where the process was used in aircraft manufacture as an adjunct to milling. It was originally used primarily to remove metal for weight reduction in areas of the workpiece that were not accessible to milling cutters and where work contours made following the surface with a cutter virtually impossible.

A Fully Chemical Process. The procedure is relatively simple. The areas of the part where material is not to be removed are first masked with an oxidation-resistant coating. The masking may be done by first coating the workpiece entirely and then removing the masking material from the desired areas by hand. When production quantities warrant, silk screening may be used to apply the maskant only where needed. The part is then immersed in a suitable *etchant*, which is usually a strong acid or alkali. After the material has been etched to the required depth, the work is removed and rinsed and the maskant removed.

Deep Straight Cuts Impossible. One of the most widely used applications is in the manufacture of printed circuit boards for electronic assemblies. The process is also competitive with conventional press blanking for short runs, especially in thin material. One of the principal drawbacks is the undercutting that occurs along the edges of the mask. Depth control is reasonably good, but straight vertical sides or sharp corners cannot be achieved in the cavity produced.

Variations in circulation of the etchant, variations of temperature, or differences in the material being worked upon may cause variable rates of chemical action. NDT by ultrasonic tests may therefore be necessary on critical parts to check possible thickness variations.

9.4.3 ELECTRICAL DISCHARGE MACHINING

Old Concept—New Development. The oldest, most successful, versatile, and widely used of the new removal processes is electrical discharge machining, often abbreviated EDM. As early as 1762, it was shown that metals were eroded by spark discharges. Electric arcs have been used to some extent for cutting operations in connection with welding, as well as practical application to the controlled shaping of metals.

High Electrical Voltage Creates Ionized Current Path. EDM is based on the observation that if an electrical potential exists between two conductive surfaces and the surfaces are brought toward each other, a discharge will occur when the gap is small enough that the potential can cause a breakdown in the medium between the two surfaces. The temperature developed in the gap at the point of discharge will be sufficient to ionize common liquids or gases so that they become highly conductive. It is this ionized column that in the welding process permits a welding arc to be maintained at considerable length, even over short periods of zero voltage when alternating current is used. The condition of maintained ionization is desirable for welding but cannot be tolerated for controlled shaping, as the discharge would tend to remain at one place so long as a low conductive path were present.

Intermittent Direct Current Required. For EDM, the electrodes are separated by a dielectric hydrocarbon oil. The elements of the electrical circuitry are shown in Figure 9.21. A capacitor across the electrodes is charged by a direct-current power

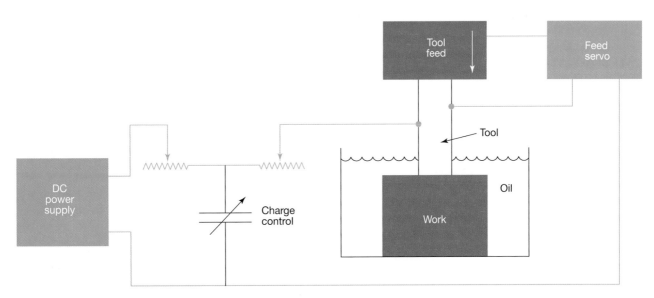

Figure 9.21: Electrical discharge machining.

supply. With the electrodes separated by about 0.025 mm (0.001 in.), a discharge will occur when the voltage reaches 25 to 100 V, depending on the exact nature of the dielectric and the materials of the electrodes. The essential element of the process is the discharge occurring at the point where the electrodes are closest together. Whether the discharge should be defined as an arc or a spark is a matter of some debate, but the fact remains that small amounts of material are removed from both electrodes, probably largely as the result of surface vaporization caused by the high temperature developed locally. As soon as the capacitor is discharged, the oil extinguishes the arc (deionizes the path), and the capacitor is then recharged.

Servomechanism Advances Tool. Subsequent discharges will occur at other points that are then closer together. As material is removed from the electrodes, the distance between them becomes greater, and the voltage required to initiate a discharge rises. This rise in voltage can be used to actuate a servocontrol that feeds the electrodes together to maintain a constant discharge voltage or, stated another way, to maintain a constant distance between he electrodes. The *amount* of material removed by each discharge is determined primarily by the amount of energy released from the capacitor. The *rate* of material removal is determined by the individual quantity and the cyclic frequency. The frequency of discharges on most machines ranges between 20 000 and 300 000 Hz.

Both Workpiece and Tool Are Eroded. The applications for the process depend on the fact that one of the electrodes can be a workpiece, the other a tool that produces a shaped hole, cavity, or external surface in the work. The relative rate of material removal on the workpiece and tool depends on their melting points, latent heats of evaporation, thermal conductivities, and other factors. Ideally, the material of the tool would be eroded very slowly or not at all. In practice, wear ratios range from as low as 0.05 (20× as much workpiece material removed as tool material) when cutting a steel workpiece with a silver tungsten alloy tool, to 2.0 or more when cutting cemented carbides. Because of its low cost and ease of shaping, brass is a more common tool material, although wear ratios are much higher. Graphite provides very favorable wear ratios when used for cutting steel.

Useful for Special Shapes and Hard Materials. The EDM process offers two principal advantages when compared to more traditional methods of machining: (1) some shapes are more easily produced and (2) workpiece hardness offers no problems (Figure 9.22). EDM may be used for producing almost any shape if the proper electrode can be made.

(a)

(b)

Figure 9.22: CNC-controlled wire EDM machine: (a) with the operator deflecting the conductor out of the coolant flow for visibility while the cabinet is open; (b) in operation with full coolant flow while the cabinet is closed.

Noncircular through-holes that would otherwise require a broach or very time-consuming handwork are often made by first removing as much material as possible with a circular drilling operation, then finishing by EDM. The advantage comes in making the electrode because the conventional machining can be done to an external shape. A square or splined electrode, for example, is more easily machined than a square or splined hole if a broach is not available. EDM is sometimes a simple and convenient way to fabricate discontinuities in a standard or test specimen for nondestructive testing.

Multiple Duplicated Electrodes Often Needed. If the hole goes through the workpiece, electrode wear creates few problems. The electrode is simply made with additional length that is fed through the work material to compensate for the wear. For a blind hole with straight sides, the electrode would also be made with additional length but would be removed periodically to have its forward end refaced. If the cavity is to have a three-dimensional contour, the problem is more severe. The number of electrodes required would depend on the materials used and on the geometrical precision required. As many as 10 electrodes are often used.

All Electrically Conductive Materials Workable. Aside from its ability to cut complex two- or three-dimensional contoured shapes, EDM has the ability to shape any material that has a reasonable amount of electrical conductivity. Hardened steels and cemented carbides present problems no greater than soft ductile materials that could easily be cut by machining. Materials are as easy to shape in a hardened state as they are in an annealed condition.

Slow Removal Process. The process has one drawback in addition to relatively high equipment cost and the problem of electrode wear discussed previously. An inverse relationship exists between the quality of the surface finish produced and the cutting rate. Surface finishes as good as 0.254 μm (10 μ-in.) are obtainable, but only with metal removal rates on the order of 0.005 cm^3 (0.0003 $in.^3$) per min. Maximum metal removal rates at present are about 5 cm^3 (0.3 $in.^3$) per min, but when this rate is achieved, surface finish quality measures about 12.7 μm (500 μ-in.)

9.4.4 ELECTROCHEMICAL MACHINING

Electrochemical machining (ECM) is somewhat newer than electrical discharge machining (EDM) and offers great potential, particularly because of the greater metal removal rates possible than with EDM.

A Special Reverse Plating System. In this process, as in EDM, both the tool and the workpiece must be conductive, or at least the workpiece must be conductive and the tool must have a conductive coating. With a suitable electrolyte between them, the tool and workpiece form opposite electrodes of an electrolytic cell. The workpiece is connected to the positive terminal of a direct-current supply and the tool to the negative terminal. The electrical circuit is identical to that used in metal plating where metal is removed from the anode and deposited on the cathode.

There are two major differences. Different electrolytes are used so that the material removed from the anode forms insoluble oxides or hydroxides. In electroplating, the unagitated electrolyte permits metal ions to leave the anode only as fast as they can diffuse into the electrolyte. The low rate of diffusion restricts the maximum current flow that can be efficiently used. In ECM the electrolyte is made to flow rapidly between the tool and the work by pressures up to 4 MPa (600 psi). Currents up to 10 000 A are used on an area 30 cm^2 (5 $in.^2$) with a resulting metal removal rate of about 16 cm^3 (1 $in.^3$) per minute. With adequate power supplies, there appears to be no reason that the metal removal rate could not be even greater.

Work Energy Efficiency Low. The ECM is used for many of the same jobs that could be done by EDM, including the making of irregularly shaped holes, forming shaped cavities, and machining very hard or abrasive materials. Figure 9.23 gives an outline of the process. Compared to EDM, tolerances must be greater, particularly incavity shaping, and tool design is more critical to obtain proper flow of the electrolyte between the tool and the work. In addition, as much as 119 kW (160 hp) per 16 cm³ (1 in.³) per min of metal removal is required. This is about 4× that required by EDM, and more than 100× that needed by most conventional machining. On the other hand, tools do not wear, and the metal removal rate is much greater than with EDM.

9.4.5 ULTRASONIC MACHINING

A Mechanical Forming Process. The term *ultrasonic machining* is used to denote an abrasive machining process used for cutting hard materials by projecting tiny abrasive particles at the work surface at high velocities. Figure 9.24 shows the details of the process. The abrasive is carried in a liquid flowing between the shaped tool and the workpiece. The tool is made to oscillate along its axis at a frequency of about 20 000 Hz.

   Transducer Motion Amplified by Horn. The heart of the equipment is the *transducer* that converts the high-frequency electrical power into mechanical energy. Most transducers are made with nickel laminations that are placed in an oscillating magnetic field. Nickel has the property of *magnetostriction* and undergoes a change in length when placed in a magnetic field. The amplitude of vibration of the nickel is insufficient for practical use and must be amplified by attaching a suitable *horn* to one end. The tool is then brazed, soldered, or mechanically fastened to the end of the horn. The entire assembly must be mechanically tuned to resonate at the frequency produced by the electronic amplifier. When so tuned, the amplitude of the tool motion is from 0.05 to 0.1 mm (0.002 to 0.004 in.).

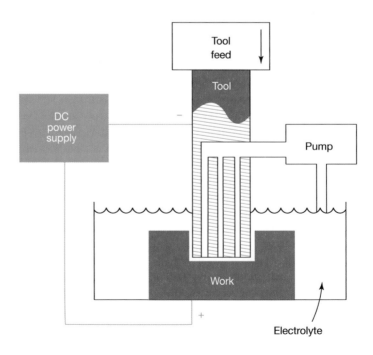

Figure 9.23: Electrochemical machining.

Produces Good Finishes. The tool itself is most often made of soft steel and is given the negative shape of the cavity to be produced, as in EDM or ECM. The most common abrasive used is boron carbide in grit size ranging from 240 (coarse) to 800 (fine). The cutting rate and finish produced both depend on the size of the abrasive. With 800-grit abrasive, finishes as fine as 0.254 μm (10 μ-in.) may be attained. Tolerances as close as 0.01 mm (0.0005 in.) are possible for size and contour with fine abrasives.

Best for Hard, Brittle Materials. Unlike conventional machining, which works only with material below a certain hardness, and EDM or ECM, which work with any conductive material, ultrasonic machining is best suited to materials that are both hard and brittle. However, the work material need not be a metal or otherwise conductive. The process has been used for engraving, slicing, drilling, and cavity sinking on hardened steel, gemstones, cemented carbides, ferrites, aluminum oxide, glass, and other ceramics.

Not Competitive with Usable Conventional Methods. The metal removal rate is presently the principal drawback, being only about 0.3 mm³ (0.02 in.³) per min. It could possibly be increased considerably with better transducers, but the process is likely to remain in the special-purpose category.

9.4.6 HIGH-ENERGY-BEAM MACHINING

EDM, ECM, chemical milling, and ultrasonic machining are commercially used processes for which equipment is available. Much development work still remains to be done on all these processes, but their current value is sufficient to warrant their existence. Other potential removal processes, such as laser and plasma arc cutting, offer alternatives to more traditional processes.

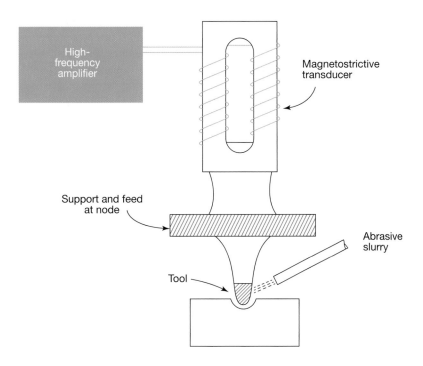

Figure 9.24: Ultrasonic machining.

The *laser* (light amplification by stimulated emission of radiation) was invented about 1960. It quickly received much attention and publicity, hailed as the greatest invention of the century. At first, it found a number of uses in measuring, in holography, and as a signal carrier, but, due mainly to limited capacity and high cost, only later became valuable for machining and welding on a commercial scale.

Development since 1970 has increased the power capability and reduced the cost to make it more competitive with conventional equipment. Some hole-making, cutting, and other types of operations are being performed industrially. The market for industrial laser use continues to grow. Uses of laser cutting and removal are mostly with materials difficult to manufacture with more common methods.

Plasma arcs and *electron beams* are heating sources for welding. Plasma arcs are also capable of sufficiently localized energy inputs so that surface material may be melted and vaporized with relatively small heating of the adjacent material. The arcs are being used for some straight-line cutting operations, where control is simple and tolerance requirements are not too high. Some experimental work has been done in lathe turning, using a plasma arc as a cutting tool.

9.5 NUMERICAL CONTROL

Numerical control (N/C) systems are auxiliary machine control equipment that may be applied to almost any kind of mechanical device that can function by repeating a certain cycle of operation. This development is especially important in the manufacturing field because it can be applied to most machine tool types and some other machine equipment, such as punches, welding equipment, cutting torches, and even drafting machines. Although N/C tapes are not entirely obsolete, most N/C systems today are now either *computer numerical control* (CNC) or *direct numerical control* (DNC) systems that are integrated into *computer-aided design* (CAD) or computer-aided programming.

Programming produces a computer file that is interpreted to extract the commands needed to operate a particular machine via a post processor. The commands are then loaded into the CNC machines for production. Since a component or part might require the use of a number of different tools—for example, drills, lathes, plasma cutters, electric discharge machines—modern machines often combine multiple tools into a single cell or unit. In other installations, an external controller oversees a sequence of machines, and human or robotic operators move the component from machine to machine. In either case, the series of steps is highly automated and produces a part or component that closely matches the original CAD design.

Greatest Value for Small to Medium Quantities. Although it would be possible to retrofit a standard machine with N/C, the results obtained would be very limited in scope, accuracy, and time saving so that only rarely would such action be economically justified. Practically all N/C equipment is of special design with an integrated control system such that the total cost may be many times that of a conventional machine designed to perform similar product work. Because the cost is high, it seems unusual that it is most economical to use N/C equipment on relatively small-quantity lots, only occasionally exceeding one or two hundred pieces.

The major benefits received from N/C include reduction of the human element in relation to the product with resulting improvement of consistency, requiring less inspection. The reason for its value in small lot sizes is based on the short setup time, particularly when the program has already been prepared for previous runs. The equipment can therefore be shifted from one product part to another by changing the programmed instructions and available tools with very little time loss.

Large-quantity manufacturing of the continuous type can be done most inexpensively with specialized, single-purpose machines, usually tied together with mechanical handling equipment and, in many cases, including most of the inspection equipment needed to maintain quality.

Principles of Operation. Numerical control consists of storing information in the form of numbers and supplying that information in proper order to the machine to cause the machine to go through some predetermined cycle of operation. Some machines are of conventional design and may be operated manually as well as by N/C. Others are so special that manual control is very difficult and in order to exhibit their greatest value may need to use a computer-generated program.

Program Storage. Several storage media, such as magnetic tape, punched cards, and others, can and have been used, and, until the advent of more sophisticated computers, industry has generally accepted a 25.4 mm (1 in.) wide eight-channel tape as a standard input medium. Figure 9.25 shows a short section of such a tape displaying two words of information to describe X- and Y-axis positions. The presence or absence of holes at various locations along the eight channels are bits of information that make up characters and words, which can be interpreted by the machine reader to initiate action.

Most Machines of Closed-Loop Design. A small number of machines have been designed to obey their commands without response to the control system. Most, though, are designed with transducers in the machine elements, which generate feedback signals for the control system. As long as error exists between the comparer feedback and command signals, movement continues. As soon as the comparison error disappears, the next command takes over.

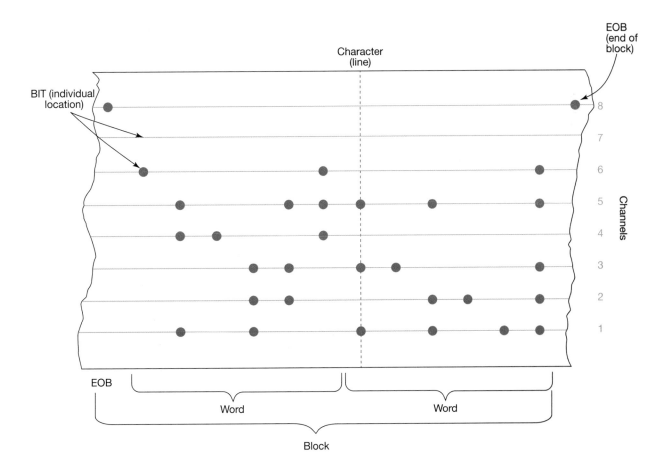

Figure 9.25: Section of N/C tape.

Controlled Motions Called Axes. Some machines such as a simple N/C drill, which moves the work only through an X and Y axis under a spindle that moves with a single position stop, are called two-axis machines. An example is shown in Figure 9.26. Others are more complex with a Z axis (spindle control) and sometimes rotational motion of the work about one or more axes to present different faces of the work to the cutting tool.

Many machines are also constructed with multiple tool holding racks and the capability of selecting and using particular coded tools as called for by the programmed instructions.

Some machines move from one point to another with no control over the path traveled to arrive at the new position. Others differ from the simpler "point to point" machine by operating through a continuously controlled path, permitting the generation of accurate curves and shapes. Figure 9.27 pictures an N/C lathe of this type.

Machine Types. Most of the machine tools fitted with N/C fall in the general categories of lathes, drilling machines, and milling machines, although many are combinations of the drilling and milling types and have been given the general name of *machining center* because of the great variety of work that can be accomplished on a workpiece in a single setup.

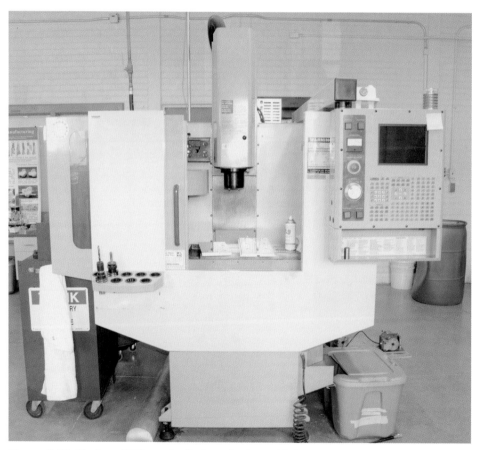

Figure 9.26: Modern CNC-controlled vertical machining center with automated tool changer (10-tool capacity) and as many as five axes of movement.

N/C Advantages. Advantages of N/C include reduced tooling costs by use of simplified jigs and fixtures; low setup time and cost (most important values); excellent repeatability with relatively good accuracy, fewer errors from human fallibility; and reduced lead time.

N/C Disadvantages. Use of N/C has several drawbacks. Original machine is more costly. Machines are more complex, thus requiring more maintenance. Operators and maintenance personnel require special training and skills. Machines usually require more floor space than conventional types. Effective use necessitates coordination of design with the equipment.

Computers. Many programs prepared for N/C can best be done by use of a computer to perform lengthy computations and turn out programming instructions ready for use. In addition to computer-assisted programming, some equipment is designed to be directly operated by a computer, which uses its own memory bank for program storage and eliminates the need for a tape and tape reader. The N/C equipment may be connected directly to its own small computer or may be included in a bank of machines controlled by a large computer. In either case, the program can normally be edited or corrected at the computer keyboard or can be quickly shifted to an entirely new program.

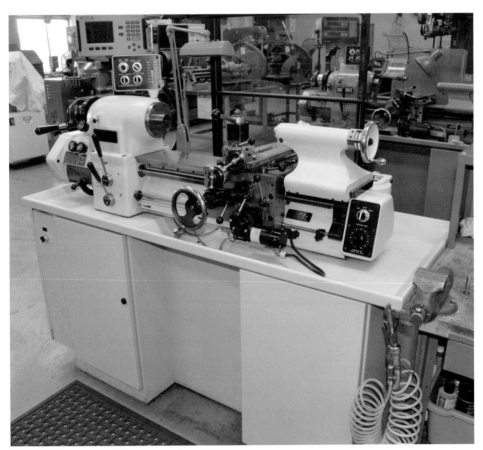

Figure 9.27: Small CNC-controlled toolroom lathe.

10 Surface Treatments and Coatings

10.1 INTRODUCTION

Products that have been completed to their proper shape and size frequently require some type of surface finishing to enable them to satisfactorily fulfill their function. In some cases, it is necessary to improve the physical properties of the surface material for resistance to penetration or abrasion. In many manufacturing processes, the product surface is left with dirt, chips, grease, or other harmful material upon it. Assemblies that are made of different materials, or from the same materials processed in different manners, may require some special surface treatment to provide uniformity of appearance.

Surface finishing may sometimes become an intermediate step in processing. For instance, cleaning and polishing are usually essential before any kind of plating process. Some of the cleaning procedures are also used for improving surface smoothness on mating parts and for removing burrs and sharp corners, which might be harmful in later use. Another important need for surface finishing is for corrosion protection in a variety of environments. The type of protection provided depends largely upon the anticipated exposure, with due consideration to the material being protected and the economic factors involved.

Satisfying the above objectives necessitates the use of many surface-finishing methods that involve chemical change of the surface, mechanical work affecting

"Some of the cleaning procedures are also used for improving surface smoothness on mating parts and for removing burrs ..."

surface properties, cleaning by a variety of methods, and the application of protective coatings, both organic and metallic.

10.2 SURFACE FINISHING

10.2.1 CASE HARDENING

Case Hardening Results in a Hard, Shell-like Surface. Some product applications require surface properties of hardness and strength to resist penetration under high pressure and to provide maximum wear qualities. Where through-hardness and the maximum strength associated with it are not necessary, it may be more economical to gain the needed surface qualities by a *case-hardening* process. Case hardening involves a change of surface properties to produce a hard, wear-resistant shell about a tough, fracture-resistant core. This is usually accomplished by a change of surface material chemistry. With some materials, a similar condition can be produced by a phase change of material already present.

   Multiple Benefits from Case Hardening. Case hardening may be more satisfactory than through-hardening in those cases where a low cost, low carbon steel with a hard shell may be used instead of a higher cost, high carbon or alloy steel needed for through-hardening. The process is much less likely to cause warping or cracking, and the product, because of its soft, ductile core, is less subject to brittle failure than a through-hardened product. Case hardening is often suitable for heavy sections that would require very special high alloy steels for through-hardening to be effective.

   Case depth measurement is sometimes checked by destructive methods: cutting the object, etching the cut surface, and checking the cut depth with a measuring microscope. A faster and more usable method when knowledge is needed directly for service parts is by use of electromagnetic tests.

10.2.2 CARBURIZING

Case hardening of steel may be accomplished by a number of methods. Choice between them is dependent on the material to be treated, the application, and the desired properties. One of the more common methods is carburizing, which implies an increase or addition of carbon, which is actually the basis of the process.

   Performed on Low Carbon Steels. Carburizing is usually performed on a low alloy or plain low carbon steel. If an alloy steel is used, it usually contains small quantities of nickel or some other element that acts as a retardant to grain growth during the heating cycle. Low carbon steels are commonly used to minimize the effect of subsequent heat treatments on the core material. It is possible to carburize any steel containing less than the 0.70% to 1.20% carbon that is produced in the surface material.

   Carbon Diffusion Is Time-Temperature Dependent. Carbon is caused to diffuse into the steel by heating the material above its critical temperature and holding it in the presence of excess carbon. Temperatures used are usually between 850 °C and 930 °C (1562 °F and 1706 °F) with the choice most dependent on the desired rate of penetration, the desired surface carbon content, and the permissible grain growth in the material. Penetration is dependent upon both the temperature and time, with variation of case depth from 0.25 to 1.0 mm (0.010 to 0.040 in.) possible in the first 2 h by varying the temperature between the two extremes. The rate of penetration slows down as the depth increases, as shown in Figure 10.1, so that for large depths, relatively long periods of time are necessary.

   Carbon May Be Supplied from a Gas, Liquid, or Solid Environment. The excess carbon for diffusion is supplied from a carbon-rich environment in solid, liquid, or gas form. Parts to be carburized may be packed in carbon or other carbonaceous material in boxes that are sealed to exclude air and then heated in a furnace for the required length of time, in a process sometimes referred to as *pack hardening.* The liquid method makes use of molten sodium cyanide, in which the parts are suspended to take on carbon. The cyanide method is usually limited to shallow case depths of about 0.25 mm (0.010 in.) maximum. The third method—often the simplest for production operations requiring heavy case depth—supplies gaseous hydrocarbons from an unburned gas or oil fuel source to the furnace retort in which the product is heated. The product is usually suspended on wires or rolled about in order that all surfaces will be exposed uniformly.

Grain-Size Control Necessary for Best Properties. Carburizing steels containing grain-growth inhibitors may be quenched directly from the carburizing furnace to harden the outside shell, but plain carbon steels must be cooled and reheated through the critical temperature range to reduce grain size. Even the alloy steels will have better properties if treated in this manner. Quenching from above the critical temperature will produce a hard martensitic structure in the high carbon surface material but will have little or no effect on the low carbon core. As in the case of most through-hardened steels, tempering is usually required to toughen the outside shell. The complete cycle for case hardening by carburizing is illustrated in Figure 10.2.

10.2.3 FLAME HARDENING

Surface Must Be Heated above Transformation Temperature. Another case-hardening process that does not require a change of composition in the surface material is *flame hardening.* This method can be used only on steels that contain sufficient carbon to be hardenable by standard heat-treating procedures. The case is produced by selectively heating part or all of the surface with special high-capacity gas burners or oxyacetylene torches at a rate sufficiently high that only a small depth from the surface goes above the critical temperature. Following immediately behind the torch is a water-quenching head that floods the surface to reduce the temperature fast enough to produce a martensitic structure. As in the case of carburizing, the surface may be then reheated to temper it for toughness improvement. The depth of hardness is controlled by the temperature to which the metal is raised, by the rate of heating, and by the time that passes before quenching.

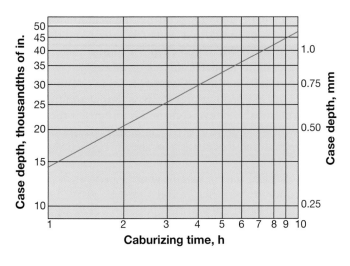

10.1: Typical carburizing case depth-time relationship.

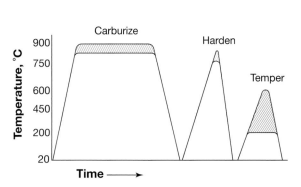

10.2: Heating cycle for case hardening by carburizing.

10.3 CLEANING OF SURFACES

Few, if any, shaping and sizing processes produce products that are usable without some type of cleaning unless special precautions are taken. Hot working, heat treating, and welding cause oxidation and scale formation from high temperatures in the presence of oxygen. For the same reason, castings usually are coated with scale or oxides. If made in sand molds, they may have sand grains fused or adhering to the surface. Residue from coolants, lubricants, and other processing materials is common on many manufactured parts. In addition to greasy films from processing, protective coatings of greases, oils, or waxes are frequently used intentionally to prevent rust or corrosion on parts that are stored for some period of time before being put to use. Even if parts are clean at the completion of manufacturing, they seldom remain that way for long. After only short storage periods, corrosion and dust from atmospheric exposure necessitate cleaning for best condition or to permit further processing.

When using NDT such as penetrant testing and ultrasonic testing, good precleaning may be necessary to get accurate results, and postcleaning is often needed to leave the surface in suitable condition. In some applications, such as on stainless steels and nickel-based alloys, ultrasonic coolants and penetrant materials must be made of only certain material so that the NDT materials are not one of the causes of stress-corrosion failure.

Cleaning sometimes has finish improvement associated with it. Some shape-producing methods result in unsatisfactory surface characteristics such as sharp corners, burrs, and tool marks, which may affect the function, handling ease, and appearance of the product. Some cleaning processes at least partially blend together surface irregularities to produce uniform light reflection. Improvement of surface qualities may be accomplished by removal of high spots by cutting or by plastic flow as cleaning is performed.

10.3.1 CHOICE OF CLEANING METHOD

As indicated by the list in Figure 10.3, many different cleaning methods are available. The one most suitable for any particular situation is dependent upon a number of factors. Cost is, of course, always a strong consideration, but the reason for cleaning is bound to affect the choice. Convenience in handling, improvement in appearance, elimination of foreign material that may affect function, or establishment of a chemically clean surface as an intermediate step in processing might all call for different methods. Consideration must be given to the starting conditions and to the degree of improvement desired or required. Methods suitable for some materials are not at all satisfactory for use on other kinds of material.

Cleaning and Corrosion Protection Sometimes Associated. Some cleaning methods provide multiple benefits. As pointed out previously, cleaning and finish improvements are often combined. Probably of even greater importance is the combination of corrosion protection with finish improvement, although corrosion protection is more often a second step that involves coating an already cleaned surface with some other material.

10.3.2 LIQUID AND VAPOR BATHS

Liquid and Vapor Solvents Common. The most widely used cleaning methods make use of a cleaning medium in liquid or vapor form. These methods depend on a solvent or chemical action between the surface contaminants and the cleaning material.

Many cleaning methods and a variety of materials are available for choice, depending on the base material to be cleaned, the contaminant to be removed, the importance and degree of cleanliness, and the quantity to be treated.

Petroleum Solvents Good for Greases and Oils. Among the more common cleaning jobs required is the removal of grease and oil deposited during manufacturing or intentionally coated on the work to provide protection. One of the most efficient ways to remove this material is by use of solvents that dissolve the grease and oil but have no effect on the base metal. Petroleum derivatives such as stoddard solvent and kerosene are common for this purpose, but as they introduce some danger of fire, chlorinated solvents, such as trichloretholene, that are free of this fault are sometimes substituted.

Conditioned Water Usually Inexpensive. One of the most economical cleaning materials is water. However, it is seldom used alone even if the contaminant is fully water soluble because the impurity of the water itself may contaminate the work surface. Depending on its use, water is treated with various acids and alkalis to suit the job being performed.

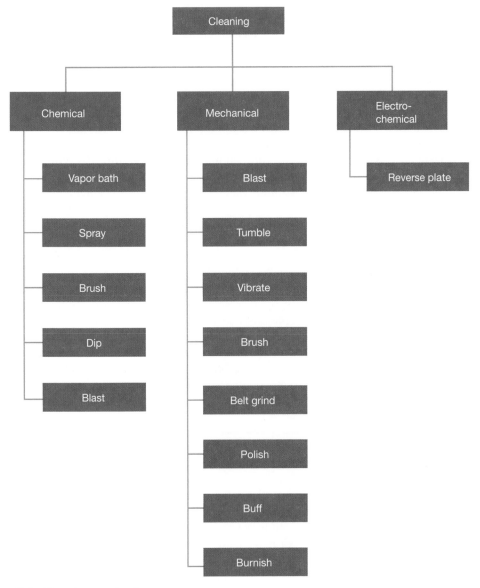

10.3: Cleaning methods.

Proper Pickling Can Selectively Remove Iron Oxides. Water containing sulfuric acid in a concentration from about 10% to 25% and at a temperature of approximately 65 °C (149 °F) is commonly used in a process called *pickling* for removal of surface oxides or scale on iron and steel. The work is immersed in the solution contained in large tanks for a predetermined period of time, after which it is rinsed to stop the chemical action.

Improper control of the timing, temperature, or concentration in the pickling bath is likely to result in pitting of the surface because of uneven chemical reaction. Most pickling baths are treated with chemical inhibitors that decrease the chemical effect of the acid on the base metal but have little effect on the rate at which the oxides are attacked.

Many Water Additives Are Proprietary Mixtures. Many of the common cleaning liquids are made up of approximately 95% water containing alkaline cleaners such as caustic soda, sodium carbonate, silicates, phosphates, and borates. The proportions are varied for different purposes and are available under different brand names for particular applications.

Application Dependent on Material and Purpose. Liquid cleaners may be applied in a number of ways. *Degreasing*, particularly on small parts, is frequently done with a vapor bath. This does an excellent job of removing the grease but has the disadvantage of not being able to remove chips and other kinds of dirt that might be present. *Vapor degreasing* is usually done in a special tank that is heated at the bottom to vaporize the solvent and cooled at the top to condense the solvent. Cold work suspended in the vapor causes condensation of the solvent, which dissolves the grease and drips back into the bottom of the tank. The difference in volatility between the solvent and the greases permits the vapor to remain unchanged and to do a uniform cleaning job.

Mechanical Work Frequently Combined with Chemical Action. Spraying, brushing, and dipping methods are also used with liquid cleaners. In nearly all cases, mechanical work to cause surface film breakdown and particle movement is combined with chemical and solvent action. The mechanical work may be agitation of the product as in dipping, movement of the cleaning agent as in spraying, or use of a third element as in rubbing or brushing. In some applications, sonic or ultrasonic vibrations are applied to either the solution or the workpieces to speed the cleaning action. Chemical activity is increased with higher temperatures and optimum concentration of the cleaning agent, both of which must in some cases be controlled closely for efficient action.

Important That Chemicals Be Removed. Washing and rinsing away of the cleaning liquids is usually necessary to prevent films and spots. Fast drying of water solutions on iron and steel products is sometimes needed to prevent the formation of rust. If the product mass is large enough, heat picked up from the cleaning bath may be sufficient to cause fast drying; otherwise, air blasts or external heat sources may be required.

10.3.3 BLASTING

Blasting Provides Large Mechanical Action. The term *blasting* is used to refer to all of those cleaning methods in which the cleaning medium is accelerated to high velocity and impinged against the surface to be cleaned. The high velocity may be provided by air or water directed through a nozzle or by mechanical means with a revolving slinger. The cleaning agent may be either dry or wet solid media such as sand, abrasive, steel grit, or shot, or may be liquid or vapor solvents combined with abrasive material.

Operator Safety Must Be Considered. The solid media are used for the removal of brittle surface contamination such as the heat-treat scale found on forgings and castings. Steel grit has replaced sand and other refractory-type abrasives to some extent because of the reduced health hazard (silicosis) and a reduced tendency for pulverization. Sand, however, can be used without danger to the operator when parts are small enough to be handled by hand inside a properly designed chamber fitted with a dust collector.

Surface Stressed and Work Hardened. In addition to cleaning, solid particles can improve finish and surface properties of the material on which they are used. Blasting tends to increase the surface area and thus set up compressive stresses that may cause a warping of thin sections, but in other cases, it may be very beneficial by reducing the likelihood of fatigue failure. When used for this latter purpose, the process is more commonly known as *shotpeening*.

Water Slurries. Liquid or vaporized solvents may, by themselves, be blasted against a surface for high-speed cleaning of oil and grease films with both chemical and mechanical action. Water containing rust-inhibiting chemicals may carry, in suspension, fine abrasive particles that provide a grinding cutting-type action for finish improvement along with cleaning. The blasting method using this medium is commonly known as *liquid honing*.

10.4 PLATINGS AND COATINGS

10.4.1 METALLIZING

10.4.1.1 THERMAL SPRAYING

Metal spraying, or *metallizing,* is a process in which metal wire or powder is fed into an oxyacetylene heating flame and then, after melting, is carried by high-velocity air to be impinged against the work surface. The small droplets adhere to the surface and bond together to build up a coating.

Bond Mostly Mechanical. The nature of the bond is dependent largely on the materials. The droplets are relatively cool when they make contact and can in fact be sprayed on wood, leather, and other flammable materials. Little, if any, liquid flow aids the bonding action. If, however, sufficient affinity exists between the metals, a type of weld involving atomic bonds may be established. The bond is largely mechanical in most cases, and metal spraying is usually done on surfaces that have been intentionally roughened to aid the mechanical attachment.

Anodic Materials Cause Selective Corrosion. Zinc, aluminum, and cadmium, which are anodic to steel and therefore provide preferential corrosion protection, are usually sprayed in thin layers, averaging about 0.25 mm (0.010 in.) in thickness, as protective coatings. Because sprayed coatings tend to be porous, coatings of two or more times this thickness are used for cathodic materials such as tin, lead, and nickel. The cathodic materials protect only by isolating the base material from its environment.

Buildup by Metal Spraying. Another important application for metal spraying is in salvage operations for which a wide variety of metals and alloys may be used. Surfaces, usually after first being roughened, are built up to oversized dimensions with metal spray. The excess material is then machined away to the desired dimension. Expensive parts with worn bearing surfaces or new parts that have been machined undersized can sometimes be salvaged by this relatively cheap procedure.

10.4.1.2 VACUUM METALLIZING

Some metals can be deposited in very thin films, usually for reflective or decorative purposes, as a deposit. The metal is vaporized in a high-vacuum chamber containing the parts to be coated. The metal vapor condenses on the exposed surfaces in a thin film that follows the surface pattern. The process is cheap for coating small parts, considering the time element only, but the cost of special equipment needed is relatively high.

Aluminum is the most-used metal for deposit by this method and is used frequently for decorating or producing a mirror surface on plastics. The thin films usually require mechanical protection by covering with lacquer or some other coating material.

10.4.2 ELECTROPLATING

Coatings of many metals can be deposited on other metals, and on nonmetals when suitably prepared, by *electroplating*. The objectives of plating are to provide protection against corrosion, to improve appearance, to establish wear and abrasion-resistant surfaces, to add material for dimensional increase, and to serve as an intermediate step of multiple coating. Some of the most common metals deposited in this way are copper, nickel, chromium, cadmium, zinc, tin, silver, and gold. The majority are used to provide some kind of corrosion protection, but appearance also plays a strong part in their use.

Complex Electrical and Chemical System. Figure 10.4 is a schematic diagram of a simple plating setup. When direct-current power of high enough voltage is applied

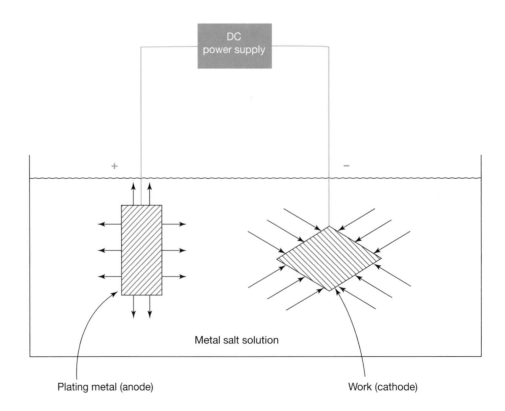

10.4: Electroplating.

to two electrodes immersed in a water solution of metallic salt, current will flow through the circuit, causing changes at the electrodes. At the negative electrode, or cathode (the workpiece), excess electrons supplied from the power source neutralize positively charged metallic ions in the salt solution to cause dissolved metal to be deposited in the solid state. At the positive electrode, or anode (plating metal), metal goes into solution to replace the metal that is removed at the other electrode. The rate of deposition and the properties of the plated material are dependent on the metals being worked with, the current density, the solution temperature, and other factors.

Coating Thickness Usually Low. Thickness of plating is usually low, in the range of 2.5 microns to 0.025 mm (0.0001 to 0.001 in.). Chromium applied for appearance only may be used in a thickness of only about one-tenth these amounts, but when used to provide wear resistance and to build up dimensions, as on gages, may be applied in thickness as much as 0.25 mm (0.010 in.).

When plating thickness is a critical consideration, measurement and control may be established with NDT. Both electromagnetic techniques and radiation backscatter are useful.

Multiple Metals for Maximum Properties. Layers of different metals are sometimes plated for maximum properties. For example, an object such as a steel bumper for an automobile may first be copper plated to provide good adhesion and coverage of the steel and to facilitate buffing to a smooth surface necessary for a high-quality final finish. Nickel is then plated over the copper to serve as the principal corrosion protection. Finally, chromium is plated over the nickel to serve as a hard, wear-resistant, bright, blue-white color coating over the softer, tarnishable nickel.

Many Problems Even Though a Common Process. Some problems exist with electroplating. Deposits on irregular shapes may vary widely in thickness. Projections and exposed surfaces may plate readily, but recesses, corners, and holes can sometimes be coated only by using specially located electrodes or electrodes shaped to conform to the workpiece shape. Electroplating can be costly because it involves payment for considerable electric power and the metal plated and lost. Because plating thicknesses are usually very small, the coating has little hiding power.

10.4.3 CONVERSION COATING

10.4.3.1 CHEMICAL CONVERSIONS

A relatively simple and often fully satisfactory method for protection from corrosion is by conversion of some of the surface material to a chemical composition that resists attack from the environment. These converted metal surfaces consist of relatively thin (seldom more than 0.025 mm [0.001 in.] thick) inorganic films that are formed by chemical reaction with the base material. One important feature of the conversion process is that the coatings have little effect on the product dimensions. However, when severe conditions are to be encountered, the converted surface may offer only partial protection, and coatings of entirely different types may be applied over them.

10.4.3.2 CHROMATE COATINGS

Zinc Dimensions Increase with Corrosion. Zinc is usually considered to have relatively good corrosion resistance. This is true when the exposure is to normal outdoor atmosphere where a relatively thin corrosion film forms. Contact with either highly aerated water films or immersion in stagnant water containing little oxygen causes even corrosion and pitting. The corrosion products of zinc are less dense than the base material so that heavy corrosion not only destroys the product appearance but also may cause malfunctions by binding moving parts.

Chromium Salts Improve Corrosion Resistance and Paintability. Corrosion of zinc can be substantially slowed by the production of chromium salts on its surface. The corrosion resistance of magnesium alloys can be increased by immersion or anodic treatment in acid baths containing dichromates. Chromate treatment of both zinc and magnesium improves corrosion resistance but is used also to improve adhesion of paint.

10.4.3.3 PHOSPHATE COATINGS

Used Mainly as a Paint Base. Phosphate coatings, used mostly on steel, result from a chemical reaction of phosphoric acid with the metal to form a nonmetallic coating that is essentially phosphate salts. The coating is produced by immersing small items or spraying large items with the phosphating solution. Phosphate surfaces may be used alone for corrosion resistance, but their most common application is as a base for paint coatings. Two of the most common application methods are called *parkerizing* and *bonderizing*.

10.4.3.4 CHEMICAL OXIDE COATINGS

A number of proprietary blacking processes, used mainly on steel, produce attractive black oxide coatings. Most of the processes involve the immersing of steel in a caustic soda solution, heated to about 150 °C (300 °F) and made strongly oxidizing by the addition of nitrites or nitrates. Corrosion resistance is rather poor unless improved by application of oil, lacquer, or wax. As in the case of most of the other chemical conversion procedures, this procedure also finds use as a base for paint finishes.

10.4.4 ORGANIC COATINGS

Paint-type materials are applied by dip, brush, and spray.

Minimum Labor Cost by Dipping. *Dipping* is common for applying protective coatings to forgings and castings to prevent rust during storage and processing and to serve as primers for the final finish. Many other products made in large quantities also are finished by dipping. Dip application is limited to parts that do not have recesses, pockets, or shapes that will hold the liquid paint or prevent its flowing to an even coat.

Brushing Costly. *Brush painting* is slow and used little in manufacturing work except on large, heavy, or odd-shaped parts that cannot be moved or manipulated in a spray-paint area. Brushing and rolling are commonly used for coating structural surfaces such as walls and ceilings of buildings. Brushing does provide efficient use of coating material, as practically none is wasted, and the mechanical rubbing of a brush or roller provides some cleaning action that may provide better adhesion.

Speed and Quality by Spraying. By far, the greatest amount of organic coatings are applied industrially by *spraying*. This method is used most with lacquers and fast-drying enamels. The short drying time causes parts to become dust-free very quickly so that they can be moved away from the spray area and advantage can be taken of this fast application method. Spraying is done in booths designed for this purpose where adequate ventilation carries fumes and spray particles away from the operator (Figure 10.5). Spray painting of automobile bodies and other large objects that are conveyorized is often done automatically with a number of spray heads, some stationary and some movable, adjusted to spray a uniform layer over the entire object.

In many cases spray application of penetrant materials is the fastest and best way of obtaining uniform coverage. Spraying aids particularly on parts containing recesses and corners difficult to contact with a brush.

Uniform Coating by Electrostatic Spraying. For *electrostatic spraying*, the paint particles are sprayed through a high-voltage electrostatic field. Each paint particle takes on an electric charge from the field and is attracted toward the grounded article to be painted. This method provides better efficiency of paint use than ordinary spraying but, even more importantly, causes the coating to distribute itself more evenly over the entire object. Electrostatic force can also be used to pull off drips or tears that form by gravity along the bottom edges of newly painted objects.

Heat Often Used to Speed Drying. As indicated previously, organic coating is often done in free air. Some solvents and vehicles are so volatile that drying is accomplished almost immediately. Others require several days for drying, and still others require elevated temperatures for necessary polymerization to take place. Heat for drying and speeding chemical reaction may be provided by various types of ovens. Some ovens are batch types in which racks of parts are placed for specific periods of time. Others are continuous types built over conveyor systems that regulate the time of exposure by the length of oven and the speed of conveyor operation.

10.4.4.1 PAINTS, VARNISHES, AND ENAMELS

Painting is a generic term that has come to mean the application of almost any kind of organic coating by any method.

Paint. As originally defined and as used most at present, *paint is* a mixture of pigment in a drying oil. Color and opacity are supplied by the pigment. The oil serves as a carrier for the pigment and in addition creates a tough continuous film as it dries.

Varnish Is Normally Clear. *Varnish* is a combination of natural or synthetic resins and drying oil, sometimes containing volatile solvents as well. The material dries by a chemical reaction in the drying oil to a clear or slightly amber-colored film. A solution of resin in a volatile solvent without the drying oil is called *spirit*, or *shellac*, varnish.

Figure 10.5: Paint spraying of an automotive part in a booth where exhaust air draws the waste paint and fumes away from the operator through filters to clean the air.

Pigment in Varnish Creates Enamel. *Enamel* is a mixture of pigment in varnish. The resins in the varnish cause the material to dry to a smoother, harder, and glossier surface than produced by ordinary paints. Some enamels are made with thermosetting resins that must be baked for complete dryness. These baking enamels provide a toughness and durability not usually available with the ordinary paints and enamels.

10.4.4.2 LACQUERS

Lacquers Easily Removed. The term *lacquer* is used to refer to finishes consisting of thermoplastic materials dissolved in fast-drying solvents. One common combination is cellulose nitrate dissolved in butyl acetate. Present-day lacquers are strictly air-drying and form films very quickly after being applied, usually by spraying. No chemical change occurs during the hardening of lacquers; consequently, the dry film can be redissolved in the thinner. Cellulose acetate is used in place of cellulose nitrate in some lacquers because it is nonflammable. Vinyls, chlorinated hydrocarbons, acrylics, and other synthetic thermoplastic resins are also used in the manufacture of lacquers.

Common Because of Fast Drying. Clear lacquers are used to some extent as protective films on such materials as polished brass, but the majority are pigmented and used as color coats. The pigmented lacquers are sometimes called *lacquer enamels*. Lacquers are widely used for coating manufactured products because of their ease of application and speed of drying.

10.4.5 ANODIZING

Aluminum, magnesium, and zinc can be treated electrically in a suitable electrolyte to produce a corrosion-resistant oxide coating. The metal being treated is connected to the anode in the circuit, which provides the name *anodizing* for the process. Aluminum is commonly treated by anodizing that produces an oxide film thicker than, but similar to, that formed naturally with exposure to air. Anodizing of zinc has very limited use. The coating produced on magnesium is not as protective as that formed on aluminum but does provide some protective value and substantially increases protection when used in combination with paint coatings.

Purposely Created Oxide Better Than Naturally Formed Oxide. Because of their greater thickness and abrasion resistance, anodic films offer much better protection against corrosion and mechanical injury than do the thin natural films. Aluminum is usually treated in a sulfuric acid electrolyte that slowly dissolves the outside at the same time it is converting the base metal to produce a porous coating. The coating can be impregnated with various materials to improve corrosion resistance. It also serves as a good paint base and can be colored in itself by use of dyes.

The usual commercial anodizing methods used on aluminum cause formation of billions per square centimeter (inch) of aluminum oxide cells, which grow above the original metal surface and at the same time extend below that original surface. Each of those cells has a pore in its center that extends to a solid barrier layer near the bottom of the cell. These numerous pores permit impregnation of the surface with various desirable materials, but they are also a source of problems for penetrant testing of anodized aluminum surfaces. The penetrant can enter the pores to such an extent that an extremely high background is produced. Special care to interpret the results may be necessary.

Checking for cracks is often called for because aluminum oxide is brittle and subject to cracking particularly if deformation of the material occurs after anodizing.

10.4.6 OTHER SURFACE TREATMENT PROCESSES

10.4.6.1 VITREOUS ENAMELS

Porcelain Consists of Fused Glass. Vitreous, or *porcelain,* enamel is actually a thin layer of glass fused onto the surface of a metal, usually steel or iron. Shattered glass, ball milled in a fine particle size, is called *frit.* Frit is mixed with clay, water, and metal oxides, which produce the desired color, to form a thin slurry called *slip.* This is applied to the prepared metal surface by dipping or spraying and, after drying, is fired at approximately 800 °C (1472 °F) to fuse the material to the metal surface. For a high-quality coating, more than one layer is applied to guard against pinhole porosity.

Excellent Corrosion Protection. Glass applied in this way has high strength and is usually flexible enough to withstand bending of the steel within the elastic limits of the base metal. The coatings have excellent resistance to atmospheric corrosion and to most acids. Vitreous enamels can be made suitable for use over a wide range of temperatures. Some special types have been used for corrosion protection on exhaust stacks for aircraft engines. Considering their high quality protection, vitreous enamels are relatively inexpensive and find many uses.

Ceramic Coatings for Special Protection. The aerospace industry is a field in which high temperature corrosion protection is essential. Porcelain enamel has been satisfactory in some of these applications, but ceramic coatings with better refractory characteristics are more commonly used. Some are applied in the same way as porcelain enamel. Others are fused to the metal surfaces with the intense heat of a plasma jet.

Porosity of porcelain or ceramic coatings can be checked with penetrants and coating thickness determined by use of electromagnetic testing techniques, such as eddy current.

10.4.6.2 HOT DIP PLATING

Several metals, mainly zinc, tin, and lead, are applied to steel for corrosion protection by a *hot dip process.* Steel in sheet, rod, pipe, or fabricated form, properly cleansed and fluxed, is immersed in molten plating metal. As the work is withdrawn, the molten metal that adheres solidifies to form a protective coat. In some of the large mills, the application is made continuously to coil stock that is fed through the necessary baths and even finally inspected before being recoiled or cut into sheets.

Zinc Applied in Many Ways. Zinc is one of the most common materials applied to steel in this manner. In addition to protection by exclusion, electrochemical protection (the source of the term *galvanized iron)* occurs when exposed steel and adjacent zinc are connected by conducting moisture. Zinc is one of the most favored coatings for corrosion protection of steel because of its low cost and ease of application. In addition to hot dipping, zinc can also be applied by electroplating, spraying, and *sherodizing.* Sherodizing is a process by which steel, heated in the presence of zinc dust, becomes coated with zinc.

Tin plating and *terne plating*, the latter using a mixture of approximately four parts lead to one part tin, are also done by hot dipping.

NONDESTRUCTIVE TESTING

CONTENTS

11 Introduction to Nondestructive Testing

11.1 BASIC DEFINITIONS

The previous chapters provided the reader with a background on materials and how they are processed, fabricated, shaped, and assembled into useful forms. We will now explore *nondestructive testing* (NDT), which is a discipline focused on the quality and serviceability of those materials and structures. NDT, which may be considered a branch of engineering, reveals hidden properties and discontinuities without affecting the future usefulness of the specimen. This discipline is vital to the production of engineering materials and to the safe and efficient operation of engineered structures.

NDT can be referred to by several different names depending on industrial application. *Nondestructive inspection* (NDI) is the term commonly used in the military, aviation, and some utility industries because those groups feel that "inspection" reinforces the idea that maintenance is being performed on something currently in service. *Nondestructive evaluation* (NDE) is preferred in research and academia because these groups often interpret higher-level test data or develop new techniques. The acronym NDE, in this instance standing for nondestructive examination, is employed in nuclear and some other industries because the term "testing" carries a connotation of performance trials (for example, proof testing) of equipment. No matter the preferred terminology, all refer to the same inspection methods.

"... vital to the production of engineering materials and to the safe and efficient operation of engineered structures ..."

11.1.1 METHODS VERSUS TECHNIQUES

The term "method" is used to describe a collection of inspection "techniques." This classification system is useful, because a method is defined by the probing energy that is used, whereas techniques are particular ways that the probing energy is applied or detected. Probing energy and materials used in NDT include electromagnetic waves, mechanical vibrations or waves, particles, and liquids. An example is the ultrasonic testing (UT) method, where the probing energy is high-frequency sound waves (mechanical vibrations). The UT method includes single-probe techniques, dual-probe techniques, tests where the probe directly touches the test object or where the test object is immersed in water, and many others.

ASNT currently recognizes 15 NDT methods in Section 3.1 of *Recommended Practice No. SNT-TC-1A* (2011) with a sixteenth method, microwave (MW) testing, to be added with the 2016 edition. "Recognition" in this instance refers to the ability to be formally certified in the method. The techniques within these methods can be classified by five factors: (1) the probing energy or material used, (2) the effect that the test object has on the probing energy (for example, attenuation or reflection), (3) the detection mechanism (for example, human eye or inductance coil), (4) the display mechanism (such as a radiologic image or needle deflection), and (5) the basis for interpretation of results.

11.1.2 PREDICTIVE MAINTENANCE

Predictive maintenance (PdM) strives to save money and lower maintenance costs by collecting data as events occur and predicting potential future problems before they occur. PdM is closely associated with nondestructive testing, in part because of method overlap (for example, thermal and infrared testing, vibration analysis, acoustic leak detection, and acoustic emission), in part because of common end goals. Various techniques are used to determine and monitor the condition of inservice equipment over time. Telltale changes in the data signature can signal when corrective actions should be taken. PdM comprises four elements: detection, analysis, correction, and verification. Although NDT certification and PdM certification paths differ—the Basic certification examination is not the same but Method examinations are—awareness of this discipline is beneficial.

Types of Test Indications. Generally, test indications are produced when a nondestructive inspection is performed. Test indications may be classified as *relevant, nonrelevant,* or *false.* A relevant indication is formed because of a discontinuity in the test object; this indication must then be reproducible and evaluated against a set of acceptance criteria by a qualified inspector for disposition. A discontinuity is classified as a defect when it falls outside of acceptance limits. A nonrelevant indication is unrelated to a flaw in the test object but is formed due to some other factor, such as test object geometry or thickness change, and can be disregarded. A false indication may be confused with, or mask, a relevant indication but is formed because the technique was misapplied, or is the result of some other factor unrelated to a discontinuity, such as magnetic writing in magnetic particle testing or a smudge in radiographic or liquid penetrant testing.

11.2 VALUE OF NDT TO MATERIALS AND PROCESSES

Nondestructive testing techniques were developed to detect discontinuities, to measure significant material properties, and to monitor processes, structures, and equipment. The range of test specimens includes research test objects, finished components and assemblies, products in service, and even scrap materials requiring sorting before being recycled for the production of new materials. NDT is often applied to determine if there is something wrong with the specimen, in contrast to performance or proof testing, which is concerned with whether the specimen functions as designed. NDT is utilized across a seemingly endless list of industries, among which are aviation, construction, original equipment manufacturing, power generation, refineries, chemical and petrochemical pipelines, and railways.

Uses of NDT. It costs money to purchase equipment, train and maintain NDT professionals, and implement inspections, so one might wonder what is gained from the exercise. NDT is used to (1) ensure product integrity and reliability, (2) avoid failures and prevent accidents, (3) make a profit for the user, (4) ensure customer satisfaction and maintain the manufacturer's reputation, (5) aid in product design, (6) control manufacturing processes, (7) lower manufacturing costs, (8) maintain uniform quality levels, and (9) ensure operational readiness.

The accurate and efficient performance of NDT is essential to the satisfactory performance and life of engineered components and structures. Engineering materials are pushed to their limits as industrial designers strive toward performance and efficiency. Customers demand high reliability and low cost, and because NDT can often locate and size discontinuities throughout a component, it is called on to ensure that raw materials and fabricated components meet design expectations for quality, reliability, and longevity. NDT is applied to find discontinuities, identify structural or geometric problems, identify issues with material properties or chemistry, provide information on stress state, conduct signature analysis, and identify heat sources. NDT can also be applied to provide chronological information, for example, whether a crack is growing over time or the thickness in a critical region is decreasing with service life.

Difference from Destructive Testing. Inherent in the definition of NDT is that the specimen's future usefulness is not affected, and the strictest definition of *nondestructive* means that no material from the sample is destroyed. A test cannot be considered nondestructive if it requires material to be removed from the specimen by shaving, sanding, vaporizing, or chemical action. Nondestructive tests also do not leave behind indents or other evidence of past testing (as, for example, with hardness testing).

Because NDT does not affect the sample's future usefulness, it may be freely applied for the quality control practice of *sampling*. This practice evaluates a subset of parts and then draws statistical conclusions about the unsampled population. Sampling rates vary, but because the specimen isn't affected, the rate can be as high as 100% without precluding production.

Limitations of NDT Methods. As outlined above, there are many advantages to using NDT, but there are limitations for each method as well. These limitations include physical access to, or contact with, one or both sides of the specimen, the need for surface preparation, and discontinuity size and orientation. In some cases, a single NDT method or technique is adequate, but no one NDT method or technique is all-revealing. It generally takes a series of methods or techniques for full evaluation of a specimen. If, for example, you are required to find all detectable discontinuities within a casting, you may use visual, penetrant, or magnetic particle testing for surface discontinuity detection and one or more additional methods, such as radiographic or ultrasonic testing, for the detection of internal discontinuities. The exact method or technique chosen depends on the thickness and nature of the material, and on the types of discontinuities that must be detected.

Detection of Discontinuities. Discontinuities sought often include cracks, voids, inclusions, delaminations, disbonds, and corrosion. Structural information of interest could be micro-scale (state of curing, crystal structure of a material, grain size, or hardened case depth) or macro-scale (proper assembly or dimensions). Physical and mechanical properties are often of interest (for example, electrical conductivity, elastic modulus, or reflectivity), as is identification of the elemental makeup of a specimen, such as alloy identification. Signature analysis, for instance acoustic or vibration signatures, and thermal analysis are important predictive maintenance tools.

One of the objectives of NDT is to detect discontinuities as early as possible in the processing sequence, thus avoiding expenditure of effort and money on materials that will later be rejected. Manufacturing processes, from production of metal from its ore and alloying elements, to the last finishing operation, have the potential to introduce or expose discontinuities. NDT can reveal many of these, thus preventing anomalous components from entering into, or returning to, service. NDT may be applied during and between processing operations, and often as a final test to ensure that all detrimental discontinuities have been detected.

To illustrate the benefit of NDT to industry, we'll examine a single application: the production of high-quality steel hot forgings. Bar stock is an input in this process, and quality is verified by a battery of destructive and nondestructive tests prior to delivery. Quality includes such aspects as microstructural cleanliness, mechanical properties, and lack of internal and external discontinuities, grain size, and microstructural homogeneity. Mixed material at the forging shop is a potential problem, so NDT in the form of positive material identification may be used for assurance that the correct alloy is being used.

The bar stock is heated to, and then held or soaked at, a target temperature prior to forging. Too low of a forging temperature can lead to cracks and tears; on the other hand, excessive temperature may cause a hot-short condition, create incipient melting, or form undesirable microstructural phases. Excessive soak time can cause microstructural changes, such as grain growth or carbide coarsening, which reduce fatigue life, machinability, and ductility. Plastic deformation from the forging operation and subsequent thermal processing tend to reduce and refine the size of microstructural grains.

NDT is used to detect undesirable conditions and properties because many of these changes alter the material's test response. NDT—for instance, magnetic particle, ultrasonic, or electromagnetic testing—is applied to detect discontinuities prior to shipping to the customer. All inspections are useful for cost avoidance, decreasing the number of scrap parts produced, and increasing customer satisfaction.

11.3 REQUIREMENTS AND CERTIFICATION FOR NDT PERSONNEL

Two of the most important attributes for those performing and overseeing inspections are attitude and integrity. The American Society for Nondestructive Testing (ASNT) recognizes this fact and therefore requires candidates for ASNT certification to sign and abide by a Code of Ethics. Aside from the expected loss of colleague respect, lapses in these two key traits have led to economic losses to affected employers and even prison time and thousands of dollars in fines for the NDT personnel responsible.

Qualification is the demonstrated skill and knowledge, as well as documented training experience, required for personnel to properly perform the duties of a specific job. Because certification is written testimony of qualification, one obviously must be qualified before he or she can be certified. Qualification is based on four factors: (1) physical attributes; (2) knowledge, including education level and additional training; (3) experience; and (4) practical ability. NDT practitioners can be divided into three categories: those who are strong in practical application but weak on theory; those who are weak in practical application but strong on theory; and those who are strong on both.

From a quality management standpoint, it is difficult and/or expensive to evaluate the quality of inspection simply by observing the process or by reviewing the inspection's output. Because it is difficult to verify conformity, the NDT community generally relies on the inspector's skills, knowledge, and integrity. The effectiveness of NDT depends, at least in part, on the capabilities of NDT personnel; their qualification and certification are necessary steps to achieving the proper performance of NDT.

When NDT is conducted in most industries, it must be performed by qualified inspectors. This requirement is generally driven by the customer or code requirements, or inspection complexity. The level of qualification scales with how safety-critical the component under test is. Sometimes industry-specific qualification and certification needs may mean additional credentials are needed for an inspector to gain unescorted access to the worksite. An example is the Transportation Security Administration (TSA) and U.S. Coast Guard's Transportation Worker Identification Credential (TWIC) for access to secure areas of the nation's maritime transportation system.

11.3.1 CERTIFICATION PROGRAMS

Various organizations have developed NDT certification schemes, which enable employers to ensure their personnel are correctly trained and qualified. A company has two basic schemes to choose from when written testimony of qualification is required: internal or external certification. Each scheme has unique requirements for inspector training, work experience and examinations. The employer is responsible for authorizing NDT personnel to perform tasks; for determining the necessary training, experience and examinations; and for documenting those requirements in a written practice.

Employer-Based Certification. In an *employer-based internal (second-party) program*, NDT personnel are certified by the employer. In the U.S., such programs may be based on a suggested framework—for example, *Recommended Practice SNT-TC-1A* or *ATA 105*—or they may follow the mandates specified in a standard, such as *ANSI/ASNT CP-189, NAS 410,* or *EN 4179*. While there are significant differences between the two types of systems, both require the employer to establish a certification control and administrative framework, and require the employer to act as the certifying agency or authority. Actual administration of the program can be performed by employees of the certifying agency, or this duty may be subcontracted to a third-party consultant. A second-party scheme is optimal when a significant number of personnel must be trained to perform specific inspections in the employer's facility. Internal certification schemes work well when there is a workforce in a fixed location, the employer has long-term inspection needs, and the system is administered by a competent certifying authority or outside agency that provides quality training and rigorous examinations. Employer-based certifications are not portable, and certification is revoked when employment is terminated.

Central Certification. *Third-party external certification* by a centralized organization is portable and recognized across a wide range of companies, industries, and countries. Central certification is administered by an impartial organization that is separate from the NDT practitioner and his or her employer. This type of certification is popular, in part, because it is standardized and the employer cannot arbitrarily alter qualification requirements. There are several third-party certification options available worldwide—to name a few, ASNT NDT Certification; ASNT Central Certification; Canadian General Standards Board (CGSB), as administered by Natural Resources Canada (NRCan) National NDT Certification Body; TWI

Certification Limited's Certification Scheme for Welding and Inspection Personnel (CSWIP); the Federal Republic of Germany's (DAkkS) SECTOR certification; and the British Institute of Non-Destructive Testing's (BINDT) Personnel Certification in Non-Destructive Testing (PCN).

While there are many certification brand names, the key for central certification programs is the requirements of the standard that they incorporate, such as ISO 9712 or ISO 11484. Because of the variety of national and international standards in use, groups of countries have begun establishing standards (for example, DIN EN ISO/IEC 17024) and Multilateral Mutual Recognition Agreements (MRA) to formalize acceptance (or at least acknowledgement) of other nation's NDT personnel certification schemes. Regardless of certification scheme, the prudent employer assesses an inspector's practical ability using parts that will be typically encountered.

The tolerance for component failure is extremely low in some industrial sectors and additional qualification measures have taken root there. An honest person would admit that infrequently used skills and abilities deteriorate over time, and an inspector with decreased skills is not a good fit for critical applications. To combat this concern, these industry sectors have developed performance-based qualification (ISO/TS 11774), which is useful for ensuring that equipment, procedures, and personnel continue to meet expectations for safety-critical applications. Performance-based qualification mandates that inspection personnel demonstrate that they can perform inspection tasks under real-world conditions, and this approach replaces much of the tedium of monthly certification record upkeep with regular—for instance, annual—practical examinations.

11.3.2 VISION TESTING

In addition to integrity and a positive attitude, NDT personnel must have sufficient visual acuity, blueprint-reading skills, mathematical knowledge, communication skills, an ability to interpret codes, strong attention to detail, and extensive practical experience. Blueprint-reading skill allows the inspector to understand the types of schematics used in an industrial environment and how to comprehend and decipher standard symbols and abbreviations. Math skills are a must for many methods—for example, radiographers calculating exposures, ultrasonic testing personnel determining discontinuity location from a reference position, or electromagnetic testing personnel calculating the standard depth of penetration for a given situation.

Good vision is of obvious importance because test indications on a specimen or radiograph, as well as peaks displayed on a screen, must be detected and properly classified by the inspector. Visual acuity stems from the physiology of the human eye—much of which is outside the scope of this book. Inspection standards mandate a minimum illuminance for a valid test.

Vision Tests. *Visual acuity* is the ability to distinguish fine details visually at a given distance. There are four basic types of acuity: smallest feature detectable (visible minimum); smallest resolvable separation between two lines (resolution); recognition of the relative positions of vernier lines, referred to as hyperacuity; and recognizing letters or reading text. NDT standards don't generally agree on which vision examination to use. Common near-vision tests—meaning within an arm's length—used in the U.S. were developed by Jaeger (Schrift-Scalen or Test-Types, circa 1854) and Snellen (letter-based optotypes, circa 1862). Jaeger's test, available in a variety of languages, was developed around the notion that vision should be assessed by how well daily functions are performed, such as reading continuous lines of text. (See Figure 11.1.) Snellen's test, which uses isolated uppercase letters, was based on how well letters of a particular size and shape could be resolved at a specific distance. Standards calling for Jaeger J-1 are generally satisfied by a Snellen 20/22 or 20/20 result. Standards requiring Jaeger J-2 are generally satisfied by a Snellen 20/27 or

20/25. European standards may call for circle-based optotypes called landolt rings (or landolt C, circa 1909), which may be presented in eight different positions (ISO 8596).

Color Differentiation. The need for *trichromatic vision* in inspectors is less straightforward. Internal certification documents generally require an inspector to be able to distinguish and differentiate contrast between the colors or shades of gray used in the method as determined by the employer. Red-green color discrimination (deficient in approximately 10% of males) is often evaluated using the Ishihara Color Test (circa 1917), which consists of a number of colored plates containing figures only visible to those with normal color vision. (See Figure 11.2.) If the Ishihara test is failed, it is generally necessary to validate the candidate's practical ability to distinguish contrast (that is, see indications on the display or see an indication against the background).

11.3.3 CODE INTERPRETATION

NDT has been used successfully for decades during component fabrication. Industry- or customer-driven requirements sometimes mandate use of a particular code. A code is a set of legal obligations that must be complied with when manufacturing or maintaining certain types of goods. Common types are nuclear; pressure containment, for example, unfired pressure vessels, power boilers, and pipelines; and large structures, including bridges, buildings, ships, lifting equipment, and heavy off-road equipment. Code interpretation skill is useful because these documents facilitate the reliable and proper application of inspections. New procedures must conform to guidelines and many codes offer acceptance criteria that must be followed closely. Welding-related codes include those by the American Welding Society (AWS), American Petroleum Institute (API), and the American Society of Mechanical Engineers (ASME).

Figure 11.1: Jaeger reading card for performance examination of near vision acuity.

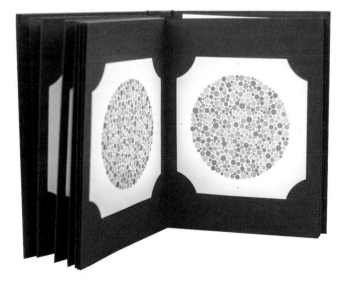

Figure 11.2: Ishihara 14 color plate test.

Personnel involved in the application and management of NDT are likely to be confronted with requirements originating in standards or codes. Proper interpretation of these documents requires knowledge of written requirements and technique applications. Codes and standards govern the inspection of new products, and some have adopted inservice inspection requirements. Engineers use NDT to locate, characterize, and monitor the growth of discontinuities; NDT can also provide data for optimization of safety factors and reducing component cost. NDT ensures the structural integrity of critical operating components and allows continued service of expensive components. Safely extending lifetimes reduces operational costs without degrading operational safety.

11.3.4 IMPORTANCE OF TRAINING

No matter which certification scheme is chosen, the quality and comprehension of standardized training programs are key factors in the probability that a given discontinuity will be detected. Training seeks to impart the body of knowledge pertinent to a particular industry segment, method, or technique. A significant portion of the training must include time using physical inspection equipment so that the student gains hands-on experience with process controls used by that method, learns about practical applications and performs actual inspections on demonstration parts. For industry- or company-specific training, the program can be application or task specific, for example, pipe welds or light metal castings. This can be more effective than a generalized approach. Generalized training of candidates can be bolstered by on-the-job-training (OJT) under a certified mentor. These mentors should be selected based on their knowledge of, and experience in, the method, and based on their ability to effectively convey that knowledge and experience to others.

11.4 REFERENCES AND INFORMATION AVAILABLE

American Society for Nondestructive Testing. There are many electronic and print sources of information for nondestructive testing personnel. One primary source of information is the *NDT Handbook* series, which was first developed in 1944. Each book in this series strives to provide the basic knowledge necessary for an understanding of the technology, principles, and application techniques of a given method. The *NDT Handbook* series has volumes on all of the major methods, as well as an overview volume that touches on some of the minor methods. ASNT also has begun developing industry-specific handbooks for the aerospace, chemical, and petroleum industries.

ASNT's Technical and Education Council method committees develop and maintain topical outlines and suggested resources for each method within *ANSI/ASNT CP-105: ASNT Standard Topical Outlines for Qualification of Nondestructive Testing Personnel*. This resource is coordinated using American National Standards Institute (ANSI) approved consensus procedures. Certification candidates seeking to increase their background knowledge of a particular method may refer to one of the many references listed in *CP-105*.

Conference and symposia attendance is an excellent way to stay informed on the latest research and development efforts. Attendance also allows direct contact with colleagues in the NDT field. Annual conferences include ASNT's Fall Conference, ASNT's Annual Spring Research Symposium, Iowa State University's Review of Progress in Quantitative Nondestructive Evaluation (QNDE) conference, and the American Petroleum Institute's Inspection Summit. More globally, the International Committee for Non-Destructive Testing (ICNDT) hosts an annual World

Conference, the Institute of Electrical and Electronics Engineers (IEEE) holds regular conferences on a variety of topics, and many regional conferences are offered by NDT societies worldwide.

Internet Resources. The World Wide Web offers a wealth of information compiled by researchers, educational institutions and inspection equipment manufacturers and vendors. An excellent web resource is NDT.net (www.ndt.net), which provides a comprehensive glossary of terms, job board, NDT news, calendar of upcoming NDT conferences, repository of new and archived technical articles, and a discussion forum that facilitates sharing of information. Since its 1997 launch with a handful of collaborators, this site has attracted more than 6000 registered forum users and many thousands more unregistered users from across the globe. Registered participants include technicians (novice through expert), consultants, engineers, and educators, as well as equipment manufacturers, vendors, and NDT service providers. ASNT's website (asnt.org) also offers a broad variety of resources, including information about certification, an events calendar, and educational and reference materials. Another excellent source of information is ASNT's quarterly newsletter, *The NDT Technician (TNT)*, which is written and reviewed by NDT practitioners for NDT practitioners. ASNT's monthly magazine, *Materials Evaluation (M.E.)*, also highlights up-to-date information on NDT methods and cutting-edge techniques.

A widely used educational site is the NDT Resource Center (www.ndt-ed.org), which is maintained by Iowa State University and other members of the Collaboration for NDT Education. Launched in 2006, the site contains information on the underlying science of NDT with material written at different education levels and for different target audiences; some applications for many of the major inspection methods; and a mathematics refresher. This site is quite popular and has grown from 16 000 visitors per month to more than 370 000 unique visits per month in 2012.

Another valuable website is MatWeb (www.matweb.com). Initiated in the mid-1990s, this site contains a searchable database of materials properties for over 92 000 engineering materials, including polymers, composites, metals, ceramics, and semiconductors. Metal information includes alloy chemistry; mechanical properties, such as hardness, tensile strength, elongation, elastic moduli, Poison's ratio, machinability, and weldability; and electrical and thermal properties.

Specifications and Standards. Although the purpose of specifications and standards is to define the minimum requirements that goods or services must meet, they are also a source of information on proper NDT techniques and procedures. Standards are developed by subject matter experts and are vetted through peer review. Standards can be broken down into three main categories, those covering equipment, processes, and personnel. There is a broad range of standards available from a variety of organizations worldwide, including ASNT, ASTM, SAE, CSA, EN, BS, ISO, DIN, CEN, WES, and SAC.

ASTM International (formerly the American Society for Testing and Materials) is a major domestic source for industrial standards; ASTM has approximately 200 guides, standards, and specifications related to NDT. ASTM's NDT-related documents are developed by approximately 550 technical expert and business professional volunteers, currently representing 37 countries.

SAE International has approximately 30 NDT-related standards. While the primary end users of SAE's standards are within the aerospace industry segment and the military, several of their documents have far-reaching applicability—for example, the qualified products listing (QPL) for liquid penetrant testing, and particle and carrier fluid specifications for magnetic particle testing. Several years ago, the U.S. military began reducing their number of independent standards, and some military standards were superseded by industry-consensus SAE documents; one example is MIL-I-25135 superseded by SAE AMS-2644 in 1989.

Subsequent chapters in this book will provide the reader with a basic overview of the most common NDT methods and techniques, including their advantages and limitations, as well as a cursory view of how reliable NDT fits with engineering and design. This text will touch on a variety of problems that materials, components, and structures encounter, and common NDT methods used to detect these problems. Nondestructive testing is crucial to material selection, product design, testing of completed and inservice parts, and everything in between. Let's now delve into these methods to see how they are industrially relevant.

12 Nondestructive Testing Methods

12.1 VISUAL TESTING

12.1.1 INTRODUCTION AND PRINCIPLES

Visual testing (VT) the oldest and most common NDT method, is important in the discipline of nondestructive testing and is widely used on a variety of specimen types. At its core, VT is the observation of a specimen, either directly or indirectly. Observation may be used to locate and size surface and surface-breaking discontinuities in opaque materials, detect subsurface discontinuities in translucent or transparent materials, detect structural problems, observe or measure clearance, detect leaking, and judge conformance to a specification (for example, a missed operation or improper assembly). Everyone is familiar with the basic principles of direct visual testing, as we regularly apply this technique in our personal lives. For example, we use VT to select the best fruit at the grocery store, with the aid of the additional senses of touch and smell, and to detect the door ding that our vehicle may have received while we were shopping inside.

"At its core, VT is the observation of a specimen, either directly or indirectly."

Electromagnetic Radiation. The probing medium for VT is electromagnetic radiation with wavelengths that are visible to the human eye. Wavelengths within the range of 380 nm – 780 nm are called visible light. Photons (packets of light energy) with wavelengths within this range excite photodetectors in the human retina and cause the sensation of vision. Photon wavelength controls the observed color. As examples, a 450 nm photon is perceived as blue light, 550 nm as yellowish green, and 750 nm as red. White light is a relatively balanced mixture of all colors of the visible light spectrum. *Illuminance*, the intensity of visible light upon a surface area at a given angle, as observed by the human eye, is measured in lumens per square meter or lux (lx).

The eye's spectral response to bright light—technically referred to as *photometric spectral responsivity*—is used as a weighting function for the luxmeter's integral sensor. This function is most sensitive to photons with a wavelength of 555 nm. It is also possible to measure the irradiance of visible light, which is the total radiant power, in watts per square meter (W·m −2), falling upon a surface area at a given angle (Figure 12.1). Radiometers and luxmeters used in NDT employ integral sensors, which are assemblies consisting of a photodiode, aperture, filter set, and light-diffusing cover. The ideal radiometric sensor has a top-hat-shaped spectral responsivity (0-1-0); however, sensor cost increases as top-hat responsivity is approached. Radiometric visible light and ultraviolet integral sensors are both commercially available for NDT use.

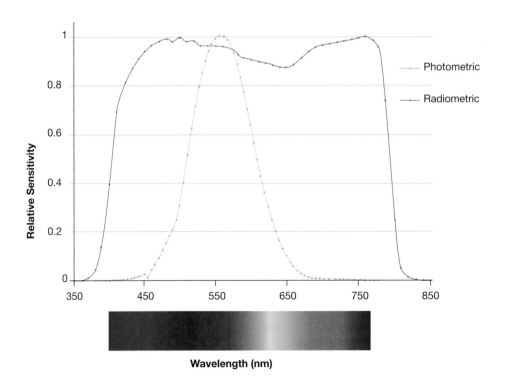

Figure 12.1: Actual normalized spectral responsivity of high-quality photometric and radiometric sensors designed to evaluate visible light.

12.1.1.2 VISUAL TESTING APPLICATIONS

Industries Where VT Is Most Used. VT may be applied to any material or within any industry, but it is most commonly applied in the power generation, aerospace, and oil and gas industries. Aside from industry experience, prerequisites necessary for the competent visual testing of an object are knowledge of the manufacturing processes by which the specimen was made, its service history, and its potential failure modes. For example, if a specimen's service history includes varying levels of induced stress, one might look for signs of fatigue crack initiation—possibly beginning the visual search around stress concentrators, for example, holes, sharp radii, changes in cross-sectional thickness, surface roughness or damage, or a weld toe. In bending and torsional fatigue applications, the operating stresses are highest on the surface of the component, which is not the case for contact fatigue. Stress concentrators increase the localized stress, and this is why many fatigue cracks initiate at the surface and are detectable with VT.

VT is the first NDT method applied to an item, and even when other NDT is performed, visual testing provides complementary information. VT may be combined with other inspection methods that are more sensitive to small surface cracks or to subsurface discontinuities. Such method combinations often lead to cost savings due to reduced inspection frequency. An example recounted to this author dealt with parts being inspected at a maintenance, repair and overhaul facility for military aircraft. A component that had just passed fluorescent penetrant testing was returned to the inspector as nonconforming. Closer visual examination under white light revealed a large bullet hole cleanly penetrating the aluminum structure, which caused no penetrant indications and so had been overlooked in the darkened penetrant inspection booth.

Frequency of VT Inspections. An example of how frequently visual testing is called for may be illustrated through a review of U.S. Federal Aviation Administration (FAA) airworthiness directives (AD). This author analyzed the nearly 3000 ADs issued from January 2000 through the end of December 2006; 1479, or 50% called for nondestructive testing. Of these NDT-related ADs, visual testing, either general visual or detailed visual, was called for 59% of the time—25% and 34%, respectively. It is expected that smaller discontinuities are found with a detailed visual test, as compared to its general counterpart. Electromagnetic testing, the third-most called-for method after visual testing, was specified 14% of the time.

12.1.1.3 VISUAL ACUITY

Visual acuity of the inspector, lighting, and surface condition of the specimen—all are of critical importance with this method. Proper lighting conditions are important for many NDT methods, and the purpose of lighting during visual inspection is to provide adequate contrast so that relevant objects or discontinuities may be observed. *Contrast detection* is the most basic of visual tasks; contrast is the difference in color, brightness, reflectance, or transmittance between a test indication and its background. The contrast ratio is the relationship between the perceived luminance of the target versus its surroundings; an example of luminance contrast is the difference in intensity of reflected light between the discontinuity and its background. Figure 12.2 offers a qualitative overview of the effect of illumination on inspection sensitivity.

Image Quality. Contrast sensitivity is a measure of how well a stationary indication of a certain size stands out visually against its surroundings; the probability of detection (POD) increases with contrast ratio, illuminance, and magnification. VT is most

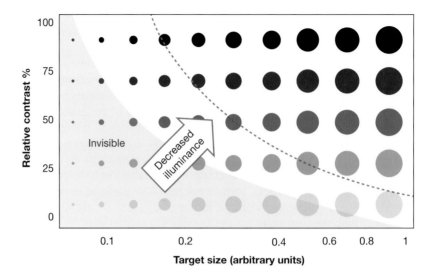

Figure 12.2: Effect of illuminance on target visibility.

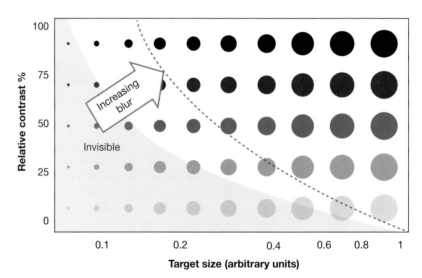

Figure 12.3: Effect of blur on target visibility.

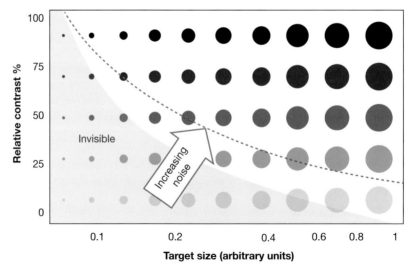

Figure 12.4: Effect of noise on target visibility.

effective when the surfaces have been cleaned prior to testing, as the presence of interfering materials—for example, spatter, slag, scale, oil, and grease—can greatly reduce
test effectiveness. Increased surface texture causes more visual distraction, and this
background noise decreases test sensitivity. For example, a direct visual inspection of
rough surfaces may struggle to find discontinuities greater than 12.7 mm (0.5 in.), but
discontinuities half that size may be located when surfaces are much smoother. Image
magnification improves sensitivity to smaller discontinuities, but it unfortunately also
reduces the amount of area inspected per unit time.

Applicable image quality, viewing conditions, and observer performance characteristics govern the ability to detect an indication. A basic characteristic of an image
is contrast. The target is visible when contrast, a function of the object and the imaging system, is adequate. Image quality is based on contrast, distortion, noise, arti-
facts, and blur. The relative effects of blur, noise, and illumination are presented in
Figures 12.3 and 12.4.

The role of an imaging system is to convert a visible environment into shades of
gray or color. Aided inspections are generally evaluated for resolution to ensure
that minimum requirements are met. Resolution evaluation tools include the USAF
1951 target (positive, negative, and fluorescent versions are available), National
Bureau of Standards (NBS) 1963A target, IEEE target (ISO 12233), DIN 25435-4,
Marconi No. 1 test chart, ronchi linear rulings, and sinusoidal (constant or variable)
line pair targets. These tools can help to define the system's resolution; some may
be useful for detecting image distortion.

Absorptivity and Reflection Modes. Absorptivity is the proportion (from a low
of 0 to a high of 1) of the light radiation incident on a material's surface that is
absorbed. Some portion of the light is reflected when it strikes a surface whose
absorptivity is less than 1; the theoretical perfect blackbody, which absorbs all incident light, has an absorptivity of 1.0. Specular reflection is caused when light is incident on a smooth surface; the angle of a specular reflection is equal to the angle of
incidence (Figure 12.5). Diffuse reflections occur at rough surfaces. While the reflection angle remains equal to the incident angle, a rough surface has many different
surface planes and angles. Each incident light beam strikes a different plane and is
reflected at a variety of angles. A perfectly diffuse surface is called *lambertian* if the
observed luminance does not vary with viewing angle. When new VT applications
are being established, it is prudent or sometimes mandated, as it is in EN 13018, to
use a demonstration piece that closely approximates the reflectivity, surface texture,
contrast ratio, and accessibility of the actual application.

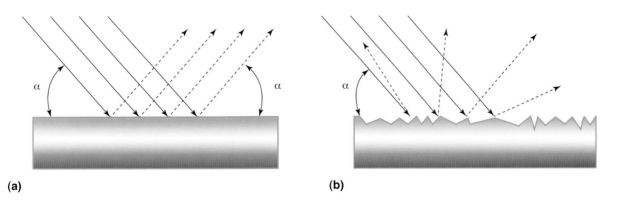

(a)   (b)

Figure 12.5: Reflection modes for light that is incident on a surface: (a) specular; (b) diffuse.

12.1.2 EQUIPMENT AND TECHNIQUES

Much of visual testing's success depends on the specimen's surface condition and on lighting arrangements, but a test may have up to five interdependent elements: the inspector, specimen, light source, recording mechanism, and an optical aid. The inspector's eye is a key component; visual acuity has been previously discussed in Chapter 11. As a broad overview, the visual testing procedure is to clear obstructions to the target, provide adequate illumination, and then simply observe.

Limitations of Viewing Angle. The human eye is very good at detecting small discontinuities, but there are situations where the inspector's eye does not have direct optical access to the test surface and assisting instruments may be beneficial or mandatory. VT techniques are divided into "direct" and "indirect." Indirect techniques may also be referred to as "remote visual testing." Direct techniques may incorporate inspection aids, while indirect techniques must use inspection aids. Choice of technique may be controlled by whether the inspector can be in the presence of the target, without environmental or physical constraints, and whether it is possible to have an unmediated optical path to this target. Unaided direct visual testing techniques have no interruption between the target and the inspector's eye.

Minimum illuminance and viewing angle, as well as maximum direct viewing distance, are often specified in standards. For example, a standard may call for an illuminance of at least 500 lux, minimum angle of vision of 30° with respect to the plane of the specimen, and a maximum viewing distance of 600 mm for general visual inspection (Figure 12.6). Aided direct visual testing techniques allow visual access to normally inaccessible areas, and these techniques may benefit from filtering, magnification, or improvements in optical path accessibility. Indirect visual testing techniques do not provide an optical path between the inspector and the target, so the aid must modify the image—for example, convert it to a digital signal—before delivering it to the inspector.

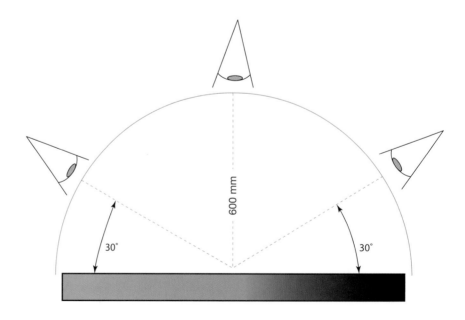

Figure 12.6: Typical constraints for direct unaided general visual testing, showing minimum angle of vision and maximum viewing distance.

12.1.2.1 OPTICAL AIDS

Aids for visual testing may be optical, mechanical, or specialized to a particular task. Optical aids include a mirror, magnifying glass or loupe (2× – 10×, with 5× being common), lighting equipment, optical flats, measuring magnifier (pocket optical comparator or measuring loupe), lenses, borescope (rigid or flexible), optical attenuator or filter (for example, neutral density, bandpass, shortpass, or longpass filters), opto-electronic devices (for example, diode arrays), image sensor, camera (photographic, video, solid state, tube, or thermal imaging), video monitor, and image recording, archiving, or processing equipment. Visual testing aids may be accompanied by rules, tape measures, calipers and micrometers for gaging linear dimensions, levels, and plumb (plummet) bobs. Examples of specialized tools would be those for evaluating pre- and post-welding configuration, such as bevel angle, fillet weld leg sizing, undercut depth, weld profile, gaps, and misalignment.

Mirrors. The mirror is a common direct-aid inspection tool, which reflects the optical path through ports or behind objects. Mirrors for VT often have telescoping and jointed handles that allow telescoping and angle adjustment. Light sources include flashlights, portable light sources, and light-emitting diodes (LEDs) including those that couple to a borescope. Light sources provide illumination, but users must avoid reflected glare. Measuring magnifiers are useful for determining the size or relative angle of features of interest. Pocket-sized magnifiers often have a variety of interchangeable reticles, and these transparent reticles are etched or printed with scales. Some models offer reticle scales in white or black so that the user may choose the one offering the best contrast against the test-object surface.

Borescopes. A *borescope* is a device consisting of fiber bundles, lenses, and/or mirrors that allow viewing of objects not accessible to unaided direct viewing. The three most common classifications of borescopes are rigid, fiber optic (fiberscope), and video (videoscope). Borescopes have two ends: the distal tip (nearest the specimen) and the eyepiece (nearest the inspector). The light train in a rigid borescope is a relatively simple straight line of mirrors and lenses. Video borescopes, which may be rigid or flexible, incorporate a camera and LEDs at the distal tip and display the camera image on a viewing screen. A rigid optical path is not always adequate, so borescopes are available with rotating distal tip optics—that is, a swing prism—and bending/rotating articulation. Borescope articulation may allow simple bidirectional movement, such as left-right or up-down, but higher-end devices have four-way articulation/panning. Current flexible borescopes may offer 120° – 140° of articulation in each of four directions.

Fiberscopes and Videoscopes. When flexibility is required, either optical fibers, as in a *fiberscope*, are used to form the optical path, or a camera at the distal tip may be coupled via electrical wires, as in a *videoscope*. A robot is called for when long-distance inspections are required. Robotic crawlers, which are used for pipe inspection, are essentially self-propelled videoscopes. Such robots have imaging and lighting in the front, and pull their electrical tether along behind. Fiberscopes use coated glass or quartz fibers to transmit illuminating light and the optical path to and from the test object. Generally used in areas where tortuous bends or curves necessitate a flexible device, a fiber optic borescope consists of a coherent fiber optic bundle, light guide fiber, and flexible protective sheath. The eyepiece of a borescope may be coupled to a charge-coupled device (CCD) camera so that the target is viewed on a display screen, rather than through the eyepiece. Specialized borescopes may incorporate working channels that have grasping and retrieval tools; facilitate blending, such as the smoothing of stress risers; or facilitate NDT, for example, using liquid penetrant or eddy current, in restricted access areas.

Imaging aids, such as videoscopes and robots, have developed significantly over time and now incorporate substantial computing power and measurement techniques. Cameras, whether coupled to the eyepiece or integral to the distal tip, allow capturing, saving, and analysis of images. The latest devices incorporate solid-state memory capacity, high-density removable media compatibility, the ability to annotate images with text or voice, and easy connectivity to a personal computer or the internet.

12.1.2.2 TECHNIQUES

There are four techniques used by visual aids for characterizing the shape, orientation, and size of a feature: (1) direct comparison, (2) stereo, (3) shadow (two-dimensional techniques), and (4) structured light (a three-dimensional technique). These measurement techniques generally employ triangulation, comparison, and/or pixel counting.

Direct Comparison Technique. Direct comparison uses a reference dimension that is observed in the same frame and focal distance, such as a nearby feature of known dimension or a scale introduced by the borescope, to compare the relative sizes of the target and reference. Measurement accuracy of the comparison technique depends on viewing distance to the target and whether observation is perpendicular to the surface—as the apparent relative proportions may vary with viewing angle.

Stereo Technique. Stereo measurements use a prism to divide the optical path into two, and when these paths converge on the target at a known angle, triangulation and computer vision calculations facilitate accurate measurements. Stereo vision and triangulation are similar to the way that human vision works. Stereo measurement accuracy does not depend on viewing angle but is governed by separation distance of the optical paths; image quality, meaning sharpness and contrast; and viewing distance. Some stereo measurement borescopes offer tip-to-target distance detection that improves accuracy.

Two-Dimensional Measurement. As its name suggests, a *shadow measurement probe* projects a shadow onto the target surface and then triangulation and computer vision calculations are used to determine dimensions. The position of the shadow is related to the viewing distance, and this distance is used as the basis of dimensional calculations. Shadow measurement accuracy does not depend strongly on image quality, but viewing distance and angle are important. Two-dimensional measurement techniques are powerful and useful, but there is one primary limitation: it is often necessary to change borescope end optics, that is, general viewing and measuring probe tips, between the detection and measurement phases of an inspection. Changing to the measurement probe tip may greatly reduce illumination at the target. A related technique uses a line projected onto the target by a laser, and elevation of the target surface distorts this line so that dimensional measurements can be made.

Use of Structured Light. Three-dimensional phase vision scanners sequentially project multiple light patterns onto the target surface; then distortions in the observed pattern are used to calculate a three-dimensional map of the surface. The combination of structured light and optical phase shifting has existed in large format for some time, but miniaturization of the technique into the format of a small-diameter borescope is a recent advancement. The structured light is often in the form of linear sine wave patterns, and the angular orientation of this pattern is varied between image captures. Multiple images, each with a different structured light orientation, are then incorporated into computer algorithms. The computer then produces a virtual representation of the target surface—for example, a point cloud—that is used for measurement and/or viewing purposes. Point cloud data may be viewed from any user-defined angle or in the form of a virtual cross section.

Machine Vision. Inspectors are prone to fatigue, distraction, and other human factors; in high-volume production environments, it is sometimes necessary to replace humans with machines. *Machine vision*, which is the application of computer-vision techniques to the industrial environment, can be deployed via robot guidance, automatic inspection and analysis, and process control. Applications of automated visual testing are diverse but include object recognition/detection, such as the liquid level in a container, the presence of a semiconductor on a printed circuit board or parts with a missed hole-drilling operation; one- and two-dimensional data or barcode readings; measurements; and motion tracking of particle or liquid flow. Inspection rates are generally far higher than is humanly possible. Special lighting—for example, a particular color of light or a shaped array of light-emitting diodes—and filtering may be useful in providing optimal image quality for rapid image processing. Nonconforming test objects may be removed from the production line pneumatically by using an air blast or mechanically by diverting them into a holding area.

12.1.3 ADVANTAGES AND LIMITATIONS

Visual testing is a sensitive method for detecting and sizing surface and surface-breaking discontinuities in a wide variety of material types. The method is flexible so that essentially any test object size or shape may be examined. VT can be low-cost, quick and mobile, and does not require a great deal of inspector training. Documentation of indications is relatively easy with photography, including image- or video-capture techniques. Proper interpretation of indications generally requires inspector skill and industrial knowledge. Visual testing requires a direct or indirect view of the target; surface uncleanliness or roughness may degrade test sensitivity. Precleaning the target surface may be necessary; however, the cleaning technique selected may reduce discontinuity visibility.

12.2 LIQUID PENETRANT TESTING

12.2.1 INTRODUCTION AND PRINCIPLES

Liquid penetrant testing (PT) is a powerful method for detecting surface-breaking discontinuities and through-thickness leak paths in nonporous materials. This method uses a dye-loaded fluid, which easily finds its way into clean and dry discontinuities. After sufficient penetrant dwell time has been allowed for the test medium to enter discontinuities, the excess surface penetrant is removed. A blotting material (developer) is then applied to draw the highly contrasting liquid out onto the specimen's surface where it forms visible indications. Test indication visibility is governed by contrast against its surroundings—that is, signal-to-noise ratio—so inspections must be performed under proper lighting conditions. PT can be extremely sensitive to surface discontinuities, and, unlike some other NDT methods, orientation of the discontinuity does not affect penetrant testing detectability.

12.2.1.1 PENETRANT TYPES

Color-Contrast versus Fluorescent. Liquid penetrants come in two basic forms: color-contrast and fluorescent. *Color-contrast penetrant*—that is, dye penetrant—contains a dark red dye and this test medium is used under bright white-light illumination. *Fluorescent penetrant testing* is generally performed under a negligible amount of ambient light with the aid of an ultraviolet (UV-A) excitation radiation source (Figure 12.7). UV-A is chosen because this band of electromagnetic radiation is largely invisible to the inspector and it is relatively safe compared to shorter wavelength ultraviolet radiation. Electromagnetic radiation is simply electric and magnetic energy in transit from a source.

Electromagnetic radiation is characterized by its wavelength; each photon of a given wavelength has a finite amount of energy. Shorter wavelength photons are more energetic. The electromagnetic radiation spectrum is divided into regions because the photobiological effect—either beneficial or detrimental—of a photon varies with wavelength. The ultraviolet (UV) spectrum is commonly divided into three regions: UV-C, UV-B, and UV-A. The 1932 Second International Commission on Illumination (CIE) defined UV-C, UV-B, and UV-A as wavelengths ranging from 100-280 nm, 280-315 nm, and 315-400 nm, respectively. The division between UV-C and UV-B is based on the point where sunlight is longpass filtered by the ozone layer, meaning shorter wavelengths are blocked. The division between UV-B and UV-A is a bit more arbitrary. Most ultraviolet energy is undetectable to the human eye—recall that visible light has a wavelength between 380 and 780 nm—so when used in nondestructive testing, the contrast of a fluorescent indication against its background is high.

Dangers of UV Radiation. UV radiation exposure presents a measureable health risk, including chance of cataracts, retinal burns, and skin cancer. This risk varies greatly with photon wavelength. These photobiological effects have been studied and defined by health and safety organizations. One domestic authority, the American Conference of Governmental Industrial Hygienists (ACGIH), maintains and periodically updates guideline values and indices for exposure to hazardous chemicals and physical agents. One of ACGIH's guidelines offers recommendations on safe exposure to UV radiation, visible light, and infrared radiation. In NDT, there are two main concerns when working with nonionizing radiation: retinal photochemical injury due to blue-light exposure of wavelengths between 400 nm and 500 nm, with sensitivity peaking at 435 nm to 440 nm; and extended UV exposure to the skin and eyes of wavelengths between 180 nm and 400 nm, with sensitivity peaking at 270 nm.

Color Contrast. When all other variables are held constant, test indications that are brighter or more contrasting against their background are easier for the inspector to detect. To incrementally improve indication visibility, the tools and consumables utilized in NDT have evolved with time. For example, PT indication sensitivity was improved in 1946 by adding red dye to the historic "oil and whiting" test medium, and visibility was again improved when fluorescent dye was introduced. Further penetrant improvements were realized when two cascading fluorophores began to be employed in 1960. *Fluorophores* are components—dyes, for example—that absorb energy and then rapidly release this absorbed energy, or fluoresce, as longer wavelength visible light.

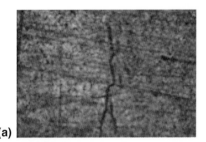  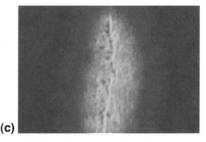

(a) (b) (c)

Figure 12.7: Appearance of a 2.54 mm (0.10 in.) long surface-breaking low-cycle fatigue crack in a nickel-chromium-based superalloy (Inconel™ 718): (a) prior to inspection; (b) with a dry-powder-developed fluorescent penetrant test indication as viewed under white light; (c) when the same test indication is observed under ultraviolet radiation.

Luminescence. Standard dyes are colored because they selectively absorb visible light, while fluorescent dyes not only absorb but also emit light when electronically excited. *Luminescence* is the low-temperature emission of light from a substance caused by electronic excitation of a molecule. Luminescence may be in the form of fluorescence (used in NDT) or phosphorescence, depending on the relaxation mechanism. A complex combination of factors controls whether a dye is fluorescent, including the structure of the molecule and the properties of its surroundings.

Absorption of a photon excites the fluorophore into an excited state and a photon is generally released when the molecule returns to the ground state—its lowest energy state. There are several distinct excited energy levels that a fluorophore can attain and the electronically excited level depends on the wavelength or energy of the incident photon. Absorption and emission of energy by a fluorophore are based on the probabilities of various events. Fluorophores prefer to absorb particular wavelengths and an excitation spectrum may be constructed by evaluating absorption at each wavelength. The wavelength and number of incident photons control fluorescent brightness, so maximum detection of medium luminance is only attained when preferred excitation wavelengths are supplied by the excitation radiation source or exciter.

Fluorophores absorb specific wavelengths of excitation energy and release that energy quickly—in the order of 10 ns – generally in the form of longer wavelength visible light. Once the fluorophore is excited, there are competing modes of relaxation. Transition between the unstable, semistable and ground state is accomplished though internal conversion—that is, nonradiative deactivation—or by releasing a photon. Fluorescent emission wavelengths are generally longer than excitation wavelengths; the difference between peak excitation and peak emission wavelengths is known as *stokes shift*. The amount of shift varies with the fluorophore, fluorophore/surrounding-medium combination, and competing nonradiative deactivation mechanisms.

Modern fluorescent penetrants contain at least two fluorophores. This teamwork approach to fluorescence is known as the *cascade effect*, which produces a much brighter indication than is possible when only one fluorophore is used. The cascading fluorophore, or optical brightener, emits pale blue light that is absorbed by its counterpart, and the cascaded fluorophore then emits light at its preferred longer yellow-green wavelengths. Synergy occurs when light emitted from one fluorophore acts as excitation energy, which transfers energy from the cascading fluorophore to the cascaded fluorophore.

12.2.1.2 LIQUID PENETRANT PROCESS

Liquid penetrant testing excels at locating all types of surface-breaking and through-thickness discontinuities in nonpermeable solid materials. PT has been successfully used on ferrous and nonferrous metals, fired ceramics and cermets, powdered metal products, glass, and some types of plastics and synthetic organic materials. The success of a test depends on thorough precleaning and drying, choice of test materials, lighting conditions, and adherence to established procedures.

Basic Steps. The penetrant testing process consists of six basic steps regardless of the type of penetrant and removal method:
1. Preclean and dry the test object.
2. Apply liquid penetrant to surfaces of interest and allow sufficient dwell time.
3. Carefully remove excess penetrant from the surface without removing penetrant from discontinuities.
4. Apply developer to the prepared surface and allow adequate development time for test indication formation.
5. Visually examine surfaces for test indications; interpret and evaluate indications.
6. Postclean the specimen if process residues will be detrimental to subsequent operations—for instance, painting—or the part's intended function.

Precleaning. The importance of precleaning cannot be overstated because adverse surface conditions, including paint, oils, and surface soils, or corrosion products, chemically active residues, and moisture, can interfere with the following: wetting of the test surface by the liquid penetrant, entry of the liquid penetrant into discontinuities, and the subsequent bleedout of liquid penetrant to form discontinuity indications. Precleaning and postcleaning methods include chemical and mechanical techniques. Examples of chemical techniques are detergents, solvents, vapor degreasing, steam cleaning, and acid or alkaline cleaning. Mechanical techniques entail abrasives or media blasts. Chemical cleaning agents are sometimes assisted by ultrasonic vibrations, which increase cleaning effectiveness through cavitation.

Cleaning technique selection is based on the type of contaminant to be removed, specimen material type, degree of cleanliness required, and cost and time factors. Some materials are sensitive to halogens, sulfur, sodium and/or potassium, so these elements may need to be avoided in cleaning products. NDT personnel must be aware that preliminary manufacturing operations—for example, sanding, honing, and shot blasting—as well as some cleaning operations, including vapor blasting, tumble deburring, and some mechanical cleaning techniques, have the potential to smear closed surface-breaking discontinuities. Such operations are either avoided, or they must be followed by a chemical etching, milling, or electropolishing step. All chemical-cleaning residues should be neutralized prior to penetrant application.

Importance of Drying. Water must be completely evaporated prior to penetrant application, generally using a pre-inspection drying step. Efficient drying techniques include a forced air oven set to a temperature between 66 °C and 121 °C (150 °F and 250 °F) and flash drying at a temperature between 66 °C and 93 °C (150 °F and 200 °F). Flash drying immerses the specimen in hot deionized water, with a chloride content less than 10 parts per million, for a sufficient length of time for the part to reach the water temperature. The term "flash" describes the appearance of residual water quickly evaporating as the part is removed from the hot water tank. It is important to note that drying temperature with penetrant trapped within discontinuities using a pre- or post-developer application, depending on developer type, is limited to 71 °C (160 °F). Fluorescent penetrant exposed to excessive drying time or temperature will have reduced luminance, referred to as *heat fade*.

The PT process relies on the ability of the test medium to enter a discontinuity, then be subsequently drawn back out and made easily visible on the surface. Small discontinuities with little width or length will only hold a tiny volume of penetrant; in other words, there is very little penetrant available to be drawn out onto the surface to form an indication. Detection is only possible if the small amount of penetrant is highly visible. Some of the light, either visible or ultraviolet, incident on the test surface is absorbed by the penetrant and some is reflected. Much of PT's sensitivity is derived from penetrant's ability to absorb light even with a minimal liquid layer thickness.

12.2.1.3 LIQUID PENETRANT INDICATIONS

The amount of light absorbed by a liquid penetrant (I_A) can be predicted, but the mathematical constants cannot be determined by inspectors in the field. The *beer-lambert law*, more simply referred to as *Beer's law*, is widely used in the unrelated field of spectrophotometry, specifically for determination of the concentration within a liquid sample. In NDT, a modified form of the beer-lambert relationship (Equation 12.1) is used to describe light absorption (I_A) by a liquid penetrant. This equation, which is wavelength dependent, is based on the absorption coefficient of the dye (e), dye concentration in the penetrant (c), layer thickness of the penetrant film (t) and the amount of incident light (I_O). Therefore, in color-contrast penetrants, for example, the concentration of red dyes directly influences inspection sensitivity.

(Eq. 12.1) $\qquad I_A = I_o\left(1-10^{-ect}\right)$

For fluorescent penetrants, this theoretical analysis can be taken one step further by considering how efficiently absorbed light is converted into detectable fluoresced light, forming a test indication. Efficiency of a fluorophore and solvent combination is known as quantum yield, which can vary depending on the solvent it's dissolved in or contaminants it's exposed to. Fluorescent brightness of a penetrant varies with the *quantum yield* of the dye, which is the ratio of photons absorbed versus photons reemitted. If a fluorophore were able to convert each absorbed photon into a photon of visible light, its efficiency would be 100%, a quantum yield of 1.0, and it would fluoresce intensely. Because of competing relaxation processes, no fluorophores attain a quantum yield of unity.

Any material class—metal, ceramic, or polymer—is potentially testable with PT as long as porosity is low and it is chemically compatible with the test media. *Porosity* is void space within a material that coalesced from a gas or is inherent to a manufacturing process, for example, powder metallurgy. Background noise is proportional to the number of surface-breaking pores, although the noise due to porosity may be reduced by selecting a different penetrant test fluid.

Capillary Action. Liquid penetrant enters surface-breaking discontinuities through the phenomenon of capillary action, and this action is likely if surface wetting occurs. Surface wetting is generally described in terms of the contact angle made between a drop of the liquid and the target surface. Good wetting approaches an ideal 0° angle, while poor wetting approaches a 180° angle (Figure 12.8). When liquid wets a target surface, it will tend to seep into surface-breaking discontinuities; discontinuity-filling speed is controlled by the liquid's kinematic viscosity. The ability of a given liquid to flow over a surface and enter surface cavities depends on the cleanliness of the surface, surface tension of the liquid, configuration of the cavity, contact angle of the liquid, ability of the liquid to wet the surface, cleanliness of the cavity, and size of the surface opening of the cavity. The amount of pressure drawing the liquid into discontinuities is proportional to surface tension and inversely proportional to the width of the discontinuity.

Surface Tension. The terms *surface energy* and *surface tension* are equivalent since both are energy per unit area; however, the former is more general in that it applies to both solids and liquids, and the latter requires an air interface. Surface wetting is a function of intermolecular attractive forces of cohesion and adhesion between the liquid and solid surfaces, and it varies with the relative surface energies

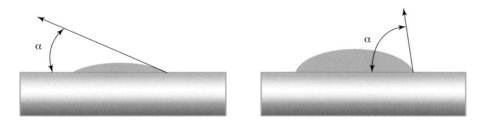

Figure 12.8: Contact angle (α) varies inversely with surface wetting; larger angles indicate poorer wetting.

of the liquid and solid. In other words, wetting is a delicate balance between the air and liquid, liquid and solid, and solid and air interfaces. As an example, water, which has a low surface energy, spreads out on the high-energy surface of an unwaxed car. Waxing the car decreases its surface energy, and consequently water will bead up. Adding a surfactant, or wetting agent, to the water may decrease its surface energy enough that, wetting, of the waxed surface could occur. Surfactants and many other impurities in pure water decrease surface tension by reducing cohesion between water molecules.

12.2.2 MATERIALS, EQUIPMENT, AND TECHNIQUES

12.2.2.1 CLASSIFICATION OF PENETRANTS

A classification system for liquid penetrant test materials was established by the U.S. Department of Defense, and this system has been carried over to current SAE and ASTM standards (Table 12.1). Liquid penetrants are classified by the type of dye that they contain—either color contrast or fluorescent. ISO-3452-2:2006 uses a similar classification, with the addition of dual-use penetrant as Type III, which may be used under white light or UV-A, and a sensitivity division within Type II penetrants: normal-sensitivity level 1 and high-sensitivity level 2. Penetrant systems are qualified according to test sensitivity level, heat fade resistance, and ultraviolet irradiance fade resistance, among other factors, and those meeting the requirements within SAE AMS 2644 are included in the standard's qualified products list (QPL-4).

			Sensitivity	
Table 12.1: Penetrant test media classification system (SAE AMS 2644, and ASTM E1417).				
Penetrant	Type I	Fluorescent[1]	Ultra-low	Level 1/2
	Type II	Color Contrast[2]	Low	Level 1
			Medium	Level 2
Removal	Method A	Water washable	High	Level 3
	Method B	Postemulsifiable lipophilic	Ultra-high	Level 4
	Method C	Solvent wipe		
	Method D	Postemulsifiable hydrophilic		
Removers	Class (1)	Halogenated[3]		
	Class (2)	Nonhalogenated		
	Class (3)	Specific application		
Developers	Form a	Dry powder		
	Form b	Water soluble		
	Form c	Water suspendible		
	Form d	Nonaqueous wet for Type I penetrant		
	Form e	Nonaqueous wet for Type II penetrant		
	Form f	Specific application		

Notes:

1 Only Type I penetrants are divided by their test sensitivity.

2 Type II penetrants are not classified by sensitivity level within the SAE and ASTM documents.

3 Not for use on titanium or nickel-based alloys.

Post-Dwell Removal. In addition to dye type, liquid penetrants are further classified by post-dwell removal technique. Many liquid penetrants cannot be removed without applying an emulsifier in a separate process step, normally by dipping or spray application. Because postemulsifiable liquid penetrants do not contain any emulsifying agent, they are less likely to be removed from a discontinuity during water rinse. Depending on the type used, the emulsifier either converts the excess surface liquid penetrant into a mixture that forms an emulsion with the addition of water (lipophilic) or acts directly with the liquid penetrant to form an emulsion subsequently removed with water (hydrophilic). Other liquid penetrants are carefully compounded with water or a surfactant as a base, and these are directly removable with water after the liquid penetrant dwell time.

Color contrast (Type II) penetrant contains a dye tracer, usually red, and is generally chosen when it is impractical to make the inspection area free of ambient light. The dye penetrant indication, when viewed under the appropriate lighting, sharply contrasts against a white background of developer. Color-contrast penetrant residue will degrade the sensitivity of a subsequent fluorescent penetrant inspection by decreasing or eliminating fluorescent luminance, so the inspector must be cognizant of prior inspections.

12.2.2.2 DEVELOPER

Developer is the final test medium applied to a sample during the inspection process; this test material wicks penetrant out of discontinuities where it can spread and scatters fluoresced light from the test indication to greatly increase its luminance. Developers come in several forms, including dry powder, water-soluble, water-suspendible, nonaqueous wet (NAWD), and specific application, such as peelable developer applied as a resin/polymer in a volatile carrier. Choice of liquid penetrant helps guide developer selection. For example, water-suspendible or -soluble developers are not used with water-washable penetrant, as the developer's water carrier could remove penetrant from discontinuities. Furthermore, dry powder developer is not used with Type II dye penetrant, as the negligible developer layer thickness won't provide enough test indication contrast.

12.2.2.3 ILLUMINANCE OF INDICATIONS

Exciter. The *exciter* is an essential component of penetrant testing. Both the total power output—evaluated as illuminance for color-contrast inspections or as irradiance and illuminance for fluorescent penetrant inspections—and the wavelengths at which energy is emitted are important. A white light source is used for dye penetrant inspections, but for maximum fluorescent penetrant excitation efficiency, the exciter's radiation should center on the fluorophore's wavelength of peak fluorescent excitation. Fluorophore and solvent combinations for fluorescent penetrant detection media have been carefully established by test media manufacturers. Today's fluorescent penetrants exhibit peak excitation with 362 nm – 371 nm photons.

Fluorescent nondestructive testing has historically been performed under negligible ambient lighting with the aid of an ultraviolet radiation source. Mercury vapor excitation radiation sources, or exciters, which exhibit strong UV-A emission lines, are still in widespread use today. A UV-A bandpass filter, such as Wood's glass, eliminates several mercury vapor emission lines that fall outside of the 315 nm – 400 nm range. Consequently, the majority of energy exiting a mercury vapor exciter is centered at 365 nm. The number of excitation source types has changed with time. In addition to medium-pressure mercury lamps, xenon, ultraviolet light-emitting diode (UV-LED), blue-light LED, and luminescent tube-based exciters are all available. UV-A filtering is used with xenon and luminescent tube sources, and may be incorporated into UV-LED sources. The spectral emission characteristics—intensity versus wavelength, as shown in Figure 12.9—and consequently the respective excitation efficiency vary among exciter types.

The output of an exciter is most often measured by its irradiance, and a radiometer is used for this measurement. A minimum UV-A irradiance of 10 watts per square meter ($W \cdot m^{-2}$) is generally mandated within fluorescent penetrant testing standards. Converting between $W \cdot m^{-2}$ and the non-SI unit of microwatts per square centimeter ($\mu W \cdot cm^{-2}$) is accomplished by multiplying the former by 100. Fluorescent test indication luminance increases with irradiance from the exciter. High irradiance (above 100 $W \cdot m^{-2}$) will, however, quickly fade a fluorescent test indication's luminance with exposure time, with the UV fade following an exponential decay relationship.

Light Measurement. The illuminance of ambient white visible light must also be evaluated using a calibrated luxmeter prior to fluorescent inspections. Radiometers and luxmeters used in NDT employ integral sensors, which are assemblies consisting of a photodiode, aperture, filter set, and light-diffusing cover. Integral sensors are designed to replicate a desired action spectrum—in other words, they use a weighting function. For example, a luxmeter's photometric response replicates human daylight color vision, whereas an ideal radiometer strives for a top-hat function spectral responsivity. Specially filtered integral radiometer sensors replicating blue light hazard and ACGIH UV-hazard action spectra are both commercially available.

Fluorescent NDT should be performed with the aid of safety glasses to protect the operator from adverse health effects and to increase an indication's contrast ratio: indication luminance versus background luminance. Some visual background noise occurs when UV-A reaches the inspector's eyes, which causes intraocular *veiling glare*. Longpass filtering glasses, which may be clear or amber in color, eliminate

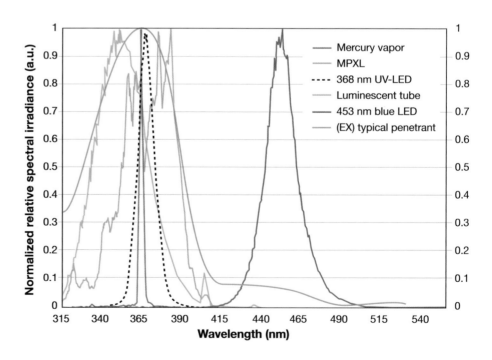

Figure 12.9: Normalized relative spectral irradiance of various exciters, shown overlaid by the excitation spectrum of a typical fluorescent liquid penetrant detection medium.

visual distraction and eye fatigue due to fluorescence within the eye. Amber-colored safety glasses block UV radiation and much of the leaked visible light emitted by the exciter. Leaked visible light is generally violet in color, but red wavelengths may also be emitted by some types of lamps and would not be blocked by longpass lenses. Leaked visible light leads to increased luminance of the test surface and a reduced signal-to-noise ratio for the indication; however, a small amount of visible light in the dark inspection booth also allows the inspector to safely move about.

Portability. PT can be extremely portable to accommodate very large or low numbers of specimens. Portable kits generally consist of aerosol cans and handheld light sources. PT may also be performed by processing batches of specimens through stationary equipment, which consists of a combination of spray booth and/or dip tanks, drain/dwell station, rinse stations, dryer, developer station, and inspection booth. Spray application of penetrant or developer may incorporate electrostatic ionization to increase the efficient use of the test medium.

12.2.2.4 SYSTEM PERFORMANCE

Many types of testing aids are available for comparing two liquid penetrants or for process monitoring. A penetrant comparator in the form of a quench-cracked aluminum block is used to compare the effectiveness of two penetrants, for example, inservice versus unused or one brand versus another. The 50 mm × 76 mm × 9.5 mm (2 in. × 3 in. × 0.375 in.) block is fabricated from Al-2024 alloy aluminum. It has a dividing groove to separate the "A" and "B" sides and is designed to be a single-use item (Figure 12.10). Common multiuse aids include penetrant testing and monitoring (TAM) or penetrant system monitoring (PSM) panels, twin known discontinuity standards (twin KDS), and nickel-chrome cracked panels.

Discontinuity Standards. Regular system performance checks commonly employ the TAM panel known discontinuity standard (Figure 12.11). TAM panels are 10.2 cm × 15.2 cm (4 in. × 6 in.) stainless steel—for example, type 321 alloy—pieces, which are divided into a smooth chrome-plated side with cracks and a rough grit-blasted side for evaluating liquid penetrant washability. The brittle chrome plating is

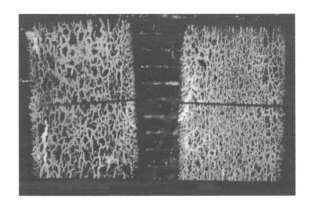

Figure 12.10: Test indications in two aluminum penetrant comparators, when processed with "Type I" fluorescent penetrant and developed using "form a" dry powder.

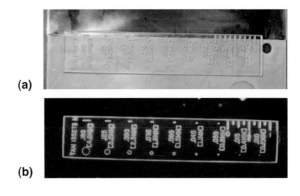

(a)

(b)

Figure 12.11: Typical penetrant system monitoring panel as processed using ultra-high-sensitivity fluorescent penetrant and developed using dry powder developer as viewed under: (a) white light; (b) ultraviolet radiation. Also shown is a typical comparator used to estimate starburst indication diameters.

cracked by indenting the reverse side in five places to produce starburst patterns of varying sizes. For example, the "A" crack is 0.38 mm – 0.79 mm in diameter and the "E" crack is 4.57 mm – 6.35 mm in diameter. The TAM panel is processed in the same manner as production parts. The number of starburst cracks detectable is noted, as is the diameter of each pattern, for example, using quantitative image analysis or some type of comparator. The TAM panel is not designed to evaluate the sensitivity of a test medium or system.

Some industry standards call for regular comparisons between in-use and unused liquid penetrant. The manufacture of TAM panels is not controlled closely enough to assume that two panels will produce similar test results. There are, however, two types of twin known discontinuity process monitoring aids that can be used. First is the twin KDS set, which is designed to compare two liquid penetrants or two testing conditions—for example, different drying times, drying temperatures, or penetrant removal parameters—rather than evaluate test sensitivity. Twin KDS panels look like narrow TAM panels; similarly, the stainless steel panels have a cracked plated side—nickel plating, in this case, approximately 1/3 as thick as the TAM panel plating—and a grit-blasted side for washability. Twins are manufactured in the form of a single panel; then the panel is cut into an "A" side, with five starburst cracks of varying sizes, and a "B" side, also with five cracks. Essentially, both sides are identical. Twin KDS panels may be repeatedly processed through the production line.

Twin nickel-chrome (Ni-Cr) test panels can also be used for comparisons between in-use and unused liquid penetrant. The only commercially available test aid useful for evaluating penetrant system or process sensitivity, these panels have two main drawbacks: they are expensive and they are primarily a laboratory tool. Twin Ni-Cr panels are 2 mm × 100 mm × 35 mm (0.08 in. × 3.9 in. × 1.4 in.). A brass substrate is first plated with nickel, then overlaid with a thin chrome plating flash. The resultant coating varies along its length. Full-width cracks are produced by temporarily bending the panel over a curved mandrel or by applying a tensile stress. Then the panel is sheared into a matching set. Twin Ni-Cr panels are available with maximum plating thickness of 10 (sensitivity level 4), 20, 30, or 50 (sensitivity level 1) microns.

12.2.3 ADVANTAGES AND LIMITATIONS

Liquid penetrant testing is one of the most sensitive nondestructive test methods for detecting surface discontinuities. Discontinuity test indications can be found regardless of the configuration of the test object or orientation of the discontinuity. PT may even be performed remotely through the working channel of a borescope. Discontinuities of interest are generally small and invisible to the unaided eye. Liquid penetrant testing can quickly examine all accessible surfaces of objects. In addition, it may be used for localized regions or locating through-thickness leaks. Liquid penetrant testing can be accomplished with relatively inexpensive, unsophisticated equipment. Small areas may be tested using portable equipment, or large batches and parts may be processed through dedicated semi-automated testing systems. The sensitivity of a liquid penetrant testing process may be adjusted through appropriate selection of liquid penetrant, removal technique, and type of developer.

Liquid penetrant testing, however, depends on the ability of liquid penetrant to enter and fill discontinuities. PT will only reveal discontinuities that are open to the surface. Specimens and their discontinuities must be clean and dry. Some machining and mechanical cleaning operations may smear or peen the surface of metals, thus closing off discontinuities and preventing their detection. Surface deformation may also occur when a component is in service, which could also smear discontinuities closed. Chemical etching or electropolishing is generally mandatory if surface deformation has occurred prior to liquid penetrant testing.

12.3 MAGNETIC PARTICLE TESTING

12.3.1 INTRODUCTION AND PRINCIPLES

Magnetic particle testing (MT) would technically fall within the topic of electromagnetic testing, but given its widespread usage and historic separation as a method of its own, this book will follow suit by considering it independently. The closely related technique of magnetic flux leakage testing, which mainly differs from MT in the detector—a hall effect sensor versus magnetic particles—will be included in a separate section. All electromagnetic tests are described by the mathematical equations derived by James Clerk Maxwell in 1864. Maxwell's equations provide a common ground from which all electromagnetic inspection techniques, including microwave and eddy current, may be explained. As a method, MT is no exception.

Ferromagnetic Test Objects. MT is applied to ferromagnetic test objects to detect surface and near-surface discontinuities. Ferromagnetic materials are most strongly affected by magnetism, and have a relative permeability considerably greater than unity. In MT, magnetic flux is induced within the test object during inspection using available magnetization techniques. These techniques may be divided into those where the specimen receives electrical current flow and those that incorporate magnetic field flow. A discontinuity of a given size, orientation, and depth in the specimen can disrupt the normal flow of magnetic flux lines. This disruption causes the localized magnetic flux leakage necessary for the collection of detection media or particles.

Ferromagnetic particles are introduced onto the specimen's surface at the proper time according to the inspection technique's process. Particles are then attracted to any magnetic poles on the specimen, including the localized flux leakage caused by discontinuities, where they collect to form test indications. These indications are viewed by the inspector, who judges their relevance and rejectability. Viewing conditions under which judgment is made must be controlled; industrial standards are generally used for guidance. For example, the minimum amount of ambient light at the specimen surface is mandated for visible particles, while the levels of ambient light and ultraviolet radiation must both be controlled for fluorescent particle inspections.

Flux Leakage Field. For discontinuities to be detected, the *flux leakage field* must be sufficiently strong to attract and hold a noticeable concentration of particles. Indication formation depends strongly on the discontinuity dimensions and position, magnetizing field strength, magnetizing waveform, and loosely on the material's magnetic permeability. In general, orientation and depth of the discontinuity determine its detectability. The strongest magnetic flux leakage field is formed when induced flux lines are oriented perpendicular to the discontinuity. Magnitude of magnetic leakage flux, and consequently the probability that it will be detected, diminishes quickly as the angle of incidence between discontinuity and flux decreases from perpendicular.

An inspector should be aware of the range of discontinuities inherent in the sample, because material type, manufacturing operations, and heat-treatment influence the types of discontinuities expected. For example, wrought steels may have laps, folds, and nonmetallic inclusions; high-chromium steels may have ferrite stringers; and precipitation-hardened (PH) steels may have longitudinal indications from segregation or banding of alloying elements.

Magnetic Domains. Because MT can only be applied to ferromagnetic materials, such as many iron- and nickel-based alloys, it is not a universal method. It can be used on most, but not all, steels, which are iron-based alloys. Limited applicability stems from the fact that ferromagnetic materials are composed of numerous individual *magnetic domains*, which are small volumes of magnetically saturated material.

These domains rotate, change size, and align as an external magnetizing force is applied. Domain orientation is random in demagnetized materials, and this randomness leads to cancellation so that the net magnetic moment of the bulk material is zero. As a ferromagnetic material is exposed to an increasing external magnetic field, the individual magnetic domains align and magnetization of the bulk can occur. Ferromagnetic domains only exist below a threshold called the *curie temperature*, which is unique for each base material. For example, the curie point for steels, where the material changes from ferromagnetic to paramagnetic, is approximately 760 °C (1400 °F). Paramagnetic materials or crystal structures have a relative permeability that is slightly greater than unity, and their permeability is practically independent of the magnetizing force.

Permeability and Flux Density. Magnetic permeability is the ratio of flux density versus field strength (B/H). Magnetic permeability for ferromagnetic materials, however, varies with flux density. A hysteresis curve, also referred to as a *B-H* curve (Figure 12.12), illustrates how a ferromagnetic material reacts when exposed to an external magnetic field. Metallurgical changes to a specimen, such as carbon content, cold work, thermal treatments, residual or applied stress, and welding, change its permeability and magnetic saturation level. Easily magnetized and demagnetized, or soft, ferromagnetic materials have low coercivity ($\overrightarrow{ad}$), while very strong, or hard, permanent magnets have a high coercivity. Key points on a hysteresis curve are:

- Point a: Demagnetized initial state.
- Point b: Point of magnetic saturation.
- Point c: Retentivity; remanence or remnant magnetization.
- Point d: Coercivity or coercive field.

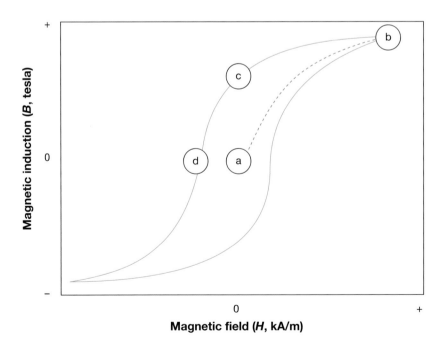

Figure 12.12: Hysteresis curve for a ferromagnetic material with the virgin curve highlighted as the $\overrightarrow{ab}$ portion.

Penetration depth for a magnetic particle test relies, in part, on the sample's permeability. The type and thickness of coatings, test equipment and magnetizing waveform used, induced magnetic field strength, particle type and size, and the dimension and location of the discontinuity sought also play a role in detectability. For example, a given discontinuity at the test sample surface forms a sharper indication than one located below the surface. In addition, indications become more diffuse with discontinuity depth. Sample surface condition is also important and can adversely affect MT sensitivity. Surface contamination and coatings can prevent indications from forming, while rust, scale, and surface roughness may form false indications.

If the size of discontinuity sought is large, thicker coatings present less of an impediment. Particle-holding power of a discontinuity is governed by the strength and curvature of the magnetic leakage field. Coated parts, or subsurface discontinuities, do not create highly curved magnetic leakage fields at the inspection surface, so an increase in magnetizing field strength is required to form an indication. In general, test sensitivity is not greatly diminished when paint or chrome thickness is less than 0.076 mm (3 mils) or nickel plating is less than 0.025 mm (1 mil).

12.3.2 MATERIALS, EQUIPMENT, AND TECHNIQUES

MT techniques can be categorized by several factors: direction of induced magnetism; magnetizing current waveform, whether the particle is introduced to the specimen surface while suspended in a carrier fluid (wet) or sprinkled as a powder (dry), whether particles are introduced to the specimen before or after magnetization, and whether the specimen completes an electrical (current flow) or a magnetic (field flow) circuit. Technique selection is primarily based on the size, depth, and orientation of the discontinuity sought. Depending on the desired effect, magnetic flux may be induced in the whole specimen or just in select areas. The goal of MT is to collect magnetic particles to a discontinuity so that a highly contrasting indication is visible to the operator. Magnetic particles must be positioned near enough the discontinuity so that the attraction force is greater than hindering forces. Indication visibility varies with its dimensions, the quality of illumination, background contrast, and the observer's vision.

Ferromagnetic Particles. No discontinuities would be detected in MT without *ferromagnetic particles*; the particles may be used dry or wet. Ferromagnetic particles may also be colored such that inspections are performed under ambient visible light, under ultraviolet radiation, or under a combination of the two, referred to as dual use. Dry powders often utilize iron filings, while wet particles generally employ some form of iron oxide. Wet fluorescent oxide particles are encapsulated within an epoxy shell; a fluorescent pigment in this shell absorbs excitation energy, often UV-A radiation, and emits visible light. Typical yellow-green particles emit visible light with a wavelength of approximately 520 nm.

12.3.2.1 WET BENCH

A horizontal or vertical wet bench must constantly agitate the bath to keep particles suspended; suspension is only possible when particle size is below a certain limit. Particle size is very important, but particle size distribution could be a delicate balance. Finer particles can offer enhanced wet bath sensitivity, but when the test sample surface is rough, too many fine particles cause excessive background fluorescence. Also, the small particles tend to agglomerate and cluster together during use. MT particles are often a mixture of spherical and rodlike particles. Spherical particles are highly mobile, but due to their lack of pronounced north and south magnetic poles, they exhibit a weaker attraction to a given magnetic leakage field. Rodlike particles have reduced mobility but are readily attracted to magnetic leakage fields.

Wet bath particles must be suspended in an oil or a treated - water bath. With either carrier fluid, regular maintenance steps must be performed. The wet method bath must be monitored for particle concentration, generally 0.1 – 0.4 mL of fluorescent particles, or 1.2 – 2.4 mL for color contrast visible particles, per 100 mL sample in a centrifuge tube. Loss of liquid due to drag-out or evaporation, as well as contamination by dust and debris, must also be monitored. MT is generally performed on ferrous components. Corrosion of the specimen is undesirable. The pH level of the carrier fluid should therefore be slightly alkaline to offer corrosion protection but should not exceed 9.0, above which skin irritations may occur. Oil is used when test standards demand it, when corrosion-sensitive parts are being tested, and in equipment that sees only periodic use. Oil-based carrier fluid has excellent wetting characteristics, doesn't require additives, and penetrates light oil contamination on the sample surface. Water-based baths have cost and environmental advantages over oil, but additives must be used not only for corrosion protection but also to enhance surface wetting, avoid bath foaming, provide anti-fungal properties, and provide a measure of alkalinity for ferrous metal corrosion resistance. Surface cleanliness is especially important when inspecting with a water-based carrier fluid or when using dry powder.

12.3.2.2 MAGNETIZING WAVEFORM AND CURRENT FLOW

Many magnetization techniques allow the inspector to select a specific magnetizing waveform. Alternating current, half-wave rectified alternating current, single-phase full-wave rectified alternating current, three-phase full-wave rectified alternating current, direct current, pulsed direct current, and capacitive discharge—all are available for MT. Each waveform type has advantages and limitations. For example, AC has minimal penetration (1 mm to 3 mm) below the specimen surface, a limitation referred to as the *skin effect*. On the other hand, AC can follow along complicated sample geometry and form well-defined test indications for surface and near-surface discontinuities. Direct current (DC) has deep penetration but tends to bypass complex geometry.

Hybrids of AC and DC have unique characteristics, which are sometimes preferable. Choice depends on wet versus dry inspection, specimen surface finish and geometry, and the depth of the expected discontinuities from the surface. For example, half-wave rectified AC is generally considered best when seeking subsurface discontinuities. While DC-type waveforms offer increased subsurface penetration, this potential advantage may be offset by the difficulty in fully removing the deep magnetization. Residual AC fields can be removed by simple pass-through demagnetization coils, but residual DC fields require multistep down-cycle demagnetization.

Electrical current flow magnetization techniques pass current directly through the specimen, and the directional relationship between flowing electrical current and the resultant magnetic field is known as the *right-hand rule*. As the rule's name suggests, one may use the right hand to visualize perpendicular relationships between a circular magnetic field (that is, curled fingers) surrounding a straight current-carrying conductor (that is, thumb), or a longitudinal magnetic field (thumb) formed within a current-carrying solenoid (curled fingers). Electrical contact is made during a *head shot* on stationary equipment and when using prods that contact the specimen's surface. Common magnetic field flow magnetization techniques include electromagnetic yokes, rigid or flexible coils, induction coil pole extenders, internal conductor, or cable passing through a hole in the specimen and permanent magnets. More than one magnetization technique may be used nearly simultaneously with the goal of detecting discontinuities lying in any orientation.

Circular Magnetization. Circular magnetic fields may be generated by passing current directly through the part (Figure 12.13) or with an internal conductor—that is, a central conductor, or threader bar—passed through a hole or hollow section. The amount of current required for an adequate inspection varies with specimen diameter. Some critical components do not allow for the possibility of localized heat damage caused by electrical arcing. This may disallow a head shot; however, an internal conductor can induce a magnetic field without threat of localized heat damage. While a head shot produces no field strength on the interior of a hollow part, an internal conductor yields the highest magnetic flux density on the inside surface and lesser amount on the exterior. Several details must be considered when adopting the internal conductor technique, such as the size of the conductor, its placement within the specimen and the number of inspections required for complete coverage.

Longitudinal Magnetization. Field-flow longitudinal magnetization may be induced with a coil or using an electromagnetic yoke. A rigid five-turn coil or a flexible conductor may be wrapped around the specimen. Sample geometry, relative diameter of a specimen versus the magnetizing coil (fill factor), and sample position within the coil—each plays a significant role. Specimen shape is generally described in terms of an aspect ratio, which is length (L) divided by diameter (D). When magnetic poles formed at the ends of a coil-magnetized part are very close together, as would be the case when the aspect ratio (L/D) is less than 3, their opposing fields work fiercely against the magnetizing force, and this opposition decreases the overall field strength within the part. The other field-flow longitudinal magnetization option for wet horizontal benches is a set of *flux flow* coils, which also act as the headstock and tailstock. This type of field-flow longitudinal magnetization uses two copper-covered laminated cores surrounded by induction coils as pole extenders, which induce the magnetic field into the test object.

Electromagnetic yokes are available in many different configurations. For example, when the legs are flexible, the yoke may be called a *contour probe*. Nevertheless, the basic idea is always the same: at least one current-carrying coil is wrapped around a U-shaped core, which forms a longitudinal magnetic field between the core

 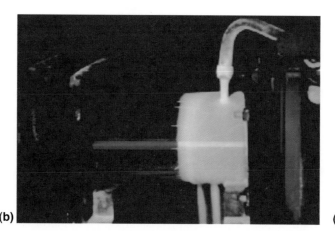 

(a) (b) (c)

Figure 12.13: Current flow (head-shot) magnetization of a solid steel bar that had been poorly induction hardened using alternating current on a horizontal wet bench: (a) pre-inspection appearance; (b) particles in the wet bath being attracted to the encircling residual leakage fields; (c) resultant test indications.

ends (Figure 12.14). Yoke options include power source (battery versus wall socket), magnetizing waveform, lifting power, and leg conformability. Yoke-to-discontinuity orientation, contact leg spacing, and leg coupling are all critical to the success of the inspection. The dead-weight lifting power of a yoke has a direct effect on the test sensitivity. Flux density is inversely proportional to pole-spacing distance.

Induced Current. Another magnetization technique is *induced current*, or *toroidal*, magnetization. This technique is useful for ring-shaped samples because it eliminates the chance for electrical arcing, reduces the number of shots for complete coverage and removes the opportunity for specimen deformation during multiple headshots. To perform induced-current magnetization inspection, a ferromagnetic core is used to greatly increase the induction efficiency. Ring-shaped test objects with a very low aspect ratio, such as gears and bearing races, are aligned so that the coil and test-object axis are parallel. In this configuration, the coil's magnetic field induces a current flowing around the test object. This induced current then forms its own magnetic field, which encircles the test object in a toroidal fashion to detect shallow or surface-breaking circumferential discontinuities. (See Figure 12.15a.)

Multidirectional magnetization on a wet bench can induce a magnetic field that changes direction with time. *Note:* Only one magnetization direction is possible at a given time (Figure 12.15b). This can reduce the number of inspection steps without decreasing omnidirectional sensitivity to discontinuities. Multidirectional magnetization uses at least two independently variable power supplies triggering slightly out of phase with each other to impart magnetic flux that varies rapidly in orientation. Multidirectional equipment offers increased discontinuity detectability as a result of fewer blind spots and can offer a 50% – 70% time savings per inspection when properly applied.

12.3.2.3 ACCESSORIES

In addition to informal rules of thumb for guidance, there are tools available for establishing test parameters. These include gauss or tesla meters, quantitative quality indicators, and a bank of parts with known discontinuities. The strength of a

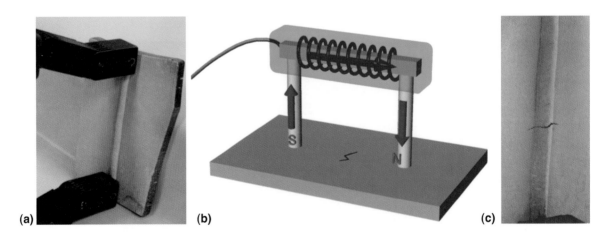

(a)   (b)   (c)

Figure 12.14: Electromagnetic contour probe inspection: (a) of a steel weld test plate containing a low-cycle fatigue crack; (b) alternating current is used; (c) white contrast paint makes the visible dry powder test indication highly visible against its surroundings.

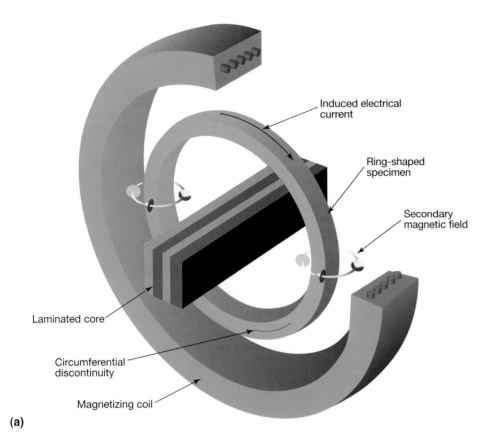

Induced electrical
current

Ring-shaped
specimen

Secondary
magnetic field

Laminated core

Circumferential
discontinuity

Magnetizing coil

(a)

(b)

Figure 12.15: Magnetizing with induced current: (a) toroidal technique to locate circumferential surface discontinuities in ring-shaped parts; (b) an engine block positioned for multidirectional magnetization.

tangential magnetic field is equal on both sides of a boundary, and a few devices exist to indicate the direction, and sometimes the magnitude, of this tangential magnetic flux. The universally accepted tool for determining active and residual uniaxial magnetic field strength outside of the test object is the hall effect probe. Shared flux indicators, which use artificial discontinuities or gaps and are held in intimate contact with the test object, include flexible laminated strips, pie gages, berthold penetrameters, and quantitative quality indicators (Figure 12.16).

Quantitative quality indicators (QQI) may be used to establish how many parts may be stacked end-to-end while maintaining an effective flux-flow coil magnetization, evaluate equipment performance, verify particle performance, verify adequate wet bath particle concentration, and ensure adequate magnetic field strength and direction—especially in a multidirectional application. QQIs are either 0.05 mm (0.002 in.) or 0.10 mm (0.004 in.) thick and contain chemically milled discontinuities whose depth is expressed in percent of shim thickness—for example, 20%, 30%, and 40% deep. Some QQIs have three concentric artificial discontinuity circles, while other large and small QQIs have a circle and crosshairs. The QQI is applied discontinuity side down, in intimate contact with the test object, with all four sides sealed to keep fluid and particles out.

12.3.3 ADVANTAGES AND LIMITATIONS

MT is a widely used method that may be applied to ferromagnetic parts of nearly every size and shape. There are four essential aspects for a successful inspection: (1) the part must be suitably magnetized in strength and orientation, (2) the particles must be introduced to the cleaned specimen surface, (3) lighting must be correct, and (4) the operator must be qualified. With the proper magnetizing

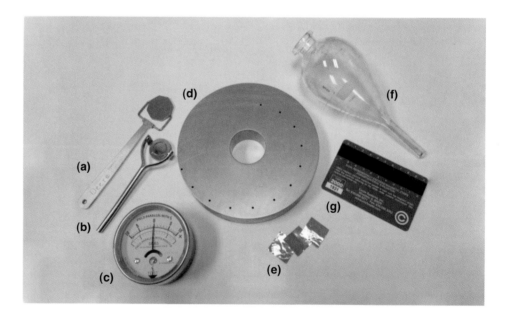

Figure 12.16: Examples of typical MT accessories include (a) the pie gage, (b) berthold penetrameter, (c) pocket magnetometer, (d) tool steel ring with side-drilled holes, (e) quantitative quality indicators, (f) centrifuge tube, and (g) magnetic stripe card.

waveform, MT may be used to inspect complex shapes, such as gears, splines, and crankshafts. This method is sensitive to surface and near-surface discontinuities, and the inspection process is quite rapid. Inspections may be performed in nearly any location and across a wide temperature range. Unlike many other NDT methods, MT indications are visible directly on the surface of the specimen, so documenting length and location is straightforward.

MT is limited to ferromagnetic parts and may miss large discontinuities if the magnetic flux and discontinuity are not properly oriented. Coatings on the sample also limit test sensitivity; a coating may need to be removed prior to testing if it is too thick or if the highest sensitivity possible is required. Post-inspection demagnetization is generally required, as strong residual magnetism can cause problems later during machining or during end use. Post-inspection cleaning is sometimes required to remove the particles and also to apply corrosion inhibitor.

12.4 ULTRASONIC TESTING

12.4.1 INTRODUCTION AND PRINCIPLES

Ultrasonic testing (UT) is a powerful volumetric inspection method based on the propagation of acoustic waves. Acoustic waves are mechanical vibrations passing through solid, liquid, or gas. Such waves may be reflected or refracted at interfaces. An interface is a change in medium—for example, metal versus a nonmetallic inclusion or void—or dramatic change in a material's properties. During UT one may monitor for the presence of a sound pulse or echo, for the amplitude of the signal received, or for the elapsed time between sending a pulse and receiving an echo. Bats using echolocation and anglers using portable sonar fish finders are both proficient at detecting and locating targets using acoustic energy, and nondestructive testing practitioners regularly employ similar acoustic techniques.

12.4.1.1 WAVE TYPES

Audible sound comprises vibrations propagating through a medium, such as the air, and energy is transferred away from its source in the form of waves. There are many different wave modes, and the frequency of waves used in UT varies widely. Frequency is measured in hertz (Hz), where one Hz is one cycle per second, and the period is the time required to complete one cycle. While sound that is audible to humans has a frequency between 20 and 20 000 Hz, ultrasonic waves used in UT have a frequency of 50 000 Hz to 50 000 000 Hz. Most inspections are performed with a test frequency between 1 MHz and 15 MHz. A wave is the coordinated oscillation of atoms about their resting position that transfers mechanical energy while the resting position of the atoms remains in the same place. Common modes of mechanical vibration in NDT are compression (longitudinal), shear (transverse), rayleigh (surface), and lamb (plate) waves.

Media for Wave Propagation. A medium must have density for a liquid or gas, and/or elasticity for solids, to support an acoustic wave. The velocity of acoustic waves varies proportionally with elasticity—that is, bulk and shear modulus mechanical material properties—and inversely with density. Some types of waves also require rigidity, so not all states of matter or materials can support all wave modes. Audible sound is transferred as *compression waves*, which propagate through all materials. Compression waves, which travel in the same direction as the atomic motion, are composed of compressions (particles that are squeezed together) and rarefactions (particles that are pulled apart). The distance between two equivalent positions on a wave—for example, two compressions—is the wavelength

(Figure 12.17). Acoustic energy propagates through a homogenous material at a constant velocity. Wavelength (λ) for all types of waves is directly proportional to acoustic velocity (*V*) and inversely proportional to test frequency (*f*). For example, a 7.5 MHz compression wave traveling through a gold bar at a velocity of 3.25 km/s would have a wavelength of 0.43 mm as calculated using the formula:

(Eq. 12.2) $$\lambda = \frac{V}{f}$$

Therefore:

(Eq. 12.3) $$\lambda = \frac{3250 \text{ m/s}}{7\ 500\ 000 \text{ Hz}}$$

$$\lambda = 0.00043 \text{ m}$$

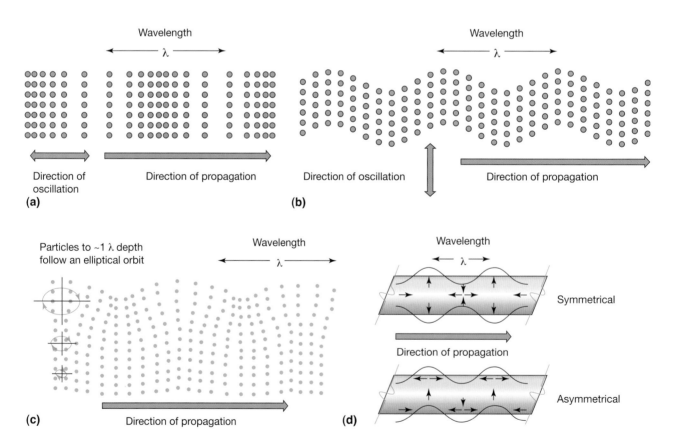

Figure 12.17: Common modes of wave propagation used in NDT include: (a) compression; (b) shear; (c) rayleigh; (d) two lamb wave modes.

This is approximately six orders of magnitude larger than the crystal lattice spacing of the atoms in the material (~4 Å or 0.0000004 mm).

Shear waves, *rayleigh waves*, and *lamb waves* can only propagate through a medium with an appreciable shear modulus (modulus of rigidity). Particle motion in a shear wave is transverse, or perpendicular, to its propagation direction. Atoms within a rayleigh wave travel in an elliptical path whose displacement decreases with depth. This type of wave only penetrates to a depth approximately equal to one wavelength. Lamb waves are a special wave mode that may only be generated in a test object with free boundaries. These waves have an infinite number of modes for both symmetric (longitudinal) and asymmetric (antisymmetric or flexural) displacements within the layer.

Wave Velocity. Compression and shear wave modes propagate with a phase speed that varies with the elastic properties of the medium. Shear wave velocity is approximately 50% of that for the compression mode, whereas rayleigh waves travel at about 90% of shear wave velocity. Many engineering materials have essentially equal mechanical properties in all directions, referred to as *elastic isotropy*, because they comprise a multitude of randomly oriented crystallites. Other engineering materials, such as composites or directionally solidified single-crystal structures, are designed to take advantage of elastic anisotropy. The difference in mechanical properties as a function of direction has a dramatic effect on wave propagation. Acoustic velocity also varies minimally with temperature and, because most engineering materials have a positive thermal expansion coefficient, velocity generally varies inversely with temperature; for example, the wave velocity in steel decreases approximately 1% per 55 °C (131 °F).

12.4.1.2 MECHANICAL VIBRATIONS

Transducer Types. Mechanical vibrations are introduced into the test object by an external energy source, such as transducers or lasers. Transducer types include piezoelectric, electromagnetic, magnetostrictive, and capacitive. Because it is so commonly used, when this text refers to an external energy source, it will be the piezoelectric crystal transducer type, referred to as a probe or search unit, unless stated otherwise. Piezoelectric materials—for example, quartz; lithium sulfate, an efficient detector; or barium titanate, an efficient emitter—accumulate an electrical charge in response to applied strain. Conversely, they produce mechanical strain due to an applied electrical potential. Transducers may be used to produce and detect ultrasonic signals; however, they must be coupled to ultrasonic testing equipment to function. The test equipment produces voltage pulses, which the transducer converts into mechanical vibrations, and these vibrations are transferred into the specimen. Detection of vibrations occurs in reverse.

Near and Far Fields. A piezoelectric element (crystal) has a specific atomic lattice structure, and the parameters of how the element is excised control whether it will preferentially produce compression waves (X-cut) or shear waves (Y-cut). Its central oscillation frequency is based on the thickness of the element. When the transducer vibrates, oscillations occur at points across the whole area of the face. The waves produced by each point source constructively and destructively interact; consequently, the distribution of sound intensities within the beam close to the face of the transducer varies dramatically. This is referred to as the *near field* or *fresnel zone*. Unexpected sound field intensity in the near field can lead to misinterpretation of discontinuity size. The length of the near field effect varies proportionally with the crystal's diameter and test frequency, and inversely with acoustic velocity. Sound field intensity reaches a maximum at the end of the near field, and this point marks the beginning of the *far field*, also called the *fraunhofer region*. Intensity decreases in a predictable manner in the far field (Figure 12.18).

Wave Boundaries. Mechanical vibrations must be transferred from the transducer, through at least one boundary, and into the test object to be useful for NDT. To make this transfer, the energy must pass through boundaries. Boundaries are changes in *acoustic impedance*—that is, changes in acoustic velocity. Recall that velocity is based on density and elastic properties. Energy transmission and reflection both occur at a boundary that is perpendicular to the sound field. The amount of mechanical energy transferred varies inversely with the difference in acoustic impedance. Greater impedance mismatch causes more of the energy to be reflected and less to be transmitted.

Use of Couplant. UT techniques, other than laser based, must use a *couplant* to transfer energy between the transducer and test object or use *electromotive force*, in the case of electromagnetic acoustic transducers. Couplant for contact and immersion transducers is generally a room-temperature liquid (water, glycerin, gel, or honey) or grease. Its purpose is to remove air from the region between the transducer and specimen. The acoustic mismatch is greater for an air-specimen boundary than it is for a couplant-specimen boundary, so the amount of energy transferred is increased. For example, 99.99% of an incident sound field is reflected at an air-quartz boundary, with characteristic acoustic impedance values of 0.0004×10^6 kg·m^{-2}·s^{-1} and 15.2×10^6 kg·m^{-2}·s^{-1} respectively, whereas only 68% is reflected at a water-quartz boundary. The acoustic impedance of water is 1.48×10^6 kg·m^{-2}·s^{-1}. This is why some ultrasonic probes employ *matching layers* to decrease acoustic impedance mismatch and increase energy transfer efficiency.

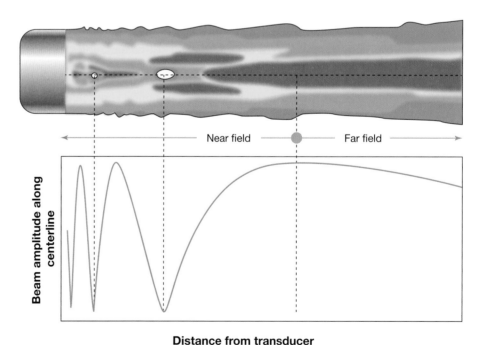

Figure 12.18: Intensity of the sound field has nodes (low amplitude) and antinodes (high amplitude) within the near field, reaches a maximum at the transition point, and then decreases in the far field.

12.4.1.3 ULTRASONIC WAVEFORMS

The packet of mechanical energy has a characteristic waveform (intensity, or amplitude versus time), and the shape of the *initial pulse* (IP), as shown in Figure 12.19, is governed by the electrical excitation waveform—for example, square or sinusoidal—provided by the ultrasonic testing equipment and by the amount of mechanical damping assembled into the transducer to reduce the amount of ringing. The packet waveform is the resultant sum of progressing waves, each with their specific frequency and amplitude. In other words, some components of the pulse are lower and others higher than the central frequency (f_c) marked on the transducer. A mathematical operation called *fourier transformation*—also referred to as *fast fourier transform* (FFT)—is used to graphically observe the spectral amplitude, that is, frequency components of a waveform expressed as amplitude versus frequency. The width of this peak, often at 50% of maximum or –6 dB, is known as the *bandwidth* (f_2 - f_1).

   Attenuation of Waves. The *pulse waveform* is distorted as it propagates through the specimen. This is known as *pulse broadening*. Distortion is due to several factors including attenuation or weakening, dispersion, diffraction, and boundary geometry. Attenuation is caused by absorption and scattering, and their relative effects vary with material properties and test frequency. Higher frequency offers improved

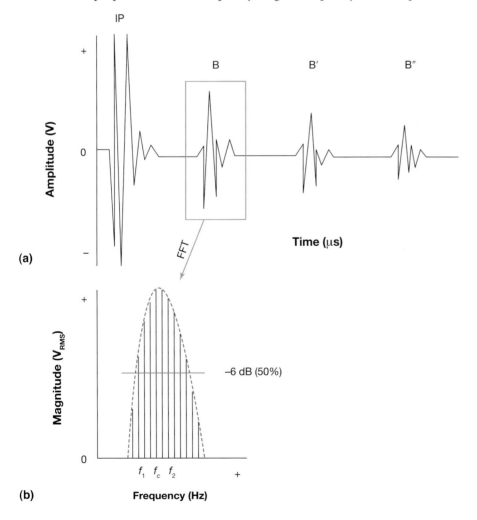

Figure 12.19: Radio-frequency (RF) display of an acoustic signal with multiple reflections presented in two ways: (a) signal amplitude versus time; (b) the frequency content of a single pulse analyzed using an FFT (V = voltage; RMS = root mean square).

inspection resolution, but higher-frequency components of the pulse are attenuated more quickly. A lower test frequency may be required to fully penetrate a large specimen or to decrease the amount of scattering due to boundary reflections, such as crystallite grain boundaries within a coarse-grained specimen material, internal porosity, or material changes within a composite. As the sound field attenuates, it also increases in diameter with distance—that is, diverges—in the far field. Increased test sensitivity is possible when a greater amount of sound energy is focused onto the discontinuity of interest. The rate of divergence increases proportionally with acoustic velocity of the medium and inversely with crystal diameter and test frequency. It is sometimes desirable to focus the acoustic energy—for instance, the spherical or linear focus—at a particular depth within the near field.

Because a variety of frequencies make up the energy pulse—recall that frequency and velocity are interrelated—the pulse will have an average velocity in spite of some components traveling more quickly or slowly. This variety of individual wave velocities—that is, phase velocities due to their unique frequency—leads to *peak broadening* because faster waves will return an echo more quickly than slower waves. When the pulse travels through a dispersive material, which tends to preferentially attenuate higher-frequency components, the inspector may observe a decrease in acoustic velocity. In other words, dispersion is a frequency-based velocity change interrelated with attenuation.

Dispersion of Waves. Lamb waves in particular are affected by *dispersion*, which means that wave packet velocity varies with test frequency, as well as the density and elastic constants of the medium. An infinite number of vibration modes exist for a specific plate thickness and test frequency. Lamb wave propagation characteristics are described graphically by experimentally determined dispersion curves that plot oscillation mode versus phase velocity. Nonuniform materials, as well as nonelastic materials where applied stress is not proportional to resultant strain, are often dispersive.

12.4.1.4 REFLECTION, DIFFRACTION, AND REFRACTION OF SOUND WAVES

NDT practitioners are generally concerned with two phenomena that occur when a sound field encounters a discontinuity: *reflection*, by which some incident sound pressure rebounds back toward its source, and *diffraction*, by which the discontinuity boundary itself oscillates and acts as a low-amplitude point source of acoustic energy. In many UT applications the amplitude, or pressure, of the reflected sound field is monitored and then compared against a known reflector, such as a side-drilled hole, flat-bottom hole, or notch. Returned signal amplitude depends on the depth, size, roughness, orientation, and contour of the reflecting area, as well as the *impedance mismatch* at the reflection boundary—for example, reflectivity of an air-filled pore versus a nonmetallic inclusion of equal size and shape.

Decreased signal amplitude due to attenuation is illustrated in Figure 12.19 as subsequent backwall echoes (B′, B″, etc.), which have lower amplitudes compared to the first backwall signal (B). Due to the many factors that affect discontinuity echo amplitude, it is often difficult to determine the precise size of a discontinuity. Flat reflectors perpendicular to the sound field are ideal, while actual discontinuities may be rough, spherical, or tilted and return less pressure. For example, a casting pore may be essentially spherical, whereas inadequate weld fusion is likely to be aligned with the bevel rather than parallel to the external surface.

Normal versus Angled Incidence. Acoustic energy may be introduced at a variety of angles with respect to the external surface of the specimen. Normal incidence waves perpendicular to the exterior, by convention, are said to propagate at zero degrees. Angled incidence is sometimes desirable to (1) induce shear waves,

(2) insonify at or direct the sound beam toward an angle that provides maximum reflection from angled discontinuities, (3) avoid specular reflection from the test object's front surface, (4) induce surface waves, and (5) induce lamb waves or diffracted waves.

Snell's Law. Reflection and refraction, both of which involve a direction change of transmitted waves, occur when the sound field encounters a boundary at an angle (θ_1), as shown in Figure 12.20. The angle of reflection is always equal to the angle of incidence, while the angle of refraction varies with the relative acoustic velocities on both sides of the boundary. Faster compression waves refract at a greater angle than slower shear waves. Mode conversion occurs at angled boundaries, which means more than one wave mode may be transmitted. Refraction angles are calculated using a relationship known as Snell's law:

(Eq. 12.4)
$$\frac{\sin\theta_1}{\sin\theta_2} = \frac{V_1}{V_2}$$

Based on the variables shown in Figure 12.20, the calculation determines one unknown based on three known values—for example, acoustic velocities of wave modes of interest in the two media and one incident or refracted angle.

Critical Angles. Inspections generally use a single wave mode, so Snell's law is also useful for determining the minimum and maximum incident angles that produce only shear waves within the test object. Compression and shear waves will both be present at angles less than the first critical angle, making signal interpretation challenging. The first critical angle is the incident angle where the faster compression wave component is no longer present—in other words, $\theta_C \geq 90°$. For example,

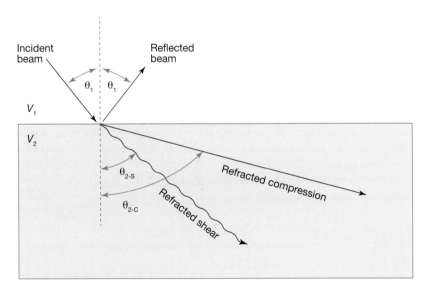

Figure 12.20: Sound field incidence at an angle smaller than the first critical angle; Snell's law is useful for determining one refraction unknown based on three known values (velocities [*V*] and angles [θ]).

the first critical angle at a water-aluminum interface, with 1.48 km/s and 6.3 km/s respective compression wave velocities, occurs when the incident sound field is oriented 13.59° off perpendicular. This is calculated using Snell's law as follows:

$$\frac{\sin\theta_1}{\sin\theta_2} = \frac{V_1}{V_2}$$

$$\sin\theta_1 = \sin\theta_2 \cdot \frac{V_1}{V_2}$$

(Eq. 12.5)
$$\theta_1 = \sin^{-1}\left(\sin\theta_2 \cdot \frac{V_1}{V_2}\right)$$

$$\theta_1 = \sin^{-1}\left(\sin 90° \cdot \frac{1.48 \text{ km/s}}{6.3 \text{ km/s}}\right)$$

$$\theta_1 = 13.59°$$

The second critical angle is the incident angle at which the slower shear wave is refracted at 90°. In our water-aluminum example, a shear wave in gold propagating at 1.2 km/s would be refracted at 90°—this is the second critical angle—with an incident angle of 28.52°.

Use of Wedges. The incident angle of the sound field may be modified electronically and/or mechanically, for example, with water coupling and a variable angle-probe manipulator or with an angled wedge. Wedges are common on conventional single-angle transducers—for example, 45°, 60°, and 70°—and they are also useful in the higher-end phased array (PA) systems, also referred to as *phased array ultrasonic testing* (PAUT) systems. The wedge angle for single-angle probes is fabricated based on Snell's law to produce a shear wave within the test object at a desired angle. Recall that velocity, and consequently the angle, will change with temperature. Wedges for PAUT probes also have a particular angle, but these systems have the capability to alter the direction and shape of the sound field. PAUT systems can electronically sweep the sound field through a range of angles in what is known as a *sectorial scan*, focus the acoustic pressure at desired depths within the near field, and scan an area without moving the probe as in a linear scan.

12.4.2 MATERIALS, EQUIPMENT, AND TECHNIQUES

Ultrasonic testing techniques for nondestructive testing have three general purposes: (1) detection and characterization of discontinuities in materials, (2) evaluation of material properties or thickness, and (3) bond characterization. Techniques have been developed to economically evaluate large or small test objects of nearly every material type and across essentially every industry. Techniques may be divided by application, such as thickness gaging or discontinuity detection; by type of transducer, such as immersion, contact, or noncontact; by how the transducer is manipulated, that is, manual versus automated; and/or by the number and configuration of transducers used.

12.4.2.1 TRANSDUCER CONFIGURATIONS

Examples of transducer configurations are shown in Figure 12.21. The number of individual or paired transducers may be multiplexed for rapid wide-area coverage, and computer-controlled systems can follow complex shapes by automatically changing the insonification angle to maintain a constant angle of incidence. The combination of proper technique and appropriate equipment results in ultrasonic tests that may be highly sensitive, penetrate very thick samples or long sections, provide required information to accurately measure the location and size of discontinuities, and provide rapid evaluation of materials by manual or automated means, including materials that require access from only one side of the test object.

Dead Zone. A wide variety of piezoelectric transducer styles are commercially available. X-cut compression wave and Y-cut shear wave contact transducers have already been discussed, as has the variety of incident angles possible as well as probes designed for air or water coupling. When a piezoelectric crystal is excited, it vibrates and generates an elastic wave. A finite amount of time is required for the crystal to cease vibrating, or ringing, and during this time the crystal cannot act as a receiver. This nonsensitive time results in a layer of the test object being uninspected—a region referred to as the *dead zone*. When water coupling using immersion, bubbler, or squirter systems is not an option, there are two choices for inspecting the near surface of a specimen: a *dual-element probe* or a *delay-line probe*.

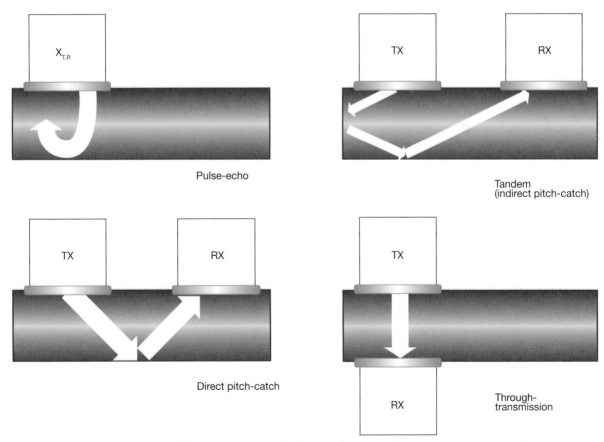

Figure 12.21: Typical transmitting (TX) and receiving (RX) transducer configurations, where coupling may be contact or noncontact but basic orientation of probes remains the same.

Use of Dual-Element Probes. Dual-element transducers were developed to overcome problems encountered by single-crystal transducers, such as the interference between the initial pulse and echo, when measuring very thin materials or when seeking near-surface discontinuities. A dual-element probe contains two crystal elements, a transmitter and a receiver, separated by an acoustic barrier. The crystals are electronically and mechanically separated so that the receiver can start detecting echoes before the transmitter ends transmission, and they are often angled slightly toward each other in what is known as a roof angle so that the sound field has a V-shaped path within the test object.

Delay-Line Probes. Plastic coupling pieces may be used between the face of a contact transducer and the specimen surface to mechanically separate the initial excitation pulse from the material interface. These delay-line pieces, namely, buffer rods or standoffs, are intended to propagate compression waves within the specimen and are therefore different from angle-beam wedges. Although plastic attenuates the signal slightly, the coupling piece removes all of the dead zone, as well as much of the near field, from the inspection of the test object. Delay lines are useful for thin or hot parts and may be incorporated into single-crystal as well as dual-element probes.

12.4.2.2 THICKNESS GAGING AND DISCONTINUITY DETECTION

Thickness gaging, also known as cross-section evaluation, is a common technique for manufacturing environments, as well as inservice verifications. Material thickness is determined by measuring the time interval between signals of interest. For example, the interval, or *time of flight*, between the interface echo and the first back-surface echo (Mode 1) or between two subsequent back-surface echoes (Mode 2 or 3) may be measured. Echoes are not always observed by the inspector on the display screen because many thickness testing instruments offer only a numerical display.

Acoustic velocity in a material is related to its physical and mechanical properties. Thickness gaging, where velocity is already known, is interrelated with velocity measurements, where the speed of sound in a material is determined by using a reference mechanical dimensional measurement, such as with calipers. Thickness testing may be performed on nearly any type of engineering material, including metal, glass, polymer, ceramic, or composite. With some devices, it is possible to simultaneously measure multiple individual layers, such as paint and substrate thickness. Due to the interdependence of material properties, velocity measurement techniques may be applied to estimate microstructure—that is, percent nodularity in ductile cast iron.

Flaw Detectors. Portable ultrasonic probes for detecting discontinuities, commonly referred to as *flaw detectors*, are flexible devices that may perform a variety of functions. These instruments often have user-selectable bandpass filters. Filter selection may be based on the central resonant frequency of the transducer, and transducers must be carefully selected for the application, such as incident angle, damping and bandwidth, test frequency, and diameter. Flaw-detector electronics are divided into six subassemblies: (1) video display, (2) pulse generator, (3) pulse transmitter, (4) time-base sweep generator, (5) receiver amplifier, and (6) signal processor. The name of the subassembly indicates its function. For example, the pulse generator acts as a clock by providing reference pulses to the pulse transmitter and the time-base sweep generator so that their actions are coordinated. The pulse transmitter energizes the piezoelectric element with a carefully controlled high-voltage electrical pulse. Discontinuity detection uses normal incidence for planar discontinuities parallel to the test surface, and an angled beam is used for nonparallel discontinuities. If the discontinuity angle is unknown or expected to vary widely, then multiple angles of inspection may be performed in succession or advanced techniques, such as *phased array* (PA) scanning or *time of flight diffraction* (TOFD), may be employed.

12.4.2.3 PHASED ARRAY

Phased array, also referred to as *phased array ultrasonic testing* (PAUT), can optimize discontinuity detection while minimizing test time. PA has four advantages over conventional single-angle inspections: the beam may be (1) electronically steered, (2) electronically swept, (3) electronically scanned, and/or (4) electronically focused. The piezocomposite configuration and a set of focal laws govern which of these advantages will be employed. Beam steering, for example, 35° to 75°, used in sectorial scanning allows a single PA probe to selectively insonify a specimen volume. This ability replaces a multitude of conventional wedges. Electronic beam focusing improves the signal-to-noise ratio by optimizing beam shape and size at a single depth or varying depth within the near-field zone.

Array Configurations. While conventional probes contain a single piezoelectric element, the term *array* denotes the use of multiple elements, referred to as a *piezocomposite*. Arrays have a variety of flat- and curved-surface configurations, including linear one-dimensional (1D), 1.5D, 2D, annular, and so on. Typical PA probes operate at 2 MHz to 10 MHz and contain 16 to 128 elements. Note that the actual frequency and element count may be outside these common ranges, however. Of the total number of elements available, a sound field is produced by a set of active elements and channels—for example, 16 element groups in a 128-element probe (a 16:128 system) or 32 active channels of 32 total (a 32:32 system).

Focal Law. An individual element must be connected to an active channel in the test equipment for it to be excited; grouping and precise timing of active channel excitation produce a sound field of interest (Figure 12.22). The set of active channel delays for a group is known as a *focal law* and a given 16-element focal law may be repeated, or multiplexed, up to eight times down the length of a 128-element probe by activating subsequent 16-element groups. Elements have a finite width, and there is a finite spacing between the centers of adjacent elements, referred to as *pitch*. The

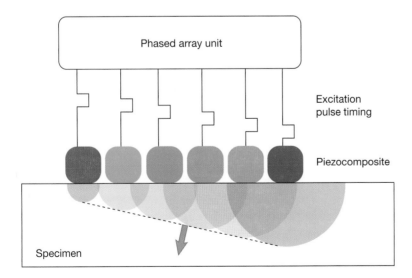

Figure 12.22: Carefully controlled excitation pulse timing of the piezocomposite leads to customizable sound field propagation.

total active area for a given focal law is known as the *aperture*. Many small elements can increase sound field steering; reduce undesirable off-angle sound fields, called *side lobes*; and improve focusing. However, probe and equipment cost is proportional with array complexity and with the number of total elements.

Tandem Probe Arrangement. The time of flight diffraction (TOFD) technique generally employs a tandem probe configuration. TOFD is the most accurate UT discontinuity sizing technique available. Depending on its configuration, the sensitivity of TOFD to small discontinuities may exceed that for radiographic testing. The transmitting TOFD probe emits a wide-angle compression wave, and, unlike echo-based techniques, TOFD primarily relies on the presence of the discontinuity itself to generate a detectable signal. Some of the transmitter's incident wave propagates along the surface as a lateral wave and some rebounds off of the backwall; these two signals offer visual boundaries when TOFD data is later plotted. These two high-amplitude signals do, however, cause near- and far-surface dead zones. Consequently, some codes, such as ASME, mandate that TOFD be supplemented by an additional inspection technique.

Through-Wall Extent. As discussed previously, a sound field striking a discontinuity causes oscillation of the discontinuity tips, and this oscillation produces low-amplitude diffracted signals (Figure 12.23). For discontinuities perpendicular to the surface, the time of flight difference between upper and lower tip-diffracted signals is directly related to the discontinuity's *through-wall extent* (TWE). The signal's depth and TWE will later be plotted with respect to the lateral and backwall echo signal locations. As will be discussed in section 12.4.3, data collected during TOFD scanning include signal response (amplitude versus time) as well as location data acquired by a positional encoder.

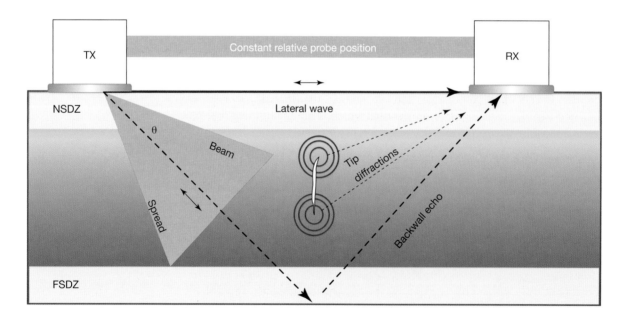

Figure 12.23: General probe configuration and mechanisms involved with TOFD, as well as the positions of the near-surface (NSDZ) and far-surface (FSDZ) dead zones.

12.4.2.5 LONG-RANGE ULTRASONIC TESTING

Long-range ultrasonic testing (LRUT) is finding increased application in some industries, such as petrochemical. The technique uses guided waves that can propagate for long distances and insonify a large volume of a test object from a single position, eliminating the need for scanning. *Guided wave* is a generic term that may refer to rayleigh, lamb, or other wave modes that propagate between two well-defined boundaries, such as inner and outer walls of a pipe or the skin of an aircraft fuselage, that act as a waveguide. Test frequency is as low as 20 kHz to 800 kHz. Considered a test method in its own right in *SNT-TC-1A* (2011), guided wave (GW) is generally applied to seek or monitor discontinuities that encompass 5% or more of the cross-sectional area. (Section 12.5.) Higher test frequencies are sensitive to smaller discontinuities, but this improvement sacrifices propagation distance.

Because guided waves may propagate for long distances, sometimes unaffected by the material or structure outside of the waveguide boundary surface, depending on wave mode, LRUT may be applied to inspect hidden structures, such as those that are insulated, under water, or obscured by support structures. Coatings and sharp changes in the form of 45° or 90° bends can be significant challenges to LRUT. Wavelength dispersion—that is, a change in pulse duration versus position and/or test frequency—is key because of the wave modes used, and development of experimental frequency-dependent dispersion curves leads to selection of the optimal test frequency for successful inspections.

12.4.2.6 ELECTROMAGNETIC ACOUSTIC TRANSDUCERS

The *electromagnetic acoustic transducer* (EMAT) is a noncontact, couplant-free method for exciting and detecting ultrasonic waves in conductive or magnetic materials. EMATs differ from piezoelectric transducers in that sound is generated within the sample itself, as opposed to within the probe. An EMAT probe holds an electrical winding, as well as a mechanism such as a single magnet, array of magnets, or an electromagnet for forming a bias magnetic field. Alternating current pulsing through the winding generates electrical fields, commonly referred to as *eddy currents*, in the outermost layer of the test object. Alternating current frequency is the UT test frequency (up to 5 MHz – 7.5 MHz). Particles of charge moving within the eddy currents experience a force due to the bias magnetic field, and this force is propagated through the specimen as an advancing sound field. EMAT probes may be designed to produce a variety of incident angles and wave modes (compression, shear, rayleigh, and lamb), including shear horizontal, which is unique to this probe type.

12.4.2.7 LASER ULTRASOUND

Laser Ultrasound Is Another Noncontact Technique. Laser UT offers the potential for even more standoff distance than EMAT probes, but high relative cost and low signal amplitude have historically limited its application to specialized cases. Optical generation and detection of sound within a test object are accomplished by two different lasers. Transduction of light into acoustic energy is performed by the sample during rapid heating of the surface caused by radiation absorption. In other words, rapid thermal expansion with low-intensity lasers or ablation with high-intensity lasers leads to the formation of mechanical waves. *Ablation*, the melting and vaporization of surface material, while useful, would not be classified as nondestructive. Surface vibrations and echoes are encoded into the detection light beam to provide echo signal detection. Advantages of laser UT include its wide range of possible test frequencies (kHz through GHz) and its ability to operate effectively in spite of curved surfaces. All four common wave modes may be generated using lasers, and phased laser arrays have been experimentally developed.

12.4.3 DATA PRESENTATIONS

Data gathered in ultrasonic testing may be presented in a variety of ways. All presentations are based on signal amplitude—that is, transduced voltage—versus time of flight for a given test position on the sample. One-dimensional amplitude-versus-time data plots are called A-scans (previously shown in Figure 12.19a) that provide information on the distance between reflector and probe, indicate whether the signal changes phase from positive to negative polarity, and may offer clues about reflector area. One or more data collection gates may be configured on an A-scan display, and a flaw detector's electronic logic will then monitor the gate for signals that exceed its threshold.

A- and B-Scans. If a set of one-dimensional A-scans was collected as the transducer was linearly traversed, then a two-dimensional B-scan data representation may be compiled. Probe position is represented along the B-scan's X axis and travel time of the ultrasonic pulse—that is, depth or time of flight—is represented on the Y axis. X-axis positional data may be gathered with an encoder or similar device. Events plotted in the B-scan may indicate when echo amplitude exceeds the gate's threshold in black and white or may denote gate-triggering echo amplitude with varying shades of grayscale or color. A B-scan offers a cross-sectional view of the sample, where the cutting line is along the linear transducer path.

Simple straight-beam B-scan data representation is useful for thickness gaging, positioning, and sizing. The same data format is also useful for linear phased array scanning. Figure 12.24 illustrates the linear transducer manipulation that leads to

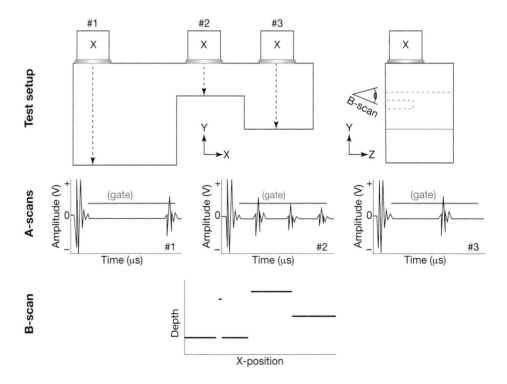

Figure 12.24: A cross-sectional B-scan is compiled by plotting the time interval noted for an A-scan data gate to be triggered with respect to transducer position along a single linear manipulation path (note that the front surface echo was outside of the gate in this illustration). (V=voltage.)

collection of A-scans, as well as compilation of a straight-beam B-scan. Angle-beam B-scan representation is useful for angled linear phased array scans with a fixed incident angle while sequencing apertures along the array and is widely used for TOFD data. For TOFD, the two angle-beam probes generally straddle a weld, and data is collected as the pair traverses the length of a welded joint. Shape is at least as important as amplitude when identifying TOFD test indications of interest.

C- and D-Scan Presentations. If the same sample used in Figure 12.24 were scanned in a *raster pattern* (an efficient means of covering an area by traversing in parallel straight lines) while collecting A-scan data, then a *top-* or *plan-view C-scan* data representation can be compiled (Figure 12.25). Time of flight, or echo amplitude, for signals exceeding the A-scan data gate may selectively be displayed with respect to a position. C-scans allow for top-view reflector area and depth estimation using the time of flight information. C-scan data may be obtained manually with the aid of an X-Y probe position encoder, but automated scanning is generally a faster and more robust approach. A *D-scan* data representation is produced when the area scan data is plotted as an end view of the component, incorporating all data, as opposed to a slice. The D-scan is perpendicular to B- and C-scan views and is three-dimensional unlike the B-scan, which is a 2D linear slice representation.

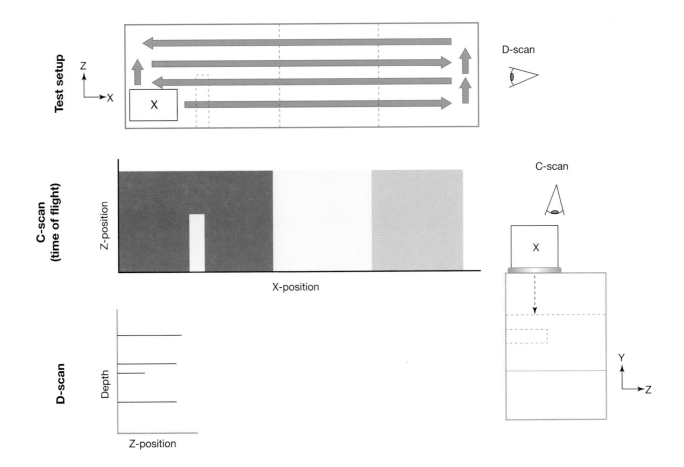

Figure 12.25: C- and D-scan representations based on a raster scan of the sample in Figure 12.24. *Note*: **This particular C-scan would represent the time of flight interval of signals triggering the A-scan data gate.**

S-Scans Used with Phased Array. The *sectorial* or *S-scan*, is unique to phased array ultrasonic testing. Familiar to many from medical prenatal imaging, the S-scan is a pie-shaped representation of each A-scan acquired as the sound field is steered through a range of angles. The PAUT inspector defines the start and end angle, as well as the angle-stepping resolution (for example, 0.5° or 1° steps), while the aperture remains constant. A-scan echo amplitude is mapped to a false-color scale. For example, low amplitude may be blue, while high amplitude is red. This allows the intensity and location of test indications to quickly be judged by the inspector. One may selectively view each A-scan on PAUT units. For visual convenience, the depth axis of A-scans is compressed to varying amounts so that echo locations directly correlate to their S-scan locations (Figure 12.26).

12.4.4 ADVANTAGES AND LIMITATIONS

The volumetric interrogation abilities of ultrasonic testing have led to the method's widespread adoption and many industries' reliance on its techniques. Acoustic energy may be imparted into a test object of essentially any material type with a variety of propagation angles and vibration modes. These waves can quickly and accurately detect and locate discontinuities, measure thickness, estimate mechanical properties or microstructure, and monitor processes. Penetrating power, with some wave modes and when the sample material is conducive, far exceeds that of any other test method.

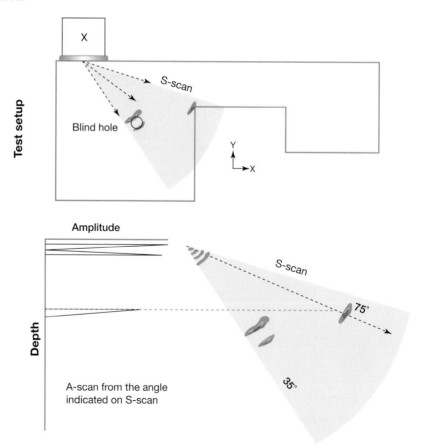

Figure 12.26: The same sample shown in Figures 12.24 and 12.25 scanned with a beam-steering (sweeping through a 35° – 75° range) phased array probe from a single position. A collection of A-scans is then compiled into a sectorial S-scan display.

However, most UT techniques require couplant between the transducer and specimen, and coupling can be a challenge when geometry is unfavorable or the surface is rough. The underlying physics of UT operation can be fairly complex. Properly deciphering test results, therefore, requires significant inspector training and experience. Computer simulation modeling may be called on for interpretation of results or the development of techniques or procedures. Echo amplitude is based on reflector size, shape, orientation, and acoustic impedance mismatch at the reflector boundary, so estimating discontinuity sizes can be challenging, especially with discontinuities that are smaller than the diameter of the sound field or beam diameter.

12.5 GUIDED WAVE TESTING

Guided wave (GW) testing is an NDT method that uses a type of ultrasonic wave mode that propagates under the guidance of one or more boundaries. For the situations where reflection and refraction are neither sufficient nor convenient to describe the wave interaction with the boundary, guided wave interpretation can be used to significantly simplify the description of the wave-propagation phenomenon.

As shown in Figure 12.27, if a wave propagates from position A to position B in a plate, describing it with bulk-wave reflection and mode conversion becomes almost impossible since hundreds of reflections must be considered. As an alternative method, wave mechanics may be used to analyze the boundary constraints and then describe the rule of wave propagation as possible wave modes in the plate. In this way, it is considered a guided wave, which may be as simple to analyze as a single mode of propagation.

Propagation in Waveguide. By definition, *guided wave* is a general term used to describe the wave propagation phenomenon where the guidance of a boundary plays a very important role. The structure in which a guided wave may propagate is called a *waveguide*. Many everyday structures are natural waveguides, for example:

- Surface of a billet, casting, or forged structure.
- Plate or thin sheet.
- Bar or rod.
- Tube or pipe.

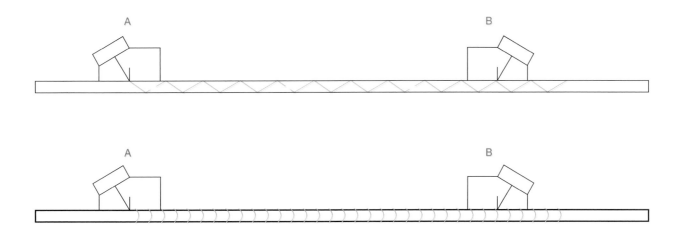

Figure 12.27: Comparison of wave propagation: (a) bulk waves; (b) guided waves.

Therefore, several types of guided waves are used in nondestructive testing, namely:

- Lamb waves in plates, classified as either symmetric or asymmetric based on their displacement fields.
- Shear horizontal (SH) guided waves having particle motion only in the direction that is perpendicular to the wave propagation direction and parallel to the surface in a plate.
- Wave modes in tubular structures in either the axial (longitudinal, torsional, or flexural mode) or circumferential (lamb-type and SH-type) directions.

Dispersion as Main Principle. The key to guided wave analysis is to understand dispersion. *Dispersion* means the wave velocity is a function of frequency. Although this appears to be in conflict with the understanding of the constant velocities of bulk waves, it is a very important feature of guided wave analysis.

Because of boundary constraints, many guided wave modes may exist in a plate. Each mode is represented with a curve showing the relationship between wave velocity and frequency. The set of curves of possible guided wave modes plotted together is called a dispersion curve plot. Dispersion curves for a given material can be plotted to show the relationship of velocity to frequency and test-object thickness. Here, velocity can be either phase velocity or group velocity:

- **Phase velocity:** the speed at which a specific point or phase on the wave propagates through a test object.
- **Group velocity:** the velocity measured from the propagation of the entire wave package.

Advantages of Guided Wave. The main advantages of GW as an NDT method include the capability to propagate sound waves over a comparably long range with no need for scanning, as all data are acquired from a single probe position. In addition, GW may be used to inspect areas not easily accessible with other methods as well as thin structures with improved sensitivity over conventional UT.

12.6 RADIOGRAPHIC TESTING

12.6.1 INTRODUCTION AND PRINCIPLES

Radiographic testing (RT) is a powerful volumetric inspection method, which employs ionizing radiation as its probing medium. Although there are many safety considerations for the use of ionizing radiation, an advantage of RT over other methods is that many RT techniques provide a permanent record of test results. Specimens may be individual components or assemblies, virtually any material type may be tested, and the range of sample size is considerable. Most RT techniques have the radiation source and radiation detector on opposite sides of the test object. The localized attenuation of penetrating radiation indicates changes in cross-sectional thickness and/or density. A few techniques allow single-sided access, with source and detector on the same side, and such techniques generally provide information about the test object's material composition.

12.6.1.1 ATOMIC STRUCTURE

Components of the Atom. The underlying principles of RT are based primarily on the structure of the atom. An *atom* is the basic building block of all substances. The conventional representation of the atom is that its core comprises protons, with a positive electrical charge, and neutrons, with no charge, within the nucleus, where essentially all of the atom's mass is concentrated. Electrons, with a negative charge and negligible mass, orbit the nucleus in specific paths. A substance made up of only one type of atom is called an element. The periodic table (refer to Figure 2.14) provides a list of all known elements ordered by their atomic number.

Atomic Number and Mass. The atomic or *Z* number refers to the number of protons. The atomic mass number is the total number of protons and neutrons, such that mass varies between isotopes of a given element. Isotopes of an element all have the same number of protons but different numbers of neutrons. Isotope identification provides its unique atomic mass as a superscript preceding the element's symbol or separated by a hyphen after the element's name, for example, cobalt-60 versus ^{60}Co or iridium-192 versus [192]Ir. Some isotopes are stable and thus not useful for NDT, whereas others are unstable and consequently radioactive. These isotopes are called *radioisotopes*.

12.6.1.2 IONIZING RADIATION

Ionizing radiation commonly used in RT includes X-rays, gamma rays, and neutrons. (Neutron radiography is discussed in Section 12.7.) X-rays and gamma rays are part of the electromagnetic spectrum and have wavelengths shorter, meaning with a higher frequency, than ultraviolet light. Wavelength is the reciprocal of frequency. The wavelength of an electromagnetic photon is directly related to its energy; a photon's energy is the product of its frequency (ν) and Planck's constant (*h*). The high energy of X-ray and gamma photons can excite electrons surrounding an atom such that they are removed from their orbits, leaving that atom with a positive net charge. In this case, the atom is ionized. An atom has a net neutral charge if the numbers of protons and electrons are equal, but positive and negative net charges are possible. Atoms or molecules with a net charge are called *ions*, for example, Cl^-, Al^{3+}, and O^{2-}.

Electron Shells. Electrons exhibit characteristics of both waves and particles. It is not possible to know the exact position of an electron at a given time. Statistical probability does, however, limit the possible location to particular regions, or shells, around the nucleus of an atom. Electron energy increases with distance from the nucleus, and the difference between quantum energy levels of two shells is useful for analytic NDT purposes. Inner K-shell electrons have less energy than L- or M-shell electrons and those in the outermost shell are called *valence electrons*. These electrons are important for the electrical conductivity of a material. When a K-shell electron is ejected from its location by an incident (primary) X-ray or gamma photon, then that space will be backfilled by a higher-energy L- or M-shell electron (Figure 12.28).

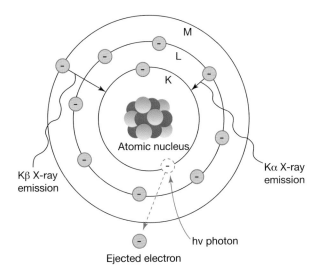

Figure 12.28: An incident photon may dislodge an electron from the atom, leaving a vacancy to be filled by an outer shell electron; characteristic X-ray photons are emitted as the higher-energy electron drops into the lower energy position.

Excess energy of the outer-shell electron is discarded as a secondary—that is, fluoresced—X-ray photon with a characteristic wavelength, for example, Kα for an L-to-K transition or Kβ for an M-to-K transition. Characteristic X-ray wavelengths are unique, although transitions between two elements may directly overlap.

Radiation Sources. Common sources of radiation for industrial radiographic testing include X-ray tubes, radioisotopes, and nuclear reactors. An X-ray tube holds a cathode (source of electrons) and anode (target for the electrons) under high vacuum. Electrons are accelerated toward the positively charged anode, and those electrons that are deflected and slowed as they interact with nuclei of a high-density metallic target material emit X-ray photons in the form of *bremsstrahlung*, or *braking, radiation*. Bremsstrahlung radiation is a continuous spectrum of X-rays with sharp peaks corresponding to secondary X-ray wavelengths of the tube's target material. Very few photons have energies equal to that of the incident electron, and most have much lower energy.

The shortest wavelength X-ray emitted by the X-ray tube is governed by the maximum kinetic energy imparted to the electron. Kinetic energy is controlled by the electron-accelerating voltage potential, often measured in thousands of electronvolts (keV), between the cathode and anode (Figure 12.29). Radiation flux emitted by an X-ray tube varies with current, measured in milliamps, while voltage controls the penetrating power—which is to say, the quality—and flux of the beam. As the voltage is increased, X-rays of shorter wavelength with more penetrating power are produced, as well as more X-rays of the same wavelength as at lower voltages. Increasing the Z number of the X-ray tube target also increases the quantity of photons and the quality of the beam. On the other hand, filtering the beam decreases flux while increasing quality. X-ray tubes are available in a huge variety of sizes and power levels; they may be small enough to incorporate into handheld devices or large enough that they are held stationary within specially designed rooms or cabinets.

12.6.1.3 RADIOISOTOPES

Radioisotopes that are practical for NDT have a combination of useful emitted energy and long useful lifetime. Unstable isotopes tend to become stable elements with less energy, and this transformation occurs through spontaneous decay processes, which emit gamma-ray energy, as well as other less energetic radiation types, such as alpha and beta particles. Many radioactive decay processes lead to the formation of

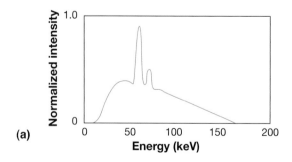
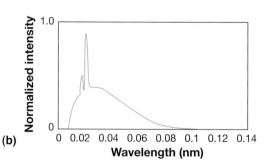

Figure 12.29: Bremsstrahlung emission with characteristic X-ray peaks from a tungsten-target 160 kilovolt X-ray tube fitted with a 1 mm aluminum filter when spectra are viewed as energy versus intensity (a) or wavelength versus intensity (b); low-energy photons are filtered out, and the highest energy emitted is governed by voltage potential (keV).

daughter elements that are different elements from the parent radioisotope. Gamma-ray photons originate in the nucleus of a radioisotope, and each radioisotope emits photons of one or more specific energy levels. Although a single radioactive decay event is random, when a large number of a given radioisotope's atoms are present, statistical probability may be applied to establish its unique decay rate.

Half-Life of Radioisotopes. The speed of an RT examination can vary with the number of photons or neutrons emitted by the source. For radioisotopes, the number of photons produced is controlled by the number of unstable atoms present (activity) and their *half-life*, which is the time required for half of the radioactive material to decay or transmute into daughter elements. For example, the half-lives for two common radioisotopes used in industrial radiographic testing are 5.27 years for cobalt-60 (emits photons with energies of 1.33 MeV and 1.17 MeV) and 73.8 days for iridium-192 (emits photons with energies of 0.6 MeV, 0.47 MeV, and 0.31 MeV). Source activity is measured in becquerels (1 Bq = 1 decay event per second). Unlike X-ray sources, gamma-ray sources cannot be turned off. They can only be safely contained within specialized storage "cameras" until needed.

Inverse Square Law. When the radiation source is small, and minimal scattering and absorption occur along the path, then the *inverse square law* (Equation 12.6) applies. This law states that the radiation intensity (*I*), or dose rate, is inversely proportional to the square of the distance (*D*) from the source—for example, one-fourth as intense when distance is doubled.

(Eq. 12.6)

$$\frac{I_1}{I_2} = \frac{D_2^{\,2}}{D_1^{\,2}}$$

When X-rays and gamma rays encounter a material, they can have significant penetrating ability. Like light, X-ray and gamma-ray photons can be refracted, focused (though not easily), scattered, and absorbed.

Linear and Mass Attenuation. Each propagation medium or material has a characteristic exponential absorption of these rays that is based on attenuation and scattering. The linear attenuation coefficient has units of cm^{-1}, and mass attenuation coefficients have units of $cm^2 \cdot g^{-1}$. Reference tables provide typical attenuation coefficient values for engineering materials. Two values are useful, especially when considering health and safety aspects of the usage and storage of radiation sources: the *half-value layer* (HVL), and the *tenth-value layer* (TVL). An HVL is the thickness of a particular material required to reduce the intensity of radiation of a particular energy to half of its original level. Likewise, the TVL is the thickness required for a tenfold decrease. For example, the HVL for a cobalt-60 source is 12.5 mm of lead, while the less intense gamma rays from an iridium-192 source require only 4.8 mm of lead, roughly equivalent to a 660 keV X-ray source, to decrease the dose rate by half. The TVL for a cobalt-60 source is approximately 41 mm of lead.

12.6.2 MATERIALS, EQUIPMENT, AND TECHNIQUES

A radiograph is a static image record produced by the passage of penetrating radiation in straight lines through an object and onto a detection medium. Some of the radiation photons pass through, while other photons are attenuated or scattered. The amount of radiation transmitted depends on the test object's material and thickness. For example, an internal void would reduce the apparent material thickness, and more photons would pass through the section containing the void than through the surrounding material. After interacting with the sample, the radiation must be detected and analyzed. Radiation detectors may sense the beam's spatial distribution, or spectrum (wavelength or energy), or flux (photons per second).

Types of Detectors. Most radiographic applications are shadow images produced by the localized attenuation of penetrating radiation. Different portions of the specimen may have unique levels of radiation absorption. Such applications monitor the unattenuated radiation that passes through the specimen. Detectors include flexible radiation-sensitive film, photostimulable phosphors, digital detectors, fluorescent screens, X-ray sensitive cameras, and other imagers. Some detectors offer static images, while others provide the ability for rapidly refreshing real-time digital radioscopic data capture. Most detectors convert photon flux into variations in grayscale on an image—for example, high flux shown as dark spots projected onto a film or light spots projected onto an image intensifier.

When ionizing radiation strikes the sensitive silver-based grains of film, a physical change occurs in the grain that makes it reactive with an alkaline chemical developer. This chemical reduction reaction converts the grain to black metallic silver. Unexposed grains are not reduced to opaque black, and when viewed with backlighting, the film produces an image of the test object. Although film has been popular for decades, alternatives to film have quickly been gaining acceptance.

Photostimulable *phosphor imaging plates* are somewhat flexible, reusable, and store the radiation-induced charge within the crystal structure of the material as metastable discontinuity color centers—that is, electrons and holes. As the term *photostimulable* suggests, the latent image held by the plate is recovered later by raster scanning with a laser, which stimulates a spontaneous emission of light. Localized color center phosphorescence, the intensity of which is proportional to the number of radiation photons absorbed, is recorded to produce a digital radiographic image.

Viewing in Real Time. Real-time radiographic viewing may use fluorescent screens, which are viewed directly through a radiation-blocking port as they emit light caused by radiation excitation. However, such detectors offer no ability to retain data for later analysis. *Radioscopy* is an inspection technique that also allows for real-time, or live, viewing of objects and structures, and for the imaging of dynamic events, during irradiation. Radioscopic techniques use an image intensifier or a flat panel detector. Data from several different perspectives often allow determination of the relative position or depth of discontinuities. Image intensifiers also fluoresce, but such devices use video cameras to remotely view, and sometimes capture, the radioscopic image produced. Solid-state flat panel detectors—for example, amorphous silicon or amorphous selenium—act as large-area integrated transistor circuits. Ionizing radiation photons are indirectly detected by the amorphous semiconductor material as follows:

1. The photon encounters a scintillation layer, for example, gadolinium oxysulfide or cesium iodide, which converts ionizing radiation into visible light.
2. The visible light photon is detected by an array of photodiodes (pixels).
3. The photodiode converts the visible light photon into an accumulated electrical charge in the amorphous semiconductor layer.
4. Finally, a computer reads the electrical charge pattern to produce a radiographic image.

High flat panel *detective quantum efficiency* (DQE) leads to rapid image acquisition and higher frame rates (images per second). *Binning,* which is the electronic grouping of adjacent pixels, can increase the frame rate by sacrificing image resolution. *Note*: Such digital techniques are referred to as digital radiography (DR) and computed radiography (CR) in *SNT-TC-1A* (2011).

Image Definition and Resolution. Images produced by radiographic testing may be larger than the physical size of the test object by altering the distance between the test object and detector. The source of radiation has a finite size based on such factors as the radioisotope pellet dimension, collimator port diameter, or X-ray tube focal spot size. Increased specimen-to-detector distance with larger spot sizes will lead to poor edge definition, as in Figure 12.30. Low detector resolution—for example, a low number of pixels per inch or faster large-grained film—can also lead to poor radiographic image sharpness. Several *image quality indicator* (IQI) styles are available, and these are used to demonstrate that the radiographic testing procedure has met a required quality level. IQIs, including hole-in-plaque, wire-diameter, step-wedge with holes, and duplex wire pair types, help to assess three factors: image sharpness, image contrast, and image noise.

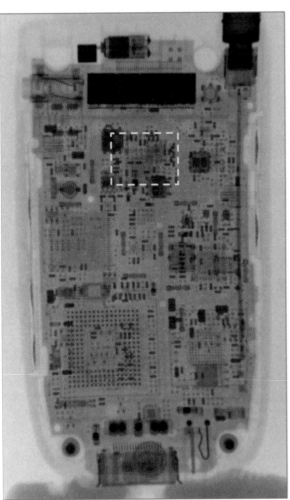

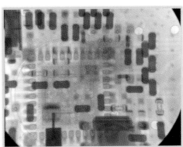

12 micron focal spot size

200 micron focal spot size

3000 micron focal spot size

Figure 12.30: Radioscopic images of a cellular telephone's circuitry demonstrating the relative magnification abilities of three different X-ray tube focal spot sizes, as captured with an image intensifier.

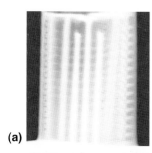

(a)

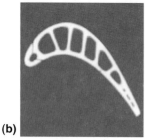

(b)

**Figure 12.31:
Evaluation of casting
turbine blade with
400 kV computed
tomographic system
showing internal
feature condition and
wall thickness
measurement:
(a) digital radiograph;
(b) computed
tomographic slice.**

Computed Tomography. Tomography is the most powerful RT technique for obtaining three-dimensional radiographic data. Digital data is collected at a multitude of projection angles, often by rotating the sample, and at a multitude of levels along the height of the sample. This digital data is compiled by computer into virtual cross-section slices, called *tomograms*, or three-dimensional representations of the sample's interior and exterior. Acquiring data from multiple angles facilitates calculation of the relative linear attenuation coefficient for each volume pixel element (voxel). Computed tomography can provide quantitative information about the density, composition, and dimensions of the features imaged. A comparison between a digital radiograph and computed tomograph is shown in Figure 12.31.

12.6.3 BACKSCATTER IMAGING

Unlike transmission techniques, backscattered X-rays allow for single-sided evaluation techniques. There are three common X-ray *backscatter techniques*: (1) elastic scattering for low-energy diffraction; (2) compton scattering for detecting dense materials, such as opiate drugs or high explosives; and (3) X-ray fluorescence used to analyze surface chemistry. X-ray fluorescence is quite common in industry and is often referred to as *positive material identification* (PMI). PMI directs X-rays or gamma rays toward the specimen, and this radiation induces characteristic X-rays to be produced within the sample's material. Incident photons interact with electrons orbiting atoms of the sample material, and when electrons are ejected from their orbits, the sample material emits radiation energy. The emitted energy has characteristic wavelengths that vary with the element(s) being interrogated. This energy is detected by the test unit. The spontaneous production of fluoresced characteristic X-rays is therefore called *X-ray fluorescence* (XRF). After mathematically processing the detected energy, the unit provides its interpretation of the chemistry of the sample.

12.6.4 ADVANTAGES AND LIMITATIONS

Radiographic testing is a powerful volumetric examination method that provides image results that are easily archived. Images may be static shadow images, or results may be viewed in real time. RT can inspect parts of essentially any shape, size, and material type for internal or external discontinuities. Specimens may be individual parts or full assemblies—for example, a full suitcase at an airport. Results may be obtained at a variety of angles, and this flexibility provides the ability to accurately size and locate discontinuities.

However, radiographic testing presents significant health and safety concerns because of the potential exposure to significant levels of ionizing radiation. In addition, the initial capital investment is significant. Most RT techniques require access to at least two sides of the specimen because transmitted radiation must be detected. RT is sensitive to changes in density or thickness; therefore, cracks and delamination-type discontinuities are only detectable when imaged nearly parallel. Furthermore, many RT techniques have delayed results as images are chemically or electronically processed.

12.7 NEUTRON RADIOGRAPHY

Sources of Neutrons. Neutron sources for industrial radiographic testing include nuclear reactor research facilities; particle accelerators, or cyclotrons; tubes projecting a deuteron beam onto a tritiated target (D-T tube); and radioisotopes—the least powerful and popular option. Neutrons useful to NDT are called *thermal neutrons*, which have collided enough times with a moderator material—for example, graphite or water—until their kinetic energy, or velocity, is equal to the thermal energy of the moderator nuclei. Similar to X-ray and gamma-ray sources, neutron sources may employ a collimator, which decreases the apparent size of the radiation source and increases the image sharpness as well as acquisition time. Neutrons may be scattered or absorbed—that is, captured—as they propagate, but materials do not attenuate thermal neutrons at the same rate as they do X-ray and gamma-ray photons. Therefore, neutrons have their own attenuation coefficients. Because neutrons, unlike X-rays, may quickly be attenuated by water and carbon, and can penetrate very thick sections of high-*Z* elements such as lead, a high degree of contrast between the elements in an object is possible. Neutron radiographic testing is sometimes the only radiographic option for an application, such as inspecting radioactive materials. Note that neutron radiographic testing is considered an NDT method in its own right apart from radiographic testing per *SNT-TC-1A* (2011).

Direct Transfer Technique. Although the use of neutrons for radiographic testing is less common than use of gamma rays and X-rays, there are two general techniques for static neutron radiographic imaging: direct and transfer. The *direct technique*, often called the direct method, is useful only for nonradioactive samples, as radioactive samples would spontaneously expose, or fog, the film. Direct neutron radiographic testing exposes the sample and film to the neutron radiation beam, although the film is exposed by radiation emitted by a conversion screen, for example, made of gadolinium. The conversion screen, which is held in intimate contact with the film, absorbs neutrons and then decays by emission of beta particles and gamma rays, which ionize the radiation-sensitive grains of the film. The exposed film is then processed in the typical manner. Other detector options are also possible, including neutron-sensitive photostimulable phosphor plates, track-etch imaging using a boron converter and cellulose nitrate film, and neutron-sensitive image intensifiers. An example of a neutron radiograph compared with an X-ray of the same object is shown in Figure 12.32.

Indirect Technique Uses Conversion Foil Screens. *Indirect neutron radiographic testing*, useful for radioactive samples, does not present the film to the radiation beam. Instead, a conversion foil screen—for example, dysprosium or indium—is irradiated by the neutron beam and thus activated. No other type of radiation will activate the screen; therefore, it is sensitive only to the neutrons passing through the sample. Later, the film and screen are introduced, and the film is exposed as the screen radioisotope decays. The latent image is thus transferred from the screen to the film. Because indirect imaging relies on radioactive decay events rather than beam transmission, it is much slower than direct imaging, for instance, eight hours versus five minutes.

Figure 12.32: Radiographs of full- size motorcycle: (a) neutron radiograph; (b) x-radiograph.

12.8 ELECTROMAGNETIC TESTING

12.8.1 INTRODUCTION AND PRINCIPLES

Electromagnetic testing (ET) techniques offer several advantages over competing inspection methods, including freedom from chemicals or liquids as well as rapid inspection rates. ET techniques can also offer low-cost, noncontact evaluation of samples of widely varying temperature. ET is used to evaluate the quality of conductive and nonconductive samples. Conductive samples may be ferrous or nonferrous. Electromagnetic testing is a catchall method, comprising several diverse techniques. The ET method most often refers to magnetic flux leakage (MFL) testing, eddy current testing, and microwave testing (MW), although magnetic barkhausen noise, ground penetrating radar (GPR), and others may fall within this category. *Note:* MFL, GPR, and MW are considered separate methods.

Vectors. All ET techniques, as well as the variety of electromagnetic waves and fields that are encountered daily, are described by the set of partial differential equations known as Maxwell's equations. These equations integrate electric, magnetic, and electromagnetic induction theories, which, before being advanced by James Clerk Maxwell, had been considered as separate disciplines with independent constants. Vector calculus is needed to fully grasp the underlying mathematics of Maxwell's equations, but at their core they simply describe the interdependence of time-varying electric and magnetic fields.

An electromagnetic field is a vector quantity, which means that it has both magnitude and three-dimensional direction. Fields may be described by their rotation, or curl, and the nature of their source—that is, divergence. For example, the mathematics behind the magnetic flux leakage and DC potential drop techniques is based on elliptic partial differential equations with zero curl and zero divergence, meaning static magnetic fields, where the magnetic and electric fields are coupled. Quasi-static, time-varying conditions of eddy current, such as remote field testing (RFT) or multifrequency eddy current testing, are described by parabolic equations. When an electric field changes with very high frequency, there is another current within the specimen, which is known as a *displacement current*. This displacement current is proportional to the frequency and the dielectric permittivity of the material.

Test Frequencies. Each technique varies in its test frequencies, transducer type, and signal analysis methods employed. For example, magnetic flux leakage often uses test frequencies between 0 Hz and 60 Hz, eddy current testing uses frequencies between 100 Hz and 10 MHz, and microwave testing employs test frequencies as high as 300 MHz. As described by Maxwell's equations, the underlying physical process changes with test frequency. Electromagnetic fields with a frequency below 10 MHz are said to be *quasi-static*, which means that displacement current is negligible. At higher frequencies, the probing energy propagates as waves. Sensor technologies used in ET vary; for example, MFL uses hall effect sensors, eddy current testing uses one or more coiled wire sensors, and microwave testing and ground penetrating radar use antennae.

ET variables generally vary nonlinearly with frequency; at times, the rate of change can vary from a positive slope to a negative slope. Because of this complicated relationship between test variables, most ET applications, such as alloy sorting, heat-treatment verification, hardness determination, or thickness measurement, require reference standards that properly match all changes that may exist in the test objects. Equipment standardization, with the proper reference standards, is important to discontinuity detection.

Electrical Conductivity. Most metals are good conductors of electricity, and electrical conductivity of the test object is an important factor in many ET techniques. For simplicity, a change in conductivity is generally associated with a change in the ability of electrons to flow. Conductivity can be anisotropic and it varies with several factors, including temperature, alloying elements and their concentrations, lattice structure or strain, and the number and concentration of dislocations within the atomic lattice structure. While conductivity—the inverse of resistivity—may be described in absolute terms, in siemens per meter, the relative International Annealed Copper Standard (% IACS) scale is often used. This relative scale uses annealed, or soft, copper with a sample temperature of 20 °C as the basis of comparison, identifying this material as 100% IACS. Other conductors are then attributed a value relative to annealed copper.

Lattice strain and dislocation density may be modified by the thermal and mechanical history of the test object. An example of a thermal process is annealing, which reduces dislocation density and consequently the number of obstacles to the flow of conduction-band electrons. A mechanical modification may be room-temperature plastic deformation, such as cold rolling, which increases atomic lattice strain and dislocation density and changes the material's electrical resistivity. The conductivity of aluminum alloys is of particular interest in some industries. Aluminum alloys may be thermally and/or mechanically processed using special recipes to induce a desired strength, corrosion resistance, or other property. Each alloy and recipe combination (temper) produces a somewhat unique electrical conductivity; therefore, ET is useful for rapid estimations of material properties in aluminum and other nonferromagnetic materials.

12.8.2 EQUIPMENT AND TECHNIQUES

To obtain information about a sample, an inspection might include different test frequencies, a variety of types or configurations of probes, multiple probe orientations, or different procedures. Many electromagnetic test techniques may be applied at all stages of forming, shaping, and heat treating of metals and alloys, where the effectiveness of processing steps can be quickly evaluated. Materials damaged during processing or improperly treated can be detected and removed from production without incurring further processing costs. There are several electromagnetic testing methods and techniques, and we will briefly touch on some of the most common ones.

12.8.2.1 EDDY CURRENT TESTING

The eddy current technique uses inductive test coils to observe an induced alternating magnetic field, as modified by the test object and its discontinuities. Time-varying current applied across the test coil produces a magnetic field, and this changing magnetic field induces a time-varying alternating current—that is, an *electromotive force* (EMF)—in the near surface of the test object. EMF amplitude varies with the applied voltage and with the driving frequency. Electrical impedance may be described as how much an electrical circuit opposes the passage of current when voltage is applied. *Impedance* of a test coil varies with the conductivity of a nearby material. Impedance is the complex sum—referring to vector addition rather than simple algebraic addition—of electrical resistance, inductive reactance, and capacitive reactance. Similar to the concept of inertia, *inductance* is an electrical circuit's opposition to a changing current flow.

Impedance. Electrical impedance has both magnitude, or amplitude, and phase. The phase relationship within an inductor coil stems from the current due to electrical resistance and the current due to inductive reactance occurring at different times. In fact, these two contributors are 90° out of phase, with voltage leading current. Vector addition allows the signal from the test coil to be represented as a phasor on the complex impedance plane with an associated amplitude and phase angle. The impedance plane display is called "complex" because real resistance values are plotted against an imaginary inductive reactance part. In some electromagnetic tests, such as sorting based on conductivity, the response of the test coil is balanced (nulled) in air (point Z_1 in Figure 12.33); then the coil is placed near the sample (point Z_2). Electrical balancing is accomplished with bridge circuits, such as a wheatstone bridge.

Eddy Currents and Skin Depth. When the test coil, which is carrying alternating current, is placed near a conductive test object, an alternating electromagnetic field is induced. This electromagnetic field comprises electrical current flowing in closed loops, referred to as *eddy currents*, within the test object and a resultant magnetic field that opposes the primary field of the test coil. (This opposition is described by Lenz's law.) Eddy currents only flow in the near surface of the test object—a phenomenon referred to as the *skin effect*—and their depth of penetration into the thickness is known as the *skin depth*. Therefore, eddy current testing is limited to surface and near-surface evaluation of materials and products. Skin depth varies inversely with test object conductivity, magnetic permeability, and test frequency. Terminal impedance of the test coil is modified by the test object.

Self-Inductance. Eddy current test equipment excites the test coil with alternating current and also allows the technician to analyze the observed change in terminal impedance. Due to the opposing direction of primary (test coil) and secondary (test object) magnetic fields for nonferromagnetic samples, a decrease in overall magnetic flux density occurs. Self-inductance of a coil is measured by the flux lines per ampere of electrical current. When the test coil is near a nonferromagnetic specimen, the self-inductance of the coil decreases. A change in coil inductance is accompanied by a change in its resistance. Both variables are monitored by the eddy current test equipment. Variations in the test coil's electrical impedance may indicate changes in structure, mass, chemistry, and mechanical properties, as compared to some reference value. For example, it may be possible to distinguish two samples made from the exact same material when the hardness and, consequently, electrical conductivity vary (points Z_{5a} and Z_{5b} in Figure 12.34).

When the test coil is near a ferromagnetic conductive sample, the typical decrease in self-inductance of the coil due to eddy current losses, described above, as well as hysteresis losses in the magnetic specimen, is counteracted by a self-inductance increase caused by the large magnetic permeability of the specimen. The magnetic permeability effect dominates the test response and, consequently, the overall test coil's self-inductance change is positive. Because the test coil impedance change is opposite for nonferromagnetic and ferromagnetic samples, the eddy current signal deflection will be in opposite directions (Figure 12.34).

Detection of Discontinuities. To detect small changes in impedance caused by discontinuities, the test coil is generally balanced while near the specimen (point Z_3 in Figure 12.34). A discontinuity causes a reduction and redistribution of the eddy currents within the specimen, and the resultant impedance is altered. One challenge with eddy current testing is that numerous variables can cause similar impedance changes in the test coil, and it may be difficult to ensure that the test response is solely due to the variable of interest. The impedance change may not be large, so the signal may be amplified in the resistance and/or inductive reactance directions. Eddy current instruments may use a fixed frequency for testing a single property, such as

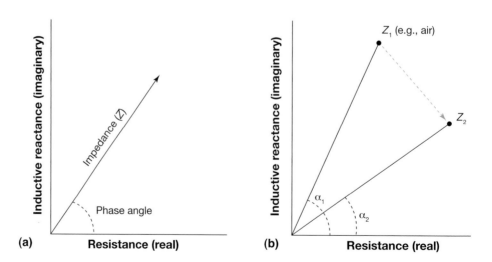

Figure 12.33: Complex impedance plane display showing: (a) resultant phasor; (b) an example change in response ($\overline{Z_1 Z_2}$) as a test coil that was balanced in air (Z_1) is placed near a conductive nonferromagnetic specimen (Z_2).

conductivity, or it may use multiple test frequencies for discrimination of multiple conditions, for sorting heat-treated materials or inspecting heat exchanger tubing, for example.

Coil Configurations. Eddy current testing uses two test coil configurations: *absolute* and *differential.* Probes may be designed to inspect an external surface or the inside surface of a hole, or to encircle the circumference of a cylindrical part, such as a rod, bar, or pipe. Absolute eddy current probes consist of a single test coil, whereas a differential probe requires at least two coils. Probes may have a combination of absolute and differential coils, and may even contain an array of multiple coils.

An absolute coil responds to the test variables of the specimen exposed to the effect of the coil's electromagnetic field. In this type of probe, the impedance or the induced voltage in the coil is measured directly, meaning the absolute value rather than changes in impedance or induced voltage is considered. In general, absolute eddy current probes are the simplest and, perhaps for this reason, are widely used. Absolute coils can, however, struggle to indicate small changes in coil impedance, and changes in the distance between the coil and sample—referred to as *liftoff*—can result in nonrelevant test indications.

Differential coils are connected in such a way that differences between the regions under the coils cause an electronic imbalance. This imbalance is the test indication of interest. Differential eddy current probes consist of a pair of coils connected in opposition so that the net measured impedance or induced voltage is cancelled out when both coils experience identical conditions. Differential probes are sensitive to relative changes in the specimen, and their sensitivity to

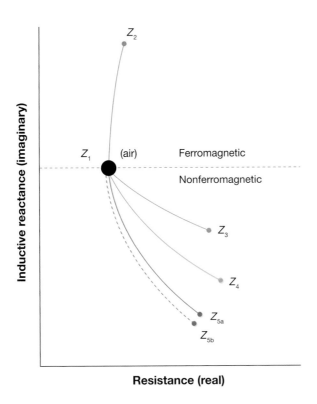

Figure 12.34: Test coil impedance will change from a balance point obtained away from conductive materials (air, point Z_1) to some other value with decreased (for ferromagnetic materials) or increased (nonferromagnetic materials) inductive reactance.

discontinuities is higher than that of absolute probes. Differential probes are fairly immune to liftoff signals as well as probe wobble, noise, and other unwanted signals that affect both coils.

12.8.2.2 POTENTIAL DROP TECHNIQUES

Alternating current and direct current *potential drop techniques* (ACPD and DCPD, respectively) may be used to determine the conductivity or effective permeability of a metal. These techniques use probes with four aligned spring-loaded pins, which directly contact the metallic test surface at defined distances from each other. The outer two pins pass electrical current through the specimen, while the voltage potential difference (drop) is measured across the inner two pins. Pin spacing is closely related to the maximum depth of interrogation, and magnitude of measured voltage varies with input current, spacing between the pins, test frequency, and specimen conductivity and geometry. The potential drop is generally converted to conductivity, or resistivity, and this value is displayed numerically. As with eddy current conductivity measurements, results may use absolute or relative values.

Crack Sizing. The potential drop technique is excellent for crack sizing. A discontinuity beneath the probe alters the electrical resistance of the material as current is forced around and underneath it. The altered resistance leads to a change in the voltage potential. Because of the skin effect, ACPD is useful for surface and near-surface discontinuities, whereas DCPD has a deeper depth of effect. Epoxies, paints, and other nonconductive surface coatings as well as surface oxides, dirt, oil, and grease must be removed or they will prevent the current from entering the material. To avoid errors, the surface must be free of moisture and remain at a uniform, known temperature.

12.8.2.3 ALTERNATING CURRENT FIELD MEASUREMENT

Because electrical contact is mandatory for ACPD, it is not suited for discontinuity detection while scanning. However, the closely related technique of *alternating current field measurement* is quite adept at locating and sizing surface-breaking discontinuities in conductive metals, such as low-carbon steel, stainless steel, or titanium. Alternating current field measurement may be used in conditions that are either dry or deeply submerged in water. Similar to the eddy current technique, an alternating current is induced in the sample's surface, and this current produces a uniform magnetic field. The term uniform means that, at least in the area under the probe, lines of current in the absence of a discontinuity are parallel, unidirectional, and equally spaced. Unlike eddy current testing, which monitors test coil impedance, alternating current field measurement monitors for variations in the magnetic field using flux density sensors.

Magnetic Field Components. Two components of the magnetic field are monitored: B_X along the direction of the discontinuity and B_Z perpendicular to the surface of the specimen. The combination of these signals offers insight into the depth or aspect ratio of the discontinuity. (See Figure 12.35.) Relative, rather than absolute, amplitudes of components of the magnetic flux density are used to minimize variations caused by material properties, instrument calibration, and other circumstances. Calibration by the inspector is not necessary, but discontinuity-sizing algorithms are most accurate for linear, non-branching discontinuities.

Although initial capital cost is higher than the competing MT and PT methods, alternating current field measurement inspection speed is high and does not require electrical contact, so coatings up to several millimeters in thickness may remain in place. Scans with conventional probes are performed parallel to expected discontinuity orientation. Array probes can allow larger areas of interrogation and multi-axis sensitivity.

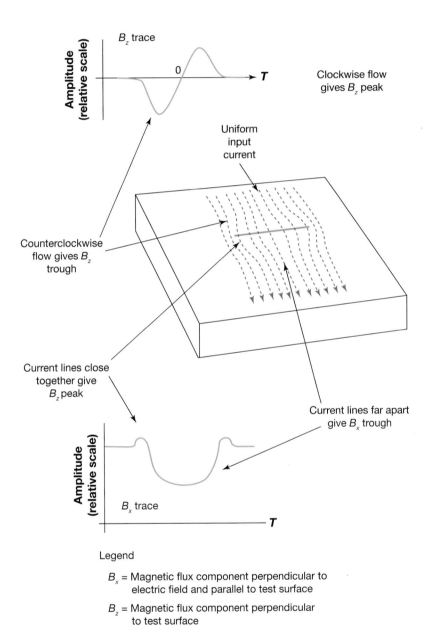

Figure 12.35: Effect of a surface-breaking discontinuity on a magnetic field.

12.8.2.4 REMOTE FIELD TESTING

Remote field testing (RFT) uses the *through-transmission effect* with two widely separated coils: one exciter coil and one detector coil. This effect produces a resultant field that is affected by anomalies. RFT is used primarily for the inspection of ferromagnetic tubular products and pipes.

Testing Coils. RFT ignores the direct coupling between the excitation (drive) and sensing (pickup) coils in favor of detecting a signal propagating through an indirect path. RFT coils are generally spaced much farther apart than configurations for typical eddy current testing. For example, a distance of two or three times the tube diameter may be used while seeking internal or external discontinuities, or loss of wall thickness. RFT operates at relatively low frequencies, with typical test frequencies in the range of 40 Hz to 500 Hz. Special probes are also available for flat geometry components. An example of such an application is fatigue cracks around fastener holes in multilayer aluminum structures. Signal phase indicates discontinuity depth and signal amplitude indicates discontinuity volume.

The changing primary magnetic field induces strong circumferential eddy currents that extend axially as well as radially in the tube wall. These eddy currents in turn produce their own magnetic field that opposes the magnetic field from the exciter coil. Because the tube wall is magnetic, the magnetic field travels in tight loops near the exciter, within the tube wall. However, at distances between one and two tube diameters (1D and 2D), the magnetic field lines change direction and travel far down the tube before eventually looping back to the other side of the exciter in the space outside the tube.

Three Zones Identified. The exciter coil magnetic field is dominant near the exciter coil and the eddy current magnetic field becomes dominant at some distance away from the exciter coil. The receiving coils are placed where they are unaffected by the magnetic field from the exciter coil but still adequately measure the field that is in the tube wall at distances from the exciter coil of 2D or more. Thus, it is possible to map the strength and distribution of the exciter (driver) coil's flux density as it travels down the tube wall. In an attempt to define the variations in the alternating current (AC) energy distributions that are present in the tube wall, three zones have been identified, as diagrammed in Figure 12.36:

- **Near field zone:** 0 to 1.5 tube diameters from the exciter coil.
- **Transition zone:** 1.5 to 2 tube diameters from the exciter coil.
- **Remote field zone:** 2 to 3 tube diameters from the exciter coil.

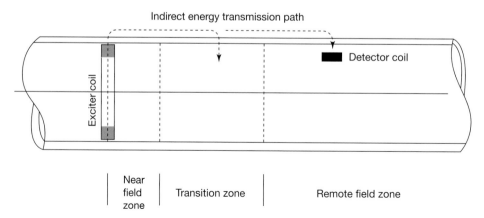

Figure 12.36: Zones in remote field testing.

Electromagnetic induction occurs as the changing magnetic field cuts across the pickup coil array. By monitoring the consistency of the voltage induced in the pickup coils, changes in the test object can be detected. Although the strength of the magnetic field at a distance from the excitation coil becomes very weak, it remains sensitive to changes in the tube or pipe wall thickness.

12.8.3 ADVANTAGES AND LIMITATIONS

Electromagnetic testing comprises many diverse methods and techniques, but all are based on the same set of Maxwell's equations. Electromagnetic methods and techniques may be applied to conductive and nonconductive specimens, although the best known—the eddy current technique—is only applied to conductors. Otherwise, ET is used to identify or differentiate among a wide variety of physical, structural, electronic, magnetic, or metallurgical conditions.

ET offers high sensitivity to discontinuities at or near the surface, with the potential for deeper penetration when lower test frequencies are selected. Decreased test frequency, however, leads to a decrease in resolution. ET requires no chemicals and thus offers environmental, health, and safety benefits over competing inspection methods.

12.9 MAGNETIC FLUX LEAKAGE TESTING

The *magnetic flux leakage* (MFL) method induces a magnetic field within a ferromagnetic specimen, then seeks localized magnetic flux leakage fields along the surface. (See Figure 12.37.) There are four steps in MFL: (1) magnetize the test object in a direction such that the lines of magnetic flux are disturbed by discontinuities, (2) scan the surface of the test object with a magnetic flux sensitive detector, (3) process the data to accentuate discontinuity signals, and (4) present the test results clearly for interpretation. The method is based on the principle that magnetic flux is locally distorted by the presence of a discontinuity. This localized distortion causes some of the magnetic field to exit, and then reenter, the test object at surface and near-subsurface discontinuities. The magnetic dipole caused by field distortion is called a *magnetic flux leakage field*. There are limits to deep-discontinuity sensitivity using this method. However, these limits are controllable to some extent by the intensity of the induced magnetic field; by features of the discontinuity, such as depth, size, and shape; and by the relative orientations of the discontinuity and magnetic flux lines (refer also to Section 12.3).

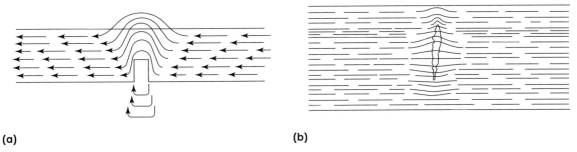

(a)   (b)

Figure 12.37: Magnetic flux leakage fields: (a) slot or keyway on reverse side of magnetized bar; (b) internal or midwall discontinuity in magnetized test object.

Detection of Flux Leakage Fields. Unlike the particles used in the closely related magnetic particle testing method, MFL employs a *hall effect sensor* to detect flux leakage fields. The core of a hall effect sensor is its semiconductor crystal, which has a constant current applied to it. The hall sensor is a four-terminal solid-state device, which produces an output voltage proportional to the input current, magnetic flux density, and the cosine of the angle between the flux lines and the face of the semi-conductor crystal. For example, a 10° off-angle orientation results in ~1.5% decrease in measured flux density. Magnetic flux lines passing the hall probe induce an electrical voltage potential. The polarity of the voltage potential changes with the direction of the magnetic flux, with one side of the sensor crystal becoming the negative portion and the other side positive. Hall probes may be configured to sense magnetic flux density oriented parallel to the test object's surface, using a transverse probe, or oriented perpendicular to the magnetic field with an axial probe.

12.10 MICROWAVE TESTING

Microwave testing (MW) and *millimeter wave NDT* are most often applied to electrically insulating, dielectric materials, such as rubber, many composites, and ceramics. However, they may also be applied to conductive metals. These techniques are useful for (1) measuring and controlling the distance from or geometry of a specimen, involving microwave imaging or holography; (2) evaluation or spectroscopic analysis of moisture content or chemistry; and (3) detection and sizing of discontinuities in metals. Microwave measurement setups may be contact or non-contact and are divided into three categories: reflection, transmission, and scattering. (See Figure 12.38.) Reflection measurements generally use one antenna for transmitting and receiving signals. Transmission measurements place an antenna on each side of the specimen, and scattering measurements are obtained using several transmitters or several receivers positioned at key locations.

Changes in Dielectric Constant. The interrogating microwave energy is emitted from the transducer, and signals of interest may be caused by localized changes in the dielectric constant of the sample, including delaminations, surface-breaking discontinuities, moisture content, and impurities, or by polarization of the signal due to discontinuity or sample material orientation effects. Test frequencies are between 300 MHz and 300 GHz, so wavelengths range from 1 m down to 1 mm. Microwaves in the frequency range below about 40 GHz are generally referred to as *millimeter waves* because that is the length scale of their wavelengths in free space. Microwaves reflect almost completely—that is, they do not penetrate—when they encounter conductive materials. However, these interrogating waves can penetrate dielectric test objects. The depth of penetration is governed by the material's ability to absorb microwave energy.

12.11 GROUND PENETRATING RADAR

Ground penetrating radar (GPR) is widely used for investigation of the ground surrounding, and the composition and integrity within, engineered structures, such as buildings, bridges, earthen dams, and road beds. GPR systems typically include a radar pulse generator, transmitter, receiver, antenna, and equipment for electronic data acquisition and storage. The electromagnetic radar pulse propagates into the specimen, and wave reflection occurs at localized changes in dielectric properties. Test frequency generally varies between 500 MHz and 2 GHz. Higher frequencies allow for shallow interrogations at high resolution; however, resolution must be sacrificed when the penetrating ability of lower test frequencies is required.

Position Encoder for Data. Data collection is usually triggered by a *position encoder*, such as a survey wheel. (See Figure 12.39.) The encoder triggers data acquisition at regular intervals. Individual waveforms collected along the path of the radar antenna can be viewed collectively in a B-scan data presentation (refer to Section 12.4.3). Depending on the application, systems are described as either *ground-coupled* or *air-coupled*. Air-coupled or -launched systems use antennae positioned at or above a height related to the central test frequency, whereas most ground-coupled antennas are positioned with the housing directly in contact with the ground. Air-coupled systems offer higher inspection speed, but ground coupling offers greater depth of penetration at a given test frequency.

12.12 INFRARED AND THERMAL TESTING

12.12.1 INTRODUCTION AND PRINCIPLES

Noncontact *infrared and thermal testing* (IR) techniques are used to determine the temperature of a point or a surface. Such measurements may be performed once or many times in succession. Many are familiar with the basic ideas of IR testing due to the common application of similar technology for home inspection services and military or sporting applications of night vision. Infrared and thermal testing is a powerful predictive maintenance (PdM) method that is used in many nondestructive testing applications.

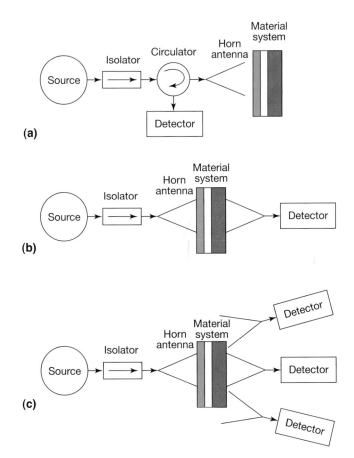

Figure 12.38: Measurement setup for microwave testing: (a) reflection; (b) transmission; (c) scattering.

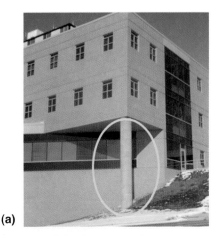

(a)

(b)

Figure 12.39: Scanning a full-scale reinforced concrete column: (a) column location; (b) equipment setup and use.

Heat can be described as the energy associated with the random and chaotic motions of the atomic particles which compose matter. Temperature is a measure of the intensity of particle motion in degrees celsius (°C) or fahrenheit (°F), or in the absolute scales of kelvin (K) or rankine (°R). At a microscopic length scale, the thermal energy of a substance is the vibrational kinetic energy of its constituent atoms or molecules. Increased thermal energy causes increased vibration or motion. The atomic or molecular velocities are proportional to temperature, and the lowest point on the kelvin temperature scale where atomic/molecular motion essentially ceases—that is, absolute zero—indicates a thermal energy of zero. Heat always flows from a warmer to a cooler region, and it may be transferred between two points via conduction or convection within a substance and via radiation as the thermal motion of particles emits electromagnetic radiation.

Convection and Conduction. *Convection* is thermal energy transfer through the motion of fluids, which is the dominant transfer mode for liquids and gases, for example, heated air rising as a result of its lower density, while cooler air sinks. While convection is limited to fluids, conduction and radiation occur in all forms of matter: solid, liquid, gas, or plasma. *Conduction* is the transfer of thermal energy by diffusion and by collisions between constituents. All matter with a temperature greater than absolute zero (0 K or –273 °C) emits thermal radiation. The total energy emitted, the peak wavelength, and the spectral energy distribution of this thermal radiation may be predicted mathematically based on the object's temperature. Total emitted energy and the energy of electromagnetic radiation photons emitted increase proportionally with temperature. The amount of radiated energy also varies with the material and surface properties of the specimen.

Emissivity and Blackbody Radiation. Emissivity is the ratio of total energy radiated by a specimen's surface at a given temperature, as compared with the total energy radiated by a blackbody radiator of the same temperature. A hypothetical *blackbody* emits the maximum radiation energy theoretically possible at a given temperature; consequently, it has an emissivity of 1.0. A blackbody would also absorb all incident radiation falling upon it. Emissivity is inversely proportional to reflectivity and is a key variable in IR.

All real materials have emissivities greater than 0.0 and less than 1.0. Poor understanding of emissivity will lead to poor measurement results. In other words, no real surface will absorb all incident radiation, so it will also emit less radiation that an ideal blackbody. Coatings, such as tape, carbon black, paint, or metallic surface treatments, alter a sample's emissivity. One example is low-emissivity glass, which uses a metallic coating to keep more thermal energy on the source side of the pane. The operator must be aware that discontinuities may be missed or obscured due to reflections, emissivity, or spatial variations due to the viewing angle or interference from wind, sunlight, moisture, or personnel.

12.12.2 EQUIPMENT AND TECHNIQUES

Contact and Noncontact Thermography. Infrared and thermal testing is the measurement or mapping of surface temperatures when heat flows from, to, or through a test object. *Contact thermography* techniques are available for mapping the temperature distribution of an area, possibly using a liquid crystal panel of the type that has been useful in medical applications to screen patients for deep-vein thrombosis. *Noncontact IR techniques* detect infrared wavelengths of electromagnetic radiation emitted by the test object. Noncontact techniques are useful for moving targets, when the target is in a controlled environment, such as in a vacuum or held within an electromagnetic field, and when the target temperature exceeds the capability of contact techniques.

Noncontact equipment varies from low-cost and limited-range infrared thermometers, similar to the device inserted into an ear to see if a child has a fever, through higher-quality and higher-range infrared pyrometers that offer instantaneous point measurements, to high-end thermal cameras. Advanced noncontact techniques have the ability to map the instantaneous distribution of surface temperatures or integrate multiple surface maps to illustrate localized temperature changes over time.

Pyrometers. There are two basic types of pyrometers: optical and electronic. *Optical pyrometers*, which are essentially outmoded, are adjusted manually until the incandescent brightness of an electrical resistance-heated filament matches that of a target within the same field of view. The target must have a temperature greater than 700 °C (1292 °F) and when the brightness of the filament and target matches, the filament disappears from view. Current supplied to the filament is directly related to filament temperature. Because the human eye is the detector and the eye must be protected, only the visible red wavelengths are used in this comparative measurement. Other screens, called *photoscreens*, can be used to control the intensity of light allowed to reach the eye and increase the useful temperature range of the instrument.

Electronic pyrometers are automatic and focus the thermal radiation from a source onto a detector, such as a photocell, photomultiplier tube, thermopile, pyroelectric device, or bolometer. Arrays of detectors, such as micro-bolometers, which change their electrical resistance with temperature, are commonly used within thermal imaging cameras. A thermographic map of the energy of a surface is then compiled into image form, known as a *thermogram*, when the array is queried. (See Figure 12.40.) The imaging or study of surface thermal patterns is known as *thermography*. Thermal imaging is most successful on samples with high emissivity.

Passive and Active Thermography. Thermography has quickly gained acceptance as an inspection technique because interpretation of inspection results is generally straightforward, its inspection resolution may be varied according to needs and sample dimensions, and it is applicable to a wide range of material types. Two thermography techniques are common in industry: passive and active. *Passive imaging* is solely the observation, in image or real-time mode, of the energy of a surface. Examples of *passive thermography* applications include observing the heat signatures of a home and measuring the distribution of thermal energy on a recently landed aircraft for indications of water ingression into its honeycomb composite structure.

(a)

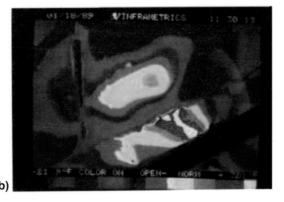

(b)

Figure 12.40: Damaged refractory on inside of a boiler with skin temperature of 465 K (192 °C [377 °F]): (a) photograph; (b) thermogram.

The passive thermography technique is cost-effective and quite commonly applied. When applied under the umbrella of predictive maintenance, passive thermography applications are divided into two groups: *electrical* and *mechanical.* Resistance to electrical flow causes an increase in temperature, sometimes due to a loose, corroded, or undersized connection, so electrical components are common test objects. Specimens that are not electrical are usually described as mechanical, a category with four subsets: (1) friction heating, (2) valve leakage or blockage, (3) insulation, and (4) buildings. Interpretation may be complex because of the presence of unknown materials, as the result of inserts or repairs, or time-dependent contrast reversal because of thermal capacitance (mass) or other thermal property interactions. Discontinuities may be detected primarily through pattern recognition or image interpretation by an experienced operator.

Active thermography does not rely on the native thermal energy of the sample but rather introduces heat with an external source. Once heat is introduced, the sample surface is then thermographically monitored as the localized temperature decreases with time. Temperature differentials, or changes in temperature over time, are related to heat transfer characteristics. The rate of heat flow away from the test surface is altered by discontinuities and subsurface geometry. A region with a temperature different than its surroundings may indicate a discontinuity. External heat sources vary widely but include hair dryers, flash lamps, infrared light-emitting diodes, lasers, and induction heating coils. Thermogram sensitivity varies with heating time, specimen material, observation time, heating intensity, and the nature of the discontinuity.

Vibro-Thermography. A slight twist to the technique of active thermography is known as *vibro-thermography* or *sonic IR*. Rather than introducing the test energy in the form of heat, the interrogating test energy is acoustic in nature. Heat generation may be caused by some combination of friction, plasticity, and viscoelastic losses. As discussed in Section 12.4, acoustic waves are vibrations, which can propagate through a test specimen. Vibrations caused by high-power acoustic waves can cause the opposite faces of a discontinuity, such as a delamination or crack, to vibrate against one another, like rubbing your hands together, and this friction causes heat. Samples are thermographically monitored during a vibro-thermographic inspection for telltale heat signatures of cracks during acoustic excitation. Inspection results are generally collected over a time period, and a series of images may be combined into a single composite or be viewed sequentially.

12.12.3 ADVANTAGES AND LIMITATIONS

Infrared and thermal testing measures the localized temperature or heat flow to diagnose problems with a process as well as detect discontinuities in materials or products. Measurement devices may be contact and/or noncontact; techniques are passive or active. Essentially, any type of material may be evaluated with infrared and thermal testing techniques; inspection results can be immediate and interpretation of these results is straightforward. The IR method is safe, as no harmful radiation is involved, and techniques may be chemical-free. However, materials with low emissivity generally require a coating of some type to reduce measurement error and reflections. Measurement error may be significant when observing a sample with varying emissivity.

12.13 ACOUSTIC EMISSION TESTING

Imagine quietly ice fishing on a cold winter day, when you feel a vibration, hear a deep boom, and immediately see that a crack propagated from your drilled hole off into the distance. The same basic principle for detecting damage may be applied to industrial components. Most engineering materials emit audible or inaudible acoustic waves when stressed, and when cracks initiate or grow. As discussed in section 12.4, acoustic waves are mechanical vibrations that propagate through a medium, and such vibrations may be detected with transducers that convert mechanical energy into an electronic signal.

Instrumentation. *Acoustic emission* (AE) instrumentation is designed to detect the structure-borne sound generated by a source. The signals from one or more sensors are amplified and measured to produce data for display and interpretation, and an array of AE leak detectors may be used to detect and then triangulate the source. AE techniques have the potential to detect discontinuities, increase productivity, and reduce maintenance costs. (See Figure 12.41.)

Sources of Signals. Acoustic signal sources include crack initiation, in-surface mill scale, crack tip yielding, crack extension, certain phase changes or growth in microstructural phases, turbulent flow or leakage, boiling, chemical reaction, friction or fretting, impact, matrix cracking, delamination, active corrosion, and matrix disbonding or fiber breakage. Acoustic emissions are omnidirectional, and most acoustic emission sources act as point source emitters that radiate energy in spherical wave fronts. AE differs from most NDT methods in that the sample itself is the source of test energy, it can be a whole-body evaluation in spite of limited access, and discontinuity orientation is irrelevant to detectability.

Application Methods. The method of acoustic emission may be divided into two common applications: detection of discontinuities and detection of leaks. Discontinuity detection monitors the sample for transient or short-lived burst signals, while leak detection is concerned with signals of longer duration. In both cases,

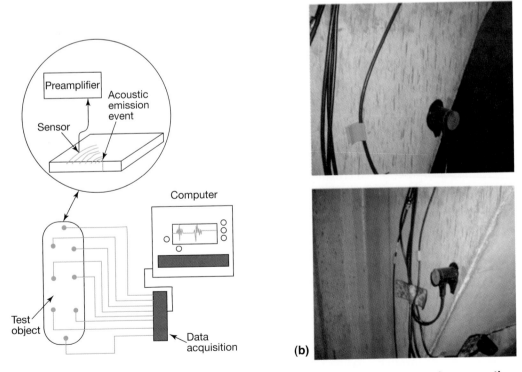

(a)　　　　　　　　　　　　　　　　　　　　　　**(b)**

Figure 12.41: Acoustic emission testing: (a) setup with eight sensors to locate crack propagation; (b) sensors affixed on concrete walls of a cable saddle.

the acoustic energy detected has propagated through the sample's structure. Increases in a material's strength, anisotropy, and grain size tend to increase AE signal amplitude.

Transient AE waves are produced by the application, and sometimes relaxation, of localized or long-range stress within an object; AE signals are also produced by the activation and motion of dislocations in the specimen's atomic structure. Because acoustic emission events are produced by dynamic mechanisms of deformation and fracture, an unstressed specimen will produce no emissions. AE tests may monitor an object over time or short-term tests can be performed while applying a controlled load, such as proof load, fatigue testing, hydrostatic pressure test, or creep test.

Some materials emit AE signals upon loading, but once a given load has been applied and the acoustic emission from accommodating that stress has ceased, additional acoustic emissions will not occur until that stress level is exceeded—even if the load is completely removed and then reapplied. This is known as the *kaiser effect*. However, the kaiser effect, if present, may also disappear with time.

AE techniques for leak detection are based on the principle that the flow of fluid, as caused by a pressure differential, changes from laminar to turbulent as it passes through an orifice. The sample may have a higher or lower pressure than its surroundings. Other signal sources include crack or orifice growth, cavitation, and the movement of solid particles at the leak. Leaks, therefore, produce a continuous detectable acoustic signal.

Comparison with LT and VA. The technique of *acoustic leak testing* is closely related to acoustic emission for leak detection. While they both may seek similar discontinuities, for acoustic emission, the test signal is transmitted through the sample—that is, it is structure-borne—but a leak-testing (LT) signal is transmitted through the air. Acoustic emission is also closely related to the method of vibration analysis (VA). However, AE is considered more sensitive and sometimes able to indicate problems earlier than the VA. Also, AE is concerned with transient acoustic events, while vibration analysis (VA) monitors signals with a longer time base and a lower frequency.

12.14 LEAK TESTING

A *leak* is the unintended transfer of fluid through a barrier—a fluid being any liquid or gas capable of flowing. Leaks due to cracks, crevices, or holes are often undesirable in engineered structures. Functional requirements may define the smallest leakage rate that must be detected or the highest rate allowable. There are several leak testing (LT) techniques that have been developed for locating, and sometimes quantifying, such discontinuities. Choice of technique depends on required sensitivity, whether the position of the leak must be known, and whether the leakage rate must be determined.

Techniques. Basic LT techniques include bubble solution (Figure 12.42), airborne ultrasonic or acoustic, voltage discharge, pressure and pressure change, ionization, conductivity, radiation absorption, chemical-based, halogen detector, radioisotope, and mass spectrometer. All of these techniques may be further subdivided depending on the hardware or test media employed. For example, airborne acoustic leak detection may apply a pressure differential to the sample or hold a battery-powered test signal emitter within an unpressurized sample, such as a vehicle cabin.

Principles. The principles of leak testing involve the physics of liquid or gas flowing through a barrier where a pressure differential or capillary action exists. LT is commonly applied to prevent the loss of costly materials or energy, to prevent contamination of the environment, to ensure component or system reliability, and to prevent an explosion or fire. Calibrated reference leaks are available for some techniques to quantify the rate of leakage.

12.15 LASER TESTING

Holography and Shearography. Since its introduction in the 1960s, the laser has found many scientific and industrial applications including laser testing methods (LM) of nondestructive testing. For example, lasers may be used to generate or detect high-frequency acoustic waves (see Section 12.4), induce mechanical vibrations and measure displacement or strain. It is this last application that is the focus for *holography* and *shearography moiré imaging*; the relative strain of a sample under changing stress may indicate discontinuities at or below the surface. Inspection systems require a means to provide a controlled and repeatable stress to the test object. Such stress may be applied via thermal changes of heating or cooling, partial vacuum (Figure 12.43), internal pressure, vibration, and microwave irradiation.

Destructive Interference of Laser Light. Holography and shearography both use the destructive interference of laser light to produce a test signal. Shearography systems direct laser light and a shearing image interferometer along the same optical

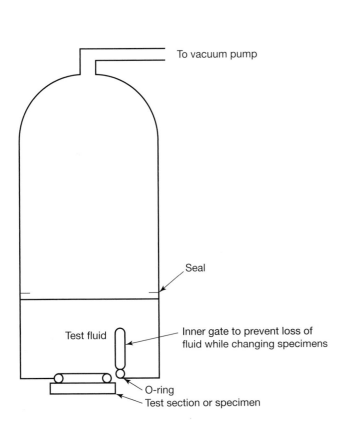

Figure 12.42: Vacuum chamber technique for providing pressure differential across leaks during bubble tests.

To vacuum pump

Seal

Test fluid

Inner gate to prevent loss of fluid while changing specimens

O-ring

Test section or specimen

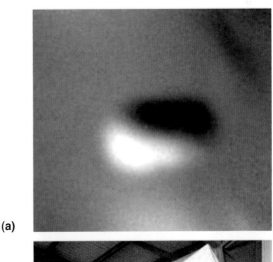

(a)

(b)

Figure 12.43: Aircraft rudder inspection: (a) shearogram of disbond; (b) portable vacuum shearography.

path. Holographic systems using a beamsplitter do not have the same optical path, which makes them more susceptible to environmental vibration and thus limits their industrial applications. For both techniques, as the distance between the optics and sample changes, the relative phase of light is altered through a process of destructive interference.

Relative Strain. Because the inspector is looking for higher than expected relative strain when stress is applied to the sample, image-based results are relatively easy to interpret. Shearography and holography provide direct measurements of discontinuity dimensions, signal-to-noise ratios, out-of-plane Z-axis deformation, and strain as a function of stress. Shearography cameras do not need to follow precision contours, can test a structure at an offset angle, and are relatively insensitive to test object bending. In addition, shearography can be performed in near real time.

Benefits of Laser Testing. Advantages of shearography and holography include full field inspection ability and high throughput. In addition, these techniques are noncontact and chemical/liquid-free. Laser-based inspection techniques inherently have a higher initial cost, but holography and shearography have found applications in the aerospace industry, for example, the testing of composite panels and control surfaces. In shearography and holography, as with other nondestructive test methods, proper reference standards are important for the development of the nondestructive test procedure.

12.16 VIBRATION ANALYSIS

Vibration Signature. Sound and vibration are interrelated; consequently, the methods and techniques of acoustic emission (AE), acoustic leak detection, and vibration

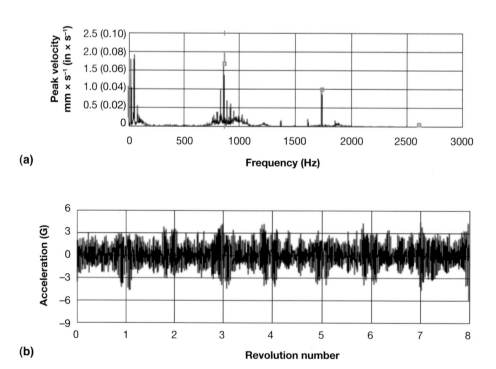

Figure 12.44: Worn gear signature: (a) frequency plot; (b) waveform.

analysis (VA) are closely related. Luckily, mechanical noise has characteristics that help distinguish it from the acoustic emission signals of cracks. A machine's vibration signature contains a significant amount of information about its health and operation. Condition monitoring, therefore, commonly analyzes either the amplitude or the frequency content of machine vibrations. Examples of vibration signatures are shown in Figure 12.44.

Mechanical problems, such as imbalance in rotating parts or deterioration of bearings; poor assembly, including misalignment or whole-engine vibration signature; or manufacturing problems, for example, dull machine tools, may be sought. Sometimes multiple data sets are collected and analyzed to monitor for a change in acoustic signature over time, referred to as a *trending analysis*. A machine's rotational speed must be known so that the frequency of events noted during data analysis can be correctly attributed.

Sensors. The sensor—which may be an accelerometer, piezoelectric transducer or linear variable displacement transducer, or eddy current probe—is subjected to periodic (repeating) and random (transient) vibration energy propagating to it. Many variables, including the sensor type, mounting method, and location, control what the transducer detects. For example, it is common for test signal frequencies above 1 kHz to go undetected when using a handheld accelerometer probe. Because most sensors only detect motion in one direction, it is common to take readings in more than one axis, for example, 90° apart on a bearing race.

Data Display. Raw data is graphically viewed with time as the X axis and signal amplitude as the Y axis. Transient and *nonsinusoidal events*—that is, not resembling a mathematical curve that describes a smooth, repetitive oscillation—can be identified in time-based analysis. Random events produce noise in the signal, and the rise time of the noise signal may also help to distinguish noise from signals of interest. Because both amplitude and frequency content of the signal may be of potential interest, a fast fourier transform may be performed so that a data spectrum may be analyzed in the frequency domain—that is, the X axis is frequency and the Y axis is amplitude. (A fourier transform decomposes a time-based signal into the frequencies that make it up, much like a musical chord can be divided into the amplitude or loudness of its constituent notes.) Frequency-based analysis is useful for identifying regularly periodic events, such as impacts.

Three amplitude types are used in evaluating the vibration signal: *displacement* involving a change in position; *velocity*, meaning the rate of change in displacement; and *acceleration*, or rate of change in velocity. A rule of thumb is that displacement is key for low-frequency signals (≤ 5 Hz), velocity is often key for frequencies up to 2 kHz, and acceleration is of primary interest at frequencies above 2 kHz. This rule is not absolute, though, and choice of analysis method ultimately depends on the application.

12.17 SPECTROSCOPY

Types of Spectroscopy. Although not recognized in *SNT-TC-1A* as an independent method, *spectroscopy* is the study of how some measurable quantity changes as a function of wavelength or frequency and, thus, intersects several NDT media. Types of spectroscopy are categorized by their manner of interrogation: electromagnetic wave, electron, acoustic, dielectric, and mechanical. *Acoustic spectroscopy* and *electron spectroscopy*—for example, X-ray photoelectron spectroscopy or auger electron spectroscopy—are generally laboratory-based techniques, but electromagnetic and mechanical techniques find common industrial applications. *Mechanical spectroscopy* techniques include process-compensated resonance testing (PCRT) and bond testing, for example, mechanical impedance analysis, resonance, and pitch-catch modes.

Electromagnetic radiation comprises photons whose energy levels are based on their wavelength. Common *electromagnetic spectroscopy* techniques are absorption, emission, raman, and fluorescence. *Absorption spectroscopy* observes the wavelength-dependent attenuation of radiation passing through the sample, for example, spectral transmittance of a light filter. *Emission spectroscopy* observes the frequency content of radiation produced by a specimen, such as spectral irradiance of a light source. *Raman spectroscopy* studies the inelastic scattering of laser light, which offers insight into the types of chemical bonds present in a sample. Lastly, *fluorescence spectroscopy* studies the wavelength-dependent excitation preference of a fluorophore or studies which wavelengths are emitted by a fluorophore during fluorescence.

X-Ray Fluorescence Spectroscopy. Fluorescence spectroscopy may be performed on solid or liquid samples in a laboratory environment using a *fluorimeter*, but the development of robust handheld devices has allowed this technique to be applied to estimating the elemental composition of samples at any location. Positive material identification (PMI), for example, employs *X-ray fluorescence* (XRF) spectroscopy. XRF is based on the principle that low-energy X-rays or gamma rays can electronically excite the sample material and induce fluorescence. (See Figure 12.45.)

Incident radiation is absorbed by the sample and inner shell electrons are ejected as photoelectrons. As discussed in section 12.6, the absorbing atoms backfill the now empty position, and as an electron moves into its new position, it discards its excess energy in the form of an X-ray photon. So the fluoresced electromagnetic radiation in this case comprises X-ray photons with a wavelength longer than the incident excitation photons. X-ray photon wavelength indicates the source element, and the number of photons detected in a given time—that is, the *count rate*—indicates the relative concentration of detected elements.

XRF-based rapid alloy identification and elemental analysis applications include sorting or confirming incoming materials, detecting heavy metal content in polymers or coatings, and detecting or estimating the relative amount of alloying elements in metallic alloys. XRF primarily interrogates the sample surface, so sample preparation is often necessary, for example, lightly sanding with silicon carbide sandpaper.

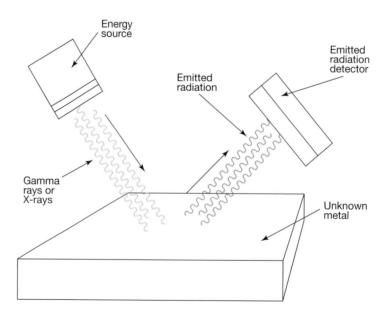

Figure 12.45: X-ray fluorescence spectrometry uses a detector that separates and identifies energy wavelengths or intensities.

13 NDT Applications

13.1 RELATIONSHIP BETWEEN NDT AND MANUFACTURING

The physical features of engineered components, such as form, orientation, location, and size, must be controlled. The level of precision or tolerance required for feature control is specified on a blueprint or other document. Such a document generally conveys requirements using *geometric dimensioning and tolerancing* (GD&T), which are unambiguously communicated using a consensus standard, such as ASME Y14.5 or ISO 7083. NDT may be applied at any stage of a component's life cycle. Raw products, including castings, forgings, and extrusions, may be inspected after they are produced; after they've received secondary processing, such as machining, welding, heat treating, grinding, plating, or assembly; or after they have been in service. NDT requirements may also be conveyed on a blueprint, and the symbols used for inspection guidance also generally follow a consensus standard, such as AWS A2.4.

Quality Level. The quality level of a product is proportional to how well its distinguishing features and attributes fulfill explicit or implicit needs. Improved quality may be sought through improvements in manufacturing, process control, and/or inspection. A potential manufacturing improvement, for example, is a change from manually operated machines to a computer numerically controlled (CNC) machining

"The level of precision or tolerance required for feature control is specified on a blueprint or other document."

center. Nondestructive testing may be incorporated for improved process control or to perform inspections at key points of a product's life.

NDT is sometimes compared to a health care system in that it may be called on in emergency situations as well as for routine checks. Noninvasive checks that do not harm the specimen may be performed without interrupting a process or removing it from service. Quality control personnel are often concerned with whether a process is in control. *Control*, in this context, means that nonconforming product is produced at the normal rate (five rejectable parts per million, for example) and variability in the process falls within normal distribution bounds, meaning upper and lower control limits.

It would not be cost-effective for a manufacturer if the scrap rate were to increase dramatically, so implementing process control feedback loops into the production line is a wise investment. Control techniques may focus on a process parameter or on a product feature, such as thickness, conductivity, or integrity. *Feature-based control* is often directly tied to product quality, but many NDT techniques do not function in real time. Human factors related to the inspector can degrade the correlation between scrap rate and control over a process.

Monitoring of Parameters. *Parameter-based measurement* is generally straightforward because of the variety of commercially available tools, but establishing control limits based on how these measurable parameters affect the product can take a significant amount of background work. The parameter of temperature, for example, is often monitored for industrial process control because thermal behavior is often directly related to the health or proper function of a part—for example, a bearing or electrical component—or process, such as carton sealing, welding, or casting. Another common example of a monitoring technique is vibration analysis, which may be used to maintain or improve product quality. Poor control of vibration in a grinding application, for example, generally leads to degraded control over the product's geometry and surface finish, and can cause localized overheating that alters the microstructure and mechanical properties of the material.

13.2 MATERIALS CHARACTERIZATION

13.2.1 ACOUSTIC VELOCITY

Mechanical wave velocity is controlled by the propagating medium's density and elastic constants—that is, bulk modulus of elasticity or shear modulus, depending on the type of wave. In steel, for example, the elastic constants are governed by the material's composition, relative fractions of individual microstructural phases, and texture. Velocity can therefore offer insight into anisotropy, texture, or residual stress—all are orientation-specific—or into a metal's microstructure, such as nodularity in ductile cast iron or retained austenite in steel. New strain-free grains form during the recrystallization stage of annealing, so ultrasound may be used to monitor heat-treatment progress for steel or aluminum. Sample temperature is generally inversely related to both density and elastic constants; therefore, acoustic velocity generally decreases with temperature.

13.2.2 MECHANICAL PROPERTIES

While ultrasonic testing is useful for determining acoustic velocity, velocity can also offer insight into the sample's mechanical properties. Depending on wave mode, acoustic velocity varies with a combination of modulus of elasticity, shear modulus, density, and Poisson's ratio—the ratio of the proportional decrease in lateral measurement to the proportional increase in length in a specimen that is elastically stretched. Acoustic velocity for a metal has experimentally been shown to vary with metallurgical properties, such as grain size, cleanliness or inclusion content, hardness, fracture toughness, and strength. As with any parameter-based measurement, establishing the signal change of interest—for example, velocity, attenuation, spectral transmittance, or backscatter amplitude—and removing the confounding effects of other variables may be difficult in practice. One approach has been to use laser-based ultrasonic testing because optical generation simultaneously produces longitudinal and shear waves; therefore, both velocities can concurrently be determined. Optical detection is also useful for measuring backscattered noise, which relates to grain size in metals.

13.2.3 ELECTRICAL CONDUCTIVITY

Electrical conductivity of a sample changes with factors such as heat treatment including aluminum temper condition, alloying elements, and integrity based on the presence of cracks, inclusions, holes, or voids. Electrical conductivity of a metal is commonly evaluated using one of two electromagnetic NDT techniques: alternating current potential drop (ACPD), or eddy current testing (See Section 12.8). The test coil of an eddy current conductivity probe changes impedance depending on whether it's over free space—that is, in air—or over a conductor. Commercial eddy-current-based instruments are capable of evaluating nonferromagnetic samples only, usually in terms of a percentage of the International Annealed Copper Standard (% IACS). Measurement error is introduced by edge effects, probe standoff distance, temperature of the probe or sample, and the magnitude of magnetic permeability in the sample. Increasing magnetic permeability, even when low, can lead to underestimation of electrical conductivity with low-frequency commercial devices. While limited by magnetic permeability, many eddy-current-based instruments can simultaneously estimate coating thickness and conductivity.

Current Proportional to Potential Difference. ACPD's four-pinned probes inject current into a conductive sample through the outer pins, while measuring the voltage potential difference (drop) across the inner two pins. Because pin distances are known and the current through two points on a conductor is proportional to the potential difference across the two points, following Ohm's law, conductivity can be determined. Linear conductivity, or resistivity, may be displayed numerically in absolute values (siemens per meter) or relative values (% IACS). Unlike eddy current, ACPD is not limited by the sample's magnetic permeability.

13.2.4 MATERIAL CHEMISTRY

Use of Spectroscopy. Radiographic techniques, such as *fluorescence spectroscopy* and *K-edge absorption spectroscopy*, may be used to evaluate the atomic composition of materials. As discussed in Section 12.6, elemental atoms are composed of electrons in orbital shells, and each shell has a unique binding energy. Incident electromagnetic photons with sufficient energy interact with the sample material to produce a detectable signal. For K-edge spectroscopy, also called *K-edge densitometry*, the signal of interest is a sharp reduction forming an "edge" in the transmitted continuous X-ray beam spectrum at the energy level of interest—for example, 88 keV for lead, 109.7 keV for thorium, or 115.6 keV for uranium. This assay technique is useful for detecting heavy metal content in pipes or containers. An example data set may be found in Figure 13.1; the energy level associated with the edge indicates the atom's identity, and the magnitude of the edge indicates its concentration.

Material Identification. X-ray fluorescence (XRF), sometimes called *positive material identification* (PMI), also directs a continuous X-ray spectrum toward the sample; gamma-ray photons may also be used. As detailed in Section 12.6, incident photons can cause the sample material to produce fluoresced X-rays with characteristic energy levels. The energy level of the fluoresced X-ray identifies the elemental atom, and the number of fluoresced X-rays detected in a given time interval gives a semi-quantitative measure of that element's concentration. Portable XRF units can generally detect elements with Z-numbers as low as 17—in the case of chlorine – when air is the propagation medium between the sample and detector. Additionally, elements with Z-numbers as low as 12 (magnesium) may be detected using a helium gas purge or special technologies (Figure 13.2).

13.2.5 POLYMER CHARACTERIZATION

As outlined previously, ultrasound may be used on polymers to estimate elastic moduli, and XRF may be used to detect heavy metals, halogens, or bromine for sorting purposes or for health and safety concerns. Additional techniques are also available for use on polymeric materials, including millimeter-wave or terahertz-wave NDT and raman spectroscopy. Terahertz frequencies are part of the far-infrared electromagnetic spectrum and generally have frequencies between 0.1 THz

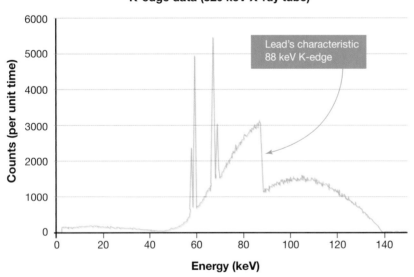

Figure 13.1: Example K-edge spectrum data showing an 88 keV edge obtained using an X-ray tube set to 140 keV; the edge indicates the presence of metallic lead. Characteristic emission lines for the X-ray tube's tungsten anode are visible. Its magnitude is used to determine the amount of lead that the X-ray beam passed through.

Figure 13.2: Portable X-ray fluorescence of a large autoclave chamber to confirm that the grade of stainless steel used matches that specified in the purchase agreement.

and 100 THz with corresponding wavelengths between 3 mm and 3 microns. While transmission is limited in humid air due to the high absorption of water molecules, terahertz waves are inherently safer than X-rays, and the signal produced within samples offers spectroscopic data about the dielectric material's molecular composition. Dielectric materials are not electrically conductive; examples include paper, polymer, wood, and most ceramics. Frequency-dependent changes in signal phase and amplitude can give insight into material properties, and a signal phase shift or time delay can indicate sample or layer thickness.

Identification of Compounds. *Raman spectroscopy* is a powerful technique for identifying molecular compounds and the type of chemical bonds present in a sample. This technique employs a laser—visible light, near infrared, or near ultraviolet—to excite inelastic scattering. Incoming laser photons may be shifted up or down in frequency after interaction with the sample. The shift in energy gives information about the vibration and stretching modes of chemical bonds in the sample. Signal amplitude from inelastic photon scattering is very weak, and these test responses must be separated from the intense laser excitation line. While laboratory units are common, applications for handheld units include confirming polymer and monomer identity or chemical fingerprint, detecting polymerization, and monitoring the polymerization rate (Figure 13.3).

13.2.6 CASE DEPTH

Abrasive wear properties, fatigue resistance, and strength of a component can be improved by increasing the hardness of its exterior. *Case hardening* may be performed by altering the chemistry of the surface layer—for example, nitriding and carburizing—or by heating and then rapidly cooling the external surface through processes such as flame hardening and induction hardening. Chemistry-altering hardening techniques result in a gradual change between the hardened case and the softer core; this gradual change presents a serious challenge to NDT.

Estimating Case Depth. Because of its rapid thermal cycle, *induction hardening* generally produces a sharply defined case/core interface, which is more readily detectable to NDT. Techniques that can vary test frequency, such as barkhausen noise, eddy current, and ACPD, have the ability to vary the depth of interrogation. Effective case depth may be estimated based on the test signal received versus the assumed depth of interrogation. Systems based on ultrasonic testing are also commercially available; dedicated UT systems insonify the sample with 5 MHz to 30 MHz sound energy with the wavelength selected to maximize signal response. Due to the

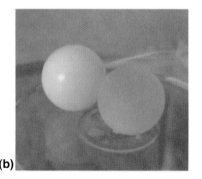
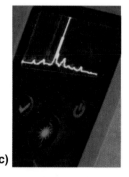

(a)   (b)   (c)

Figure 13.3: Portable raman spectroscopy: (a) display unit; (b) test objects (one ball of polystyrene and another of a different type of polymer); (c) chemical fingerprint indicates the material identification.

sharp change in mechanical properties at the case/core interface, a backscattered ultrasonic signal returns to the transducer, and the time of flight between this signal and the front surface is directly related to case depth.

13.2.7 RESIDUAL STRESS

Triaxial stress state, combined from the x-, y-, z-directions, within an engineered component is important because failure is likely when the strength or endurance limits of a material are exceeded. As mentioned in Section 13.2.1, ultrasonic testing has been used to measure orientation-specific acoustic velocity in materials, and the change in velocity is related to applied or residual stress. It is a challenge, however, for UT techniques, generally utilizing electromagnetic acoustic transducers, to distinguish the desired stress-altered velocity effect from any inherent material anisotropy (texture) that may exist. *Crystallographic techniques* based on X-ray or neutron diffraction have found wider application for estimating residual stress (Figure 13.4). Crystalline materials have an ordered structure—that is, type of unit cell—and a specific spacing between atoms, referred to as *lattice spacing*. Incident radiation photons are elastically scattered from the sample, which may be a powder or an actual component. Constructive and destructive interference of the scattered energy is three-dimensionally analyzed to determine atomic arrangement. If one assumes that strain in the lattice is elastic, then applied and residual stress can be directly related to deformation in the atomic arrangement. The photon beam interrogates a volume of material, in diameter and in depth, and for polycrystalline materials this volume will hold a number of grains. X-rays scatter due to interaction with the electron cloud surrounding an atom, but neutrons scatter after interacting with the nucleus. Thus, *neutron diffraction* has the ability to more precisely determine atomic positions.

Figure 13.4: Portable goniometer setup for in situ X-ray diffraction of a large welded structure to determine the level of residual stress.

13.3 NEW PRODUCT APPLICATIONS

13.3.1 CASTINGS

All products, including cast components, have the potential for internal and external discontinuities. Examples of casting discontinuities include undesirable thickness; external pores; spherical internal voids; shrinkage, including cavity, dendritic, filamentary, sponge, and micro-shrinkage; cracks, generally initiating at the external surface after solidification; improper or undesirable microstructure or microstructural phases; inclusions, such as sand from green sand mold, slag, or dross; core shifts; hot tears, formed during solidification due to constrained thermal contraction; misruns, or incomplete mold fillings; and cold shuts.

Verification of Casting Integrity. NDT is widely used to verify casting integrity, but tests are most effective when the inspector understands the manufacturing process and the circumstances during the part's service life so as to know what types of discontinuities to expect. Ultrasonic, radiographic, liquid penetrant, magnetic particle, visual, thermal, and other methods are commonly applied to seek, and sometimes size, such discontinuities (Figures 13.5 and 13.6). Quality class for a component or region, which strongly affects cost, is often selected based on whether the casting is vital to the assembly's longevity or safety. Class is the degree of thoroughness of testing, and different levels generally correspond to acceptable discontinuity sizes.

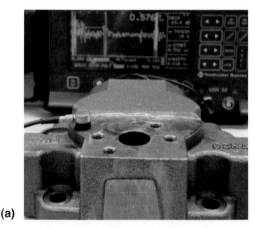
(a)
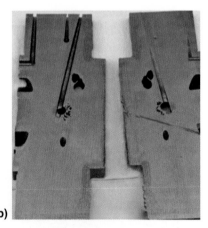
(b)

Figure 13.5: Ultrasonic testing: (a) applied to seek internal voids in a cast iron component; (b) example discontinuities exposed by cross sectioning.

(a)
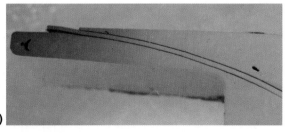
(b)

Figure 13.6: Laminations in a painted aluminum die casting: (a) visually detected on the exterior; (b) shown to extend deeply into the part when the area is cross sectioned, mounted, and polished.

13.3.2 WROUGHT PRODUCTS

Wrought components, such as forgings, drawn products, and rolled sheet or plate, may have internal or external discontinuities, as shown in Figures 13.7–13.10. Common discontinuities sought may pertain to thickness, internal bursts, cracks,

Figure 13.7: Fluorescent penetrant indications (Level 4, hydrophilic postemulsifiable): (a) on the edges of bimetallic bearing, which call attention to crack formation; (b) crack formation visible in the polished cross section (500× original magnification).

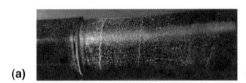

Figure 13.8: Fluorescent magnetic particle testing indications: (a) caused by superficial forming discontinuities on AISI 1018 steel fasteners; (b) 200× original magnification.

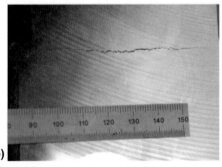

Figure 13.9: Ultrasonic testing: (a) used to detect an internal burst in this forged, heat-treated, and machined component; (b) the discontinuity is caused by a combination of steel microstructure and thermal processing procedures.

Figure 13.10: Chevron-shaped central burst: (a) in a cold-forged AISI-8620 component, which produced an acoustic emission signal during post-carburization straightening; (b) a deeply etched (using a hot mixture of hydrochloric acid and water) cross section shows material grain flow produced by the forging process.

inclusions, laminations, hardness, laps, seams, grain size, texture, conductivity, or magnetic properties. Electromagnetic, ultrasonic, radiographic, liquid penetrant, magnetic particle, visual, thermal, and other testing methods are commonly applied to seek, and sometimes size, such discontinuities.

Benefit of Early Detection. Examples of nondestructive verifications of wrought products are ultrasonic testing, using electromagnetic acoustic transducers (EMATs), and magnetic flux leakage or eddy current-based testing by a steel producer to confirm the quality of products, such as blooms, billets, rods, bar, tube, or rope. Early detection on a hot product is cost-effective because one could avoid further work on a defective product. A mill may generate rayleigh waves around the circumference of a tube using an EMAT and, with signal processing, the presence and approximate size of discontinuities, such as laps, seams, or pits, may be determined. The material's high temperature, high transit speed of the sample, and the production environment make these noncontact techniques optimal. Statistical analysis of indications is possible with computer-based inspection process monitoring in terms of discontinuities per roll or per unit length, and so on.

13.3.3 JOINTS AND BONDS

Joining and bonding methods are diverse and include fasteners, such as bolts and rivets; adhesives; welding; brazing; and soldering. Nondestructive testing—for example, visual, ultrasonic, or radiographic testing—is widely applied for weld inspection to locate and characterize discontinuities to determine if corrective action, such as air carbon-arc gouging, grinding, or rewelding, is required. Because a perfect weld is impossible, accept/reject criteria are necessary when discontinuities are noted. These criteria, which must be consistently applied according to a standard or code, are based on factors such as weld dimensions, whether the part is safety critical, and whether the joint is statically or dynamically loaded. Integrity of a weld is affected by factors such as the welding process; cleanliness of the weld in terms of grease, oil, dirt, paint, moisture, or interpass slag; choice of consumables, such as filler metal or shielding gas; joint type and geometry, for example, bevel angle, root gap, partial or complete penetration; or necessary thermal treatments, including pre-heat, proper interpass temperature, or post-weld stress relieving.

Types of Discontinuities in Joints and Bonds. Typical discontinuities in bonded or joined parts include undercut, arc strikes, lamellar tearing or laminations in the parent material, internal voids, cracks, lack of fusion or disbond, lack of joint penetration, inclusions or slag, and improper joint dimensions, such as leg size, profile, or fit-up (Figures 13.11 – 13.13). Electromagnetic, ultrasonic, radiographic, liquid

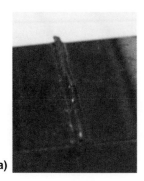 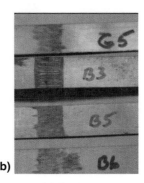 

(a)   (b)   (c)

Figure 13.11: Eddy current testing of: (a) flash butt-welded steel strip, (b) ground flush, (c) then subjected to automated eddy-current scanning with an absolute probe.

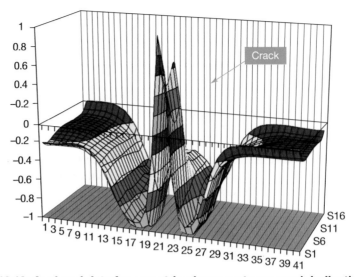

Figure 13.12: Analyzed data for one strip shows a strong crack indication.

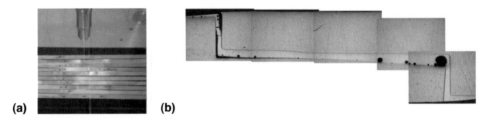

(a) (b)

Figure 13.13: Immersion ultrasound scanning of: (a) soldered lap joints in brass; (b) a typical composite micrograph showing regions of disbond and porosity (right, 50× original magnification).

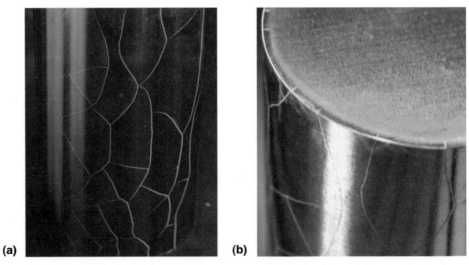

(a) (b)

Figure 13.14: Fluorescent magnetic particle testing indications: (a) on an induction heat-treated and ground steel bar; (b) indications show that the cracks terminate at the interface of the hardened case and the soft core.

penetrant, magnetic particle, visual, thermal, and other testing methods are commonly applied to seek, and sometimes size, such discontinuities. An example application is acoustic emission monitoring of resistance spot welding, where the system automatically halts the process if undesirable expulsion, such as spitting or flashing, occurs (see ASTM E751). Also, NDT may be applied to monitor fastener strain during or after installation using, for example, ultrasonic monitoring of bolts.

13.3.4 MACHINED PRODUCTS

Inspectors sometimes assume that internal discontinuities are detected in their as-cast or as-formed state, and therefore only external discontinuities are the target of inspections of machined components. Discontinuities of interest generally pertain to voids; cracks; dimensions; localized thermal damage, such as grinder burn; heat treatment; case depth; or coating thickness (Figure 13.14). Electromagnetic testing such as barkhausen noise or eddy current, liquid penetrant, magnetic particle, visual, thermal, ultrasonic, and other testing methods are often applied, and radiographic techniques may be called on.

13.3.5 ASSEMBLIES

NDT on assemblies is generally useful for determining if components or operations were missed or inadvertently included, or for measuring dimensions without disturbing the relative positions of components. Radiographic and visual testing methods are commonly applied to assemblies, but ultrasonic, thermal, vibration analysis, and other methods may be called for. For example, vibration readings may be applied to rotating, reciprocating, or electromagnetic machinery to seek problems, such as vane/impeller, electric motor, and belt-drive problems, or resonance-related issues.

13.3.6 COMPOSITES, CERAMICS, AND POLYMERS

Nonmetallic engineering materials have the potential for internal and external discontinuities to be introduced during their production, and these discontinuities can affect material properties (Figure 13.15). Advanced structural ceramics, for example, may contain pores or voids, inclusions, compositional inhomogeneity, large grains, or cracks. The distribution and size of discontinuities can strongly affect material properties, such as fracture toughness. Composite materials, such as solid laminates and bonded sandwich types, are used in the aerospace, watercraft, sporting goods, automotive, and wind power industries. Typical discontinuities in composites

(a)   (b)

Figure 13.15: Internal porosity within a die-cast polymeric dock cleat visible in (a) top- and (b) side-view real-time X-ray radiographs (a digital image subtraction technique was used to enhance contrast).

include porosity, inclusions, poor ply orientation, or layup sequence, ply waviness, and delaminations or disbonds. Ultrasonic (immersion, contact, air-coupled, polar backscatter, and bond-testing), radiographic, visual, thermal, and other testing methods, including tap testing and shearography, are commonly applied to seek, and sometimes size, such discontinuities.

Detection of Delaminations. *Delaminations* in composites are a major concern, but these discontinuities are often readily detectable. Laser-based ultrasound, for example, is well suited for delamination detection to the very edge of curved and complex geometries. UT-based detection of inclusions is more difficult due to low acoustic impedance mismatch; therefore, the proportion of incident energy reflected is low. Reference standards with intentionally planted inclusions, voids, or delaminations aid in test setup and sometimes in discontinuity sizing.

13.4 FAILURE OF MATERIALS

13.4.1 NDT'S ROLE IN DETECTING MATERIAL FAILURE

This chapter has thus far summarized how nondestructive testing methods and techniques are commonly used to verify that freshly fabricated materials and components are free from discontinuities. Products that are acceptable when new, however, may begin to deteriorate or fail when placed into service. Here again, NDT is useful for detecting or monitoring such problems. Common causes of material failure are excessive static or dynamic stress, electrochemical action, wear, cyclic loading, embrittlement, and thermal cycling.

Importance of Inservice Inspections. There is no perfect NDT method or technique capable of locating all discontinuities, and each has detection limitations of a particular length scale. Likewise, the human factors involved in many methods and techniques result in variability in the inspection process. For instance, a given weld discontinuity may be missed or may be detected and accepted today but judged as a rejectable defect during subsequent inspection. These assumptions have led to product design guidelines that are used in various industries. Many welded structures, for example, are based on the assumption that the weld itself only has a fraction of the strength of the parent metal because producing a perfect weld is not possible due to the *joint efficiency factor* or quality factor. Aerospace applications, as a further example, often use a *damage tolerant approach*, which assumes that discontinuities smaller than the detectability limit are present, but subsequent NDT during the life of the part will detect propagating discontinuities prior to their reaching fracture-critical size.

13.4.2 FAILURE MECHANISMS

Compression and Stress. Deformation occurs when a force is applied to an elastic material. *Compression* causes negative strain—that is, the body gets shorter—whereas tension causes positive strain. Forces are generally distributed across an area. *Stress* is a measure of pressure, the mathematical result of force per unit of cross-sectional area, expressed in newtons per square meter or pascals. When stress is perpendicular to the cross section, it is said to be normal; when parallel, it is said to be shear. The active failure mechanism often depends on ambient temperature, applied stress, rate of loading/unloading, and material properties, such as the elastic modulus, melting point, yield strength or grain size.

Effects of Static Stress. Excessive static stress is a common failure mechanism, which may lead to distortion failures, such as buckling, yielding or bending, or creep; cracking; or fracture. Fracture of materials may be divided into brittle and ductile. This division is based on the amount of plastic deformation that occurs prior to failure. Brittle materials exhibit negligible plastic deformation and fail when their tensile strength, which resists the maximum normal stress, is exceeded. Ductile materials may exhibit considerable amounts of plastic deformation and fail when shear stress exceeds their shear strength.

Effects of Dynamic Stress. Excessive dynamic stress can lead to fatigue cracking, impact damage, spalling, or brinelling. Fatigue cracking is a progressive mechanism of material failure in which a crack initiates, often at a surface discontinuity, then propagates under repeated or fluctuating stress cycles (Figures 13.16 and 13.17). *Low-cycle fatigue cracking* is a common problem that occurs in most alloys at stress levels above their endurance limit. *High-cycle fatigue cracking* occurs at relatively low loads. Crack initiation requires that the load be applied a large number of times—for instance, >100 000. Stresses are not always externally applied. Thermal gradients and/or differences in thermal expansion coefficients can cause failure of components and assemblies.

Corrosion Damage. *Corrosion*, the deterioration of a metal by a chemical or electrochemical reaction with its environment, for instance, the rusting of steel, is a common electrochemical failure mechanism. Several types exist, including general, crevice (touch point), pitting, and exfoliation corrosion. Corrosion is always related to material loss, and a related failure mechanism is *wear*, material loss due to liquid and/or solid flow. Wear is a complicated material failure mechanism, which is pervasive across all industries. There are many recognized wear modes including abrasive wear, adhesive wear, erosion, cavitation pitting, and fretting. These modes may occur alone or in combination with other failure mechanisms, such as erosion-corrosion or cavitation-erosion. Corrosion damage, when allowed to propagate excessively, can lead to leaking.

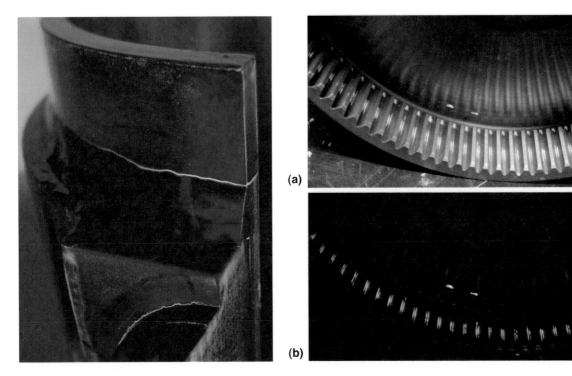

(a)

(b)

Figure 13.16: Magnetic particle testing indications on a cross-sectional portion of a garbage truck ram, which formed at a weld toe (crack had propagated through-thickness) and at a trunnion radius.

Figure 13.17: Fluorescent penetrant (Level 4, hydrophilic postemulsifiable) indications: (a) on a steel racecar component when viewed under a combination of white light and UV-A irradiation; (b) solely under UV-A irradiation.

As its name suggests, *stress corrosion cracking* (SCC) is an electrochemical failure mechanism that occurs when a susceptible material—metallic alloy, ceramic, glass, or polymer—fails due to the combined presence of tensile stress and a corrosive environment. SCC can occur without significant change in wall thickness and causes normally ductile materials to unexpectedly fail in a brittle manner, as in the case of copper-zinc alloys exposed to ammonia. While SCC is insidious, its threat may be removed by reducing the applied or residual tensile stress as a dominant player, by reducing exposure to the corrosive environment, or by reducing the corrosivity of the environment.

Embrittlement. Two common embrittling mechanisms are caused by radiation and by hydrogen. Long-term exposure to high-energy neutrons in a nuclear reactor causes *lattice defects*, which tend to diffuse into clusters. *Neutron degradation* generally increases the ductile-to-brittle transition temperature of the alloy by greater than 200 °C (392 °F) for the worst cases. The ductile-to-brittle transition temperature is the temperature where fracture toughness sharply decreases. Hydrogen damage, due to hydrogen embrittlement, hydrogen-induced cracking, or stress-oriented hydrogen-induced cracking, is more widespread across industries and can greatly reduce the fracture toughness and yield strength of structural alloys. Factors affecting susceptibility include hydrogen concentration, alloy heat treatment, stress level of the component, strain rate during deformation, and temperature—most severely at room temperature.

Hydrogen embrittlement may be caused any time a susceptible metal contacts atomic or molecular hydrogen. Common procedures of concern are electroplating, phosphating, and pickling. Special thermal treatments (holding the part above a certain temperature for some amount of time) are commonly applied to drive out the hydrogen and minimize the likelihood of a problem later.

14 NDT and Engineering

14.1 ROLE OF NDT ENGINEERS

An independent NDT talent placement organization (PQNDT) tracks benefits and compensation of nondestructive testing personnel through annual surveys completed voluntarily by NDT practitioners. Analysis of their 2006 – 2011 reports reveals some interesting details regarding the NDT discipline. The field, on average, appears to be male dominated, with only 3% – 4% of NDT practitioners expected to be female. NDT may attract fresh faces, including females, when compensation of Level III experts is considered. The organization reported that the average wage for a Level III in the U.S. was just under $100 000 in 2011, and recent historical data suggested an average annual salary increase of 7% over this six-year period.

NDT Survey Results. ASNT has also surveyed its members to learn more about their job functions. In 2012, there were 6300 ASNT NDT Level III certificate holders among a total membership of 12 000. A targeted survey received responses from 13% of these NDT practitioners, which offered a glimpse into their job roles. Based on this snapshot, most (80%) NDT Level III personnel hold more than one method certificate, and they tend to work in the petroleum or chemical (26%), aerospace (19%), manufacturing (15%), or power generation (14%) industries. Common roles for Level III personnel within these industries included developing and/or providing

"A targeted survey received responses from 13% of these NDT practitioners, which offered a glimpse into their job roles."

NDT training, developing and providing inspection solutions, generating inspection specifications, and providing guidance or aid to design and production teams. The amount of work experience held by these Level IIIs was significant, with over 87% of the respondents having greater than 11 years and 26% with more than 30 years of experience.

14.2 NDT RELIABILITY

A reliable inspection process is one that is not only repeatable and reproducible but also has a known limit of sensitivity. Applications that cannot tolerate a significant risk of component failure require highly reliable inspection processes. Human factors represent some of the most significant variables in the application of NDT. Excess variation in a process is generally undesirable, but variability is not always easy to assess. Aspects that enhance NDT reliability are proper calibrations, for instance, of equipment or of an inspection setup, as well as adequate procedures, process controls including audits, and assessments of detection capability. At its core, an inspection seeks to detect a test response amid background noise. In MT, for example, the inspector's eye is the sensor, which detects an indication based on its color contrast, brightness contrast, and length. The brain then processes the sensor's signal to classify an indication as a relevant discontinuity or as irrelevant background noise. This classification step is governed by some threshold, which could be a maximum allowable discontinuity size or some other factor.

Human Factors. Sometimes, in spite of good process controls, there is a chance that the test may not actually be performed or may not be performed according to an established procedure with a certain probability of inspection. Human factors are among the controlling aspects when an inspection is misapplied. For example, in 2011, an ultrasonic inspector was found guilty of falsifying inspection documentation for thousands of welds, including several critical welds on nuclear submarines. Such problems are not limited to the maritime industry; other industries have undoubtedly dealt with uninspected components or missed cracks that were large enough to be visible to the unaided eye.

There are four possible outcomes from a nondestructive test: (1) a relevant discontinuity is found, (2) a discontinuity-free region or sample is accepted, (3) a discontinuity is called where none exists, or (4) a relevant discontinuity is overlooked. Outcome 1 is commonly called a *hit*, while outcomes 3 and 4 are labeled as *false calls* and *misses*, respectively. Reliable inspections strive to attain outcomes 1 and 2 and strive to avoid outcomes 3 and 4. Optimal outcomes are attained with a knowledgeable, alert, and motivated inspector provided with proper equipment, a sensitive test technique, and a repeatable procedure.

Probability of Detection. NDT plays a critical role in process control and in the inspection of safety-critical assemblies, such as aircraft, pressure vessels, nuclear reactor components, and pipelines. Thus, the assessment of the performance of NDT has become important. It is not acceptable to simply assume that inspections are perfect processes of unbounded detection capability. When probability of inspection is assumed to be ideal, then inspection variability is assessed as discontinuity size versus likelihood of detection. Industries with high-performance, fracture-critical structures, as in aerospace, which have adopted damage-tolerant design and maintenance protocols, are highly concerned with a nondestructive inspection's *probability of detection* (PoD). Damage tolerance requires a thorough understanding of the material's fatigue properties, stresses applied during usage, discontinuity growth rate, critical discontinuity size, and knowledge of the inspection's detection capability. Maintenance inspection frequency could be based on how long the largest discontinuity that may be missed would take to grow to the smallest size where failure is possible.

PoD is a well-established technique for demonstrating detection capability for that inspector and procedure at that instant in time and could be considered an estimate of the largest discontinuity that could be missed during repeated inspections. A PoD value is derived from a statistical analysis of data regarding hits, when an actual discontinuity is detected, and misses, when a discontinuity is overlooked. It may also be based on analysis of test signal magnitude. The number of false calls—that is, an inspector-indicated discontinuity where none existed—is also noted. The output of this analysis is an estimate, with some level of confidence, that indicates all discontinuities of a given size or larger are highly likely to be detected. Put another way, one might be 95% confident that 90% of detectable discontinuities are being detected. Note in Figure 14.1, for example, that one discontinuity with a greater length than the calculated PoD value (A_{NDE}) was missed during this assessment (misses are indicated by the lower set of data points). Confidence, in a statistical sense, refers to how likely the results would be repeated or exceeded if the assessment were performed multiple times.

Probability of detection is sometimes referred to as an *end-to-end capability evaluation* in that it is unique to the NDT method, technique, materials, and equipment used; the operator or technician; accept/reject criteria; and the specimen including material, shape, or surface finish. PoD has historically been assessed experimentally by inspecting a number of parts, both with and without discontinuities, using the inspection procedure of interest. A PoD assessment is not a constant in that a subsequent assessment won't likely return exactly the same result. A core reason for determining PoD was to provide assurance that one or more maintenance inspections would be performed before a rogue (missed) discontinuity had propagated from its original dimensions to critical size. From a statistical standpoint, it would be ideal to have 100% probability of detection, but the number of samples required to design such an experiment would have to be prohibitively large. In an effort to balance experimental costs with statistical rigor, the point where a 95% lower confidence boundary intersects with 90% probability of detection has become standardized and is now referred to as the *90/95 PoD value* (along with the relevant number of false calls).

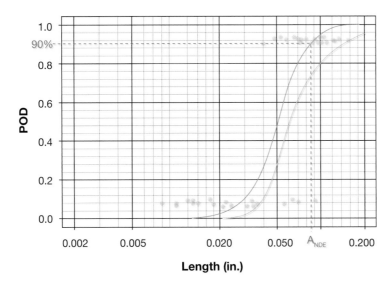

Figure 14.1: Hit-miss data and resultant PoD curve with probability of detection on the Y axis and discontinuity length on the X axis; this curve was generated for a specific fluorescent penetrant testing process that sought low-cycle fatigue cracks in Inconel™ and titanium bars.

PoD assessments are fairly expensive efforts, in part because of the cost of pedigreed samples, but also because they are time-intensive. When samples are not pedigreed, then the statistician must consider that unknown discontinuities may have been overlooked. Unknown misses tend to skew PoD values smaller, sometimes considerably, with traditional analysis methods. This type of sample set is called *truncated*—that is, the smaller discontinuity end of the distribution is unknown and assumed to be cropped—and it requires a special analytical approach to avoid a falsely conservative value. One method of decreasing the cost and time required for a PoD assessment involves the use of physics-based computer simulation models to achieve model-assisted probability of detection. The use of computer models promises to reduce the number of required samples and experiments. Use of fewer samples equates to more cost-effective, but equally robust, statistical analysis of NDT applications.

14.3 ENGINEERING APPROACH

14.3.1 DESIGN FOR INSPECTABILITY

Design engineers have historically been focused on static and dynamic stress levels applied to their components and what choice of material best copes with that stress in the most economical manner. Textbook values and a factor of safety then result in a design that generally avoids premature failure. The design engineer is keenly aware that components are not discontinuity-free, and nondestructive testing is often called on to give some assurance that no discontinuities are present, especially in critical areas.

Role of Computers in NDT. Computers have revolutionized our lives, and electronic hardware is now commonly applied for purposes as diverse as communications, entertainment, and health care. Because computing power has increased with time, *computer simulations* of industrial processes and applications are now commonplace. For example, a company may virtually simulate a user's experience in a new prototype vehicle, estimate the magnitude and location of stresses on a design, predict the useful life of a component based on expected stresses, or simulate the dynamic flow of particles and/or fluids through an environment. Simulations are also available, for example, to model material flow, microstructure, expected stresses, and likely discontinuity locations for forging and casting processes. Such software can reduce design and development time as well as decrease the amount of scrap produced.

If simulation software predicts critical locations on a component, possibly due to stress level or a potential for discontinuities, then NDT can be considered at an early stage. Input from the NDT engineer on the optimal inspection method and technique can lead to discussions about design for inspectability. Inspection problems, often due to external shape, can occur later if NDT is not involved in the early thought process. For example, perhaps it is forecast that ultrasonic testing could be called upon to confirm the quality level of a casting, but it is impossible to place a UT probe at the key location without modifying the external surface (Figure 14.2). The designer may not be aware of inspection limitations, so early involvement by the NDT expert could reduce the likelihood of rude surprises later in the production cycle.

14.3.2 INSPECTION SIMULATION

Like computer simulation models for manufacturing processes, *nondestructive testing simulations* are widespread. NDT simulations for radiographic, ultrasonic, and electromagnetic testing are commercially available; many undistributed research-based simulations have been developed as well, including time-based

Figure 14.2: Example of gray iron casting, which has the potential for an inside surface discontinuity. Although ultrasonic testing holds the promise of sorting good from bad, it is not possible to couple the transducer to the key area.

simulation of a discontinuity's magnetic particle collection and indication formation ability. Simulations are powerful tools for qualifying an inspection system,
quickly optimizing inspection parameters, exploring application feasibility, inter-
preting data obtained from complex specimens, training, and reducing the cost
involved in probability of detection assessments.

Computer-Aided Design and Ray Tracing. The complexity, capabilities, accuracy, and cost of these software packages vary. Some allow *computer-aided design*
(CAD) models to be imported, while others may require that rudimentary drawing
tools incorporated in the package be used. Some methods, such as radiographic or
electromagnetic testing, are best simulated using a physics-based approach. When it
comes to ultrasonic testing, an alternative to physics-based modeling is *ray tracing*.
Ray tracing is a simplified approach that generally requires low monetary investment
and less computing power. A ray-tracing simulation, for example, may only consider
reflection and refraction of a primary acoustic beam in homogenous materials of relatively simple geometry. A more complex physics-based approach may incorporate a
test object's heterogeneous material properties; discontinuity properties, such as
type, dimensions, location, and orientation; spectral emission characteristics of the
acoustic source; filtering; scattering mechanisms; and tools that predict a probability
of detection curve or predict what an A-scan display would look like for the virtual
situation of signal amplitude versus time of flight. Either simulation approach may
be valuable depending on the user's need.

14.3.3 UNIFIED LIFE-CYCLE APPROACH

Product Development Process. In the early days of NDT, Level III personnel generally waited until relatively late in the process of developing a new component to
become involved. Historically, the product development process is as follows: (1)
understanding the customer's needs leads to the establishment of design requirements; (2) designers offer their prototype; (3) after testing and refinements, the
design enters production; and (4) the product may encounter problems, which (5)
require assistance from NDT personnel. Problems requiring NDT assistance may
lead to increased knowledge and experience within the organization, which may
guide the development of future products or the selection of manufacturing
processes or parameters so as to avoid similar issues. However, sequential product
enhancement is a tediously slow process, and simultaneous deployment of computer-based tools could help bypass some intermediate development steps.

NDT as an Engineering Tool. Engineers constantly seek ways to reduce manufacturing costs, conserve energy, and develop high-performance materials that
decrease mass while maintaining strength and product longevity. NDT has evolved
into a powerful engineering tool for verifying product quality and safety. As may be
extrapolated from the previous sections, computer models may be used to estimate
the magnitude of stress around a three-dimensional component model, and then
NDT modeling tools may be utilized to estimate the likelihood of finding a specific
discontinuity in the high-stress regions. A *unified life-cycle approach* bundles the
power of many computer-based tools to optimize a component's design based on its
end use.

Examples of computer-based tools include computer-aided manufacturing, such
as computer numerical control; computer-aided design; numerical modeling of
stress fields or displacement, for example, finite element analysis; cost-estimate modeling; manufacturing process models; failure models, including fatigue crack initiation and propagation; product reliability modeling, involving statistical analysis of
failures and longevity; and nondestructive inspection simulations. A desirable design
and production situation is the unified life-cycle approach, which concurrently
leverages all of these tools to optimize the component and maximize profitability.

References

Allgaier, M.W. and R.E. Cameron, tech. eds., and P. O. Moore, ed. *Nondestructive Testing Handbook*, third edition: Volume 9, *Visual Testing*. Columbus, OH: The American Society for Nondestructive Testing, Inc. (2010).

American Conference of Governmental Industrial Hygienists (ACGIH). *TLVs® and BEIs® Based on the Documentation of the Threshold Limit Values for Chemical Substances and Physical Agents and Biological Exposure Indices.* Cincinnati, OH: ACGIH. (2004). 151-158.

AMS 2644-E, *Inspection Material, Penetrant*. Warrendale, PA: SAE International. (2006).

Annual Book of ASTM Standards, Volume 03.03: *Nondestructive Testing*. West Conshohocken, PA: ASTM International. (2015).

ANSI/ASNT CP-105: ASNT Standard Topical Outlines for Qualification of Nondestructive Testing Personnel. Columbus, OH: The American Society for Nondestructive Testing, Inc. (2011).

ANSI/ASNT CP-189, Standard for Qualification and Certification of Nondestructive Testing Personnel. Columbus: OH: The American Society for Nondestructive Testing, Inc. (2011).

ANSI Z-136.1, *American National Standard for the Safe Use of Lasers*. American National Standards Institute. Orlando, FL: Laser Institute of America. (2014).

Askeland, D.R. and W.J. Wright. *The Science and Engineering of Materials*, seventh edition. Johannesburg, South Africa: CL-Engineering. (2015).

ASME. *Boiler and Pressure Vessel Code*. Section V: *Nondestructive Examination*. New York, NY: ASME International. (2015).

ASME Y14.5, *Dimensioning and Tolerancing*. New York, NY: ASME International. (2009).

ASM Handbook: Volume 1, *Properties and Selection: Irons, Steels, and High-Performance Alloys*. Metals Park, OH: ASM International. (1990).

ASM Handbook: Volume 2, *Properties and Selection: Nonferrous Alloys and Special-Purpose Materials*. Metals Park, OH: ASM International. (1990).

ASM Handbook: Volume 4, *Heat Treating*. Metals Park, OH: ASM International. (1991).

ASM Handbook: Volume 6, *Welding, Brazing, and Soldering*. Metals Park, OH: ASM International. (1993).

ASM Handbook: Volume 6A, *Welding Fundamentals and Processes*. Metals Park, OH: ASM International. (2011).

ASM Handbook: Volume 8, *Mechanical Testing and Evaluation*. Metals Park, OH: ASM International. (2000).

ASM Handbook: Volume 9, *Fatigue and Fracture*. Metals Park, OH: ASM International. (1997).

ASM Handbook: Volume 15, *Casting*. Metals Park, OH: ASM International. (2008).

ASM Handbook: Volume 16, *Machining*. Metals Park, OH: ASM International. (1989).

ASM Handbook: Volume 17, *Nondestructive Evaluation and Quality Control*. Metals Park, OH: ASM International. (1989).

ASM Handbook: Volume 21, *Composites*. Metals Park, OH: ASM International. (2001).

ASNT Recommended Practice No. SNT-TC-1A: Personnel Qualification and Certification in Nondestructive Testing. Columbus, OH: The American Society for Nondestructive Testing, Inc. (2011).

ASTM E-751/E-751-M, *Standard Practice for Acoustic Emission Monitoring during Resistance Spot-Welding*. West Conshohocken, PA: ASTM International. (2012).

ASTM E-1417/ E-1417-M, *Standard Practice for Liquid Penetrant Testing*. West Conshohocken, PA: ASTM International. (2013).

ATA SPEC 105, *Training and Qualifying Personnel in Nondestructive Testing Method*. Washington, DC: Air Transport Association of America (ATA/AIR). (2014).

AWS A2.4, *Standard Symbols for Welding, Brazing, and Nondestructive Examination*. Miami, FL: American Welding Society, Inc. (2012).

AWS D1.1/D1.1M, *Structural Welding Code – Steel*. Miami, FL: American Welding Society, Inc. (2011).

Beissner, R.E., G.A. Matzkanin and C.M. Teller. *NDE Applications of Magnetic Leakage Field Methods: A State-of-the-Art Survey*. San Antonio: TX: Nondestructive Testing Information Analysis Center. (1980).

Bossi, R.H., F.A. Iddings and G.C. Wheeler, tech. eds., and P. O. Moore, ed. *Nondestructive Testing Handbook*, third edition: Volume 4, *Radiographic Testing*. Columbus, OH: The American Society for Nondestructive Testing, Inc. (2002).

Bossi, R.H., tech. ed., and P. O. Moore, ed. *ASNT Industry Handbook*: Aerospace NDT. Columbus, OH: The American Society for Nondestructive Testing, Inc. (2014).

Bowditch, W.A., K.E. Bowditch and M.A. Bowditch. *Modern Welding*, eleventh edition. Tinley Park, IL: Goodheart-Wilcox. (2012).

Bray, D. and R. Stanley. *Nondestructive Evaluation: A Tool in Design, Manufacturing and Service*. New York: McGraw-Hill. (1989).

Breen, C., F. Guild and M. Pavier. "Impact of Thick CFRP Laminates: The Effect of Impact Velocity." *Composites Part A: Applied Science and Manufacturing*. Volume 36, Issue 2 (2005). 205-211.

Chandler, H. *Metallurgy for the Non-Metallurgist*. Materials Park, OH: ASM International. (1998).

Daniels, D., ed. *Ground Penetrating Radar*, second edition. London, UK: The Institution of Engineering and Technology. (2004).

DIN EN ISO/IEC 17024, *Conformity Assessment – General Requirements for Bodies Operating Certification of Persons*. Berlin, Germany: Deutsches Institut für Normung E.V. (DIN). (2012).

DOT/FAA/AR-00/46, *Repair of Composite Laminates*. Office of Aviation Research, Federal Aviation Administration. Springfield, VA: National Technical Information Service (NTIS). (Feb. 2004).

DOT/FAA/AR-03/74, *Bonded Repair of Aircraft Composite Sandwich Structures*. Office of Aviation Research, Federal Aviation Administration. Springfield, VA: National Technical Information Service (NTIS). (Dec. 2000).

Duell, J.M. "Impact Testing of Advanced Composites." Chaper 6 in Kessler, M., ed. *Advanced Topics in Characterization of Composites*. Bloomington, IN: Trafford Publishing. (2006). 97-112.

Eisenmann, R.C., Sr., and R.C. Eisenmann, Jr. *Machinery Malfunction Diagnosis and Correction: Vibration Analysis and Troubleshooting for Process Industries*. Upper Saddle River, NJ: Prentice Hall. (1998).

EN 4179, *Aerospace Series: Qualification and Approval of Personnel for Non-destructive Testing*. Berlin, Germany: Deutsches Institut für Normung E.V. (DIN). (2011).

EN 13018, *Nondestructive Testing – Visual Testing – General Principles*. Berlin, Germany: Deutsches Institut für Normung E.V. (DIN). (2001).

Federal Aviation Administration. *Aviation Maintenance Technician Handbook – Airframe, Volume 1*, Chapter 4: "Aircraft Metal Structural Repair." New Castle, WA: Aviation Supplies & Academics, Inc. (2012). 7-1 – 7-56.

Federal Aviation Administration. *Aviation Maintenance Technician Handbook – Airframe, Volume 1*, Chapter 7: "Advanced Composite Materials." New Castle, WA: Aviation Supplies & Academics, Inc. (2012).

Federal Aviation Administration. *Composite Aircraft Structure* (Advisor Circular). AC No: 20-107B. (8 Sept. 2009).

Fruehan, R.J. *The Making, Shaping and Treating of Steel: Steelmaking and Refining Volume*, eleventh edition. Pittsburgh, PA: AISI Steel Foundation. (1998).

Hammond, C. *The Basics of Crystallography and Diffraction*. Oxford: Oxford University Press. (1997).

Harris, D.W. *A Guide to Personnel Qualification and Certification*. Columbus, OH: The American Society for Nondestructive Testing, Inc. (2008).

Hassan, M.Z., Z.W. Guan, W.J. Cantwell, G.S. Langdon and G.N. Nurick. "The Influence of Core Density on the Blast Resistance of Foam-Based Sandwich Structures." *International Journal of Impact Engineering*. Volume 50 (December 2012). 9-16.

Horns, A.A. and D.R. Wyman. *Mathematics and Physics of Neutron Radiography*. Reidel Texts in the Mathematical Sciences, Book 1. New York, NY: Springer Publishing Company. (1986).

Inspection of Metals: Understanding the Basics. Metals Park, OH: ASM International. (2013).

ISO 3452-2, *Non-destructive testing – Penetrant Testing – Part 2: Testing of Penetrant Materials*. Geneva, Switzerland: International Organization for Standardization (IOS). (2013).

ISO 7083, *Technical Drawings – Symbols for Geometrical Tolerancing – Proportions and Dimensions*. Geneva, Switzerland: International Organization for Standardization (ISO). (1983).

ISO 8596, *Ophthalmic Optics – Visual Acuity Testing – Standard Optotype and Its Presentation*. Geneva, Switzerland: International Organization for Standardization (IOS). (2009).

ISO 9712, *Non-Destructive Testing – Qualification and Certification of NDT Personnel*. Geneva, Switzerland: International Organization for Standardization (ISO). (2012).

ISO 11484, *Steel Products – Employer's Qualification System for Non-Destructive Testing (NDT) Personnel*. Geneva, Switzerland: International Organization for Standardization (ISO). (2009).

ISO/TS 11774, *Non-Destructive Testing – Performance-Based Qualification*. Geneva, Switzerland: International Organization for Standardization (ISO). (2011).

Jackson, C. N., Jr., and C. N. Sherlock, tech. eds., and P. O. Moore, ed. *Nondestructive Testing Handbook*, third edition: Volume 1, *Leak Testing*. Columbus, OH: The American Society for Nondestructive Testing, Inc. (1998).

Jol, H.M. ed. *Ground Penetrating Radar Theory and Applications*. Oxford, UK: Elsevier Science. (2009).

Kalpakjian, S. and S.R. Schmid. *Manufacturing Processes for Engineering Materials*, fifth edition. Upper Saddle River, NJ: Prentice Hall. (2007).

Maldague, X. P. V., tech. ed., and P. O. Moore, ed. *Nondestructive Testing Handbook*, third edition: Volume 3, *Infrared and Thermal Testing*. Columbus, OH: The American Society for Nondestructive Testing, Inc. (2001).

McCain, D. *ASNT Study Guide: Industrial Radiography Radiation Safety*. Columbus, OH: American Society for Nondestructive Testing, Inc. (2009).

Metalcasting Forecast & Trends. Schaumburg, IL: American Foundry Society (AFS). (2015).

Metals Handbook: Volume 11: *Failure Analysis and Prevention*. Metals Park, OH: ASM International. (1986).

MFL Compendium: Articles on Magnetic Flux Leakage: Collected from Materials Evaluation Published from 1953 to 2006. Columbus, OH: The American Society for Nondestructive Testing, Inc. (2010).

Miller, R.K. and E. v.K. Hill, tech. eds., and P. O. Moore, ed. *Nondestructive Testing Handbook*, third edition: Volume 6, *Acoustic Emission Testing*. Columbus, OH: The American Society for Nondestructive Testing, Inc. (2005).

Moore, D. G., tech. ed., and P. O. Moore, ed. *Nondestructive Testing Handbook*, third edition: Volume 8, *Magnetic Testing*. Columbus, OH: The American Society for Nondestructive Testing, Inc. (2008).

NAS-410, *Certification & Qualification of Nondestructive Test Personnel*. Arlington VA: Aerospace Industries Association (AIA/NAS). (2014).

PQNDT, *Salary Survey*. Arlington, MA. Available at: http://www.pqndt.com/.

Richardson, M.O.W. and Wisheart, M.J. "Review of Low-Velocity Impact Properties of Composite Materials." *Composites Part A: Applied Science and Manufacturing*. Volume 27, Issue 12 (1996). 1123-1131.

Roach, D. and K. Rackow. Sandia Report SAND2007-4088, *Development and Validation of Bonded Composite Doubler Repairs for Commercial Aircraft*. United States Department of Energy. Albuquerque, NM: Sandia National Laboratories. (July 2007).

Rose, J.L. *Ultrasonic Waves in Solid Media*. Cambridge, UK: Cambridge University Press. (1999).

SAE AMS-2644, *Inspection Material, Penetrant*. Warrendale, PA: SAE International. (2013).

Safri, S.N.A., M.T.H. Sultain, N. Tidris and F. Mustapha. "Low Velocity and High Velocity Impact Test on Composite Materials – A Review." *The International Journal of Engineering and Science* (IJES). Volume 3, Issue 9 (2014).

Taylor, J.L., ed. *Basic Metallurgy for Nondestructive Testing*, revised edition. Essex, England: W.H. Houldershaw, Ltd. (British Institute of Nondestructive Testing). (1988).

Tracy, N., tech. ed., and P. O. Moore, ed. *Nondestructive Testing Handbook*, third edition: Volume 2, *Liquid Penetrant Testing*. Columbus, OH: The American Society for Nondestructive Testing, Inc. (1999).

Udpa, S. S., tech. ed., and P. O. Moore, ed. *Nondestructive Testing Handbook*, third edition: Volume 5, *Electromagnetic Testing*. Columbus, OH: The American Society for Nondestructive Testing, Inc. (2004).

Van Vlack, L.H. *Elements of Material Science and Engineering*, sixth edition. Upper Saddle River, NJ: Prentice Hall. (1989).

Welding Inspection Handbook, third edition. Miami, FL: American Welding Society. (2000).

Workman, G. L. and D. Kishoni, tech. eds., and P. O. Moore, ed. *Nondestructive Testing Handbook*, third edition: Volume 7, *Ultrasonic Testing*. Columbus, OH: The American Society for Nondestructive Testing, Inc. (2007).

Workman, G.L., tech. ed., and P. O. Moore, ed. *Nondestructive Testing Handbook*, third edition: Volume 10, *Nondestructive Testing Overview*. Columbus, OH: The American Society for Nondestructive Testing, Inc. (2012).

Zoughi, R. *Microwave Non-Destructive Testing and Evaluation*. Dordrecht, Netherlands: Kluwer Academic Publishers. (2000).

Figure Sources

All figures derive from sources published or purchased by The American Society for Nondestructive Testing, Inc., except for the following figures reproduced with permission.

Chapter 2

Figures 1 – 3, 15, and 16: Peter Huffman

Figure 9: National Research Council, Boucherville, Quebec, Canada

Figure 10: MISTRAS Group, Inc.

Figure 11: thesingularityprinciple.blogspot

Figures 12, 19 and 20: Wikimedia Commons

Figure 13: California Institute of Technology, Jet Propulsion Laboratory, NASA (public domain)

Figure 17: EliseEtc, Wikimedia Commons

Figure 18: Jacek FH, Wikimedia Commons

Figures 22 – 24 and 28 – 31: NDT Resource Center and the Center for NDE, Iowa State University

Figure 26: Metallos, Wikimedia Commons

Figure 27: Christophe Dang Ngoc Chan, Wikimedia Commons

Figure 32: American Iron and Steel Institute (AISI)

Figure 33: Runningamok19, Wikimedia Commons

Chapter 3

Figures 1a and 6: NDT Resource Center and the Center for NDE, Iowa State University

Figure 2a: Wikimedia Commons

Figure 2b: Rainer Knäpper, Free Art License (http://artlibre.org/licence/lal/en/)

Figure 3a: Breakdown, Wikimedia Commons

Figure 4: Amgreen, Wikimedia Commons

Chapter 4

Figure 3: Pearson Scott Foresman, Wikimedia Commons (public domain)

Figure 4: American Iron and Steel Institute (AISI)

Chapter 5

Figures 6, 8, 16, 18, and 19: Federal Aviation Administration, U.S. Department of Transportation (public domain)

Figure 7: NASA/Larry Sammons, Wikimedia Commons (public domain)

Figures 9, 10, and 12 –15: Timothy Kinsella, Dassault Falcon Jet Corp.

Figure 11: Timothy Kinsella, Dassault Falcon Jet Corp., of University of California at San Diego project for Federal Aviation Administration (public domain)

Figure 17: Sandia National Laboratories, U.S. Department of Energy

Chapter 8

Figure 1: Long-Lok Fasteners Corporation

Figure 2: AWS A.30M/A3.0.2010, Figure A.1, reproduced with permission of the American Welding Society (AWS), Miami, FL

Figures 13, 15, and 16: AWS A2.4:2012, Annex E, Welding Symbol Chart, reproduced with permission of the American Welding Society (AWS), Miami, FL

Figure 26a: Szalax, Wikimedia Commons

Figure 26b: Pressure Welding Machines (PMW) Limited

Figure 40: NDT Resource Center and the Center for NDE, Iowa State University

Chapter 9

Figures 5 – 18, 22, 26, and 27: Richard D. Lopez

Chapter 11

Figure 2: Latham & Phillips Ophthalmic

Chapter 12

Title page: KARL STORZ

Figures 1, 5 – 15a, 16 – 26, 28 – 30, 33, and 34: Richard D. Lopez

Figures 2 – 4: Sprawls Educational Foundation, http://www.sprawls.org/ppmi2/IMGCHAR/#Contrast_Sensitivity

Figure 15b – Solid State Systems, Inc.

Figure 45: Reprinted, with permission, from ASTM standard *E-1476*, *Standard Guide for Metals Identification, Grade Verification, and Sorting*, copyright ASTM International, 100 Barr Harbor Drive, West Conshohocken, PA 19428. A copy of the complete standard may be obtained from ASTM International, www.astm.org.

Chapter 13

Figures 1 – 16: Richard D. Lopez

Chapter 14

Figures 1 and 2: Richard D. Lopez

Index

Note: Figures and tables are denoted after page numbers by *f* and *t* respectively.

A

ablation, 333
abrasives, 255–256, 262–263
absolute zero, 356
absorption spectroscopy, 364
absorption-type corrosion inhibitors, 53
absorptivity, 299
acceleration amplitude, 363
accelerometer probes, 363
accept/reject criteria for damage assessment, 130
acoustic emission (AE)
    instrumentation, 359, 359f
    testing, 358–360, 359f
acoustic impedance, 324
acoustic leak testing, 360
acoustic properties, 69–70
acoustic spectroscopy, 363
acoustic velocity
    atomic bonding strength and, 32
    in materials characterization, 366–367
    residual stress and, 370
    thickness gaging and, 330
    ultrasonic testing for, 32
    wave behavior, 322–324, 326
acoustic waves, 69–70, 321, 358, 359
activation energy, 60
active thermography, 357, 358
adhesives
    adherence properties, 120
    adherends, 120
    adhesion, 124
    adhesive bonding, 118, 118f, 124–125, 127, 203
    adhesive joining, 124, 195–196
    for composite materials, 118
    as glues or cements, 120
    as polymers, 19
adiabatic shear, 51
aerogels, 27
aerospace industry
    alloys used in, 98t
    aluminum use in, 92, 95–96
    damage tolerant approach, 376
    density in material choice, 64
    foam use in, 26
    high temperature corrosion protection in, 281
    laser testing for, 362
    moisture damage and, 127
    PoD concerns, 380
    reinforcing agents in, 118, 118f
    SAE International standards, 293
    titanium use in, 102
age hardening (precipitation hardening), 14, 19, 39, 50
air pockets, 164, 164f
air-coupled system, 355
aircraft industry, 118f, 182, 193, 361f
    See also aerospace industry
AISI (American Iron and Steel Institute) standards, 86
allergic dermatitis hazards, 133–134

allotropic (polymorphic) structures, 39, 40–41
alloys
    advantages of, 42
    alloy sorting as ET application, 346
    alloy steels, 47, 88–89
    alloying elements on steel properties, 88t
    atomic arrangements, 15
    defined, 79
    defined and described, 14–15
    examples, 42
    intermetallic compounds, 15
    interstitial alloys, 15
    solid solution strengthening, 43
    See also specific metal alloys
alpha case, 102
alternating current (AC)
    alternating current potential drop technique (ACPD), 350, 367, 369
    field measurement, 350–351
    as waveform in MT, 316
aluminum (Al)
    aluminum alloys, 92–98, 93t, 97t, 98t
    anodizing for, 280
    cast aluminum alloys, 96–98, 98t
    foamed aluminum, 26f
    microshrinkage in castings, 144
    penetrant comparator test, 311f
    properties, 96
    for vacuum metalizing, 276
    wrought aluminum alloys, 93t, 95–96, 96t
aluminum alloys
    elastic modulus of, 32
    ET for, 347
Aluminum Association, 92–93
aluminum lithium alloys, 95
aluminum oxide, 256
aluminum oxide ceramic, 23
American Conference of Governmental Industrial Hygienists (ACGIH), 304
American Foundry Society (AFS), 145
American Iron and Steel Institute (AISI), 86, 89
American National Standards Institute (ANSI) standard for aluminum alloys, 92–93
American Petroleum Institute (API) welding codes, 291
American Petroleum Institute Inspection Summit, 292
American Society for Nondestructive Testing (ASNT)
    Annual Spring Research Symposium, 292
    Central Certification, 289
    Code of Ethics for certification candidates, 288
    Fall Conference, 292
    Level III certificate holders, 379–380
    NDT Certification, 289
    NDT Handbook series, 292
    newsletter, 293
    website resources, 293
American Society of Mechanical Engineers (ASME) codes, 291, 332
American Welding Society (AWS), 210, 228, 238, 291
amorphous structures, 27, 35, 39
amorphous thermoplastics, 21
amplifiers (transistors), 19
angled incidence in UT, 326–327

angular distortions, 234f
anions, 30, 32
anisotropic behavior in crystalline structures, 41, 58, 85
anisotropic conductivity, 346
anisotropic materials, 73, 370
annealing, 49, 58–59
anodic inhibitors/protection, 53–54
anodic materials, 275
anodizing, 280
ANSI/ASNT CP-105: ASNT Standard Topical Outlines for Qualification of Nondestructive Testing Personnel, 292
ANSI/ASNT CP-189 certification standard, 289
antennae for MT and GPR, 346
antiferromagnetism, 69
appearance and function in design, 9–10
applied loads, material failure and, 184
aramid fibers, 121
arc cutting, 255
arc welding
    consumable electrode processes, 214–218
    electrodes, 216–217
    history of, 196
    modifications, 217–218
    nonconsumable electrode processes, 218–219
argon (Ar) as shielding gas, 218
array configurations, 331
A-scan data representation, 325f, 334–336
ASNT. See American Society for Nondestructive Testing
aspect ratios, 317
assemblies of parts, 6, 168, 375
assembly fastening, 204
ASTM E1417 penetrant standards, 308
ASTM International (formerly, the American Society for Testing and Materials), 57, 238, 293
atomic
    cleanliness, 198, 223
    closeness, 198
    structure, 28–29, 338–339
atomic force microscope (AFM), 29
atomic mass unit (amu), 30
atomic numbers (Z-numbers), 15, 29, 339, 340, 341
atoms
    average position of, 31f
    bonding, 30–32
    defined and described, 28, 338
    diffusion, 59–60, 59f
    flux (flow of atoms), 60
    mass, 30, 339
attenuation and signal amplitude, 325f, 326
attenuation coefficients, 345
auger electron spectroscopy, 363
austenite, 45–46
austenitic stainless steels, 90
austenitization, 237
autoclave molding, 115, 124
autofrettage, 66–67
automatic welding, 219
automotive industry
    aluminum replacing steel, 92, 165
    casting alloy uses, 98t
    continuous casting for salvage, 146–147
    drawing fenders, 182
    ferrous materials standards developed, 86

E

early detection advantages, 373
echoes, 326, 330, 332–336
economics in material considerations, 8–9
eddy current testing
  for case depth, 369
  defined and described, 333, 347–350
  edge cracks on turbine blades, 138
  as electromagnetic NDT testing technique, 345, 367
  of flash butt-welded steel strip, 373f
  remote field testing as, 346
  for surface examination, 347–348
  for wrought products, 373
edge dislocation (line dislocation), 54f, 55–56, 55f
edging operations, 171
E-glass, 121
elastic
  deformation, 41
  isotropy, 323
  limit, 10–11
  moduli, 32
  scattering, 344
elasticity as property, 8
elastomers, 19
electric arc furnaces, 81, 146
electric arc welding, 214–216
electric furnace steel, 83
electrical balancing, 347, 348, 349f
electrical conductivity, 15, 43, 67, 367
electrical discharge machining (EDM), 12, 259–261, 259f
electrical energy forming methods, 189
electrical excitation waveforms, 325
electrical properties, 67
electrical resistivity, 67
electrical thermography applications, 358
electrochemical grinding, 67
electrochemical machining (ECM), 261–262, 262f
electrochemical reactions (electrolytic reactions), 52
electrode material in welding, 214
electro-discharge machining (EDM), 67, 260
electrolytic reactions (electrochemical reactions), 52
electromagnetic acoustic transducers (EMATs), 333, 373
electromagnetic contour probe inspection, 318f
electromagnetic forming, 189, 189f
electromagnetic NDT techniques, 367
electromagnetic radiation, 69, 296, 304
electromagnetic spectroscopy techniques, 364
electromagnetic testing (ET), 345–353
  alternating current field measurement, 350–351
  in case hardening objects, 270
  complex impedance plane display, 348f
  eddy current testing, 347–350
  edge cracks on turbine blades, 138
  ET equipment and techniques, 347–352
  ET principles, 345–347
  FAA regulations for, 297
  in porcelain and ceramic coatings, 281
  potential drop techniques (ACPD and DCPD), 350
  seamless tubing, 180
  surface-breaking discontinuity on magnetic field, 351f
  tears and cracks in sheet metal, 194
  test coil impedance, 349f
  test frequencies, 346
  test material properties, 67
  thickness control and measurement, 194
  welded tubing, 180
electromagnetic transducers, 323
electromagnetic waves as probing energy in NDT, 286
electromagnetic yokes, 316–318, 318f
electromotive force (EMF), 324, 347

electron beam guns, 220, 220f
electron beam machining, 12
electron beam welding (EBW), 220, 264
electron spectroscopy, 363
electronegative elements, 31
electronegativity, 35
electronic imbalances in differential coils, 349–350
electronic pyrometers, 357
electrons
  in covalent bonding, 33
  electron cloud (sea of electrons), 34
  electron movement in metallic bonds, 34
  electron shells, 30, 339–340, 339f, 367–368
  electron spin, 30
  equal to protons in atoms, 29–30
  in ionic bonding, 32
  in metallic bonding, 34
  valence electrons, 30, 339, 339f
electroplating, 276–277, 277f
electropolishing, 257
electropositive elements, metals as, 31
electroslag welding, 224, 225f
electrostatic bonds, in adherence, 120
electrostatic spraying, 279
elements and compounds, 8, 80f, 338
embrittlement, 378
emission spectroscopy, 364
emissivity, 356
employer-based internal (second-party) certification program, 289
EN 4179 certification standard, 289
enamels, 280
end-to-end capability evaluation, 381
  See probability of detection
endurance limit (fatigue limit), 76
energy forms in shape changing, 6, 168
energy states, 18
energy vs. distance in atomic bonding, 31f
engineered materials, 287
engineering and NDT, 379–383
  engineering approach, 382–383
  hit-miss data and PoD curve, 381f
  inspectability, designing for, 382, 382f
  inspection simulations, 382–383
  NDT engineers' role, 379–380
  NDT reliability, 380–382
  unified life-cycle approach, 383
engineering ceramics, 116
engineering material densities, 65t
engineering materials, 3–4, 13
engineering plastics, 20
engineering strain, 74
engineering stress (s), 70–71
environment, 51–54
environmental damage in composite materials, 127–129
epoxies
  in casting, 114
  drying, 132
  flammability, 128
  in metal joining, 203
  moisture expansion, 127
  as nonconductive coating, 350
  in particle board, 22
  in thermosetting compounds, 120
equilibrium condition, 42
equilibrium phase diagram, 44f, 45
equilibrium phases in steel and cast iron, 42, 46–48, 46f
equipment and procedures, welding, 216
erosion protection for composite materials, 128
etchants, 258–259
etching, 57
eutectic
  alloys, 162
  composition, 144
  temperature, 92
exciter coil magnetic field, 352
exciters in PT testing, 309–310
expanded bag molding, 115

expendable plaster mold casting, 153
explosion welding (EXW), 226, 227
explosive forming, 188, 188f
external chills, 142
extrinsic semiconductors, 19
extrusion, 6, 114, 180

F

FAA (U.S. Federal Aviation Administration) airworthiness directives (AD), 297
fabrication of composite materials, 122–125
fabricators vs. mills, 169
face-centered cubic (FCC) structures, 36f, 38–39, 38f, 41, 60
facilities, availability of, 10
factories, 4
failure mechanisms, 376–378
false calls, 380–381
false test indications, 286
far field (fraunhofer region), 324, 324f, 326
fast fourier transform (FFT), 325, 363
fatigue
  defined, 76–77
  fatigue crack in superalloy, 304f
  fatigue cracking, 377, 377f
  fatigue limit (endurance limit), 76
  testing for, 360
faying surfaces, 132, 133
feature-based control, 366
Federal Republic of Germany (DAkkS) SECTOR certification, 290
feed and cutting motion, 248, 248f
feed heads/feeders, 139, 142, 142f
feliform corrosion, 52
ferrimagnetism, 68
ferrite, 45–48
ferritic stainless steel, 90
ferromagnetic particles, 315
ferromagnetic test objects, MT for, 313
ferromagnetism, 68
ferrous metals and alloys, 79–92, 82f, 87f
fiber breakage, 127
fiber pull-out, 125, 127
fiberglass, 22
fibers for composites, 19, 121
fiberscopes for VT, 301
fibrous fillers in thermosetting resins, 114–115
filler in fusion bonding, 198–199
filler metal welding, 178
fillet welds, 229f
film radiography, 194
flame hardening, 271
flammability in composite materials, 128
flash, 112, 171–172, 178
flasks (casting), 147, 149
flatback patterns, 148f, 149
flat products (steel), 176, 176f
flaw detectors, 330
flexible laminated strips, 320, 320f
floor and pit molds, 152–153
flow bonding, 200, 200f
flow molding, 114
flow-assisted corrosion (flow-accelerated corrosion), 52
fluid flow and heat transfer, 143
fluorescence, 18
fluorescence spectroscopy, 364, 367–368
fluorescent magnetic particle testing, 372f, 374f
fluorescent nondestructive testing, 307, 309–310
fluorescent penetrant testing, 303–304, 304f, 372f, 377f
fluorescent screens, 342
fluorimeter, 364
fluorophores, 304–305, 307, 309
fluoroscopic testing techniques in welded tubing, 180